Mathematical Statistics

A BLAISDELL BOOK IN

PURE AND APPLIED MATHEMATICS

CONSULTING EDITOR

Douglas Chapman, University of Washington

AN INTRODUCTION TO

Mathematical Statistics

Second Edition

BY H. D. BRUNK

University of Missouri

BLAISDELL PUBLISHING COMPANY

A Division of Ginn and Company

WALTHAM, MASSACHUSETTS · TORONTO · LONDON

Library of Congress Catalog Card Number 64-15990

Preface to the Second Edition

No change to the basic plan of the book has been made in this second edition. Chapter 11 has been expanded somewhat to include a brief introduction to Bayesian inference. Many minor additions and other changes have been made for greater clarity or completeness, and some errors have been corrected. These improvements owe much to useful comments by Professors Herman Chernoff, David Gale, Henry Gould, William Kruskal, Joseph Moser, Gordon Newell, John Randolph, and especially John Pratt, whose many helpful suggestions include that for the approach now used for the moments of the number of runs. The author is grateful to them and also to the publishers for their encouragement, patience, and skill.

June 1963

H. D. Brunk

Preface to the First Edition

The purpose of this text is to assist the student to acquire as thorough an understanding of basic concepts in probability and statistics as is compatible with his mathematical background and the time available. The aim is not only to introduce him to mathematical statistics, but also to help prepare him for further study if he desires to undertake it. Thus, concepts which the author regards as fundamental are discussed thoroughly, while the student is given only a brief introduction to specialized methods.

This text was written originally for use in a one-semester, three-hour course introductory to mathematical statistics, offered to students who have studied the calculus but who have no formal background in probability or mathematical statistics. To make the book useful for more extended courses, however, additional material has been included. This additional material is presented in starred chapters and sections which are largely independent of one another; however, all presuppose the material presented in unstarred sections in the first 95 pages. It will be seen that a desirable feature of the book is its flexibility, which permits the teacher to shape the course according to the special needs of his students and his personal preferences.

The unstarred sections in the first 95 pages cover what appears to the author to be nearly the irreducible minimum background in probability for an understanding of the basic concepts of statistical inference; it has been his practice to devote the first six or seven weeks of the semester to this material. The remainder of the semester has usually been devoted to topics in the other unstarred chapters and sections. The teacher may wish, depending on his class and on the time available, to omit some of the proofs, particularly some of those in starred chapters and sections which make greater demands on the mathematical maturity of the student.

A suggested one-semester course includes Chapters 1 through 10, 12, or 13, omitting starred sections. Either or both of Chapters 16 or 17 or selected portions of them may be included in place of one or more of Chapters 10, 12, or 13.

The teacher who wishes to take up some of the material in starred chapters or sections may do so in any order he wishes, except that the material on analysis of variance should be preceded by the chapter on sampling from a normal population, and the discussion of normal regression should be preceded by the chapter on regression as well as that on sampling from a normal population (cf. Organization Chart on page xi following Table of Contents). Also, the later chapters utilize the χ^2 distribution, which is defined in the chapter on sampling from a normal population. However, for use with those later chapters, the definition of the χ^2 distribution may be used without studying the chapter in which it appears.

Controversial questions in the foundations of probability are avoided; probability spaces are introduced as useful mathematical models. Inevitably, the teacher will feel that some topics have been omitted or slighted which he would like to include or stress. In particular, there is little work on multivariate analysis, a study of which the author feels should be preceded by more work in mathematics (in particular, matrix algebra) than is prerequisite for the course for which this text has been designed.

The author wishes to express his gratitude to the reviewers for the publisher, whose comments were very helpful; to Professor Frederick Mosteller in particular, for his many helpful suggestions for addition and revision which have markedly improved the book and made it more useful. Dr. Churchill Eisenhart, Dr. W. J. Youden, and their colleagues in the National Bureau of Standards were most helpful in making available compilations of published work of the Bureau for use as sources of problems. The author is grateful to Mr. James K. Yarnold, who prepared a number of the problems based on data taken from the literature. He is grateful also to his colleagues Professor G. B. Collier for the use of his problem lists, and Professor P. B. Burcham for his help and encouragement. The author is further indebted to Professor Sir Ronald A. Fisher, Cambridge, to Dr. Frank Yates, Rothamsted, and to Messrs. Oliver and Boyd Ltd., Edinburgh, for permission to reprint Table No. VII, from their book *Statistical Tables for Biological, Agricultural, and Medical Research.* The publishers also deserve the author's gratitude for their untiring efforts toward the goal of producing a text of maximal utility to teacher and student.

H. D. BRUNK

Contents

ORGANIZATION CHART

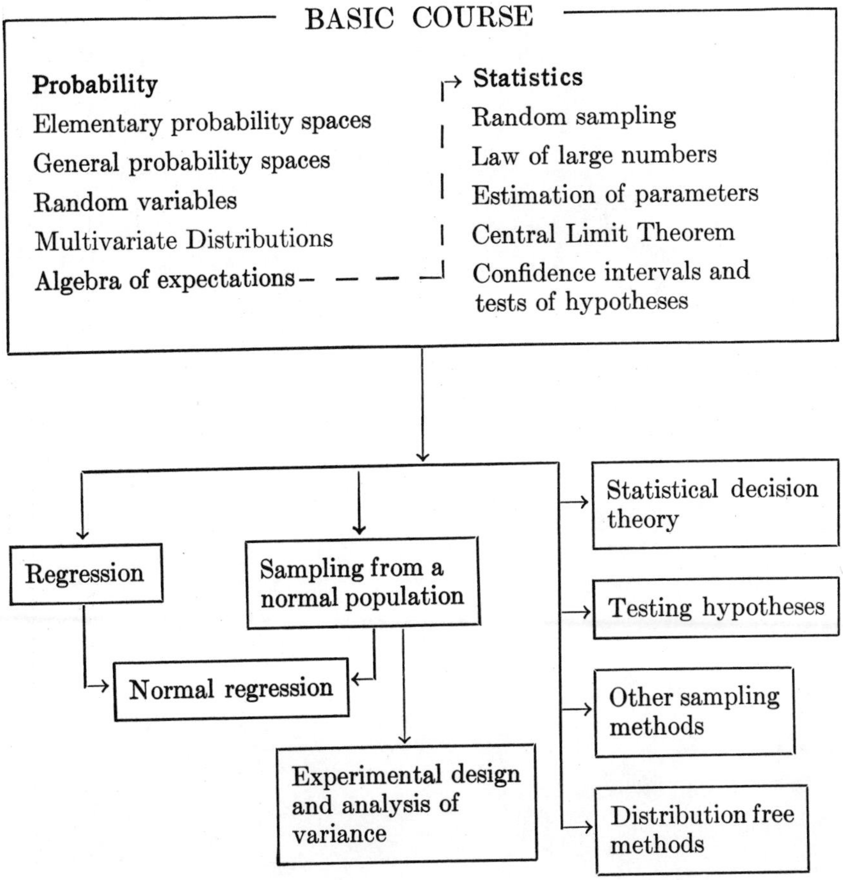
BASIC COURSE
Probability
Elementary probability spaces
General probability spaces
Random variables
Multivariate Distributions
Algebra of expectations
Statistics
Random sampling
Law of large numbers
Estimation of parameters
Central Limit Theorem
Confidence intervals and tests of hypotheses
Regression
Sampling from a normal population
Normal regression
Experimental design and analysis of variance
Statistical decision theory
Testing hypotheses
Other sampling methods
Distribution free methods

Mathematical Statistics

Part One

PROBABILITY

Introduction

Most of us manage to gain some experience with various games of chance in one way or another, and have some intuitive grasp of the kind of question with which probability theory has to deal. These concepts, made precise and integrated into a working theory—probability theory—have a great many applications in many fields, and in particular, in statistics. Indeed, probability forms the basis of the theory of statistical inference; it provides the conceptual framework within which the ideas of statistical inference may be discussed. Therefore the first part of this book is devoted to ideas arising in the theory of probability which are essential for an understanding of mathematical statistics.

Applications of a mathematical theory are made through mathematical models. That is, when faced with a "real," concrete, or physical situation to which he hopes to apply a mathematical theory, an investigator begins by idealizing the situation so as to make a mathematical model. For example, suppose a surveyor wishes to use measurements involving three trees, two on his side of a river and a third on the opposite bank, to determine the width of the river. He begins by constructing a mathematical model, in this case a geometric one. He idealizes the trees, replacing them by points, and introduces certain ideal elements, lines, which join them. He makes use of the geometric concepts of distance and angle, which have precise meanings only relative to his model and not relative to the actual existing situation. He makes readings on his instruments and incorporates the numerical results of his readings into his model as appropriate distances and angles. He then applies directly to his model the theory of plane geometry (or trigonometry).

The investigator (statistican or other) who wishes to apply the theory of probability must proceed in a similar fashion. The basic element in a mathematical model designed for the application of probability is called a probability space. The simplest of these we shall call elementary probability spaces. We shall state what we mean by an elementary probability space, and indicate some situations in which such a mathematical model seems to be (and has proved to be) appropriate. Having thus gained some experience with probabilistic concepts, we shall turn to more general probability spaces, and list axioms for the undefined elements (event, probability, etc.) of probability theory in the same spirit as one does for the undefined elements (point, line, etc.) of the theory of geometry. We shall continue throughout the book to discuss special situations in which probability models have proved useful, and shall not commit ourselves to any very general propositions concerning the utility or non-utility of such models.

CHAPTER

1

Elementary Probability Spaces

1. Introduction. When we wish to analyze mathematically a given situation, we have to begin by idealizing the situation, that is, by building a mathematical model. Consider, for example, the experiment of tossing a coin. Our particular interest is focused on the features that there are exactly two results possible, heads and tails, and that these are equally likely. These features are emphasized in the construction of a model, consisting of two *elementary events*, say H and T, and a probability $\frac{1}{2}$ associated with each. In general,

▶ *If an (idealized) proposed experiment can result in any of an exhaustive set of N equally likely and mutually exclusive possibilities, then an appropriate mathematical model is a set of N elementary events, a probability $1/N$ being associated with each.*

This ratio, $1/N$, is referred to as the probability that a performance of the experiment will result in a particular, specified one of the possibilities. We may also be interested in the occurrence of at least one of a specified subcollection of the possibilities. Such a subcollection is called an *event*, and its probability is defined to be the sum of the probabilities of the elementary events in the subcollection. The elementary events of this subcollection, we say, are *favorable* to the event, and we say the event *occurs* if the performance of the experiment results in the occurrence of one of the possibilities of that subcollection.

EXAMPLE 1. Suppose you hold a die, and propose to cast it. Thinking about the experiment before you perform it, you will set up a mathematical model containing 6 elementary events, a probability 1/6 being associated with each. The *event* consisting of the elementary events 2, 4, 6 might be described as "the event that an even number of spots will turn up." Three elementary events are favorable to this event, and its probability is accordingly 3/6, or 1/2. You might then say that you have a 50–50 chance of throwing an even number of spots.

EXAMPLE 2. You are about to draw a card from a well-shuffled, standard deck. You set up a model in which there are 52 elementary events, each with a probability 1/52. The *event* "you will draw an ace" has 4 elementary events favorable to it, so that its probability is 1/13. Another common way of describing this situation is to say that the chances are 12 to 1 against your drawing an ace.

The assumptions you must make in order to set up the probability model in Example 2 are notably (1) that you are bound to draw one of the 52 cards; (2) that you are as likely to draw one as any other; (3) that you will draw only one card. These assumptions may be described by the following statement:

▶ *The elementary events represent an* exhaustive *set of* equally likely, mutually exclusive *possibilities.*

EXAMPLE 3. Urn I contains 1 red and 2 white balls, Urn II contains 1 white and 2 red balls. You choose at random a ball from Urn I, transfer it to Urn II, mix, and then choose at random a ball from Urn II. What is the *a priori* probability (before transferring the ball) that the ball drawn from Urn II will be white?

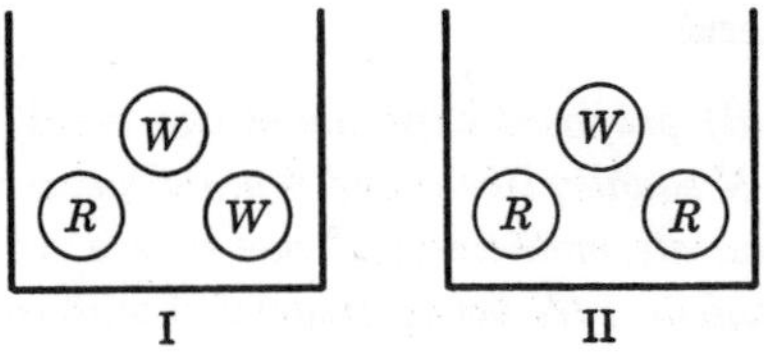

Figure 1

The phrase "at random" is intended to suggest that each ball is as likely to be drawn as any other. There are 12 distinct possible "results" of the experiment: the ball transferred may be any of the 3 in Urn I, and the ball finally drawn may be any of the 4 which are in Urn II after the transfer. In setting up a model, a probability space, we assume: these 12 possibilities are equally likely; one must occur (they are an exhaustive set of possibilities); and only one will occur (they are mutually exclusive). The probability space accordingly has 12 elementary events, each with associated probability 1/12. Of these the following 5 are favorable to the event "white will be drawn from Urn II": transfer red, draw white; transfer first white, draw first white (from the two white balls in Urn II after the transfer); transfer first white, draw second white; transfer second white, draw first white; transfer second white, draw second white. This event therefore has probability 5/12, the sum of the probabilities of the elementary events favorable to it, or the number of elementary events favorable to it divided by the total number of elementary events.

PROBLEMS

1. A certain paragraph contains 10 words of one letter, 10 words of two letters, 15 words of three letters, 15 words of four letters, 50 words of five or more letters. A word is to be chosen at random. (Can you think of a way to accomplish this?) What is the probability that (a) the word will have fewer than three letters? (b) at least three letters? (c) exactly three letters? (d) more than three letters?

2. Of 2500 freshmen in a certain school, 1000 are women; 1200 weigh over 140 lb.; of the women, 700 are taller than 5 ft. 5 in.; and of the men, 1300 are taller than 5 ft. 5 in. A student is to be chosen at random from the freshman class. What is the probability that (a) a male student will be chosen? (b) a student weighing over 140 lb. will be chosen? (c) a student taller than 5 ft. 5 in. will be chosen? (d) a man shorter than 5 ft. 5 in. will be chosen?

3. In a city with 10,000 voters, opinions on two propositions are distributed as follows: 1000 for both; 2000 for I, against II; 1000 against both; 4000 for I, no opinion on II; 1000 against II, no opinion on I; 1000 no opinion on either; none in the other categories. A voter is to be chosen at random. What is the probability that (a) he will be for I? (b) he will be against I? (c) he will have no opinion on I? (d) Explain why the sum of the probabilities in (a), (b), (c) is 1.

4. (a) Construct a model for the experiment of casting a pair of standard dice. How many elementary events are there, and what are their probabilities? What assumptions do you make in setting up the model?

(b) How many elementary events are favorable to the event "you will throw a total of 8 spots on the two dice"?

(c) What is the probability of throwing "snake eyes" (total 2 spots)?

(d) What is the probability of throwing 7 or 11?

(e) What is the probability of throwing 2, 3, or 12?

(f) Suppose one die is red, the other white. What is the probability that the number of spots on the red die will be smaller than the number on the white die?

5. You and Richard Roe each toss a 50-cent piece. You win if you match Roe.

(a) What assumptions do you make in setting up the model? What are the elementary events, and what is the probability of each?

(b) What is the probability that both will throw heads?

(c) What is the probability that you will win?

6. With reference to Problem 5, set up in another way (in which you disregard Roe) an elementary probability space in which "you throw heads" is an event, and show that its probability is the same in each.

7. Assume that in an isolated physical system there are 3 molecules, M_1, M_2, and M_3, each having 0, 1, or 2 units of energy, the sum of their energies being 2 units. Assume all distributions of energy among the three molecules equally likely. Construct a mathematical model for this situation. How many elementary events are there? What elementary events are favorable to the event: "M_1 will have energy 0"? What is its probability?

8. I have a miniature roulette wheel with 38 slots. There are a green 0, a green 00, and the first 36 positive integers. The numbers 1, 3, 5, 7, 9, 12, 14, 16, 18, 19, 21, 23, 25, 27, 30, 32, 34, 36 are red, and the others are black. They are arranged on the betting table in 12 rows and 3 columns:

1	2	3
4	5	6
.	.	.
.	.	.
34	35	36

Suppose you place the following bets; (I) on the 5 and 6; (II) on the second row; (III) on the third column; (IV) on red.

(a) What is the probability that, on a single roll of the ball, one of the bets will win? (b) What is the probability that all will win?

9. You are with two friends, matching to see who pays for the coffee. Each of you tosses an unbiased coin.

(a) Construct a probability space appropriate to this experiment, exhibiting the elementary events and stating their probabilities.

(b) What is the probability that you will be odd man, i.e., that the uppermost face on your coin will match that of neither of your friends?

10. An urn contains 2 white and 3 red balls. You plan to draw two simultaneously; what is the probability that they will be of the same color?

11. In a hand of draw poker, you hold two aces, a king, and two small cards. If you discard the two small cards, what is the probability that you will draw two more so as to have a "full house" (two aces and three kings, or three aces and two kings)? Three of a kind or better (at least three aces or at least three kings)? (The mathematical model you set up depends on the information available to you. As far as you are concerned, not knowing what cards the other players hold, any of the cards you haven't seen is as likely to be drawn as any other.)

12. Urn I contains 2 white and 3 red balls, Urn II contains 1 white and 1 red. You plan to transfer one ball from Urn I to Urn II, then to draw one from Urn II.

(a) What is the *a priori* probability, the probability before the transfer, that you will finally draw a red ball from Urn II?

(b) If you noticed that you transferred a red one, what is the probability that you will draw red?

2. Events. Events, and only events, have probabilities. So one might say an event is something that has a probability. But the questions of interest are:

(1) How do events come to have probabilities?
(2) How can one compute probabilities of complicated combinations of events, when the probabilities of the individual events are known?
(3) How does one interpret the probability of an event, once it is calculated?

(1) The answer to (1) is contained in the description of a probability space and of its purpose. A *probability space* is a mathematical model set up to aid in the analysis of a situation in which an experiment is to be performed, the result of which can conceivably be the occurrence of any one of a number of possibilities. For the present, we are supposing the situation is one in which those possibilities are equally likely. These distinct possibilities correspond to the *elementary events* in the probability space. That is, the investigator sets up a mathematical model of his actual situation; this mathematical model consists of elements he calls *elementary events*, which are the counterparts of the distinct possible results of his experiment. Thus if his experiment will consist of choosing at random one of 10,000 items, his model will have 10,000 elementary events. He will associate a probability 1/10,000 with each, and will say: "the probability of drawing any one particular item is 1/10,000." He may be interested in the probability that he will choose a defective item; that is, he may wish to know the probability of the *event* he can describe thus: "one of the defective items will be selected." Let us call this event A; A consists of all those elementary events which correspond to defective items, and its probability is the sum of their probabilities. In other words, if there are m defective items, A consists of the m elementary events which are their counterparts; and its probability is $m/10{,}000$. The elementary events which constitute A are said to be *favorable* to A. If a defective item is in fact chosen, the investigator may say: "the event A occurred," or "an elementary event favorable to A occurred."

The collection, or *set*, of all those elementary events which correspond to nondefective items is also an event, say, B. There are $10{,}000 - m$ elementary events favorable to B, and its probability is $(10{,}000 - m)/10{,}000 = 1 - m/10{,}000$.

(2) Much of this text is devoted to question (2): how can probabilities of various complicated events be computed?

(3) We hope you will develop throughout this course of study an increasingly adequate "feel" for probability, that numerical probabilities and events will gain significance for you. One may think of the probability of an event in this way: if the probability space the investigator sets up is an adequate model for the experiment he is interested in, if he makes (or if he could make) many "independent" repetitions of the experiment under identical conditions, if each time he observes whether or not a certain event A occurred, then the relative frequency of occurrence of the event A should be very close to the numerical probability of A. This is essentially an interpretation of the law of large numbers, to be discussed later. (In an alternative approach to probability theory, this "long run relative frequency" is *defined* to be the probability of the event.)

Events, and only events, have probabilities, so that the concept of event is fundamental to the theory of probability. In order to deal effectively with events, we need to introduce notations for events which are described as certain combinations of other events. We shall generally use a capital letter near the beginning of the alphabet to denote an event. If A and B are two events (two subsets of elementary events), then the symbol $A \cup B$ will refer to the combined subset of all elementary events each of which is favorable either to A or to B; some may be favorable to both. In an *Euler diagram* we represent the event A by a number of dots enclosed by a closed curve, each dot representing an elementary event favorable to A. If B is represented similarly, then the totality of all dots in A or in B (or in both) represents $A \cup B$. The event $A \cup B$ we shall call the *union* of A and B.

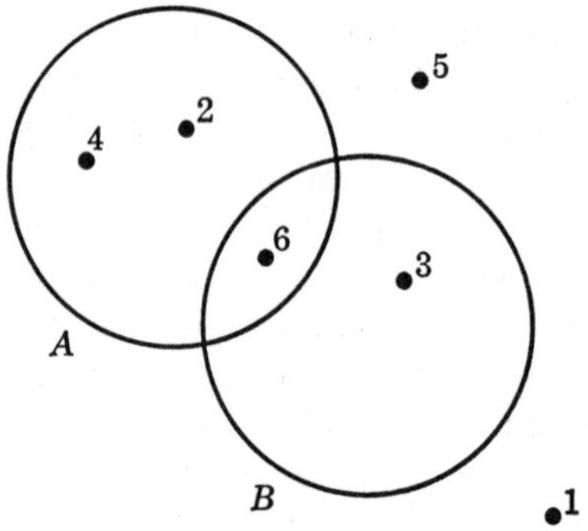

Figure 2

The *intersection* of two events A and B is the set of elementary events favorable to both, and is denoted by $A \cap B$ or simply by AB. In the Euler diagram it is represented by the collection of dots which are in both A and B.

For example, in the experiment of tossing a die, the elementary events 2, 4, 6 are favorable to the event A described by the phrase "an even number of spots will turn up." The elementary events 3, 6 are favorable to the event B, "3 or a multiple of 3 will turn up." Then 2, 3, 4, and 6 are favorable to $A \cup B$, while only 6 is favorable to $A \cap B$ (or AB).

We shall indicate the contrary of an event by placing a bar over the symbol for the event; thus $\bar{A}$ indicates the event *complementary* to A, the event which occurs if and only if A does not, the event to which those elementary events are favorable which are not favorable to A, the set of all those elementary events which are not in the event A.

It is convenient to use special symbols for two particular events: S for the set of *all* elementary events, and O for the void or null event, containing *no* elementary event. Thus the event S always occurs. Its probability, $P(S)$, the ratio of all elementary events favorable to S to the total number of elementary events, is 1, since all elementary events are favorable to S; S is the *sure event.* The event O never occurs, and its probability, $P(O)$, is 0, since the number of elementary events favorable to O is 0; O is the *impossible event.* You should verify that $\bar{S} = O$, $\bar{O} = S$, and that for every event A, $A \cup O = A$, $A \cup S = S$, $AO = O$, $AS = A$, $A \cup \bar{A} = S$, and $A\bar{A} = O$.

If A and B are two events, then $A - B$ is the event which occurs if and only if A occurs but not B; it is the set of elementary events which are favorable to A but not to B. In the accompanying Euler diagram (Figure 2), the event $A - B$ consists of the elementary events 2 and 4, while $B - A$ contains the elementary event 3 alone. For every pair A,B of events, $A - B = A - AB = A\bar{B}$; for each event A, $\bar{A} = S - A$, and $A = S - \bar{A}$.

If every elementary event favorable to A is also favorable to B, we write $A \subset B$ or $B \supset A$, and say that A is *contained in* B, or that the occurrence of A *implies* that of B. For every pair A,B of events, $AB \subset A$, $AB \subset B$, $A \subset A \cup B$, $B \subset A \cup B$.

Two events A and B are *equal* if every elementary event favorable to one is also favorable to the other: $A = B$ if and only if $A \subset B$ and $B \subset A$. In order to prove two events equal in the exercises which follow, you must show that each elementary event favorable to the left member of the equation is also favorable to the right, and conversely.

The table on page 12 gives the correspondence between the notation and the terminology.

PROBLEMS

1. Verify that

(a) $\overline{A \cup B} = \bar{A}\bar{B}$

(b) $\bar{A} \cup \bar{B} = \overline{AB}$

(c) $A(B \cup C) = AB \cup AC$

(d) $A \cup BC = (A \cup B)(A \cup C)$

(e) $AB - ABC = AB\bar{C}$

(f) $B - (B - A) = AB$

2. Which of the following are true for all events A, B, C, and which are not?

(a) $(\bar{A} \cup \bar{B})C = \overline{AB} \cup C$
(b) $(A - C)(B - C) = AB\bar{C}$
(c) $AB - C = A \cap (B - C)$
(d) $(A - C) \cup (B - C) = (A \cup B) - C$
(e) $A \cap \overline{AC} = O$
(f) $A \cup B \cup C = A \cup (B - A) \cup [C - (A \cup B)]$
(g) $A(B - C) = AB - AC$
(h) $(\bar{A} \cup \bar{B}) \cap \overline{AB} = O$
(i) $(\bar{A} \cup \bar{B}) \subset \overline{AB}$
(j) $B \subset B\bar{A} \cup A$
(k) $ABC \subset AC$
(l) If $A \subset B$, then $B = (B - A) \cup A$
(m) $AB \subset AC \cup B\bar{C}$

3. Arrange in "increasing" order, using the symbol $\subset$ between successive events: A, AB, $A \cup B$, S, O, $AB \cup AC$.

4. If $A \subset B$, arrange in increasing order the events: $\bar{A}\bar{B}$, $\bar{A} \cup \bar{B}$, $\bar{A}$, $\bar{B}$.

5. If A, B, C are events, write expressions for the event which occurs if (a) none of the three occurs; (b) all occur; (c) only C occurs; (d) A and B occur; (e) A and B occur, but not C; (f) exactly one occurs; (g) at least one occurs; (h) not more than one occur; (i) exactly two occur.

Table of Symbols

$A = O$	A is void or empty; A is impossible, cannot occur.
$A = S$	A must occur, A is the sure event.
$A \cup B$	The event which occurs if and only if either A or B (or both) occurs.
AB	The event which occurs if and only if both A and B occur.
$AB = O$	A and B are mutually exclusive events; they are logically incompatible; if either occurs, the other cannot.
$\bar{A}$	The event which occurs if and only if A does not.
$\begin{Bmatrix} A \subset B \\ B \supset A \end{Bmatrix}$	If A occurs, so does B; A implies B.
$A - B$	The event which occurs if and only if A occurs but not B.

Σ *and* Π *Notation.* The Σ and Π notations are probably already familiar to you. If $a_1, a_2, \cdots, a_n$ are numbers, then

$$\sum_{i=1}^{n} a_i = a_1 + a_2 + \cdots + a_n,$$

and

$$\prod_{i=1}^{n} a_i = a_1 a_2 \cdots a_n.$$

Similarly, if $A_1, A_2, \cdots, A_n$ are events, then

$$\bigcup_{i=1}^{n} A_i = A_1 \cup A_2 \cup \cdots \cup A_n,$$

and

$$\bigcap_{i=1}^{n} A_i = A_1 \cap A_2 \cap \cdots \cap A_n = A_1 A_2 \cdots A_n.$$

For example:

$$\sum_{i=1}^{4} i = 1 + 2 + 3 + 4;$$

$$\sum_{k=3}^{N} k^2 = 3^2 + 4^2 + 5^2 + \cdots + N^2;$$

$$\sum_{j=0}^{r} \frac{j}{1+j^2} = \frac{0}{1+0^2} + \frac{1}{1+1^2} + \frac{2}{1+2^2} + \cdots + \frac{r}{1+r^2};$$

$$\sum_{3<k\leq 7} \frac{(-1)^k}{k} = \sum_{k=4}^{7} \frac{(-1)^k}{k} = \frac{(-1)^4}{4} + \frac{(-1)^5}{5} + \frac{(-1)^6}{6} + \frac{(-1)^7}{7};$$

$$\bigcup_{i=2}^{5} B_i = \bigcup_{2\leq k\leq 5} B_k = B_2 \cup B_3 \cup B_4 \cup B_5;$$

$$\bigcup_{j=1}^{N} CA_j = CA_1 \cup \cdots \cup CA_N = C(A_1 \cup \cdots \cup A_N)$$
$$= C[\bigcup_{j=1}^{N} A_j];$$

$$\prod_{s=1}^{2} \left(1 - \frac{1}{s}\right) = \left(1 - \frac{1}{1}\right)\left(1 - \frac{1}{2}\right);$$

$$\prod_{k=2}^{N} (k^2 + 1) = (2^2 + 1)(3^2 + 1) \cdots (N^2 + 1);$$

$$\bigcap_{r=3}^{5} \bar{C}_r = \bar{C}_3 \cap \bar{C}_4 \cap \bar{C}_5 = \bar{C}_3\bar{C}_4\bar{C}_5(=\overline{C_3 \cup C_4 \cup C_5});$$

$$\bigcap_{i=1}^{N} A_i B_{i+1} = A_1 B_2 A_2 B_3 \cdots A_N B_{N+1}$$
$$= A_1 A_2 \cdots A_N B_2 B_3 \cdots B_{N+1}$$
$$= (\bigcap_{i=1}^{N} A_i)(\bigcap_{j=2}^{N+1} B_j).$$

3. Law of Total Probability. If A is an event, we shall write $P(A)$ for its probability. In an elementary probability space of the kind we are at present considering, this is the ratio of the number of elementary events favorable to A divided by the total number of elementary events.

▶ ***The Law of Total Probability.*** If A and B are mutually exclusive events ($AB = O$), then

$$P(A \cup B) = P(A) + P(B).$$

Proof. Let N be the number of elementary events; each has probability $1/N$. Let a be the number favorable to A, and b the number favorable to B. Since A and B are mutually exclusive, no elementary event is favorable to both, so that $a + b$ is the number favorable to $A \cup B$. Then

$$P(A \cup B) = \frac{a+b}{N} = \frac{a}{N} + \frac{b}{N} = P(A) + P(B).$$

You can use the principle of mathematical induction to prove the following:

▶ *If N is any positive integer, and if $A_1, A_2, \cdots, A_N$ are mutually exclusive events ($A_iA_j = O$ for $i \neq j$, $i,j = 1, 2, \cdots, N$), then*

$$P(\textstyle\bigcup_{i=1}^{N} A_i) = \sum_{i=1}^{N} P(A_i),$$

or

$$P(A_1 \cup A_2 \cup \cdots \cup A_N) = P(A_1) + P(A_2) + \cdots + P(A_N).$$

The law of total probability can be interpreted verbally as stating that if no two of the events $A_1, A_2, \cdots, A_N$ can both occur at a single performance of the experiment, then the probability that at least one will occur is the sum of their respective probabilities.

The law of total probability for two events is a most useful special case of the following formula:

▶ $$P(A \cup B) = P(A) + P(B) - P(AB).$$

(You see that when A and B are mutually exclusive ($AB = O$) this reduces to the earlier formula.)

Proof. Let N be the total number of elementary events, a the number favorable to A, b the number favorable to B, and c the number favorable to AB. Then $a + b - c$ are favorable to $A \cup B$, so that

$$P(A \cup B) = \frac{a+b-c}{N} = \frac{a}{N} + \frac{b}{N} - \frac{c}{N} = P(A) + P(B) - P(AB).$$

PROBLEM

Write a formula for $P(A \cup B \cup C)$ in terms of the probabilities of A, B, C and their intersections.

(Hint: $P(A \cup B \cup C) = P[A \cup (B \cup C)]$; use the formula above for the probability of the union of two events.)

Verify that your formula reduces to the one above if $C = B$.

4. Conditional Probability. In a probability space appropriate to consideration of a throw of two dice, there are 36 elementary events. But suppose you are told that a seven was thrown, and are asked for the probability that a three and a four came up. A new probability space appropriate for consideration of this problem has only 6 elementary events, those in the original space which are favorable to the event "a seven will be thrown." Of these only two, "three on die I and four on die II," and "four on die I, three on die II" are favorable to the event "a three and a four came up," so that this event has probability 2/6, or 1/3.

We can deal similarly with the situation in which S is the original set of N elementary events, and A and B are events, with a and b elementary events favorable to A and to B respectively, and c elementary events favorable to both A and B. Suppose you are told that the event B occurred, and asked for the probability that A did. In effect B now becomes your probability space, one containing b elementary events, of which c are favorable to the event AB. In this new probability space, then, the probability of AB is c/b. With reference to the original probability space, this is called the *conditional probability of A given B*, and will be denoted by $P(A \mid B)$. We have

$$P(A \mid B) = \frac{c}{b} = \frac{c/N}{b/N} = \frac{P(AB)}{P(B)}.$$

Similarly,

$$P(B \mid A) = \frac{P(AB)}{P(A)}.$$

5. Law of Compound Probability. The law of compound probability is contained in the formulas just given. It may be stated as follows:

▶ ***Law of Compound Probability.*** *If A and B are any two events, then*

$$P(AB) = P(B)P(A \mid B) = P(A)P(B \mid A).$$

The formulas in the paragraph above are valid only if $P(A) \neq 0$ and $P(B) \neq 0$; but the formulas in the Law of Compound Probability would be valid also if $P(A) = 0$ or if $P(B) = 0$, no matter how $P(A \mid B)$ and $P(B \mid A)$ might be defined, since then each member is 0.

PROBLEM

Prove that $P(ABC) = P(C|AB)P(B|A)P(A)$.

EXAMPLE 4. Urn I contains a white balls and b red ones; Urn II contains c white balls and d red ones. You plan to transfer a ball chosen at random from Urn I to Urn II and then to draw at random from Urn II. What is the probability that you will draw a white ball?

In an earlier problem of this kind (cf. p. 6), you set up a probability space involving $(a + b)(c + d + 1)$ elementary events, each representing the transferring of one of the $a + b$ balls in Urn I into Urn II, and the drawing of one of the $c + d + 1$ balls then in Urn II. Now we can use the laws of total and compound probability to avoid some of the counting which would be required by the more direct method. Let A denote the event that a white ball will be transferred; then $\bar{A}$ is the event that a red one will be transferred. Let B denote the event that a white one will finally be drawn from Urn II; you are asked to find $P(B)$. Now B can occur only if A occurs or if A does not occur; or again, B can occur only if both A and B occur, or if both $\bar{A}$ and B occur. That is,

$$B = AB \cup \bar{A}B.$$

Since AB and $\bar{A}B$ are mutually exclusive, it follows from the law of total probability that

$$P(B) = P(AB) + P(\bar{A}B).$$

By the law of compound probability,

$$P(AB) = P(A)P(B|A) \text{ and } P(\bar{A}B) = P(\bar{A})P(B|\bar{A}).$$

Each of these probabilities could also be written in another way, but in the present problem the probabilities $P(A)$ and $P(\bar{A})$ can readily be determined, as can the conditional probabilities $P(B|A)$ and $P(B|\bar{A})$. We have

$$P(A) = \frac{a}{a+b}, \qquad P(\bar{A}) = \frac{b}{a+b},$$

$$P(B|A) = \frac{c+1}{c+d+1}, \quad P(B|\bar{A}) = \frac{c}{c+d+1}.$$

On making these substitutions in the above formulas we find that

$$P(B) = \frac{a(c+1)}{(a+b)(c+d+1)} + \frac{bc}{(a+b)(c+d+1)},$$

$$P(B) = \frac{ac + bc + a}{(a+b)(c+d+1)}.$$

PROBLEMS

1. Given $P(A) = 1/2$, $P(B) = 1/3$, $P(AB) = 1/4$; find $P(A \cup B)$, $P(A|B)$, $P(B|A)$, $P(A \cup B|B)$.

2. Given $P(A \cup B) = 11/12$, $P(A) = 3/4$, $P(AB) = 1/2$; find $P(B)$, $P(A|B)$, $P(B|A)$.

3. A player throws two dice, one red and one black.

(a) What is the probability that he will throw 7?

(b) After the dice are thrown, an observer can see that the red die has turned up 2. He cannot see the black. What is the probability (conditioned by the red die having turned up 2) that the player has thrown 7?

(c) Illustrate the law of compound probability in computing the probability that the player will throw 7 and that the red die will show 2 points.

4. Event A can happen only if one of two mutually exclusive events B_1 or B_2 does; that is, $A \subset B_1 \cup B_2$.

(a) Show that $A = AB_1 \cup AB_2$.

(b) Express $P(A)$ in terms of $P(AB_1)$ and $P(AB_2)$.

(c) Express $P(A)$ in terms of $P(B_1)$, $P(B_2)$, $P(A|B_1)$, and $P(A|B_2)$.

5. R. Roe has an alarm which will ring at the appointed hour with probability 0.7. If it rings, it will wake him with probability 0.8. If it doesn't ring he will wake in time to make his morning class with probability 0.3. What is the probability that he will make his morning class?

6. Urn I contains 10 white and 3 red balls. Urn II contains 3 white and 5 red balls. Two balls are to be transferred from I to II, and one ball is then to be drawn from II. What are the probabilities that the two balls transferred from I will be (a) both white? (b) one white and one red? (c) both red?

(d) What is the probability that a white ball will be drawn from II?

7. Hunter Doe hunts bear. The probability that a bear will appear at range less than R_1 is 0.1, at range between R_1 and R_2 is 0.3, and at greater range than R_2 is 0.2. If a bear appears at range less than R_1, Doe will be able to kill him with probability 0.7; with probability 0.5 if the range is between R_1 and R_2; with probability 0.2 if the range is greater than R_2. What is the probability that Doe will kill a bear?

8. Jones chooses at random one of the integers 1, 2, 3, then throws as many dice as are indicated by the number he chose. What is the probability that he will throw a total of 5 points?

9. As a train approaches, a station operator will press a button with probability 0.95; if he presses the button, the switch will operate with probability 0.99; if the switch operates, a warning bell will sound with probability 0.9. What is the probability that the warning bell will sound?

10. Two cars approach each other on the highway at night. If neither driver is dozing, they will pass safely with probability 0.999. Each will be dozing with probability 0.1, the probability that both will doze being 0.01. If only driver A dozes, they will pass safely with a probability 0.7. If only driver B dozes they will pass safely with probability 0.8. If both doze they will pass safely with probability 0.4. What is the probability that they will pass safely?

11. Suppose you separate two aces and a jack from a standard deck of cards, place them with their backs uppermost, mix them, choose one at random and replace it in the deck. You then shuffle the deck and draw a card. What is the probability that you will draw an ace? Show how you use the laws of total and compound probability in obtaining your answer.

6. Independent Events. Two events are *independent* if the knowledge that one will occur or has occurred does not affect the probability of the other; more precisely, if the conditional probability of each given the other is the same as the unconditional probability. Thus events A and B are independent if $P(B \mid A) = P(B)$ and $P(A \mid B) = P(A)$. Since

$$P(AB) = P(B \mid A)P(A) = P(A \mid B)P(B),$$

the conditional probabilities will be equal to the unconditional probabilities if and only if

$$P(AB) = P(A)P(B),$$

if neither $P(A)$ nor $P(B)$ is 0. If either is 0, one of the conditional probabilities fails to be defined. For convenience, however, we shall use the multiplicative relation immediately above as the definition of independent events, even if one or both has probability 0.

▶ ***Definition.*** Events A and B are independent if

$$P(AB) = P(A)P(B).$$

If we have at hand three events, A, B, and C, we feel that a reasonable definition of independence should imply that $P(A \mid BC) = P(A)$, $P(C \mid B) = P(C)$, etc. If none of the events has probability 0, such conditional probabilities will be equal to the unconditional probabilities if and only if $P(AB) = P(A)P(B)$, $P(BC) = P(B)P(C)$, $P(AC) = P(A)P(C)$, and $P(ABC) = P(A)P(B)P(C)$. For convenience again, we shall say that A, B, C are *independent*, or *mutually independent*, if

(i) *A, B, C are pairwise independent, that is,*

$$P(AB) = P(A)P(B),\ P(BC) = P(B)P(C),\ \textit{and}\ P(AC) = P(A)P(C),$$

and if

(ii) $P(ABC) = P(A)P(B)P(C)$.

Similarly, the events of any finite collection of events are independent, or mutually independent, if and only if the probability of the intersection of every collection of distinct events from among them is the product of their probabilities. That is,

▶ *Events are* independent *if and only if the probability that any specified two or more events will happen is the product of the probabilities of the events specified.*

PROBLEMS

1. Each of four men throws a single die. What is the probability that (a) each will throw 4; (b) each will throw an even number of spots; (c) all will throw the same number?

2. Each of N individuals tosses one coin. Express in terms of N the probability that (a) none will throw heads; (b) each will throw heads; (c) at least one head will turn up.

3. How many people must draw one card each from different decks to have a probability at least 0.9 that at least one ace will be drawn?

4. Prove that if A is any event, then O and A are independent, and S and A are independent.

5. Prove that if A and B are independent, then $\bar{A}$ and $\bar{B}$ are independent, and A and $\bar{B}$ are independent.

6. Given that events A, B, and C are independent, with probabilities 1/2, 1/3, and 2/3 respectively, find the probabilities of

(a) AB. (b) $A \cup B$. (c) $C - (A \cup B)$. (d) $A - BC$.

7. One of the problems which contributed to the early growth of the theory of probability in the 17th century was posed to Pascal by a French nobleman fond of gambling, the Chevalier de Méré ([12],† p. 4). He had found experimentally that the probability of obtaining at least 1 six in 4 throws of a die is larger than the probability of obtaining at least 1 double six in 24 throws of two dice, a result which seemed to him unreasonable. Find these probabilities.

8. In a group of N members, a fraction p (a total number Np) bear a certain distinguishing characteristic C. (a) Describe an elementary probability space appropriate to the experiment of choosing a member at random, observing whether or not it bears C, returning it, and repeating the process (cf. Problem 4, p. 7). Are the events A_1: "a member bearing C will appear on the first draw" and A_2: "a member bearing C will appear on the second draw" independent? Prove your answer correct. (b) As in (a), but with three draws, and three events A_1, A_2, A_3.

† Bracketed references are to the books listed on page 372.

9. Professor Aye shuffles three cards having identical backs; one has a red face, one a yellow face, one a blue face. He lays them face down on the table. Miss Bea will attempt to name the colors of the faces in the order laid down. Assume no collusion nor clairvoyance, and that Miss Bea will not name the same color twice.

(a) Set up an elementary probability space appropriate to this experiment. What elementary events are favorable to each of the following events? A: "Miss Bea will correctly name the color of the first card." B: "She will correctly name the color of the second card." C: "She will correctly name the color of the third card."

(b) Are A, B, C pairwise independent? mutually independent? Prove your answers correct.

10. Eight tickets, numbered 111, 121, 122, 122, 211, 212, 212, 221 are placed in a brown hat and stirred. One is then to be drawn at random. Show that the events A: "the first digit on the ticket drawn will be 1," B: "the second digit on the ticket drawn will be 1," and C: "the third digit on the ticket drawn will be 1" are not pairwise independent (hence not mutually independent), although $P(ABC) = P(A)P(B)P(C)$.

11. Madame L. has a jewel box containing four ornate rings. One ring has a diamond and an emerald; another a diamond and a topaz; another an emerald and a topaz; and the other five pearls. She will reach into her box and select one ring at random. Show that the events A: "she will select a ring with a diamond," B: "she will select a ring with an emerald," and C: "she will select a ring with a topaz" are pairwise independent, but not mutually independent ([5], p. 116; [6], p. 25).

CHAPTER
2

General Probability Spaces

7. Introduction. Thus far our attention has been directed to probability spaces in which there are only a finite number of elementary events, all with the same probability. Yet modern probability theory has application to a vast range of situations to which no probability space with only a finite number of equally likely elementary events is appropriate. The spaces we have been dealing with are in a sense the simplest, and are closely related to games of chance and the early development of probability theory. Our discussion of them has been motivated by a desire to instruct the intuition; to develop an appreciation of the characteristic properties of events and their probabilities. We shall list these properties below in two sets of axioms, one list of axioms for events, and another for their probabilities. A probability space will then be any collection of elementary events, together with a family of subcollections of elementary events, called events, and their probabilities, satisfying the two lists of axioms. Not all such spaces will contain only finite numbers of elementary events, nor will all elementary events in such a space necessarily have the same probability.

Each event will still be a collection of elementary events, but it will not always be possible to preserve the properties of probability we require if we admit *all* collections of elementary events as events. The axioms for events are designed to give us freedom in operating with events, the results of operations on events such as we have discussed leading always to further events. For example, the union of a finite number of events should be an event. It is even convenient, often, to speak of the union or intersection of an infinite, but countable, set of events. A set of objects (such as events) is *countable* if they can be counted; that is, if they can be so arranged that there is a first, a second, a third, etc., each being associated with one and only one positive integer. If only a finite number of positive integers is used in this counting, the set is *countable* and *finite*. If all positive integers are used, the set is *infinite*, but *countable*. There are, of course, sets (such as the set of all real numbers) which are infinite and uncountable.

If a set of events is countable, the event associated with a particular integer can be designated by setting that integer as a subscript on a symbol for the event. Thus if N is a positive integer, $A_1, A_2, \cdots, A_N$ is a countable and finite set of events; $A_1, A_2, \cdots$ represents a countable and infinite set of events.

8. Definition of a Probability Space. We are now in a position to define a probability space.

▶ ***Definition.*** A probability space *consists of a set S (finite or infinite) of elementary events and a family $\mathfrak{F}$ of events. Each event is a set of elementary events said to be favorable to the event. The family $\mathfrak{F}$ of events satisfies the following axioms for $\mathfrak{F}$. A probability $P(A)$ is associated with each event A in $\mathfrak{F}$, satisfying the axioms for P which follow those for $\mathfrak{F}$.*

▶ **9. Axioms for $\mathfrak{F}$.**

$\mathfrak{F}1$. *O and S are events; that is, the void (impossible) event, to which no elementary event is favorable, and the (certain) event containing all elementary events, or to which every elementary event is favorable, belong to the family of events.*

$\mathfrak{F}2$. *The intersection of each countable set of events is an event; that is, the set of elementary events, each of which is favorable to every one of a given countable (finite or infinite) collection of events, is an event.*

$\mathfrak{F}3$. *The union of each countable collection of events is an event; that is, the set of elementary events, each of which is favorable to at least one of the events of a given countable set of events, is an event.*

$\mathfrak{F}4$. *If A is an event, so is $\bar{A}$; that is, the set of elementary events not favorable to a given event is an event.*

The following property of the family of events, which could be given as an axiom in place of $\mathfrak{F}4$, is a consequence of $\mathfrak{F}2$ and $\mathfrak{F}4$:

$\mathfrak{F}5$. *If A and B are events, so is $A - B$; the set of elementary events favorable to A but not to B is an event, $A - B$.*

PROBLEM

Prove $\mathfrak{F}5$ above.

▶10. Axioms for P, and Related Theorems.

Axioms for P

P1. *$P(A)$ is defined for every event A;* that is, if A is in $\mathfrak{F}$, then there is associated with A a real number $P(A)$.

This axiom states that $P(A)$ is a real-valued function of sets (each event is a *set* of elementary events) defined on $\mathfrak{F}$.

P2. $P(A) \geq 0$ *for every event* A.

P3. $P(S) = 1$.

P4. (*Law of Total Probability*). *The probability of the union of a countable set of* mutually exclusive *events is the sum of their probabilities.*

If $A_1, A_2, \cdots, A_N$ are events, and if $A_iA_j = O$ for $i \neq j$, $i,j = 1, 2, \cdots, N$, then $P(\bigcup_{i=1}^{N} A_i) = \sum_{i=1}^{N} P(A_i)$. If $A_1, A_2, \cdots$ are events, and if $A_iA_j = O$ for $i \neq j$, $i,j = 1, 2, \cdots$, then

$$P(\bigcup_{i=1}^{\infty} A_i) = \sum_{i=1}^{\infty} P(A_i).$$

The following theorems are consequences of the axioms.

P5. *If A and B are events, and if $A \subset B$, then* $P(B - A) = P(B) - P(A)$.
(Hint: $B = A \cup (B - A)$.)

P6. $P(\bar{A}) = 1 - P(A)$ *for every event* A.

P7. $P(O) = 0$.

P8. $0 \leq P(A) \leq 1$ *for every event* A.

P9. *If A and B are events, and if $A \subset B$, then $P(A) \leq P(B)$.*

P10. (*Boole's inequality*). *If $A_1, A_2, \cdots$ are events (not necessarily mutually exclusive) then $P(\bigcup_{i=1}^{\infty} A_i) \leq \sum_{i=1}^{\infty} P(A_i)$.*

★ ***P11.*** *If $B_1, B_2, \cdots$ are events, if $B_1 \subset B_2 \subset \cdots$ and if $B = \bigcup_{i=1}^{\infty} B_i$, then $P(B) = \lim_{i\to\infty} P(B_i)$.*

★ ***P12.*** *If $B_1, B_2, \cdots$ are events, if $B_1 \supset B_2 \supset \cdots$ and if $B =$* $\bigcap_{i=1}^{\infty} B_i$, then $P(B) = \lim_{i\to\infty} P(B_i)$.

PROBLEM

Prove Theorems P5 to P10. In proving each you may use those which appear earlier in the list, in addition to the axioms.

(Hint for P10: Use P4, P5; first observe that

$$\bigcup_{i=1}^{\infty} A_i = A_1 \cup [A_2 - A_1] \cup [A_3 - (A_1 \cup A_2)] \cup \cdots.)$$

★ (Hint for ★P11: Show first that $B = \bigcup_{i=1}^{\infty} A_i$ where $A_1 = B_1$ and $A_i = B_i - B_{i-1}$, $i = 2, 3, \cdots$; the events $\{A_i\}$ are mutually exclusive; apply P4 and observe that by definition $\sum_{i=1}^{\infty} P(A_i) = \lim_{n\to\infty} \sum_{i=1}^{n} P(A_i)$.)

★ (Hint for ★P12: Use P6 and P11; what is $\bar{B}$?)

Each of the probability spaces we first studied contained only a finite number of elementary events, and *every* set of elementary events was an event, so that axioms $\mathfrak{F}1$ to $\mathfrak{F}4$ (and $\mathfrak{F}5$) were automatically satisfied. We saw also that for probability as defined on page for such spaces, axioms P1 to P4 were satisfied, hence also properties P5 to P10.

Henceforth we shall frequently have occasion to deal with probability spaces in which there are infinitely many elementary events. In such cases in general not every set of elementary events can belong to the family $\mathfrak{F}$ of events if the axioms P1 to P4 are to hold; but in each such case there will be a family $\mathfrak{F}$ of events satisfying axioms $\mathfrak{F}1$ to $\mathfrak{F}4$, and a probability associated with each event, satisfying axioms P1 to P4. When there are only a finite number of elementary events in S, we shall always take for $\mathfrak{F}$ the family of all sets of elementary events; i.e., in this case every set of elementary events will be an event. However, we shall not insist even in this special case that the elementary events have equal probabilities, so long as axioms P1 to P4 are satisfied.

Following standard usage, when an event is denoted by a literal symbol such as A, its probability will be denoted by $P(A)$. But when the event is represented by a description between braces, its probability will be denoted by setting the abbreviation "Pr" immediately in front of the braces enclosing the description of the event.

EXAMPLE 1. You have been given an unbalanced coin, and by some means or other (as, for example, by observing the results of a very large number of tosses) have become convinced that the probability of throwing heads is about 0.6. An appropriate probability space for the experiment of one toss of the coin has just two elementary events, H and T. There are exactly four events, 0, H, T, and $H \cup T = S$, with associated probabilities 0, 0.6, 0.4, and 1.

EXAMPLE 2. A horizontal arm rotates about a vertical axis, a pointer on the end sweeping around a circle on which is marked a scale from 0 to 1, the points marked 0 and 1 coinciding. In the idealized situation, this device provides a means of choosing a number *at random* between 0 and 1, the scale marking at the point where the pointer comes to rest being the number thus chosen. A probability space appropriate to the consideration of one performance of the experiment which consists in spinning the pointer and noting the number where it comes to rest has infinitely many elementary events: each number of the interval [0,1), i.e., each x satisfying $0 \leq x < 1$, is an elementary event. In this space, each interval is also to be an event. An *interval* is the set of all real numbers x satisfying inequalities $a < x < b$ or $a \leq x < b$ or $a < x \leq b$ or $a \leq x \leq b$ for some pair of real numbers a and b with $a < b$; in the present situation, a and b may be any real numbers between 0 and 1 with $a < b$. Roughly, an interval is the set of all real numbers between two specified numbers. A single number itself is a degenerate interval, and is also to be an event in the probability space we are considering. In accordance with axiom $\mathfrak{F}3$, the set of real numbers in the union of two or more intervals or in the union of any countable set of intervals must be an event also.

The description of the experiment is intended to suggest that the pointer is as likely to come to rest in one of two intervals of equal length as in the other, or that events which are intervals of equal length should have equal probabilities. It can then be shown that the probability of any interval must be proportional to its length: if the event A is an interval of length s, then $P(A) = ks$, where k is a proportionality constant, the same for all intervals. Since S is the interval [0,1), its length s is 1; hence $1 = P(S) = k \cdot 1$, and $k = 1$, so that for every interval A of length s, $P(A) = s$.

In this probability space, then, the elementary events are the real numbers between 0 and 1. Each interval is an event, and each elementary event, a degenerate interval, is also an event. The probability of an event which is an interval is just its length. The complete construction and description of the family of events and the complete definition of their probabilities is beyond the scope of this text. We shall simply assume that a family $\mathfrak{F}$ of events exists with the above described properties, satisfying axioms $\mathfrak{F}1$ to $\mathfrak{F}4$, and that associated with each event is a probability with the above properties and satisfying axioms P1 to P4.

The concepts and formulas we developed for the special probability spaces we considered first are meaningful and valid in the more general context also. Consider, for example, the formula for the probability of a union:

▶ $$P(A \cup B) = P(A) + P(B) - P(AB).$$

Proof. $A \cup B = A \cup (B - A) = A \cup (B - AB)$; $B - A = B - AB$ is an event by $\mathfrak{F}5$. By the definition of the difference of two events, A and $B - AB$ are mutually exclusive events: no elementary event is favorable to both. By P4 then,

$$P(A \cup B) = P(A) + P(B - AB).$$

Since $AB \subset B$, by P5 we have

$$P(B - AB) = P(B) - P(AB),$$

so that

$$P(A \cup B) = P(A) + P(B) - P(AB).$$

11. Conditional Probability, and the Law of Compound Probability. As before, if A and B are events, we define $P(A \mid B)$ by

$$P(A \mid B) = \frac{P(AB)}{P(B)} \quad \text{if } P(B) \neq 0,$$

and have immediately

▶ $$P(AB) = P(A)P(B \mid A) = P(B)P(A \mid B)$$

even if $P(A) = 0$ or $P(B) = 0$.

12. Independence. Independence of events also is defined as before: the events of a finite set of events are *independent* if the probability of the intersection of every set of distinct events among them is the product of their probabilities; the events of a countable but infinite collection of events are independent if those of every finite subset are independent (cf. pp. 18, 19).

▶ *Events are* independent *if the probability that those of a finite collection of specified events among them will all occur is the product of the probabilities of those specified.*

PROBLEMS

1. Show that $P(A \mid A) = 1$ if $P(A) \neq 0$.

2. The driver of each of two cars has probability 0.1 of dozing. What is the probability that both will doze? What assumption is implicit in your answer?

3. Each of three guns has probability 0.6 of hitting a target. What is the probability (a) that all will hit; (b) that none will hit; (c) that the first will miss and the other two hit; (d) that exactly two will hit; (e) that at least two will hit?

4. If A is the event that a man chosen at random from a certain group will prove to be overweight, and if B is the event that he will be over 50 years of age, write in symbolic form the following events and their probabilities: (a) he will not be overweight; (b) if found to be overweight, he will also be over 50; (c) he will be overweight and over 50; (d) if found to be over 50, he will also be overweight.

5. If $\frac{1}{10}$ of 1% of the eyes of newborn calves are defective, while both eyes are defective in $\frac{1}{80}$ of 1% of newborn calves, what is the probability that a newborn calf will have at least one defective eye?

6. Assume that the N events, each that you are infected with one of N types of bacteria and virus, are independent, and that the probability of each is 1/2. What is the probability that (a) you are infected by all; (b) you are infected with none; (c) you are infected with at least one?

7. You fire three times at a target, with a probability 0.7 each time of hitting it. Assume that the events that you hit it with the first, second, and third shots are mutually independent. What is the probability that (a) you will hit the target all three times; miss it all three times; (b) you will hit it with the first or second shot?

8. At a booth at a carnival you and two friends toss one dart each at a balloon, with respective hit probabilities of 1/2, 1/4, and 1/3. What is the probability that (a) all will hit; (b) none will hit; (c) at least one will hit; (d) your two friends will hit?

9. You fire one round at a target with each of three guns. Let A, B, C respectively denote the events that you hit with the first gun, that you hit with the second gun, and that you hit with the third gun. Assume these events are independent, with probabilities 0.7, 0.6, and 0.4 respectively.

(a) Express in terms of A, B, C the event that you will not hit the target at all, and find its probability.

(b) Express in terms of A, B, C the event that you will hit the target at least twice, and find its probability.

10. Show that $P(ABC) = P(A)P(B|A)P(C|AB)$.

11. (a) Three people are present in a room. What is the probability that the birth dates of at least two will fall on the same day of the month (not necessarily the same month or year)? For simplicity assume all months have 30 days.

(b) How many people must be present in order for this probability to be at least 1/2?

12. Assume that the probability that a child born to a couple will be male is 1/2, and is thus independent of the number and sex of other children in the family. Assuming that the couple will have three children, find the probability that (a) all will be boys; (b) at least one boy will be born.

13. Assume that the probability that a child born to a couple will be male is $1/2 + mc - fk$, where c and k are certain small constants, and where

m is the number of male children already born to the couple, f the number of female children already born to the couple. If the couple are going to have three children, what is the probability that (a) all will be boys; (b) at least one will be a boy? (Your answers will be expressed in terms of c and k.)

14. You plan to perform the following experiment. You will shuffle a standard deck, and draw a card; replace it, reshuffle, and draw again; continuing in this manner until you have shuffled the entire pack and drawn a card from it 52 times.

(a) Write an exact expression for the probability, p, that you will never draw the queen of hearts.

(b) Show that $p \doteq 1/e$ (is approximately equal to), and indeed that if n independent trials are to be made of an event with probability $1/n$ in each, the probability that the event will never occur approaches $1/e$ as $n \to \infty$.

13. Bayes Formula. Suppose A is an event which can occur only if one of the mutually exclusive events $B_1, B_2, \cdots, B_N$ occurs; that is,

$$A \subset \bigcup_{i=1}^{N} B_i, \; B_iB_j = O \quad \text{if } i \neq j, \; i,j = 1, 2, \cdots, N.$$

Suppose you have at hand a problem in which the conditional probabilities $P(A \mid B_i)$ $(i = 1, 2, \cdots, N)$ can readily be determined, as can also the probabilities $P(B_i)$ $(i = 1, 2, \cdots, N)$, and that you wish to determine the conditional probability $P(B_1 \mid A)$.

First, with the aid of the law of compound probability (or the definition of conditional probability), you can write

$$P(AB_1) = P(A)P(B_1 \mid A) = P(B_1)P(A \mid B_1).$$

On dividing both sides by $P(A)$, you have

$$P(B_1 \mid A) = \frac{P(B_1)P(A \mid B_1)}{P(A)};$$

the numerator is known, and it remains to determine $P(A)$. You observe that, since $A \subset B_1 \cup B_2 \cup \cdots \cup B_N$, you have

$$A = AB_1 \cup AB_2 \cup \cdots \cup AB_N:$$

A occurs if and only if both A and B_1 occur or both A and B_2 occur or $\cdots$ or both A and B_N occur. The events $B_1, B_2, \cdots, B_N$ were given to be mutually exclusive; so also, therefore, are the events $AB_1, AB_2, \cdots, AB_N$: no elementary event is favorable to any two of them. By P4,

$$P(A) = P(AB_1) + P(AB_2) + \cdots + P(AB_N)$$

$$= \sum_{i=1}^{N} P(AB_i).$$

By the law of compound probability,

$$P(AB_i) = P(B_i)P(A \mid B_i) \quad (i = 1, 2, \cdots, N),$$

so that

$$P(A) = \sum_{i=1}^{N} P(B_i)P(A \mid B_i).$$

Since you know $P(B_i)$ and $P(A \mid B_i)$ for each i ($i = 1, 2, \cdots, N$), this gives you $P(A)$, and thus finally $P(B_1 \mid A)$:

▶ ***Bayes Formula***

$$P(B_1 \mid A) = \frac{P(B_1)P(A \mid B_1)}{\sum_{i=1}^{N} P(B_i)P(A \mid B_i)}$$

if $B_1, B_2, \cdots, B_N$ are mutually exclusive, and if $A \subset B_1 \cup B_2 \cup \cdots \cup B_N$.

It is clear that any other of the events $B_1, B_2, \cdots, B_N$ could play the role here played by B_1.

(Bayes formula is correct; its abuse through indiscriminate application has been severely criticized; cf. [11], p. 44; [3], Chapter 34; [7].)

Example 3. Jones has two bags: I, with three red marbles and two white; II, with one red marble and four white. The bags are identical in appearance. He asks you to choose one bag at random, and to draw at random a marble from it. You draw a red marble. What are the odds in favor of its having come from bag I; that is, what is the probability that it came from I?

You are to find the conditional probability of drawing a marble from bag I, given that the marble drawn is red. Let A denote the event "a red marble will be drawn," and B_1 the event "a marble will be drawn from bag I." The marble must be drawn from bag I or from bag II; let B_2 denote the event "the marble will be drawn from bag II." Then $A \subset B_1 \cup B_2$, and B_1 and B_2 are mutually exclusive. The hypotheses of Bayes' Theorem are satisfied, and the formula obtains:

$$P(B_1 \mid A) = \frac{P(B_1)P(A \mid B_1)}{P(B_1)P(A \mid B_1) + P(B_2)P(A \mid B_2)}.$$

$P(B_1)$ is 1/2, $P(A \mid B_1)$ is 3/5; $P(B_2)$ is 1/2, and $P(A \mid B_2)$ is 1/5. Substitution in the formula yields

$$P(B_1 \mid A) = 3/4.$$

If you give Jones odds of 3 to 1 that the marble came from bag I, it's a fair bet—assuming Jones doesn't know which bag it came from!

EXAMPLE 4. Your host has arranged an unusual game for you and his other guests. Unseen by his guests, his small daughter spins a pointer which must stop in one of three sectors, I of central angle 144°, II of central angle 144°, and III of central angle 72°. Also unseen by his guests, his small son throws a number of dice equal to the number of the sector in which the pointer stops. The sum of the spots is then announced, and the guests bet on the sector in which the pointer stopped. If the sum of the spots was 8, what are the odds for the various sectors?

Let A be the event "eight spots will turn up," B_i the event "the pointer will stop in the ith sector" ($i = 1, 2, 3$). You have to determine $P(B_i|A)$ ($i = 1, 2, 3$). The events B_2, B_3 are mutually exclusive, and A can occur only if at least one of the events B_2, B_3 occurs. You have $P(B_2) = 2/5$ and $P(B_3) = 1/5$. Also, $P(A|B_2) = 5/36$, $P(A|B_3) = 21/216$, so that

$$P(B_2|A) = \frac{(2/5)(5/36)}{(2/5)(5/36) + (1/5)(21/216)} = 60/81,$$

and

$$P(B_3|A) = \frac{(1/5)(21/216)}{(2/5)(5/36) + (1/5)(21/216)} = 21/81.$$

Obviously $P(B_1|A) = 0$.

PROBLEMS

1. Your friend chose at random one of three states, A, B, and C, to visit. The probability of rain in A was 1/3, in B was 1/4, and in C was 1/6. He came back with mud on his car. What is the probability that he visited state C?

2. A population of white rats contains 70% Andean rats, 30% Himalayan. Among the Andean, 30% have pink ears, while among the Himalayan, 50% have pink ears. A rat chosen at random is found to have pink ears. Use Bayes Formula to compute the probability that it is Andean.

3. I have three brown bags and two green. Each brown bag has red marbles and white marbles in the ratio 4 to 1, and each green bag has red marbles and white marbles in the ratio 1 to 4. I choose a bag at random, and a marble at random from the bag, showing it to you. It is white. What is the probability that it was drawn from a green bag?

4. In the example on page 30, a total of 5 spots appeared on the dice thrown. What are the odds for the various sectors?

5. Assume that the probability that a family chosen at random in a certain locality will have one child is 1/4; two children, 1/4; three children, 1/8. One such family is known to have three or fewer children, all of whom are boys. What is the probability that there are exactly two children? (Assume the probability that a child will be a boy is 1/2, independently of the number and sex of other children in the family.)

6. (Bertrand's Box Paradox) Each of three boxes has two drawers. Each drawer of one contains a gold coin; each drawer of another a silver coin; and of the third, one contains a silver coin, the other a gold coin. A box is chosen at random, a drawer is opened and is found to contain a gold coin. What is the probability that the coin in the other drawer of the same box is silver?

7. In Example 3 on page 29, Jones draws a marble at random from bag I and places it in bag II. You then choose one at random from bag II and find it is red. What is the probability that Jones transferred a red one from bag I to bag II?

8. My near-sighted neighbor enjoys tossing a basketball at a basket, but must rely on his small son to report whether or not he makes a goal. His probability of making a goal is 0.6, and the probability that his son will report correctly is 0.8. If his son reports a goal, what is the probability that my neighbor did make a goal?

9. In certain standard tests, I and II, it has been found that 5% and 10% respectively of 10th-grade students earn grade A. Comment on the statement that the probability is $(5/100)(10/100) = 1/200$ that a 10th-grade student chosen at random will earn grade A on both tests.

14. Summary. The elements of a probability space are called *elementary events*. Certain collections or sets of elementary events are *events*. The family $\mathfrak{F}$ of all events has the following properties:

$\mathfrak{F}1$. O and S are events; O is the void event, containing no elementary event, and S is the sure event, containing all elementary events.

$\mathfrak{F}2$. The intersection of a countable set of events is an event.

$\mathfrak{F}3$. The union of a countable set of events is an event.

$\mathfrak{F}4$. The complement, $\bar{A}$, of an event A is an event.

$\mathfrak{F}5$. The difference of two events is an event.

If there are only a finite number of elementary events, then every set of elementary events is an event, and the axioms for $\mathfrak{F}$ are satisfied.

Associated with each event A is a probability $P(A)$ with the following properties.

P1. $P(A)$ is defined for every event A.

P2. $P(A) \geq 0$ for every event A.

P3. $P(S) = 1$.

P4. The probability of the union of a countable set of mutually exclusive events is the sum of their probabilities.

P5. $P(B - A) = P(B) - P(A)$ for every pair A,B of events for which $A \subset B$.

P6. $P(\bar{A}) = 1 - P(A)$ for every event A.

P7. $P(O) = 0$.

P8. $0 \leq P(A) \leq 1$ for every event A.

P9. $P(A) \leq P(B)$ if $A \subset B$.

P10. $P(\bigcup_{i=1}^{\infty} A_i) \leq \sum_{i=1}^{\infty} P(A_i)$.

The *conditional probability* $P(B|A)$ is defined by:

$$P(B|A) = P(AB)/P(A).$$

Two events A and B are *independent* if

$$P(AB) = P(A)P(B).$$

The events of a countable collection of events are independent if the probability of the intersection of any finite number of them is the product of their probabilities.

Bayes formula applies to a situation where $A \subset \bigcup_{i=1}^{N} B$, and where the events $B_1, B_2, \cdots, B_N$ are mutually exclusive. Then we have for each k, $k = 1, 2, \cdots, N$,

$$P(B_k|A) = \frac{P(B_k)P(A|B_k)}{\sum_{i=1}^{N} P(B_i)P(A|B_i)}.$$

CHAPTER
3

Random Variables

15. Introduction. What is the number of spots which will turn up on a tossed die? What will be the weight of a man chosen at random in New York City? What force will be required to strip the threads of a screw chosen at random from a lot? None of these questions can be answered by simply a number; an element of chance, or of randomness, enters in each case. Nor is it satisfactory just to state the possible values; of primary interest in connection with each value is the *probability* that that value will be assumed.

Essentially, a *random variable,* or stochastic variable, is a variable which assumes each of its possible values with a definite probability. The number $\mathbf{y}$ of spots that will turn up on a tossed die is a random variable. The probability that $\mathbf{y}$ will assume the value 4, $Pr\{\mathbf{y} = 4\}$, is 1/6. The probability that $\mathbf{y}$ will assume a value between -2.5 and π is $Pr\{-2.5 < \mathbf{y} < \pi\} = 3/6 = 1/2$. *Only events have probabilities,* so we have to set up a structure within which $\{\mathbf{y} = 4\}$ and $\{-2.5 < \mathbf{y} < \pi\}$ are events. This can be done by defining a random variable as a function of elementary events on a probability space. Thus a random variable makes correspond to each elementary event a real number, its value at that elementary event.

If $\mathbf{x}$ is a random variable, then for each real number a, we want $\{\mathbf{x} = a\}$ to have a probability. Thus $\{\mathbf{x} = a\}$ must be interpreted as describing an event, a set of elementary events. This is accomplished by *defining* a random variable to be a real-valued *function* on the probability space. That is, the random variable $\mathbf{x}$ makes correspond to every elementary event s a real number $x(s)$, the *value* of the random variable $\mathbf{x}$ at the elementary event s. Then $\{\mathbf{x} = a\}$ is to be interpreted as the set of elementary events at each of which $\mathbf{x}$ has the value a; i.e., the set of elementary events s for which $x(s) = a$. We shall require that this set of elementary events be included in the family $\mathfrak{F}$ of events. Also, for every pair of real numbers b and c for which $b < c$, we denote by

$\{b < \mathbf{x} < c\}$ the set of elementary events at each of which $\mathbf{x}$ has a value strictly between b and c, and require that this set of elementary events be an event. Similarly, $\{b \leq \mathbf{x} < c\}$ will denote the set of elementary events at each of which $\mathbf{x}$ assumes a value not smaller than b but smaller than c, and this set is required to be an event in order for $\mathbf{x}$ to be a random variable, etc. We come thus to the definition of a random variable:

▶ ***Definition.*** A random variable $\mathbf{x}$ *is a real-valued function on a probability space: it makes correspond to each elementary event a real number, the* value *of the random variable at that elementary event. Further, for every real number* a, *the set* $\{\mathbf{x} = a\}$ *of elementary events at which* $\mathbf{x}$ *assumes the value* a *is an event; and for every pair of real numbers* b *and* c *the sets* $\{b < \mathbf{x} < c\}$, $\{b \leq \mathbf{x} < c\}$, $\{b < \mathbf{x} \leq c\}$, $\{b \leq \mathbf{x} \leq c\}$, $\{\mathbf{x} < c\}$, $\{\mathbf{x} \leq c\}$, $\{\mathbf{x} > b\}$, $\{\mathbf{x} \geq b\}$ *are events.*

If S contains only a finite number of elementary events, the condition expressed in the last sentence is automatically satisfied; for then every set of elementary events is an event.

The term "random variable" is perhaps not the best term for the concept, for the word "random" here and the phrase "at random" have different connotations. Other terms in common use are "chance variable" and "stochastic variable"; in German, zufällige Grösse; in French, variable aléatoire.

EXAMPLE 1. You match coins with Jones, winning a dime if you match, losing a dime if you don't. An appropriate probability space has 4 elementary events: HH, HT, TH, and TT. Let $\mathbf{y}$ denote the random variable verbally described as the amount you will win. This random variable is a real-valued function on the probability space: at each of the elementary events HH and TT it has the value 10 (cents), and at each of the elementary events HT and TH it has the value -10. The sure event S here contains only 4 elementary events, and accordingly every set of elementary events is an event. For example, $\{\mathbf{y} = 10\}$ consists of the elementary events HH and TT, and $Pr\{\mathbf{y} = 10\} = 1/2$; $\{\mathbf{y} = -7\}$ is the void event: no elementary event is favorable to it, and $Pr\{\mathbf{y} = -7\} = 0$; $\{-20 < \mathbf{y} \leq -7\}$ consists of the elementary events HT and TH, and $Pr\{-20 < \mathbf{y} \leq -7\} = 1/2$.

EXAMPLE 2. A point is to be chosen at random on the unit circle (with center at the origin, radius 1). Let $\mathbf{x}$ denote its abscissa (x coordinate). An appropriate probability space consists of the points on the unit circle: each such point is an elementary event. A complete description of an appropriate family of events is beyond the scope of this text. However, such a family can be determined so as to include each arc of the circle, to give each arc a probability proportional to its length, and to satisfy the axioms on the family of events and on the probability. The term "at random" is intended, in effect, to suggest that the probability that a point will be chosen on a particular arc shall be proportional to its length:

$$Pr\{\text{point in arc of length } s\} = ks.$$

Since the probability that the point will be chosen in an arc of length 2π (the whole circle) is 1, we have $1 = k \cdot 2\pi$, or $k = 1/2\pi$.

The abscissa $\mathbf{x}$ of the point chosen is a real-valued function on the probability space; to each point on the unit circle corresponds a real number, its x coordinate. The event $\{\mathbf{x} = a\}$ consists of two elementary events, the two points on the circle whose abscissa is a, if $-1 < a < 1$. The probability of this event is 0, for all elementary events in this particular probability space have the same probability, which could not be positive, or an event containing a large enough number of them would have probability greater than 1. If $-1 \leq a < b \leq 1$, then the elementary events favorable to the event $\{a < \mathbf{x} < b\}$ are those points on the two arcs of the circle between the ordinates $x = a$ and $x = b$. These arcs are mutually exclusive events; by P4, the probability of their union, $\{a < \mathbf{x} < b\}$, is the sum of their lengths multiplied by $1/2\pi$:

$$Pr\{a < \mathbf{x} < b\} = \frac{2}{2\pi}(\text{Arc}\cos a - \text{Arc}\cos b).$$

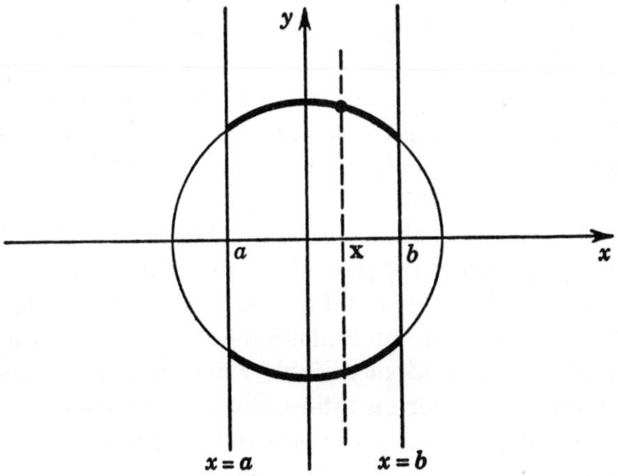

Figure 3

PROBLEMS

1. Let $\mathbf{w}$ represent "the square of the number of spots which will appear on a tossed die" ($\mathbf{w} = \mathbf{y}^2$, where $\mathbf{y}$ is the random variable discussed on page 33).

(a) Describe $\mathbf{w}$ as a random variable. What elementary events are favorable to the event $\{\mathbf{w} = 25\}$; to the event $\{0 < \mathbf{w} < 14\}$; to the event $\{-17 \leq \mathbf{w} \leq 42\}$; to the event $\{0 < \mathbf{w} < 1\}$?

(b) What are the probabilities of these events?

2. (a) Show that in the case of throwing a die, the probability of an elementary event is itself a random variable, $\mathbf{z}$.

(b) Find $Pr\{\mathbf{z} = 0\}$, $Pr\{\mathbf{z} = 1/6\}$, $Pr\{0 < \mathbf{z} < 1\}$.

(c) Draw the graph of $Pr\{\mathbf{z} < t\}$ as a function of t.

3. A point is chosen at random on the interval [0,1] ($0 \leq x \leq 1$) of the x axis.

(a) What are the elementary events in an appropriate probability space?

(b) Define "the coordinate of the point chosen" as a random variable, $\mathbf{x}$. What elementary events are favorable to the event $\{\mathbf{x} = 1/2\}$? What is its probability?

(c) What elementary events are favorable to the event $\{1/2 \leq \mathbf{x} \leq 1\}$; to the event $\{1/3 < \mathbf{x} < 4\}$? What are their probabilities?

4. An individual is to be chosen at random from a certain group of 100, and his weight, $\mathbf{x}$ pounds, is to be measured to the nearest pound. Let the probability space consist of the 100 individuals, each with associated probability 1/100. (a) Describe $\mathbf{x}$ as a random variable defined on this probability space. (b) Describe the events $\{\mathbf{x} < 150\}$ and $\{100 < \mathbf{x} \leq 150\}$.

16. Probability Space Induced on the Set of Real Numbers by a Random Variable. A random variable $\mathbf{x}$ is defined with respect to a given fundamental set S of elementary events, a family $\mathfrak{F}$ of events, each of which is a set of elementary events (a subset of S), and a probability P defined for each event, $\mathfrak{F}$ and P satisfying the axioms listed earlier. But also a random variable $\mathbf{x}$ *determines* a probability space in which the set R of all real numbers is the fundamental set, the real numbers themselves are elementary events, and intervals are events. The set of all real numbers x satisfying the inequalities $a < x < b$ is the *interval* (a,b); the intervals $(a,b]$ ($a < x \leq b$), $[a,b)$ ($a \leq x < b$), and $[a,b]$ ($a \leq x \leq b$) are defined similarly. We note that each interval is a set of real numbers, a subset of R.

The way in which the random variable $\mathbf{x}$ determines a probability space on R is as follows. Consider an interval of real numbers. It is to be an event, and its probability is to be the probability of the event in the original probability space, at each elementary event of which $\mathbf{x}$ assumes a value in the interval: $Pr\{a < \mathbf{x} < b\}$ is to be the probability assigned to the interval (a,b) of real numbers, $Pr\{a \leq \mathbf{x} < b\}$ the probability assigned to the interval $[a,b)$, etc.

It will not be necessary for us to describe completely the class of events, and it would be beyond the scope of this text to do so. It is clear that the family of intervals will not suffice, since this family does not satisfy, for example, Axiom $\mathfrak{F}4$ (nor any of the others): the union of two intervals need not be an interval. The smallest class of events which includes the intervals and which satisfies the axioms is called the class of Borel sets, and this we take for the family of events. It can be shown, though again it is beyond the scope of this text to do so, that a probability can be defined for each of these events so as to satisfy the axioms, and so that the probability associated with an interval is just the probability in the original probability space on which $\mathbf{x}$ is defined of the event consisting of those elementary events at each of which $\mathbf{x}$ assumes a value in the interval.

We note that since intervals are events in this *induced probability space*, any single number is an event too; for the real number a is the intersection of the interval $[a,b)$ and the interval $(c,a]$, and by Axiom $\mathfrak{F}2$ the intersection of events is an event.

▶ *A random variable* $\mathbf{x}$ *defined on a probability space induces on the set* R *of real numbers another probability space. In this induced probability space the elementary events are the real numbers; they are also events. Each interval of real numbers is an event. The probability of an event which is a single real number* a *is* $Pr\{\mathbf{x} = a\}$. *The probability of an event which is an interval* (a,b) *is* $Pr\{a < \mathbf{x} < b\}$, *the probability of an event* $[a,b)$ *is* $Pr\{a \leq \mathbf{x} < b\}$, *the probability of an event* $(a,b]$ *is* $Pr\{a < \mathbf{x} \leq b\}$, *and the probability of an event* $[a,b]$ *is* $Pr\{a \leq \mathbf{x} \leq b\}$.

The term *population*, or *parent population*, which we shall use later in studying random sampling, will refer to precisely such a probability space: a probability space induced on R by a random variable.

For example, suppose that you have a supply of 1000 bolts of a certain size produced by a certain manufacturer, and that you are interested in their shear strengths. In an appropriate probability space each bolt would be represented by an elementary event of probability 1/1000. Now consider the random variable $\mathbf{x}$: "shear strength of a bolt to be chosen at random." This random variable has many possible values; the probability, $Pr\{\mathbf{x} = x\}$, that it will be equal to a particular real number x, is precisely the fraction of the 1000 bolts whose shear strength is x.

This fraction is also the probability associated with the elementary event, in the induced probability space, which is the real number x. For example, if there are 5 bolts with shear strength 20, then $Pr\{\mathbf{x} = 20\} = 0.005$, and this is the probability to be associated with the point 20 on the real axis.

The probability associated with an interval (a,b) is just the fraction of the 1000 bolts having shear strengths between a and b. For example, if there are 13 bolts with shear strengths between 30 and 35, then $Pr\{30 < \mathbf{x} < 35\}$

= 0.013, and this is the probability to be associated with the interval (30,35) on the real line. This induced probability space is the *population* determined by the random variable $\mathbf{x}$ and the original probability space. We shall call $\mathbf{x}$ the random variable of the population. A particular *sample value* obtained in *random sampling* from this population is just a real number x in the population, one of the possible values of the random variable $\mathbf{x}$.

PROBLEMS

1. (a) With reference to Problem 1 on page 35, what are the elementary events in the probability space induced by $\mathbf{w}$ on the set R of all real numbers? (b) What probability is associated with the interval (0,14); (c) with the single real number 25; (d) with the interval $[-17,42]$; (e) with the interval (0,1)?

2. Let $\mathbf{x}$ be the random variable of Problem 4, page 36, and consider the probability space induced on R by $\mathbf{x}$. How would you determine, from the original probability space in Problem 4, the probabilities associated with the intervals $(-\infty,150)$ and $(100,150]$?

17. Graphical Representation of a Discrete Random Variable. A *discrete* random variable is one which has only a countable number of possible values; there may be only a finite number, or the number of possible values may be infinite but countable (see page 21). To be somewhat more precise, a random variable $\mathbf{x}$ is *discrete* if there is a finite number N of distinct real numbers $a_1, a_2, \cdots, a_N$ or if there are numbers $a_1, a_2, \cdots$ such that the probability is 1 that $\mathbf{x}$ will assume one of these values. To put it another way, $\mathbf{x}$ is discrete if $\mathbf{x}$ induces on the set R of real numbers a probability space in which each of a finite set $a_1, a_2, \cdots, a_N$, or infinite set $a_1, a_2, \cdots,$ of real numbers has a positive probability, the sum of the probabilities being 1.

The probability distribution of $\mathbf{x}$ is determined by these numbers a_i and by the probabilities associated with them. Let p_i denote the probability that $\mathbf{x}$ will assume the value a_i:

$$p_i = Pr\{\mathbf{x} = a_i\} \quad (i = 1, 2, \cdots, N, \text{ or } i = 1, 2, \cdots).$$

The *probability distribution* of such a random variable $\mathbf{x}$ consists of these values a_i together with their probabilities p_i.

We can obtain a graphical representation in the Cartesian plane of the probability distribution of $\mathbf{x}$, or of the induced probability space, by marking the points with coordinates (a_i,p_i), that is, the points with abscissa a_1, ordinate p_1, abscissa a_2, ordinate p_2, etc.

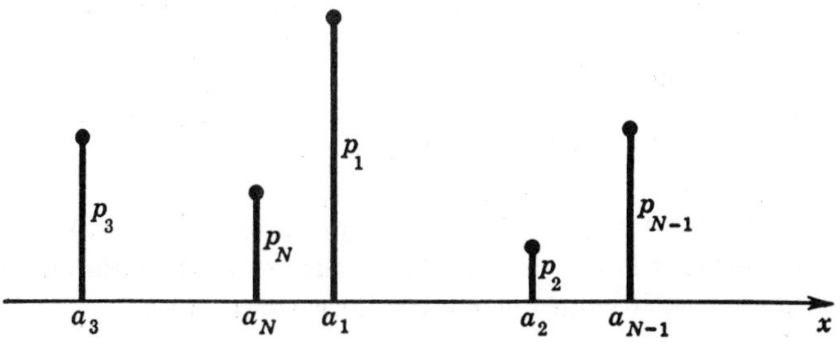

Figure 4

The situation will be easier for the eye to grasp if the ordinates themselves are filled in, from the x axis to the points, as in the accompanying sketch. These points constitute the graph of the *probability function* (also called *frequency function*) of $\mathbf{x}$, a function which has the value p_1 at a_1, p_2 at a_2, etc.:

$$f(x) = Pr\{\mathbf{x} = x\}, \quad x = a_1, a_2, \cdots, a_N \text{ (or } x = a_1, a_2, \cdots).$$

If the probability function $f(x)$ is regarded as being defined only for the N possible values $a_1, a_2, \cdots, a_N$ (or $a_1, a_2, \cdots$) of $\mathbf{x}$, then the points (a_i,p_i), $i = 1, 2, \cdots, N$ (or $i = 1, 2, \cdots$) themselves constitute the complete graph of $f(x)$. But sometimes it is convenient to think of f as being defined for all real x:

▶ $f(x) = Pr\{\mathbf{x} = x\}$, *all real* x, *is the probability function of the discrete random variable* $\mathbf{x}$,

so that $f(a_1) = p_1, f(a_2) = p_2, \cdots, f(a_N) = p_N$, while $f(x) = 0$ if x is none of the numbers $a_1, a_2, \cdots, a_N$ (or $a_1, a_2, \cdots$). The graph of $f(x)$ then consists of the points (a_i,p_i), together with the points $(x,0)$ for all other x, that is, the x axis except at points a_i.

Bearing in mind that each real number x is an elementary event in the probability space induced by $\mathbf{x}$, we may also describe the probability function $f(x)$ of the discrete random variable $\mathbf{x}$ as the function which associates with each elementary event x its probability in the induced space.

The probabilities of events such as $a < x < b$, or, in the induced probability space, the probabilities of intervals (a,b), for real numbers a,b with $a < b$, are susceptible of graphical interpretation with the aid of the graph of the probability function. The event $\{a < \mathbf{x} < b\}$ is the union of the disjoint events $\{\mathbf{x} = a_i\}$ for all i for which $a < a_i < b$, and its probability is accordingly the sum of their probabilities:

$$P(a,b) = Pr\{a < \mathbf{x} < b\} = \sum\nolimits_{a < a_i < b} p_i,$$

where the sum on the right is the sum of the probabilities p_i for all i for which a_i is strictly between a and b. This same sum can be written in terms of the probability function:

▶ $$P(a,b) = Pr\{a < \mathbf{x} < b\} = \sum_{a<x<b} f(x),$$

since $f(a_1) = p_1, f(a_2) = p_2, \cdots, f(a_N) = p_N$, and $f(x) = 0$ for all other x. The sum on the right is the same as the earlier sum, the sum of the probabilities associated with values of $\mathbf{x}$ lying between a and b.

▶ This sum is represented graphically by the sum of the heights of the spikes at points a_i between a and b.

Example 3. Consider Example 1 on page 34, in which you match coins with Jones, winning a dime if you match, and losing a dime if you don't. Your gain, $\mathbf{y}$, is a discrete random variable, having only two possible values, 10 and -10, each with probability 1/2. The probability function, $g(y)$, of $\mathbf{y}$ is given by

$$g(10) = 1/2,$$

$$g(-10) = 1/2,$$

$$g(y) = 0 \quad \text{for all other } y.$$

The graph below of the probability function of $\mathbf{y}$ exhibits the probability space induced on R (or on the y axis) by $\mathbf{y}$; a probability 1/2 is associated with each of the real numbers, -10 and 10.

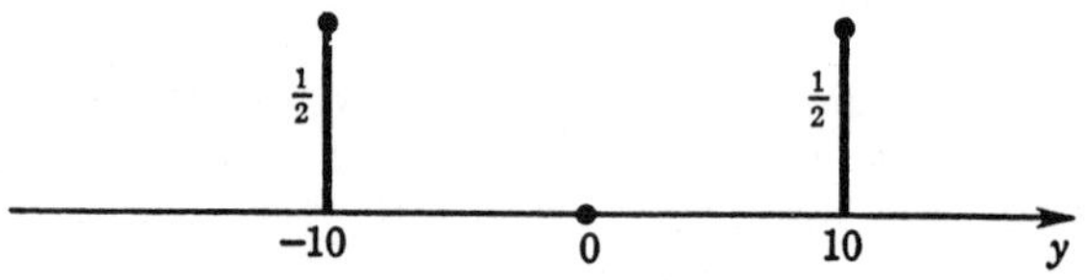

Figure 5

$Pr\{-20 < \mathbf{y} \leq -7\}$ is represented by the sum of the heights of the spikes at numbers y satisfying the inequalities $-20 < y < -7$: $Pr\{-20 < \mathbf{y} \leq -7\} = 1/2$.

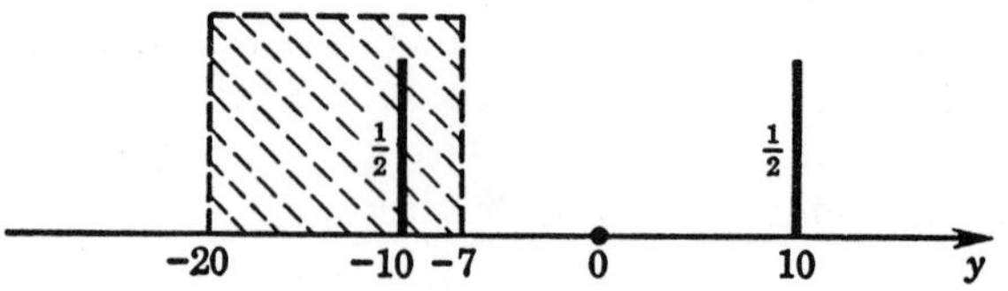

Figure 6

18. Physical Representation of a Discrete Random Variable. The probability distribution of a random variable can also be represented by means of a distribution of mass along a bar bearing a scale, or coordinate axis. This representation is particularly useful in connection with a discussion of the moments of a random variable. Let **x** again be a discrete random variable, assuming values a_i with probabilities p_i ($i = 1, 2, \cdots, N$ or $i = 1, 2, \cdots$). We idealize a bar into a straight line, a coordinate axis, and at each point whose coordinate is a value of **x** we place a point mass of magnitude equal to the probability that **x** will assume that value: at a_1 we set a mass p_1, at a_2 a mass p_2, etc.

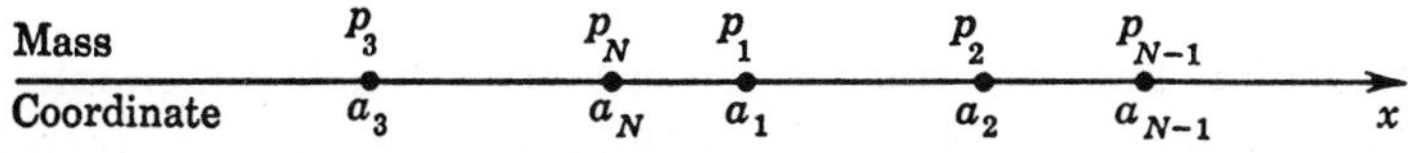

Figure 7

The total mass on the bar is then 1, for the sum of the probabilities associated with all possible values of **x** is 1. If $a < b$, then

$$P(a,b) = Pr\{a < \mathbf{x} < b\} = \sum_{a<a_i<b} p_i = \sum_{a<x<b} f(x)$$

is represented by the sum of the point masses at points lying between a and b on the bar.

▶ *The mass in any interval represents the probability that* **x** *will assume a value in that interval, or the probability associated with that interval in the probability space induced on R (the x axis) by* **x**.

Example 4. In Examples 1 and 3, pages 34 and 40, we obtain the physical representation of the distribution of **y** by placing a point mass 1/2 at 10 and another at −10. Then $Pr\{-20 < \mathbf{y} \leq -7\}$ is represented by the sum of the point masses at points y satisfying the inequalities $-20 < y \leq -7$: there is just one, and $Pr\{-20 < \mathbf{y} \leq -7\} = 1/2$.

19. Physical Representation of a Continuous Random Variable. A random variable is *continuous* if it has a probability density function with the property described below.

The probability that a continuous random variable will assume any particular value is 0, and accordingly there are no point masses in the physical representation of such a random variable. Rather, if **x** is a continuous random variable, we represent its probability distribution by placing a continuous distribution of mass on the coordinate axis in such a way that

▶ *the mass in any interval is numerically equal to the probability that* $\mathbf{x}$ *will assume a value in that interval:*

$$\textit{Mass between } a \textit{ and } b = Pr\{a < \mathbf{x} < b\} = P(a,b).$$

The *density function* $f(x)$ is a function with the property that this mass is given by the integral of $f(x)$ over the interval (a,b):

▶ $$\textit{Mass between } a \textit{ and } b = Pr\{a < \mathbf{x} < b\} = P(a,b) = \int_a^b f(x)\,dx.$$

This density function $f(x)$ *is also called the* probability density function *of the continuous random variable* $\mathbf{x}$.

20. Graphical Representation of a Continuous Random Variable. The graph of the probability density function furnishes a graphical representation of the probability distribution of a continuous random variable $\mathbf{x}$, or of the probability space induced by $\mathbf{x}$.

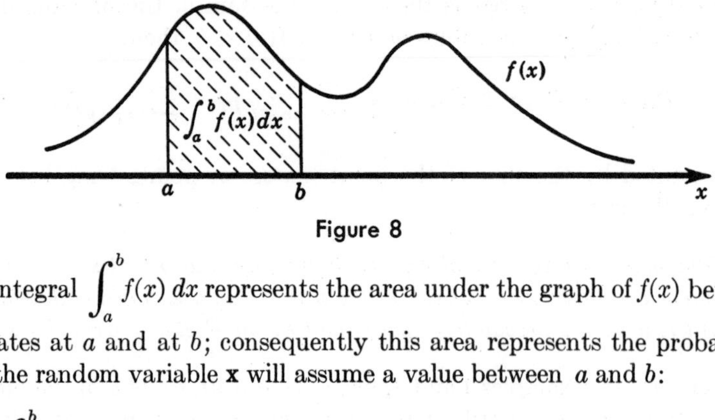

Figure 8

The integral $\int_a^b f(x)\,dx$ represents the area under the graph of $f(x)$ between ordinates at a and at b; consequently this area represents the probability that the random variable $\mathbf{x}$ will assume a value between a and b:

▶ $$\int_a^b f(x)\,dx = \textit{area under graph of } f(x) \textit{ between } a \textit{ and } b$$
$$= Pr\{a < \mathbf{x} < b\} = P(a,b).$$

Since probabilities are non-negative, the probability density function must also be non-negative; also

$$\int_{-\infty}^{\infty} f(x)\,dx = Pr\{-\infty < \mathbf{x} < \infty\} = 1.$$

Example 5. (The Uniform or Rectangular Distribution). Suppose you have a device for choosing a number $\mathbf{z}$ "at random" between 0 and 1. That is, your device will produce a number between 0 and 1 in such a way that the probability that it will lie in any given interval is proportional to the length of that interval (cf. Example 2, page 25). We may take as elementary events the real numbers between 0 and 1. The family $\mathfrak{F}$ of events will be a family including all subintervals of [0,1] and satisfying the axioms for $\mathfrak{F}$. The probability of an event which is a subinterval of [0,1] is to be proportional to the length of that subinterval. Since the probability is 1 when the length of the interval is 1, the proportionality constant must be 1.

Alternatively, we could set up a probability space in which all real numbers are elementary events, but in which every event which is an interval outside [0,1] has probability 0. The probability of an event which is an interval would then be just the length of the part of that interval in [0,1]. This alternative space is also identical to the probability space induced on R by the random variable $\mathbf{z}$.

If $0 \leq a < b \leq 1$, then

$$Pr\{a < \mathbf{z} < b\} = b - a = \int_a^b 1\,dz.$$

Accordingly, the constant 1 is the probability density function of $\mathbf{z}$ for $0 < z < 1$. If a and b are any two real numbers with $a < b$, then

$$Pr\{a < \mathbf{z} < b\} = \int_a^b h(z)\,dz,$$

where

$$h(z) = 1 \quad \text{if } 0 < z < 1,$$

$$h(z) = 0 \quad \text{if } z < 0 \text{ or if } z > 1;$$

for the integral $\int_a^b h(z)\,dz$ gives the length of the part of the interval (a,b) in [0,1] (if any) and is therefore equal to the probability of the event which is the interval (a,b). (Values may be assigned to $h(z)$ for $z = 0$ and for $z = 1$ arbitrarily, since they will not affect the probability of any event.)

The graph of the probability density function $h(z)$ of $\mathbf{z}$ is shown in the accompanying figure.

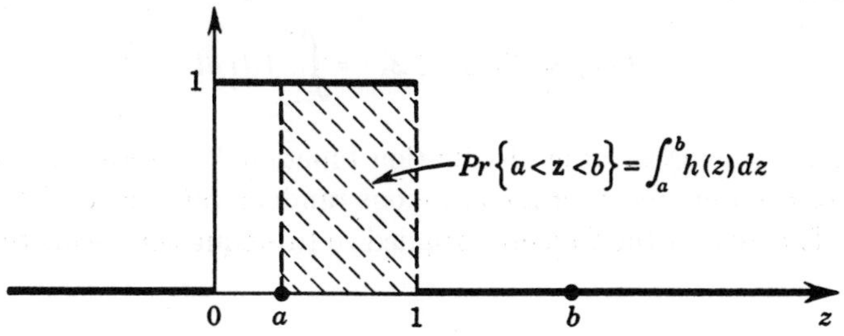

Figure 9

The area under the graph over any interval represents the probability that the number **z** will be chosen in that interval.

The distribution of this random variable **z** is called the *uniform distribution*, or the *rectangular distribution*, over [0,1].

21. Distribution Function. Only discrete random variables have probability functions, only continuous random variables have probability density functions, but every random variable has a *distribution function* (also called *cumulative distribution function*).

▶ *The distribution function* $F(x)$ *of a random variable* **x** *is defined by*

$$F(x) = Pr\{\mathbf{x} < x\}.$$

Another common definition of distribution function is: $Pr\{\mathbf{x} \leq x\}$. For each real number x, the set of elementary events at which the random variable **x** assumes values less than the real number x is an event, $\{-\infty < \mathbf{x} < x\}$ or $\{\mathbf{x} < x\}$. This event and its probability depend on the real number x, so that $Pr\{\mathbf{x} < x\}$ is a function of x, the distribution function of the random variable **x**. We must bear in mind that while it is called the distribution function of **x**, it is not a function of **x**; that is, its argument is not the random variable **x**, but the real number x.

In the physical representation of a random variable, the value of the distribution function at the real number x is represented by the total mass situated on the bar to the left of the point with coordinate x.

In the graphical representation of a discrete random variable **x**, the sum of the heights of spikes at points to the left of x represents $F(x)$. This is also the sum of values of the probability function of **x** at points to the left of x:

▶ $$F(x) = Pr\{\mathbf{x} < x\} = \textstyle\sum_{t<x} f(t).$$

In the graphical representation of a continuous random variable **x**, the area under the graph of the probability density function to the left of x represents $F(x)$:

▶ $$F(x) = Pr\{\mathbf{x} < x\} = \int_{-\infty}^{x} f(t)\, dt.$$

This equation expresses the distribution function F in terms of the probability density function f for a continuous random variable **x**. The Fundamental Theorem of the Calculus applied to this equation yields the following:

▶ $$f(x) = \frac{d}{dx} F(x) = F'(x)$$

(except at points, if any, where f is not continuous); here f, F are respectively density function and distribution function of a continuous random variable $\mathbf{x}$.

This equation expresses the probability density function of a continuous random variable in terms of its distribution function.

The graph of the distribution function provides a graphical representation of a random variable, whether discrete or continuous or neither. (Throughout this text the discussion is limited to random variables which are discrete or continuous, since the systematic study of general random variables would require concepts not usually introduced in a first course in the calculus.) If $a < b$, then the event $\{\mathbf{x} < a\}$ implies the event $\{\mathbf{x} < b\}$: $\{\mathbf{x} < a\} \subset \{\mathbf{x} < b\}$. It follows from property P9 (page 23) that $F(a) = Pr\{\mathbf{x} < a\} \leq Pr\{\mathbf{x} < b\} = F(b)$. Therefore the function $F(x)$ is nondecreasing (as x increases). Also it can be shown that $F(x) = Pr\{\mathbf{x} < x\} \to 0$ as $x \to -\infty$ and that $F(x) = Pr\{\mathbf{x} < x\} \to 1$ as $x \to \infty$. These asymptotic relations can be expressed symbolically as

$$F(-\infty) = 0, \quad F(\infty) = 1.$$

If $a < b$ then the event $\{\mathbf{x} < b\}$ is the union of the mutually exclusive events $\{\mathbf{x} < a\}$ and $\{a \leq \mathbf{x} < b\}$:

$$\{\mathbf{x} < b\} = \{\mathbf{x} < a\} \cup \{a \leq \mathbf{x} < b\}.$$

According to Axiom P4 (page 23), then,

$$Pr\{\mathbf{x} < b\} = Pr\{\mathbf{x} < a\} + Pr\{a \leq \mathbf{x} < b\},$$

or

$$F(b) = F(a) + Pr\{a \leq \mathbf{x} < b\},$$

or finally,

▶ $$Pr\{a \leq \mathbf{x} < b\} = F(b) - F(a):$$

the probability that $\mathbf{x}$ will assume a value not less than a but less than b, or the probability of the interval $[a,b)$ in the probability space induced on R by $\mathbf{x}$, is represented on the graph of the distribution function by the difference between the heights of the graph at b and at a.

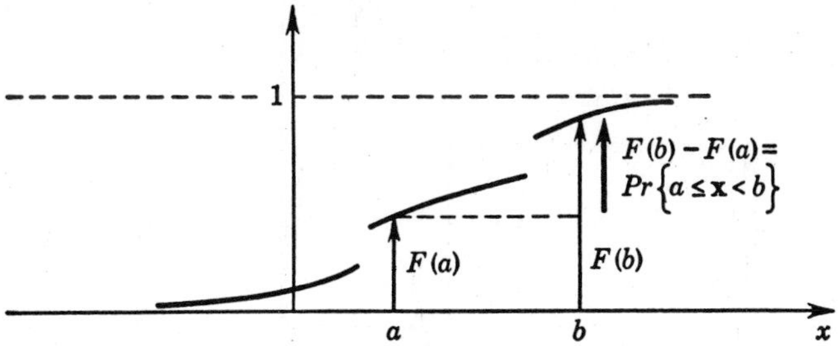

Figure 10

This is true whether the random variable is continuous or discrete or neither. If the random variable is continuous, then the probability that it will assume any particular value is 0, so that also $Pr\{a < \mathbf{x} < b\}$, $Pr\{a < \mathbf{x} \leq b\}$, $Pr\{a \leq \mathbf{x} \leq b\}$ are given by $F(b) - F(a)$.

The term *probability law*, or *probability distribution* of a random variable $\mathbf{x}$ refers to a means of specifying $Pr\{a \leq \mathbf{x} < b\}$ for every interval $[a,b]$ (or indeed $Pr\{\mathbf{x}$ in $A\}$ for every event A in the probability space induced by $\mathbf{x}$ on the real line). An appropriate response to the question: "What is the probability distribution of $\mathbf{x}$?" is to give the distribution function of $\mathbf{x}$, since this determines all such probabilities. In the case of a discrete random variable, its probability function also determines these probabilities, as does the density function of a continuous random variable.

We remark that the function $F(x)$ is *continuous from the left*. That is, if $a_1 \leq a_2 \leq \cdots$, $\lim_{n\to\infty} a_n = x$, then $\lim_{n\to\infty} F(a_n) = F(x)$. This follows from P11; for if in P11 we set $B_i = (-\infty, a_i)$, $i = 1, 2, \cdots$, then $B = \bigcup_{i=1}^{\infty} B_i = (-\infty, x)$, and $F(x) = Pr\{\mathbf{x} < x\} = P(B) = \lim_{i\to\infty} P(B_i)$ $= \lim_{i\to\infty} Pr\{\mathbf{x} < a_i\} = \lim_{i\to\infty} F(a_i)$. (With the alternative definition of distribution function, $F(x) = Pr\{\mathbf{x} \leq x\}$, a distribution function is continuous from the right.)

EXAMPLE 6. In Examples 1, 3, and 4 (pages 34, 40, 41), $\mathbf{y}$ is a discrete random variable, assuming the values -10 and 10, each with probability $1/2$. If $g(y)$ is the probability function of $\mathbf{y}$, then $g(-10) = Pr\{\mathbf{y} = -10\}$ $= 1/2$, $g(10) = Pr\{\mathbf{y} = 10\} = 1/2$, and $g(y) = 0$ if y is neither -10 nor 10. If $G(y)$ is the distribution function of $\mathbf{y}$, $G(y) = Pr\{\mathbf{y} < y\}$, then in the physical representation $G(y)$ is the total mass to the left of y, and with reference to the graph of g, $G(y)$ is the sum of the heights of the spikes at points to the left of y. For example, $G(-20)$ is the sum of the spikes to the left of -20, or the total mass to the left of -20, which is 0. $G(-10)$ also, the total mass to the left of -10, is 0. Indeed, if $y \leq -10$, then $G(y) = 0$. $G(0)$ is the total mass to the left of 0, or the sum of the spikes to the left of 0, and is $1/2$; if $-10 < y \leq 10$, then $G(y) = 1/2$. If $y > 10$, $G(y) = 1$.

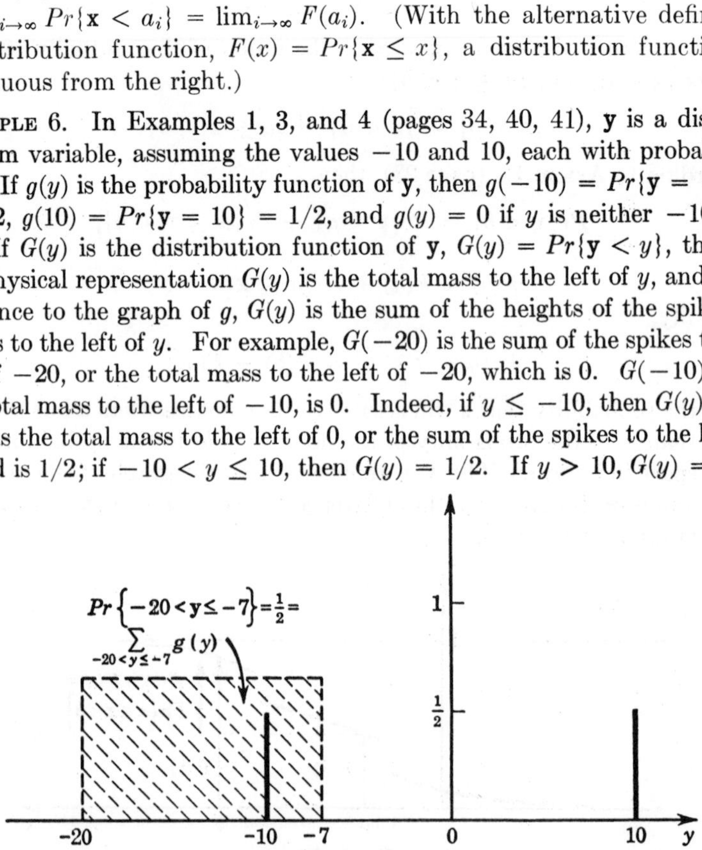

Figure 11(a)

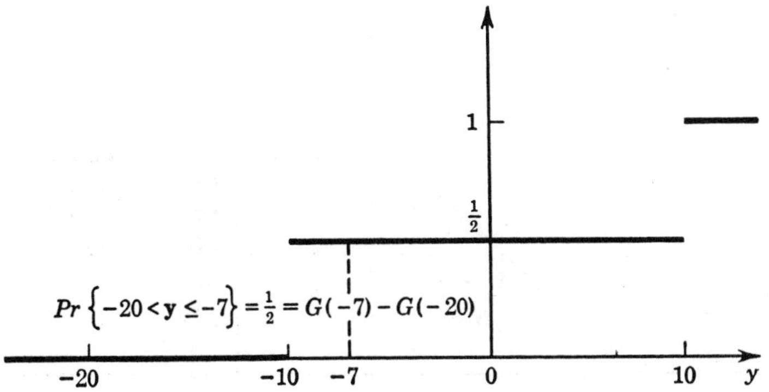

Figure 11(b)

EXAMPLE 7. (Uniform Distribution over [0,1]). In Example 5 (page 42), **z** is a continuous random variable with probability density function h given by

$$h(z) = 1 \quad \text{for } 0 < z < 1,$$

$$h(z) = 0 \quad \text{for all other } z.$$

In the physical representation we have a mass loaded bar, with no mass outside the unit interval [0,1] and mass 1 inside the unit interval; the mass in any interval is numerically equal to its length, so that the density at any point of the unit interval is 1. If $H(z)$ is the distribution function of **z**, $H(z) = Pr\{\mathbf{z} < z\}$, then $H(-4)$ is the total mass to the left of -4, which is 0; indeed, $H(z)$, the mass to the left of z, or the area under the graph of h to the left of z, is 0 if $z \le 0$. If $0 < z \le 1$, then $H(z)$ is just the mass between 0 and z, or the area under $f(z)$ from 0 to z, and is just z. If $z > 1$, then the total mass 1, or the entire area 1, lies to the left of z, so that $H(z) = 1$:

$$H(z) = 0 \quad \text{for } z \le 0,$$

$$H(z) = z \quad \text{for } 0 < z \le 1,$$

$$H(z) = 1 \quad \text{for } z > 1.$$

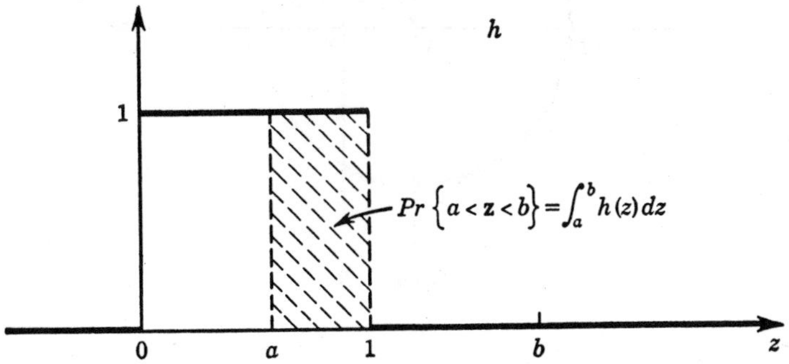

Figure 12(a)

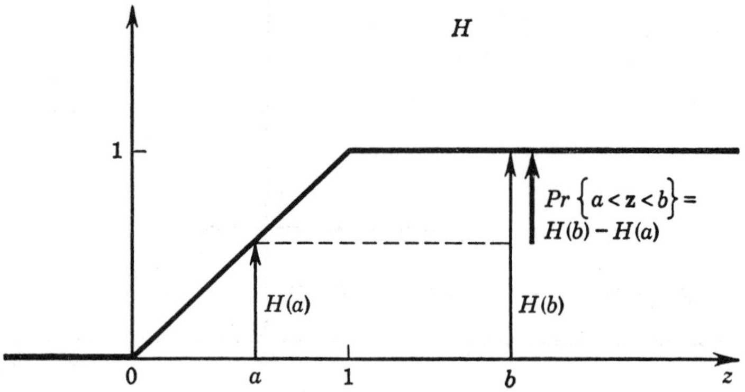

Figure 12(b)

Note that the area to the left of z under the graph of h, $\int_{-\infty}^{z} h(z)\,dz$, is just the height at z of the graph of H, for every real z; and that $H'(z) = h(z)$ for each real z except $z = 0$ and $z = 1$.

EXAMPLE 8. In order to determine the probability density function of the random variable $\mathbf{x}$ in Example 2, page 34, we shall first find its distribution function, $F(x) = Pr\{\mathbf{x} < x\}$. The event $\{\mathbf{x} < x\}$ will occur if and only if a point is chosen on the arc of the unit circle extending to the left between the two points whose abscissas are x; the elementary events favorable to this event are the points on this arc. We saw on page 35 that the probability of choosing a point on a prescribed arc is proportional to the length of the arc, and that the proportionality constant is $1/2\pi$.

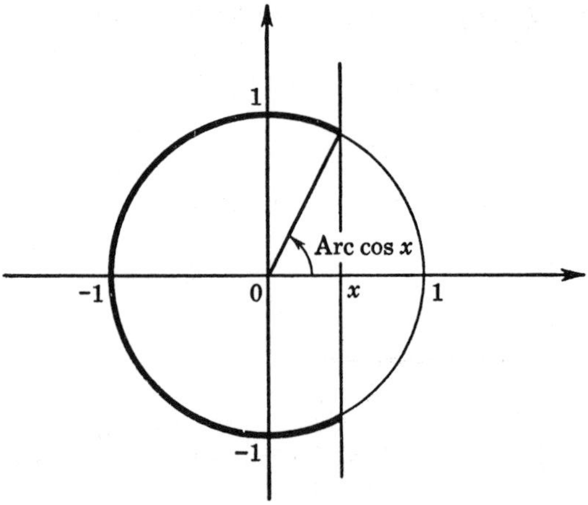

Figure 13

The length of the arc to the left of the two points with abscissa x is $2(\pi - \text{Arc}\cos x)$, so that the probability of choosing a point on this arc is

$$F(x) = Pr\{\mathbf{x} < x\} = \frac{1}{2\pi} \cdot 2(\pi - \text{Arc}\cos x)$$

$$= 1 - \frac{1}{\pi} \text{Arc}\cos x, \quad \text{for } -1 < x \leq 1.$$

Also

$$F(x) = Pr\{\mathbf{x} < x\} = 0 \quad \text{if } x \leq -1,$$

$$F(x) \qquad = 1 \quad \text{if } x > 1.$$

The probability density function f is then given by

$$f(x) = F'(x) = \frac{1}{\pi\sqrt{1 - x^2}} \quad \text{for } -1 < x < 1,$$

$$f(x) \qquad = 0 \quad \text{for } x < -1,\ x > 1.$$

We can determine the distribution function of $\mathbf{x}$ in what appears formally to be a different way, and illustrate a method of determining the distribution function of a random variable which is a function of a random variable whose distribution function is known. In order to illustrate the idea without unduly complicating the computations, let us change the problem so that the point is chosen at random on the upper semicircle. If $\boldsymbol{\theta}$ is the random variable which is the angle from the x axis to the radius vector of

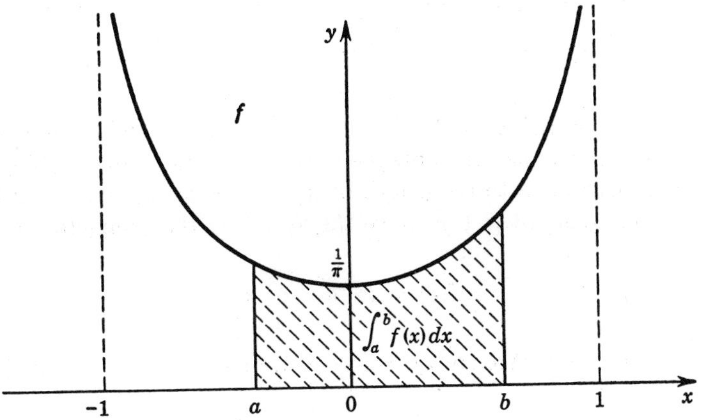

Figure 14(a)

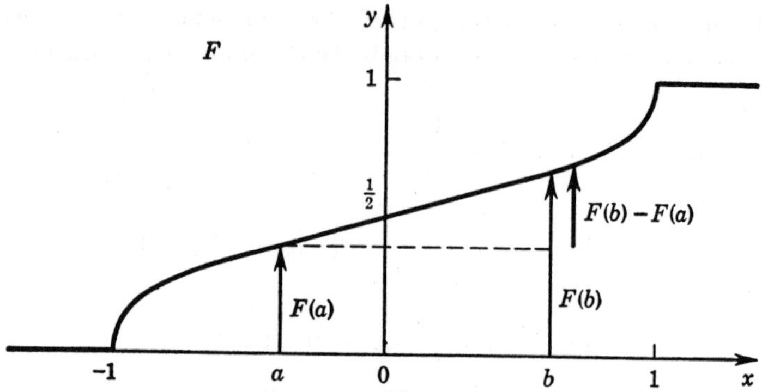

$$Pr\{a < \mathbf{x} < b\} = \int_a^b f(x)\,dx = F(b) - F(a)$$

Figure 14(b)

the point chosen, then

$$\mathbf{x} = \cos \boldsymbol{\theta},$$

and $F(x) = Pr\{\mathbf{x} < x\} = Pr\{\cos \boldsymbol{\theta} < x\} = Pr\{\boldsymbol{\theta} > \text{Arc}\cos x\}$,

since $\cos\theta$ is a decreasing function for $0 < \theta < \pi$. Let $G(\theta)$ be the distribution function of $\boldsymbol{\theta}$,

$$G(\theta) = Pr\{\boldsymbol{\theta} < \theta\}.$$

We have
$$Pr\{\boldsymbol{\theta} > \text{Arc}\cos x\} = 1 - Pr\{\boldsymbol{\theta} \leq \text{Arc}\cos x\}$$
$$= 1 - Pr\{\boldsymbol{\theta} < \text{Arc}\cos x\},$$

since $Pr\{\boldsymbol{\theta} = \text{Arc}\cos x\}$ is 0. But

$$Pr\{\boldsymbol{\theta} < \text{Arc}\cos x\} = G(\text{Arc}\cos x),$$

so that

$$F(x) = 1 - G(\text{Arc}\cos x),$$

and
$$f(x) = F'(x) = -G'(\text{Arc}\cos x)\frac{-1}{\sqrt{1-x^2}}.$$

If $0 < \theta < \pi$, then $G(\theta) = Pr\{\boldsymbol{\theta} < \theta\}$ is just the probability that the point will be chosen on the arc subtended by the central angle θ. This probability is proportional to the length of the arc, which is just θ, and the proportionality constant is $1/\pi$, since the length of the complete arc is π.

$$G(\theta) = Pr\{\boldsymbol{\theta} < \theta\} = \frac{\theta}{\pi},$$

$$F(x) = 1 - G(\text{Arc}\cos x) = 1 - \frac{1}{\pi}\text{Arc}\cos x, \quad \text{for } -1 < x \leq 1,$$

and $f(x) = G'(\text{Arc}\cos x)\dfrac{1}{\sqrt{1-x^2}} = \dfrac{1}{\pi\sqrt{1-x^2}}$ for $-1 < x < 1$,

since $G'(\theta) \equiv 1/\pi$ for $0 < \theta < \pi$.

PROBLEMS

1. Sketch the graphs of the probability function and the distribution function of the number of spots which will turn up on a tossed die. Also sketch the corresponding mass distribution, and then represent on each sketch the probability that the number of spots will be less than 5 but not less than 3.

2. (*Uniform distribution over* $[a,b]$). A real number $\mathbf{z}$ is to be chosen at random between two fixed numbers a and b with $a < b$. Find formulas for its density and distribution functions, and sketch their graphs.

3. A sack contains red marbles and white marbles in the ratio 2 to 1. You are to draw a marble at random, and to note its color. Let $\mathbf{x}$ denote the number of red marbles you will draw in a single draw; $\mathbf{x}$ is either 1 or 0; 1 with probability 2/3, 0 with probability 1/3. Sketch the graphs of the probability function and the distribution function of $\mathbf{x}$, and also the mass distribution corresponding to $\mathbf{x}$. In each sketch represent $Pr\{1/2 < \mathbf{x} \leq 3\}$.

4. Sketch the graphs of the probability function and distribution function of $\mathbf{y} = \mathbf{x}^2$, where $\mathbf{x}$ is the random variable in Problem 3.

5. Find formulas for and sketch the graphs of the density function and distribution function of $\mathbf{w} = \sqrt{\mathbf{z}}$, where $\mathbf{z}$ is the random variable in Examples 5 and 7, pages 42 and 47, uniformly distributed over the interval $[0,1]$.

6. A Poisson distributed random variable $\mathbf{z}$ has probability function $h(z) = e^{-\lambda}\lambda^z/z!$, $z = 0, 1, 2, \cdots$, $h(z) = 0$ for other values of z, where λ is a positive constant. What is the probability function of $\mathbf{w} = 2\mathbf{z} + 4$?

7. In the probability space appropriate to tossing a die, the probability of an elementary event is itself a random variable. (Problem 2, page 36.) Sketch the graphs of its probability function and distribution function.

8. An angle $\boldsymbol{\theta}$ is chosen at random between $-\pi/2$ and $\pi/2$, and a line is drawn through the point $(0,1)$ making an angle $\boldsymbol{\theta}$ with the negative direction on the y axis. Find the distribution function and density function of the point $\mathbf{x}$ where this line crosses the x axis (*Cauchy's distribution*).

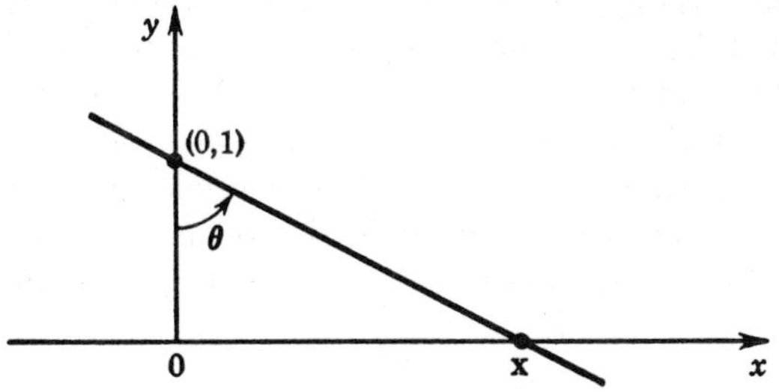

Figure 15

22. Expectation and Variance. The *expectation* (*expected value*, or *mean*) of a *discrete* random variable is the sum of the products of its values by their associated probabilities. If $\mathbf{x}$ assumes the values $a_1, a_2, \cdots, a_N$ with probabilities $p_1, p_2, \cdots, p_N$ then $E(\mathbf{x}) = \sum_{i=1}^{N} a_i p_i$. If $\mathbf{x}$ assumes the values $a_1, a_2, \cdots$ with probabilities $p_1, p_2, \cdots$ then $E(\mathbf{x}) = \sum_{i=1}^{\infty} a_i p_i$ provided this infinite series converges absolutely. (It is found to be inconvenient to define the expectation at all if the series does not converge absolutely.) If $f(x)$ is the probability function of $\mathbf{x}$ (page 39), then

$$\blacktriangleright \qquad E(\mathbf{x}) = \sum_x x f(x).$$

The *variance* of $\mathbf{x}$ is given by

$$V(\mathbf{x}) = \sum_{i=1}^{N} [a_i - E(\mathbf{x})]^2 p_i, \quad = E[(X - E(X))^2]$$

or by

$$V(\mathbf{x}) = \sum_{i=1}^{\infty} [a_i - E(\mathbf{x})]^2 p_i,$$

provided that the series converges. In either event

$$\blacktriangleright \qquad V(\mathbf{x}) = \sum_x [x - E(\mathbf{x})]^2 f(x).$$

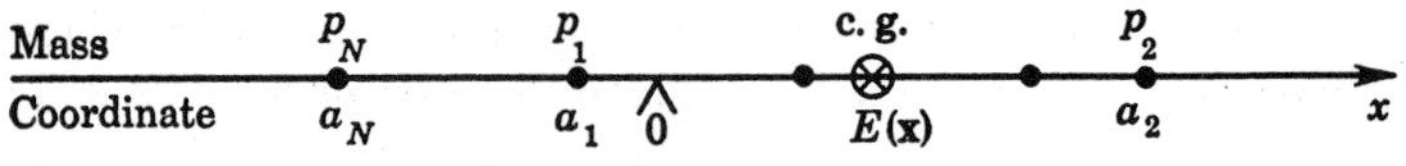

Figure 16

With reference to the associated mass distribution, $E(\mathbf{x}) = \sum_i a_i p_i = \sum_x x\, f(x)$ is just the sum of the moments about the origin of the point masses p_i at points with coordinates a_i $(i = 1, 2, \cdots, N)$; that is, $E(\mathbf{x})$ is the moment about the origin of the mass distribution associated with $\mathbf{x}$. Since the coordinate of the center of gravity is the moment about the origin divided by the total mass, and since the total mass is 1, $E(\mathbf{x})$ *is also the coordinate of the center of gravity of the mass distribution.* Also, $[a_1 - E(\mathbf{x})]^2$ is the squared distance of the mass p_i from the center of gravity, and similarly for $[a_i - E(\mathbf{x})]^2$, $i = 2, 3, \cdots, N$. The sum of these squares, each multiplied by the associated mass, is known as the moment of inertia; that is, $V(\mathbf{x})$ is the *moment of inertia of the associated mass distribution,* also referred to as the second moment about the mean.

If $\mathbf{y}$ is a continuous random variable with density function $g(y)$, then

$$\blacktriangleright \qquad E(\mathbf{y}) = \int_{-\infty}^{\infty} y\, g(y)\, dy$$

if this integral exists (i.e., $\lim_{A\to\infty, B\to\infty} \int_{-A}^{B} y\, g(y)\, dy$ exists). Note that the existence of $E(\mathbf{y})$ implies that

$$\int_0^\infty y\, g(y)\, dy, \int_{-\infty}^{0} y\, g(y)\, dy, \int_{-\infty}^{\infty} |y|\, g(y)\, dy$$

all converge. $E(\mathbf{y})$ also represents the moment about the origin of the associated mass distribution, and since the total mass is 1, $E(\mathbf{y})$ is the coordinate of the center of gravity of the mass distribution. The variance of $\mathbf{y}$ is given by

$$V(\mathbf{y}) = \int_{-\infty}^{\infty} [y - E(\mathbf{y})]^2\, g(y)\, dy,$$

if this integral exists; and again $V(\mathbf{y})$ is the moment of inertia, or the second moment about the mean, of the associated mass distribution.

It can be shown that if the variance of a random variable exists, so does its expectation; though $E(\mathbf{y})$ may be defined while $V(\mathbf{y})$ is undefined.

If $\mathbf{z}$ is a random variable having a variance $V(\mathbf{z})$, its *standard deviation* σ_z is given by

$$\sigma_z = \sqrt{V(\mathbf{z})}.$$

The standard deviation is the radius of gyration of the associated mass distribution.

The expectation $E(\mathbf{x})$ is generally a somewhat centrally located point relative to the probability distribution of $\mathbf{x}$ or the mass distribution representing it. The variance may be regarded as a measure of the compactness, or rather, of the dispersion of the distribution: if $\mathbf{x}$ assumes values far from the mean (expectation) with moderately large probabilities, then the variance will be large; while if most of the probability mass lies near the mean, the variance will be small.

23. Summary. *A random variable* $\mathbf{x}$ *is a function defined at each elementary event of a probability space, such that for every pair a,b, of real numbers with* $a < b$, *the set of elementary events for which* $a < \mathbf{x} < b$ ($a < \mathbf{x} \le b$, $a \le \mathbf{x} < b$, $a \le \mathbf{x} \le b$, $\mathbf{x} < b$, $\mathbf{x} \le b$, $\mathbf{x} > a$, $\mathbf{x} \ge a$) *is an event.*

The distribution function $F(x)$ *of a random variable* $\mathbf{x}$ *is the function of the real variable* x *defined by*

$$F(x) = Pr\{\mathbf{x} < x\}.$$

The probability function $f(x)$ *of a* discrete *random variable* $\mathbf{x}$ *is the function of the real variable* x *whose value at each* x *is the probability that* $\mathbf{x}$ *will assume the value* x:

$$f(x) = Pr\{\mathbf{x} = x\};$$

then

$$F(x) = Pr\{\mathbf{x} < x\}$$
$$= \sum_{t<x} f(t).$$

The expectation, variance, and standard deviation of the discrete random variable **x** *are given by*

$$E(\mathbf{x}) = \sum_x x\, f(x),$$

$$V(\mathbf{x}) = \sum_x [x - E(\mathbf{x})]^2 f(x),$$

$$\sigma_x = \sqrt{V(\mathbf{x})}.$$

The density function $f(x)$ *of a* continuous *random variable* **x** *is the function of the real variable* x *with the property that for every pair of real numbers* a, b, *with* $a < b$,

$$Pr\{a < \mathbf{x} < b\} = \int_a^b f(x)\, dx;$$

then

$$F(x) = Pr\{\mathbf{x} < x\} = \int_{-\infty}^{x} f(t)\, dt,$$

and

$$f(x) = F'(x)$$

at each point x *where* f *is continuous. The expectation, variance, and standard deviation of the continuous random variable* **x** *are given by*

$$E(\mathbf{x}) = \int_{-\infty}^{\infty} x\, f(x)\, dx,$$

$$V(\mathbf{x}) = \int_{-\infty}^{\infty} [x - E(\mathbf{x})]^2 f(x)\, dx,$$

$$\sigma_x = \sqrt{V(\mathbf{x})}.$$

PROBLEMS

1–7. Find expectations, variances, and standard deviations, when they exist, of the random variables in Problems 1, 2, 3, 4, 5, 7, and 8 on page 51.

8. The density function of a certain continuous random variable **x** is proportional to $x(1 - x)$ for $0 < x < 1$, and is 0 for other values of x.

(a) Show that $f(x) = 6x(1 - x)$ for $0 < x < 1$.

(b) Find the distribution function of **x**.

(c) Find $Pr\{\mathbf{x} < 1/2\}$.

(d) Find $E(\mathbf{x})$.

9. (a) In Problem 8, draw rough sketches of the density function and the distribution function of **x**; represent $Pr\{1/2 < \mathbf{x} < 3/4\}$ graphically on each.

(b) Find the distribution function and density function of **y**, if $\mathbf{y} = \mathbf{x}^2$.

10. A random variable **y** assumes values 0, 1, and 2 with associated probabilities 1/2, 1/4, 1/4 respectively. Find $E(\mathbf{y})$ and $V(\mathbf{y})$. Describe the associated distribution of point masses on a line. Sketch the distribution function of **y**.

11. Your friend agrees to give you one dollar if either of the following two events occurs on a certain day, two dollars if both occur on that day, and nothing if neither occurs:

(A) rain in Columbia, Mo. (probability 1/5);
(B) duck born in McBaine, Mo. (probability 1/10).

(a) Find the probabilities that you will be paid nothing; one dollar; two dollars. (b) Sketch the distribution function of your gain. (c) Find your expected gain.

12. The density function $f(x)$ of a certain random variable **x** is proportional to x for $0 \leq x \leq 1$, and is 0 for all other values of x. Find $f(x)$, and the mean, variance, and standard deviation of **x**.

13. The random variable **x** assumes the value a with probability 1. Sketch its distribution function. Find its mean and standard deviation.

14. The random variable **y** assumes the value 1 with probability p, the value 0 with probability $q = 1 - p$. Sketch its distribution function. Find its mean and standard deviation.

15. A whole number is chosen at random between 1 and 10. Sketch the distribution function of this number.

16. You toss a coin three times, and are paid n dollars if heads comes up for the first time on the nth throw, $n = 1, 2, 3$. Find the expectation of your gain and its variance, and show how they can be interpreted as distance from origin of the center of gravity and moment of inertia about the center of gravity respectively, of an appropriate mass distribution on a line.

17. Suppose there is a positive constant θ such that the density function $g(y)$ of a random variable **y** is proportional to $e^{-\theta y}$ for $y > 0$ and is 0 for $y < 0$. (a) Find $g(y)$. (b) Find $E(\mathbf{y})$ and $V(\mathbf{y})$.

18. Let **x** denote the annual income of a man chosen at random from among those in a certain profession. Suppose there are positive constants c and k such that the density function of **x** is $f(x) = ck^c/x^{c+1}$ for $x > k$, $f(x) = 0$ for $x < k$. Find $E(\mathbf{x})$ and $V(\mathbf{x})$.

19. Suppose you plan to choose a number **x** at random between 0 and 1, and then to draw a chord at distance **x** from the center of a circle of radius 1.

What is the probability that the length of the chord will be less than the side of an inscribed equilateral triangle?

20. Suppose you plan to choose at random a number $\mathbf{y}$ between 0 and π, and then to draw a chord having a central angle $\mathbf{y}$ radians in a circle. What is the probability that the length of the chord will be less than the side of an inscribed equilateral triangle? (The fact that Problems 19 and 20 give different answers to the ambiguous question: "What is the probability that a chord drawn at random in a circle will have a length less than the side of an inscribed equilateral triangle?" is known as Bertrand's Paradox.)

21. Let $\mathbf{x}$ have a probability density function $f(x) = \theta e^{-\theta x}(x > 0)$, $f(x) = 0$ $(x < 0)$. Show that if the positive x axis is divided into intervals of equal length h starting at the origin, then the probabilities that $\mathbf{x}$ will lie in successive intervals form a geometric progression with common ratio $e^{-\theta h}$.

22. The velocity $\mathbf{v}$ of a molecule in a gas has probability density function $f(v) = av^2e^{-bv^2}$ for $0 < v < \infty$, $f(v) = 0$ for $v < 0$, where b is a constant depending on the gas and its temperature, and where $a = 4b\sqrt{b/\pi}$. Find the mean velocity of molecules in the gas.

23. Show that if $0 < r < 1$ then $f(x) = (1 - r)r^x$, $x = 0, 1, 2, \cdots$, $f(x) = 0$ for other x, is the probability function of a discrete random variable. Find its mean and standard deviation.

Hint:

$$\sum_{x=0}^{\infty} xr^x = \sum_{x=1}^{\infty} xr^x = r\sum_{x=1}^{\infty} xr^{x-1} = r\frac{d}{dr}\left(\sum_{x=1}^{\infty} r^x\right).$$

CHAPTER

4

Multivariate Distributions

We shall find that in developing the theory of statistical inference we shall have occasion to deal with several random variables defined on the same probability space. We shall be particularly interested in situations where they are "independent." In working toward an understanding of this concept, we begin with a discussion of the concept, *joint distribution* of a pair of random variables.

24. A Pair of Discrete Random Variables. This concept is most conveniently introduced by an example.

Example 1. Suppose that in a game of coin-tossing you bet a dollar on heads on the first throw, and a dollar again on heads on the second throw. Let **x** be your gain on the first throw, **y** your gain on the second throw. A probability space appropriate to this situation has 4 elementary events: *HH*, *TH*, *HT*, and *TT*, each with probability 1/4. Each single elementary event is an event, as is each combination of elementary events, and also the void event. The table below gives the value of each of the random variables **x** and **y** at each elementary event; **x** and **y** are real-valued functions (1 and −1 are real numbers) defined on the probability space. Further, the set of all elementary events for which **x** assumes a prescribed value, or lies in a prescribed interval, is an event, since *every* combination of elementary events is an event in this probability space; a similar statement holds for **y**. Therefore **x** and **y** are random variables (page 34).

1st	2nd	Probability	x	y
H	H	1/4	1	1
H	T	1/4	1	−1
T	H	1/4	−1	1
T	T	1/4	−1	−1

We can obtain a physical representation of the pair $(\mathbf{x},\mathbf{y})$ analogous to the physical representation of a single random variable by associating with each point in the xy plane whose coordinates are a pair of possible values of $\mathbf{x}$ and $\mathbf{y}$ a point mass numerically equal to the probability that $\mathbf{x}$ and $\mathbf{y}$ will assume these values. A mass 1/4 is then associated with each of the points $(1,1)$, $(1,-1)$, $(-1,1)$, $(-1,-1)$ in the xy plane.

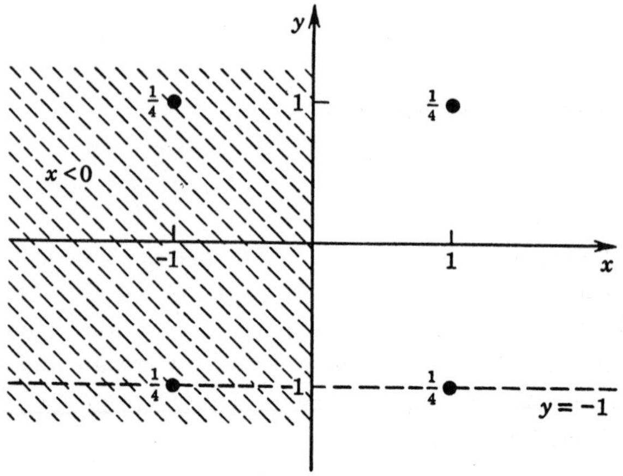

Figure 17

If R is any region in the xy plane, then $Pr\{(\mathbf{x},\mathbf{y}) \text{ in } R\}$, the probability that $\mathbf{x},\mathbf{y}$ will assume a pair of values which are coordinates of a point in R, is just the sum of the masses at points in R. As an example, $Pr\{\mathbf{x} < 0\} = 1/2$, the sum of the masses at the points in the half-plane $x < 0$. Also, $Pr\{\mathbf{y} = -1\} = 1/2$, the sum of the masses at points on the horizontal line $y = -1$.

A geometrical representation analogous to the graph of the probability function of a single random variable consists of spikes at points in the xy

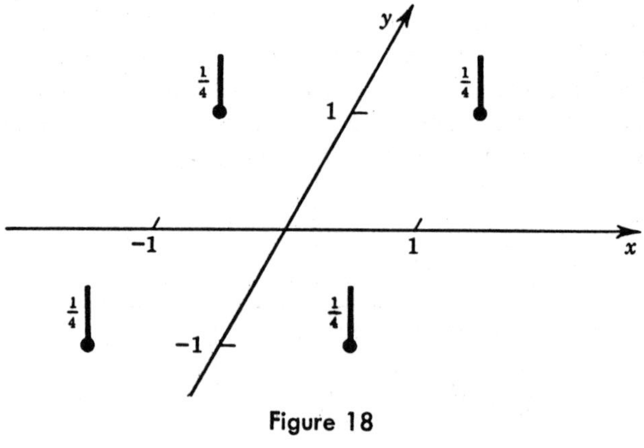

Figure 18

plane whose coordinates are possible values of $\mathbf{x}$ and $\mathbf{y}$, the height of each spike being numerically equal to the probability that $\mathbf{x}$ and $\mathbf{y}$ will assume those values.

25. Probability Space Induced on R_2 by a Pair of Random Variables. In the above example, either the physical representation or the geometrical representation gives us a picture of the probability space induced on R_2, the set of all ordered pairs of real numbers (the Cartesian plane), by $(\mathbf{x},\mathbf{y})$; a probability $1/4$ is associated with each of the events $(1,1)$, $(1,-1)$, $(-1,1)$, $(-1,-1)$. A pair $\mathbf{x},\mathbf{y}$ of random variables induces on the set R_2 of all pairs of real numbers a probability space in much the same way as a single random variable induces on the set R of real numbers a probability space. In the induced probability space, the Cartesian plane R_2 is the fundamental set of elementary events: each point of R_2, that is, each ordered pair of real numbers, is an elementary event. An *interval*, or *rectangle*, in R_2 is the set of all points or pairs (x,y) satisfying inequalities such as $(a < x < b,\ c < y < d)$, or the inequalities obtained by replacing any, some, or all of the symbols "$<$" by "$\leq$." Each interval in R_2 is an event in this probability space, and the family of events is the smallest family containing all the intervals and satisfying the axioms for $\mathfrak{F}$. This family is known as the class of Borel sets in R_2.

▶ *A pair* $\mathbf{x},\mathbf{y}$ *of random variables defined on a probability space induces on the Cartesian plane R_2 (the xy plane, the set of all ordered pairs of real numbers) a probability space. In this probability space the elementary events are the ordered pairs of real numbers, which are also events. Each interval, or rectangle, is an event. The probability of an event which is a single point or pair (x,y) is $Pr\{\mathbf{x} = x, \mathbf{y} = y\}$, the probability that* $\mathbf{x}$ *will assume the value x and* $\mathbf{y}$ *will assume the value y. The probability of an event which is an interval is the probability that* $\mathbf{x}$ *and* $\mathbf{y}$ *will assume values which are the coordinates of a point in that interval or satisfying the inequalities determining that interval.*

That is, the probability, in the induced probability space R_2, of an interval $a \leq x \leq b, c \leq y \leq d$, is the probability of the event: $\{a \leq \mathbf{x} \leq b, c \leq \mathbf{y} \leq d\}$. To fill in a gap in the logic, we need to assure ourselves that there is actually an event in the original probability space which can be described in this way. To see this, we note first that by the definition of a random variable (p. 34), $\{a \leq \mathbf{x} \leq b\}$ is an event, as is also $\{c \leq \mathbf{y} \leq d\}$. By Axiom $\mathfrak{F}2$ (p. 22), their intersection

$$\{a \leq \mathbf{x} \leq b\} \cap \{c \leq \mathbf{y} \leq d\} = \{a \leq \mathbf{x} \leq b, c \leq \mathbf{y} \leq d\}$$

is also an event.

The term *bivariate population,* which we shall use later, will refer to precisely such a probability space: a probability space induced on R_2 by a pair of random variables. The term *multivariate population* refers to a probability space induced by a random vector (two or more random variables defined on the same probability space) on R_k, the Cartesian space of k dimensions, or the space of k-tuples of real numbers, where k is the number of random variables in the combined random variable.

For example, suppose you plan to select at random one of a large group of small animals and to measure its average food intake **x** and its longevity **y**. The probability $Pr\{\mathbf{x} = x, \mathbf{y} = y\}$ associated with a particular number pair (x,y) in the bivariate population induced by the pair $(\mathbf{x},\mathbf{y})$ of random variables is the fraction of the animals each of whose average food intake is x and whose longevity is y. This bivariate population is a probability space in which the elementary events are real number pairs, a probability being associated with each in this way. The random variables **x** and **y** are called the random variables of the population, or the random variables which determine this bivariate population.

EXAMPLE 2. Suppose you are given an opportunity to play the following game: You will toss a coin twice, betting a dollar on heads in the first throw. If heads comes up you will also bet a dollar on heads in the second toss, but if tails comes up on the first, you will bet 2 dollars on tails in the second throw.

Let **x** denote your gain on the first throw, **y** your gain on the second. An appropriate probability space on which to consider **x** and **y** as random variables has 4 elementary events, HH, HT, TH, and TT, each with probability 1/4. At the elementary event HH, the random variable **x** has the value 1 and the random variable **y** also the value 1, etc. The probabilities of the 4 elementary events and the values of **x** and of **y** corresponding to each are given in the following table.

	Probability	**x**	**y**
HH	1/4	1	1
HT	1/4	1	−1
TH	1/4	−1	−2
TT	1/4	−1	2

The accompanying sketches of the physical (mass) representation and the geometrical representation give a picture of the joint probability distribution of the random variables **x** and **y**, and also of the induced probability space on R_2, the xy plane. The original probability space, on which **x** and **y** are defined, has only 4 elementary events, HH, HT, TH, and TT. The induced probability space has infinitely many elementary events; every point (x,y) in the xy plane, or every ordered pair of real numbers, is an elementary event, but the total probability mass is concentrated in just 4 of

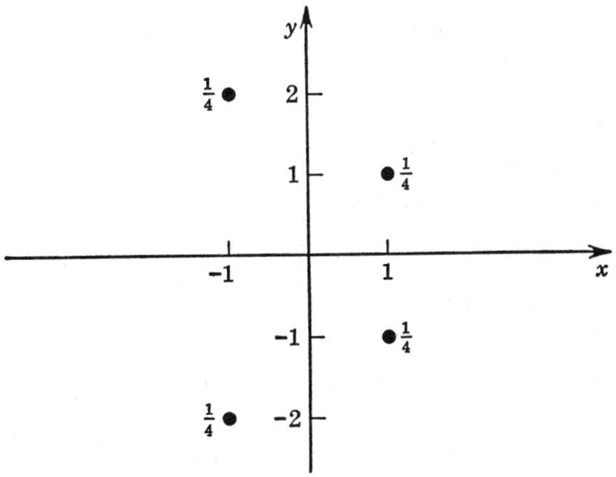

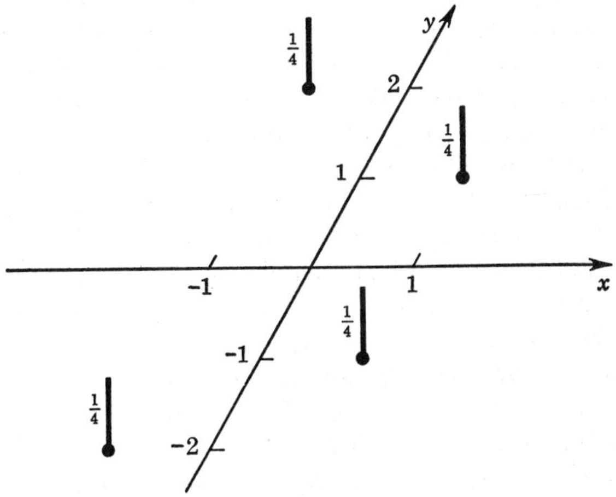

Figure 19

the elementary events: each of the points (1,1), (1,−1), (−1,−2), and (−1,2) has an associated probability 1/4.

The second representation, the geometrical one, will also serve as a graph of the *joint probability function* $f(x,y)$ of the random variables **x**, **y**. It is a function defined only for discrete random variables, whose value at each point (x,y) is the probability that **x** will assume the real number x as a value and **y** will assume the real number y as a value, or the probability in the induced probability space associated with the point (x,y):

$$f(x,y) = Pr\{\mathbf{x} = x, \mathbf{y} = y\}.$$

In the present example, $f(1,1) = 1/4$, $f(1,-1) = 1/4$, $f(-1,-2) = 1/4$, $f(-1,2) = 1/4$, while $f(x,y) = 0$ for every other pair (x,y).

The distribution of each of the random variables $\mathbf{x}$ and $\mathbf{y}$ can be determined directly from the original probability space; for example, $Pr\{\mathbf{x} = 1\} = P(HH \cup HT) = P(HH) + P(HT) = 1/2$. However, it can also be determined from the joint probability function, that is, from the induced probability space. For example, the event $\{\mathbf{x} = 1\}$ can occur if and only if one of the events $\{\mathbf{y} = 1\}$, $\{\mathbf{y} = -1\}$ also occurs:

$$\{\mathbf{x} = 1\} = [\{\mathbf{x} = 1\} \cap \{\mathbf{y} = 1\}] \cup [\{\mathbf{x} = 1\} \cap \{\mathbf{y} = -1\}].$$

The two events on the right above are mutually exclusive, so that by the law of total probability (Axiom P4),

$$Pr\{\mathbf{x} = 1\} = Pr\{\mathbf{x} = 1, \mathbf{y} = 1\} + Pr\{\mathbf{x} = 1, \mathbf{y} = -1\}$$

or

$$Pr\{\mathbf{x} = 1\} = f(1,1) + f(1,-1).$$

Note that $Pr\{\mathbf{x} = 1, \mathbf{y} = 1\}$ *means* $P(\{\mathbf{x} = 1\} \cap \{\mathbf{y} = 1\})$.

In either the physical or geometrical representation of the joint distribution we observe that the right member of this equation is just the sum of the probabilities associated with points on the vertical line $x = 1$. This tallies with the observation made earlier, that if A is an event in the probability space induced on R_2 by a pair of discrete random variables, then the probability that they will assume values which are coordinates of a point in A is just the sum of the probabilities associated with points in A. In the present situation, A is the event consisting of the elementary events or points on the line $x = 1$, and its probability is the sum of the probabilities associated with the two points $(1,1)$ and $(1,-1)$; all other points on this line have probability 0.

If $f(x)$ denotes the probability function of $\mathbf{x}$, $f(x) = Pr\{\mathbf{x} = x\}$, then the above equation can be written $f(1) = f(1,1) + f(1,-1)$. When $\mathbf{x}$ is given originally as one of a pair forming a random vector, its probability distribution is referred to as the *marginal distribution* of $\mathbf{x}$.

26. Joint Distribution of Discrete Random Variables; General. We shall never have occasion to discuss simultaneously two or more random variables unless they are defined on the same probability space; two random variables not capable of definition on the same probability space do not belong in the same discussion. The probability space, so to speak, furnishes a common background, a basis for possible relationships among the random variables. The random variables of a pair $(\mathbf{x},\mathbf{y})$ are *discrete* if each assumes only a countable (finite or infinite) number of different values at elementary events in the probability space, so that the pair assumes only a countable number of different pairs of values. We obtain a mass representation of the pair if we place a mass at each point in the xy plane equal to the probability that $\mathbf{x}$ will assume the value which is the x coordinate of that point and $\mathbf{y}$ will assume the value which is the y coordinate of that point. That is, with a point in the xy plane is associated the probability of the event consisting of those elementary events at which $\mathbf{x}$ assumes as a value the x coordinate of the point and $\mathbf{y}$ assumes as a value the y coordinate of the point. We have a geometrical representation if we place at each such point a vertical spike (perpendicular to the xy plane) whose height is the probability that $\mathbf{x}$ will assume its x coordinate as a value and $\mathbf{y}$ its y coordinate as a value. This latter, geometrical representation is also then the graph of the joint probability function of $\mathbf{x}$ and $\mathbf{y}$:

$$f(x,y) = Pr\{\mathbf{x} = x, \mathbf{y} = y\}.$$

The function $f(x,y)$ is positive at only a countable number of points (x,y) and is zero at every other point (x,y). The geometrical representation furnishes a picture of the bivariate population determined by $\mathbf{x}$ and $\mathbf{y}$, the probability space induced on R_2 by $\mathbf{x}$ and $\mathbf{y}$.

We can express the (marginal) probability function of $\mathbf{x}$ in terms of the joint probability function of $\mathbf{x}$ and $\mathbf{y}$. If x is a real number, to be held fixed for the moment, then the event $\{\mathbf{x} = x\}$ is the union of the mutually exclusive events $\{\mathbf{x} = x\} \cap \{\mathbf{y} = y\}$ for all possible values y of $\mathbf{y}$. We may represent this equality in the following way:

$$\{\mathbf{x} = x\} = \bigcup_y \{\mathbf{x} = x\} \cap \{\mathbf{y} = y\}$$

with the understanding that in forming this union y ranges over all possible values of the random variable $\mathbf{y}$, that is, over the countable number of distinct values assumed by the random variable $\mathbf{y}$. The events in the union on the right are mutually exclusive (y cannot at the same elementary event assume two distinct values), so that by the law of total probability (Axiom P4),

$$Pr\{\mathbf{x} = x\} = \sum_y P(\{\mathbf{x} = x\} \cap \{\mathbf{y} = y\}) = \sum_y Pr\{\mathbf{x} = x, \mathbf{y} = y\},$$

or

▶ $$f(x) = \sum_y f(x,y),$$

where $f(x)$ represents the probability function of $\mathbf{x}$, $f(x) = Pr\{\mathbf{x} = x\}$. Similarly, if $g(y)$ is the probability function of $\mathbf{y}$, $g(y) = Pr\{\mathbf{y} = y\}$, then

▶ $$g(y) = \sum_x f(x,y)$$

gives the marginal probability function of $\mathbf{y}$ in terms of the joint probability function. (Note that different letters must be used to represent the probability functions of $\mathbf{x}$ and $\mathbf{y}$, since in general they will not be the same function.)

If A is any event in the induced probability space, as for example a line, curve, or region in the xy plane, then A is the union of the mutually exclusive events (x,y) which are points in A. Its probability is that of the union of the mutually exclusive events $\{\mathbf{x} = x, \mathbf{y} = y\}$ in the original probability space for all pairs (x,y) in A. Accordingly,

$$\blacktriangleright \quad P(A) = Pr\{(\mathbf{x},\mathbf{y}) \text{ in } A\} = \sum_{(x,y) \text{ in } A} Pr\{\mathbf{x} = x, \mathbf{y} = y\}$$
$$= \sum_{(x,y) \text{ in } A} f(x,y)$$

where the notation with each $\sum$ sign is intended to indicate that the summation is to be carried out over all points (x,y) in A.

If we have k discrete random variables forming a random vector $(\mathbf{x}_1, \mathbf{x}_2, \cdots, \mathbf{x}_k)$, their joint probability function is given at the point $(x_1, x_2, \cdots, x_k)$ in a Cartesian space R_k of k dimensions, the set of all ordered k-tuples of real numbers, by

$$\blacktriangleright \quad f(x_1, x_2, \cdots, x_k) = P(\{\mathbf{x}_1 = x_1\} \cap \{\mathbf{x}_2 = x_2\} \cap \cdots \cap \{\mathbf{x}_k = x_k\})$$
$$= Pr\{\mathbf{x}_1 = x_1, \mathbf{x}_2 = x_2, \cdots, \mathbf{x}_k = x_k\}.$$

The marginal probability function of any particular one, say $\mathbf{x}_i$, is given at the real number x_i by

$$\blacktriangleright \quad f_i(x_i) = \sum_{x_1,x_2,\cdots,x_{i-1},x_{i+1},\cdots,x_k} f(x_1, x_2, \cdots, x_k)$$

where in the summation all variables range over their possible values, except x_i, which is fixed. The marginal joint probability function of any particular two, say $\mathbf{x}_i$ and $\mathbf{x}_j$, is given at the number pair (x_i,x_j) by

$$f_{i,j}(x_i,x_j) = \sum_{x_1,x_2,\cdots,x_{i-1},x_{i+1},\cdots,x_{j-1},x_{j+1},\cdots,x_k} f(x_1, x_2, \cdots, x_k),$$

where in the summation all variables range over their possible values, except x_i and x_j, which are fixed; etc.

If A is any event in the induced probability space in R_k,

$$P(A) = \sum_{(x_1, \cdots, x_k) \text{ in } A} f(x_1, \cdots, x_k).$$

Thus the *probability distribution* of the random vector $(\mathbf{x}_1, \cdots, \mathbf{x}_k)$ is determined by its joint probability function.

PROBLEMS

1. Determine the marginal probability functions of $\mathbf{x}$ and of $\mathbf{y}$ given the following joint probability function. Each entry in the table is the value of the joint probability function at the indicated point (x,y).

$x \backslash y$	1	2	3
1	1/8	1/8	2/8
2	3/8	0	0
3	0	1/8	0

2. As in Problem 1, for the following joint probability function.

$x \backslash y$	-1	0	1
-1	1/12	1/12	2/12
0	0	0	0
1	2/12	2/12	4/12

3. (a) In Problem 1 above, find $Pr\{\mathbf{x} < 2\}$.

(b) In Problem 2 above, find $G(y) = Pr\{\mathbf{y} < y\}$ for all y.

4. You plan to make two throws of a die. Let **x** denote the number of times an ace (one) will turn up, **y** the number of times a deuce (two) will turn up.

(a) Describe the probability space on which **x** and **y** are defined.

(b) Construct a table giving the joint probability function of **x** and **y**.

(c) Determine the marginal probability functions of **x** and **y** directly from the original probability space.

(d) Determine the marginal probability functions of **x** and **y** from the joint probability function.

5. A coin is to be tossed. If heads comes up a die will then be tossed, while if tails comes up the coin will be tossed again. Assign the number 1 to heads and the number 0 to tails, and let **x** denote the number to come up on the first toss, **y** the number to come up on the second toss.

(a) Construct a table giving the joint probability function of **x** and **y**.

(b) Determine the marginal probability functions both from the original probability space and from the joint probability function.

(c) Find $Pr\{\mathbf{x}^2 + \mathbf{y}^2 < 10\}$.

6. Two coins are tossed together, twice.

(a) Find the joint distribution of **x**, the number of tosses in which no head will appear, and **y**, the number of tosses in which one and only one head will appear. (b) Find the marginal distributions of **x** and **y**. (c) Find $E(\mathbf{y})$, $V(\mathbf{y})$, σ_y.

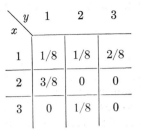

27. Continuous Random Variables. We introduce this concept by the following example.

EXAMPLE 3. (*Uniform Distribution over the Unit Square*). A point $(\mathbf{x},\mathbf{y})$ is to be chosen "at random" in the unit square, $0 \leq x \leq 1$, $0 \leq y \leq 1$. The phrase "at random" is intended to convey the idea that of two congruent figures in the unit square, the point is as likely to be chosen in one as in the other. In particular, if two rectangles in the unit square have corresponding sides equal, the probability that the point will be chosen in one is to be the same as the probability that it will be chosen in the other. It is possible to use the law of total probability to show that the probability of choosing the point in an interval or rectangle must then be proportional to its area, and since the area of the entire unit square is 1, the proportionality constant must be 1. In the probability space we are describing, the elementary events are the points (or number pairs) in the unit square; intervals or rectangles are to be events, so that the family of events is to be the smallest family containing intervals in the unit square and satisfying the axioms for $\mathfrak{F}$ (the Borel subsets of the unit square). The probability of an event which is an interval is just its area, and the probability of a single elementary event is 0.

An alternative probability space for this situation would have the whole plane R_2 as the fundamental set of elementary events, but each event entirely outside the unit square would have probability 0. This is the probability space induced on R_2 by the pair $\mathbf{x},\mathbf{y}$ of random variables.

We shall have a mass representation of the joint distribution of $\mathbf{x}$ and $\mathbf{y}$ if we spread out uniformly over the unit square a total mass 1, so that the density of the distribution of mass is 1 at each point of the unit square.

We obtain a geometrical representation if we sketch the graph of this density function; its graph is a surface of constant height 1 over each point

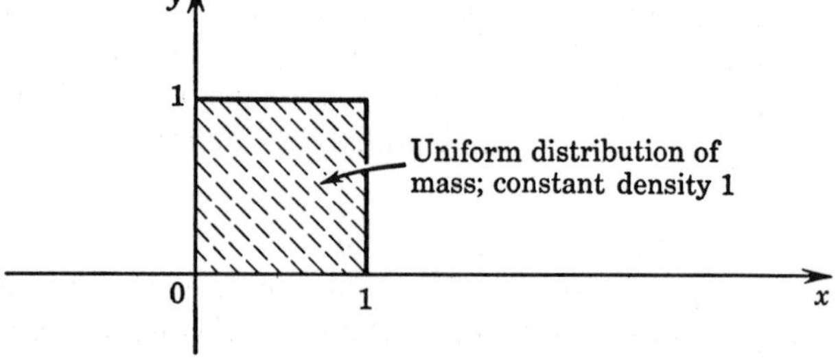

Figure 20

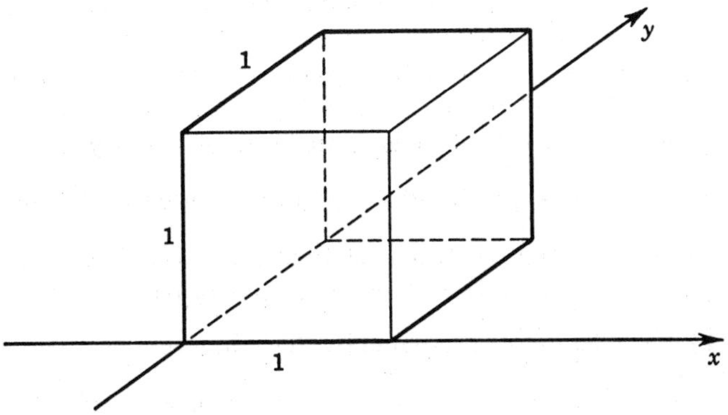

Figure 21. Graph of density function, height 1 over unit square, height 0 over other points.

of the unit square, and of height 0 (coincides with the xy plane) over every other point (Figure 21).

The probability that $\mathbf{x}$ and $\mathbf{y}$ will assume values in a certain subregion of the unit square is the area of that region, and may also be expressed as the integral of the density, which is 1, over that region. If A is any event in the induced probability space, for example, a line, curve, or region in R_2, the xy plane, its probability is the integral over A of the density, which is 0 outside the unit square and 1 inside it; thus $P(A)$ is the area of the part of A in the unit square. In particular, if a and b are real numbers with $a < b$, then $Pr\{a < \mathbf{x} < b\}$ is the probability of the event A consisting of all elementary events or points in a vertical strip determined by the inequalities $a < x < b$; in the mass representation this probability is equal to the mass in this strip; in the geometrical representation it is the volume over this strip and under the graph of the density function, or the area of the part of this strip in the unit square. If $0 \leq a < b \leq 1$, then this is just $b - a$, so that the marginal distribution of $\mathbf{x}$ is the *uniform* distribution over [0,1] (Example 5, page 42). Similarly, the marginal distribution of $\mathbf{y}$ is the uniform or rectangular distribution over [0,1].

28. Continuous Random Variables; General. A pair $\mathbf{x},\mathbf{y}$ of random variables defined on the same probability space have a continuous joint distribution if there is a function $f(x,y)$ with the property that the probability of an event A in the induced probability space on R_2 is the integral of f over A:

$$\blacktriangleright \qquad P(A) = Pr\{(\mathbf{x},\mathbf{y}) \text{ in } A\} = \iint_A f(x,y)\, dx\, dy.$$

This function f is called the *joint probability density function* of $\mathbf{x}$ and $\mathbf{y}$, or simply their *joint density function.*

In the mass representation of their joint distribution a total mass 1 is spread out over the xy plane in such a way that the density at any point is numerically equal to the joint density function of $\mathbf{x}$ and $\mathbf{y}$ at that point. Thus $Pr\{(\mathbf{x},\mathbf{y}) \text{ in } A\} = \iint_A f(x,y)\,dx\,dy$ is represented by the mass in A.

In the geometrical representation of their joint distribution, the graph of the density function $f(x,y)$ is drawn over the xy plane. Then $Pr\{(\mathbf{x},\mathbf{y})$ in $A\} = \iint_A f(x,y)\,dx\,dy$ is represented by the volume under the graph of the density function and over the region A in the xy plane.

The *marginal distribution function* of $\mathbf{x}$, $F(x) = Pr\{\mathbf{x} < x\}$, is the probability that $(\mathbf{x},\mathbf{y})$ will be in A, where A is the half-plane containing all points with abscissa less than x:

$$F(x) = Pr\{\mathbf{x} < x\} = \iint_{u<x} f(u,v)\,du\,dv = \int_{-\infty}^{x}\left[\int_{-\infty}^{\infty} f(u,v)\,dv\right]du;$$

the change of name from x and y to u and v of the variables of integration does not change the value of the integral, and by making this change we avoid confusing a variable of integration with the real number x which is

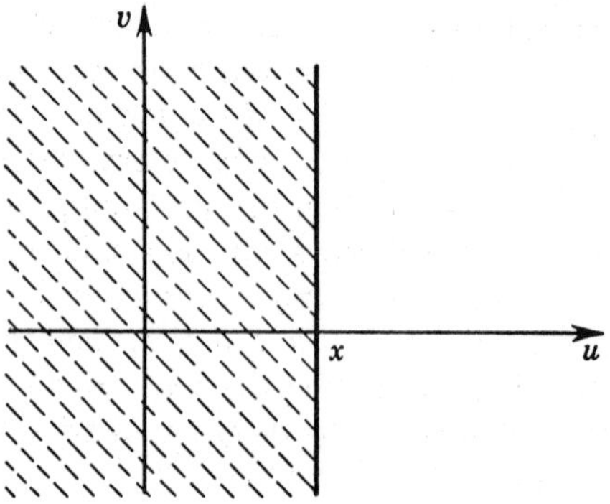

Figure 22

the abscissa of the right boundary of the region over which we are integrating. We see from the above equations that if we set

$$f(u) = \int_{-\infty}^{\infty} f(u,v)\,dv,$$

then

$$F(x) = \int_{-\infty}^{x} f(u)\,du;$$

further, if a and b are any two real numbers, with $a < b$, then

$$Pr\{a < \mathbf{x} < b\} = \iint_{a<x<b} f(x,y)\,dy\,dx = \int_a^b \left[\int_{-\infty}^{\infty} f(x,y)\,dy\right] dx$$

$$= \int_a^b f(x)\,dx.$$

But this is precisely the condition (page 42) to be satisfied if $\mathbf{x}$ is to be a continuous random variable with density function $f(x)$. Thus $\mathbf{x}$ is a random variable having a continuous distribution, with density function

▶ $$f(x) = \int_{-\infty}^{\infty} f(x,y)\,dy.$$

Similarly, $\mathbf{y}$ has a continuous distribution with density function

▶ $$g(y) = \int_{-\infty}^{\infty} f(x,y)\,dx.$$

We observe that the marginal density function of $\mathbf{x}$ at x is obtained by integrating the joint density function along the vertical line whose abscissa is x, and similarly the marginal density function of $\mathbf{y}$ at y is the integral along the horizontal line with ordinate y of the joint density function.

If we have a continuous random vector $(\mathbf{x}_1, \mathbf{x}_2, \cdots, \mathbf{x}_k)$, the joint density function is a function $f(x_1, x_2, \cdots, x_k)$ of k real variables $x_1, x_2, \cdots, x_k$ with the property that for every event A (set of points in R_k, the space of k-tuples of real numbers),

$$Pr\{(\mathbf{x}_1, \mathbf{x}_2, \cdots, \mathbf{x}_k) \text{ in } A\} = \iint_A \cdots \int f(x_1, x_2, \cdots, x_k)\,dx_1\,dx_2 \cdots dx_k.$$

Thus the *joint probability distribution* of $\mathbf{x}_1, \cdots, \mathbf{x}_k$ is determined by their joint density function. The marginal density function of any particular one, $\mathbf{x}_i$, is given at the real number x_i by

$$f_i(x_i) = \underbrace{\int_{-\infty}^{\infty}\int_{-\infty}^{\infty}\cdots\int_{-\infty}^{\infty}}_{k-1} f(x_1, x_2, \cdots, x_k)\,dx_1\,dx_2 \cdots dx_{i-1}\,dx_{i+1} \cdots dx_k.$$

EXAMPLE 4. Suppose the random vector $(\mathbf{x},\mathbf{y})$ has a joint probability density function which is proportional to the square of the distance from the origin within the circle of radius 1 centered at the origin, and is 0 elsewhere:

$$f(x,y) = k(x^2 + y^2) \quad \text{for } x^2 + y^2 < 1,$$

$$f(x,y) = 0 \quad \text{for } x^2 + y^2 > 1.$$

Since the probability associated with the entire xy plane, $Pr\{(\mathbf{x},\mathbf{y}) \text{ in } R_2\}$, is 1, we have

$$\int_{-\infty}^{\infty}\int_{-\infty}^{\infty} f(x,y)\,dx\,dy = 1.$$

This integral may be more easily evaluated in polar coordinates, r, θ, with $x^2 + y^2 = r^2$ and $dx\,dy = r\,dr\,d\theta$. We have

$$\int_{-\infty}^{\infty}\int_{-\infty}^{\infty} f(x,y)\,dx\,dy = k\int_0^{2\pi} d\theta \int_0^1 r^2\cdot r\,dr,$$

since $f(x,y) = 0$ when $r > 1$. The left member is 1 and the right member is $k\pi/2$, so that $k = 2/\pi$, and

$$f(x,y) = \frac{2}{\pi}(x^2 + y^2) \quad \text{when } x^2 + y^2 < 1,$$

$$f(x,y) = 0 \quad \text{when } x^2 + y^2 > 1.$$

The marginal density function $f(x)$ of $\mathbf{x}$ is given by

$$f(x) = \int_{-\infty}^{\infty} f(x,y)\,dy = \frac{2}{\pi}\int_{-\sqrt{1-x^2}}^{\sqrt{1-x^2}} (x^2 + y^2)\,dy$$

$$= \frac{4}{\pi}\int_0^{\sqrt{1-x^2}} (x^2 + y^2)\,dy \quad \text{if } -1 < x < 1,$$

since $f(x,y) = 0$ when $y > \sqrt{1 - x^2}$ or $y < -\sqrt{1 - x^2}$. The integration yields

$$f(x) = \frac{4}{3\pi}\sqrt{1 - x^2}(2x^2 + 1) \quad \text{if } -1 < x < 1.$$

If $x < -1$ or if $x > 1$, then

$$f(x) = \int_{-\infty}^{\infty} f(x,y)\,dy = \int_{-\infty}^{\infty} 0\,dy = 0.$$

PROBLEMS

1. Let $(\mathbf{x},\mathbf{y})$ have a uniform distribution over the unit circle (center origin, radius 1); that is, $f(x,y)$ is constant for $x^2 + y^2 < 1$ and 0 for $x^2 + y^2 > 1$. Find (a) the marginal density function of $\mathbf{y}$; (b) the marginal distribution function of $\mathbf{y}$; (c) $E(\mathbf{y})$; (d) $V(\mathbf{y})$.

2. A target for darts is to consist of a bull's-eye and two concentric rings, with associated scoring values 5, 2, 1. Let the radius of the bull's-eye be 1 inch. Determine the radii of the rings so that if the dart is thrown at random (the hit point of the dart has a uniform distribution over a square containing the target), then it is 5 times as likely to hit the outer ring as the bull's-eye, and twice as likely to hit the outer ring as the inner ring.

3. Let $(\mathbf{r},\mathbf{s})$ have joint density function $f(r,s) = e^{-(r+s)}$ when $r > 0$, $s > 0$, $f(r,s) = 0$ when $r < 0$ or $s < 0$. Find (a) the density function of $\mathbf{r}$; (b) $E(\mathbf{r})$; (c) $V(\mathbf{r})$.

4. Let the joint density function of $(\mathbf{x},\mathbf{y})$ be $f(x,y) = ke^{-(x^2+y^2)/2}$.

(a) Use integration in polar coordinates to find k.

(b) Observe that

$$\int_{-\infty}^{\infty}\int_{-\infty}^{\infty} e^{-(x^2+y^2)/2}\,dx\,dy = \int_{-\infty}^{\infty} e^{-x^2/2}\,dx \int_{-\infty}^{\infty} e^{-y^2/2}\,dy$$
$$= \left[\int_{-\infty}^{\infty} e^{-t^2/2}\,dt\right]^2,$$

and use the result of (a) to find the marginal density function of $\mathbf{x}$.

(c) Find $E(\mathbf{x})$.

(d) Find $V(\mathbf{x})$.

5. Let $\mathbf{x},\mathbf{y}$ have the joint density function $f(x,y) = 1$ for $0 < x < 1$, $0 < y < 1$, $f(x,y) = 0$ otherwise. Find the probability that (a) $\mathbf{x} < 1/2$, $\mathbf{y} < 1/2$; (b) $\mathbf{x} + \mathbf{y} < 1$; (c) $\mathbf{x} > 1/3$; (d) $\mathbf{x}^2 + \mathbf{y}^2 < 1/4$.

6. (a) In Example 3, page 66, ($(\mathbf{x},\mathbf{y})$ uniformly distributed over the unit square), find $Pr\{\mathbf{x} + \mathbf{y} < z\}$ if $z < 0$; if $0 < z < 1$; if $1 < z < 2$; if $z > 2$.

(b) Your answer in (a) is the distribution function of the random variable $\mathbf{z} = \mathbf{x} + \mathbf{y}$. Find the density function of $\mathbf{z}$.

7. Show that if $\mathbf{x},\mathbf{y}$ have joint density function $f(x,y)$ and if $\mathbf{z} = \mathbf{x} + \mathbf{y}$, then for every pair a,b of real numbers with $a < b$,

$$Pr\{a < \mathbf{z} < b\} = \int_a^b dz \int_{-\infty}^{\infty} f(x, z - x)\,dx;$$

hence that the density function of $\mathbf{z}$ is $\int_{-\infty}^{\infty} f(x, z - x)\,dx$.

8. The (cumulative) *distribution function* $F(x,y)$ of a pair $(\mathbf{x},\mathbf{y})$ of random variables is defined by

$$F(x,y) = Pr\{\mathbf{x} < x, \mathbf{y} < y\}.$$

Show that if $\mathbf{x},\mathbf{y}$ are continuous random variables with joint probability density function $f(x,y)$, then

$$\frac{\partial^2 F(x,y)}{\partial x \partial y} = f(x,y).$$

29. Conditional Distributions of Discrete Random Variables. Suppose $\mathbf{x},\mathbf{y}$ are discrete random variables having a joint probability function $f(x,y) = Pr\{\mathbf{x} = x, \mathbf{y} = y\}$ which is different from 0 for only a countable number of pairs (x,y); and marginal probability functions

$$f(x) = \textstyle\sum_y f(x,y), \quad g(y) = \sum_x f(x,y). \qquad \text{(page 63)}$$

Let us consider now how to define appropriately a conditional probability, the probability $Pr\{\mathbf{y} = y | \mathbf{x} = x\}$, where x and y are two fixed real numbers. We recall that if A and B are two events with $P(B) \neq 0$, then $P(A|B) = P(AB)/P(B)$. Our desired definition then has in effect already been given: if we take for A the event $\{\mathbf{y} = y\}$, and for B the event $\{\mathbf{x} = x\}$, then $AB = A \cap B$ is the event $\{\mathbf{x} = x, \mathbf{y} = y\}$, and we have $Pr\{\mathbf{y} = y | \mathbf{x} = x\} = P(A|B) = P(AB)/P(B) = Pr\{\mathbf{x} = x, \mathbf{y} = y\}/Pr\{\mathbf{x} = x\}$. Let us denote this conditional probability, which depends on the fixed numbers x and y, by $g(y|x)$:

► $$g(y|x) = f(x,y)/f(x) \quad \text{if } f(x) \neq 0.$$

When y varies, x being held fixed, $g(y|x)$ is a function of y; it is called the *conditional probability function* of $\mathbf{y}$, for the given value x of $\mathbf{x}$. It is defined only if x is a value assumed by $\mathbf{x}$ with positive probability, that is, only if $f(x) \neq 0$. If $f(x) \neq 0$, then $g(y|x)$ is defined for all y, but is different from 0 for only those y for which $f(x,y) \neq 0$. For example, in Example 1, page 57, $g(y|x)$ is defined for all y if and only if x is either 1 or -1. We have $g(1|1) = f(1,1)/f(1) = (1/4)/(1/2) = 1/2$, $g(-1|1) = f(-1,1)/f(-1) = (1/4)/(1/2) = 1/2$, etc.

The conditional probability function of $\mathbf{x}$ for a given value y of $\mathbf{y}$, $f(x|y)$, is defined similarly:

► $$f(x|y) = f(x,y)/g(y) \quad \text{if } g(y) \neq 0.$$

In Example 2, page 60, we have $f(1|2) = f(1,2)/g(2) = 0/(1/4) = 0$; $f(-1|-2) = f(-1,-2)/g(-2) = (1/4)/(1/4) = 1$, etc.

In many problems of interest the given data include conditional probabilities. In such situations we shall often find the law of total probability useful in expressing unconditional probabilities in terms of conditional probabilities. For example, suppose that $\mathbf{y}$ is a discrete random variable, having possible values $b_1, b_2, \cdots, b_M$, with probabilities $p_1, p_2, \cdots, p_M$: $g(b_j) = p_j$, $j = 1, 2, \cdots, M$, $g(y) = 0$ for other y. Suppose A is an event, suppose we are given the conditional probabilities $P(A|\{\mathbf{y} = b_j\})$ for $j = 1, 2, \cdots, M$, as well as the unconditional probabilities p_j ($j = 1, 2, \cdots, M$), and suppose we are required to find $P(A)$. The events $\{\mathbf{y} = b_1\}$, $\{\mathbf{y} = b_2\}, \cdots, \{\mathbf{y} = b_M\}$ are mutually exclusive and exhaustive, so that

$$A = [A \cap \{\mathbf{y} = b_1\}] \cup [A \cap \{\mathbf{y} = b_2\}] \cup \cdots \cup [A \cap \{\mathbf{y} = b_M\}],$$

and

$$P(A) = \textstyle\sum_{j=1}^{M} P(A \cap \{\mathbf{y} = b_j\}).$$

But for each j, by the definition of conditional probability (law of compound probability, page 15), $P(A \cap \{\mathbf{y} = b_j\}) = P(A | \{\mathbf{y} = b_j\})\, Pr\{\mathbf{y} = b_j\}$ so that

$$P(A) = \sum_{j=1}^{M} P(A | \{\mathbf{y} = b_j\})p_j, \quad \text{or} \quad P(A) = \sum_y P(A | \mathbf{y} = y)g(y),$$

the latter summation being extended over all values of $\mathbf{y}$ which are assumed with positive probability (the addend is 0 for each other y).

▶ *The probability of any event is the sum of products, each a probability of the event conditioned by the assumption of one of the possible values of* $\mathbf{y}$*, multiplied by the probability that* $\mathbf{y}$ *will assume that value.*

This is true for *any discrete random variable* $\mathbf{y}$.

In particular, if $(\mathbf{x},\mathbf{y})$ is a discrete random vector and if we take for A the event $\{\mathbf{x} = x\}$ where x is a real number, we find that the probability function $f(x)$ of $\mathbf{x}$ is given by

$$Pr\{\mathbf{x} = x\} = \sum_y Pr\{\mathbf{x} = x | \mathbf{y} = y\} Pr\{\mathbf{y} = y\},$$

or

▶ $$f(x) = \sum_y f(x|y)g(y).$$

Since $f(x|y)g(y) = f(x,y)$, this is equivalent to the equation discussed earlier,

$$f(x) = \sum_y f(x,y).$$

Similarly,

▶ $$g(y) = \sum_x g(y|x)f(x),$$

if $g(y)$ is the probability function of $\mathbf{y}$.

EXAMPLE 5. In Example 2 on page 60 you are to toss a coin twice, betting 1 dollar on heads in the first toss. On the second toss you will bet 1 dollar on heads if heads came up on the first, 2 dollars on tails if tails came up on the first. Let $\mathbf{x}$ be the amount you will win on the first toss: we are given directly that $Pr\{\mathbf{x} = 1\} = Pr\{\mathbf{x} = -1\} = 1/2$, or $f(1) = f(-1) = 1/2$. Let $\mathbf{y}$ be the amount you will win on the second toss: we are given $Pr\{\mathbf{y} = 1 | \mathbf{x} = 1\} = Pr\{\mathbf{y} = -1 | \mathbf{x} = 1\} = Pr\{\mathbf{y} = 2 | \mathbf{x} = -1\} = Pr\{\mathbf{y} = -2 | \mathbf{x} = -1\} = 1/2$, or $g(1|1) = g(-1|1) = g(2|-1) = g(-2|-1) = 1/2$. Applying the above formulas, we find, for example,

$$Pr\{\mathbf{y} = 1\} = g(1) = \sum_x g(1|x)f(x) = g(1|1)f(1) + g(1|-1)f(-1)$$
$$= \tfrac{1}{2}\cdot\tfrac{1}{2} + 0\cdot\tfrac{1}{2} = 1/4.$$

If we wish to find the probability that your total winnings will not exceed 1, we find on setting $A = \{\mathbf{x} + \mathbf{y} \leq 1\}$ that

$$\begin{aligned} Pr\{\mathbf{x} + \mathbf{y} \le 1\} &= \textstyle\sum_x Pr\{\mathbf{x} + \mathbf{y} \le 1 \mid \mathbf{x} = x\} f(x) \\ &= Pr\{\mathbf{x} + \mathbf{y} \le 1 \mid \mathbf{x} = 1\} Pr\{\mathbf{x} = 1\} \\ &\qquad + Pr\{\mathbf{x} + \mathbf{y} \le 1 \mid \mathbf{x} = -1\} Pr\{\mathbf{x} = -1\} \\ &= Pr\{1 + \mathbf{y} \le 1 \mid \mathbf{x} = 1\} Pr\{\mathbf{x} = 1\} \\ &\qquad + Pr\{-1 + \mathbf{y} \le 1 \mid \mathbf{x} = -1\} Pr\{\mathbf{x} = -1\} \\ &= Pr\{\mathbf{y} \le 0 \mid \mathbf{x} = 1\} Pr\{\mathbf{x} = 1\} \\ &\qquad + Pr\{\mathbf{y} \le 2 \mid \mathbf{x} = -1\} Pr\{\mathbf{x} = -1\} \\ &= \tfrac{1}{2} \cdot \tfrac{1}{2} + 1 \cdot \tfrac{1}{2} = 3/4. \end{aligned}$$

30. Independence of Discrete Random Variables. The discrete random variables $\mathbf{x}$ and $\mathbf{y}$ are independent if each conditional probability is equal to the corresponding unconditional probability: $Pr\{\mathbf{x} = x \mid \mathbf{y} = y\} = Pr\{\mathbf{x} = x\}$ for each real number y which is a value assumed by $\mathbf{y}$ with positive probability, and $Pr\{\mathbf{y} = y \mid \mathbf{x} = x\} = Pr\{\mathbf{y} = y\}$ if $Pr\{\mathbf{x} = x\} \neq 0$. In the functional notation,

$$f(x \mid y) = f(x), \quad \text{if } g(y) \neq 0,$$

and

$$g(y \mid x) = g(y), \quad \text{if } f(x) \neq 0.$$

Since $f(x \mid y) = f(x,y)/g(y)$ ($= Pr\{\mathbf{x} = x, \mathbf{y} = y\}/Pr\{\mathbf{y} = y\}$) and $g(y \mid x) = f(x,y)/f(x)$, we find that the equations $f(x \mid y) = f(x)$ and $g(y \mid x) = g(y)$ are valid when $f(x) \neq 0$ and $g(y) \neq 0$ if and only if

$$f(x,y) = f(x)g(y).$$

This last equation has meaning and is true also if either $f(x) = 0$ or $g(y) = 0$; and we take it as the definition of independence of the discrete random variables $\mathbf{x}$ and $\mathbf{y}$:

► *The discrete random variables* $\mathbf{x}$ *and* $\mathbf{y}$ *with joint probability function* $f(x,y)$ *and marginal probability functions respectively* $f(x)$ *and* $g(y)$ *are independent if and only if*

$$f(x,y) = f(x)g(y)$$

or

$$Pr\{\mathbf{x} = x, \mathbf{y} = y\} = Pr\{\mathbf{x} = x\} Pr\{\mathbf{y} = y\}$$

for every pair (x,y).

We have seen that this is equivalent to requiring the conditional probabilities mentioned above to be equal to the corresponding unconditional probabilities.

The above condition might also be stated as follows: the discrete random variables $\mathbf{x}$ and $\mathbf{y}$ are independent if and only if the events $\{\mathbf{x} = x\}$ and $\{\mathbf{y} = y\}$ are independent for every pair of real numbers x and y. An equivalent statement is the following: for each event A (set of real numbers) in the probability space induced by $\mathbf{x}$, and each event B in the probability space induced by $\mathbf{y}$, we have

$$Pr\{\mathbf{x} \text{ in } A, \mathbf{y} \text{ in } B\} = Pr\{\mathbf{x} \text{ in } A\}Pr\{\mathbf{y} \text{ in } B\};$$

or, the events $\{\mathbf{x} \text{ in } A\}$, $\{\mathbf{y} \text{ in } B\}$ are independent events. For if $\mathbf{x}$ and $\mathbf{y}$ are independent according to the above definition, then

$$\begin{aligned} Pr\{\mathbf{x} \text{ in } A, \mathbf{y} \text{ in } B\} &= \textstyle\sum_{x \text{ in } A} \sum_{y \text{ in } B} f(x)g(y) \\ &= [\textstyle\sum_{x \text{ in } A} f(x)][\sum_{y \text{ in } B} g(y)] \\ &= Pr\{\mathbf{x} \text{ in } A\}Pr\{\mathbf{y} \text{ in } B\}. \end{aligned}$$

Conversely, if the latter condition holds, then on taking for A the single real number x and for B the single real number y, we have

$$Pr\{\mathbf{x} = x, \mathbf{y} = y\} = Pr\{\mathbf{x} = x\}Pr\{\mathbf{y} = y\},$$

or

$$f(x,y) = f(x)g(y).$$

EXAMPLE 6. In Example 2, page 60, we have, for instance, $f(1,1) = 1/4$ while $f(1) = 1/2$, $g(1) = 1/4$, so that

$$f(1,1) \neq f(1)g(1).$$

This shows that $\mathbf{x}$ and $\mathbf{y}$ are *not* independent, since for independence we must have $f(x,y) = f(x)g(y)$ for *every* pair of real numbers x,y.

EXAMPLE 7. In Example 1, page 57, we have $f(1) = f(-1) = g(1) = g(-1) = 1/2$, and $f(1,1) = f(-1,1) = f(1,-1) = f(-1,-1) = 1/4$, so that $f(x,y) = f(x)g(y)$ for every pair (x,y); $\mathbf{x}$ and $\mathbf{y}$ are independent.

Discrete random variables $\mathbf{x}_1, \mathbf{x}_2, \cdots, \mathbf{x}_k$ (cf. page 64) are *independent* if and only if their joint probability function $f(x_1, x_2, \cdots, x_k)$ is given in terms of their marginal probability functions $f_1(x_1), f_2(x_2), \cdots, f_k(x_k)$, by

$$f(x_1, x_2, \cdots, x_k) = f_1(x_1)f_2(x_2) \cdots f_k(x_k) = \textstyle\prod_{i=1}^{k} f_i(x_i),$$

or

$$Pr\{\mathbf{x}_1 = x_1, \mathbf{x}_2 = x_2, \cdots, \mathbf{x}_k = x_k\} = \textstyle\prod_{i=1}^{k} Pr\{\mathbf{x}_i = x_i\}.$$

★31. Matrix Condition for Independence of Two Discrete Random Variables. Let us think of the joint probability function of two discrete random variables as given in tabular form, as in Problems 1 and 2 on pages 64 and 65, with columns headed by values of $\mathbf{y}$ and rows by values of $\mathbf{x}$, the entry in the row headed by x and in the column headed by y being $f(x,y)$, the probability that $\mathbf{x}$ will assume the value x and $\mathbf{y}$ the value y. If $\mathbf{x}$ and $\mathbf{y}$

are independent, then $f(x,y) = f(x)g(y)$; if then x_1 and x_2 are two of the values of **x**, we shall have, for each y, $f(x_1,y) = f(x_1)g(y)$ and $f(x_2,y) = f(x_2)g(y)$, so that

$$f(x_1,y) = \frac{f(x_1)}{f(x_2)} \cdot f(x_2,y)$$

for each y. That is, if **x** and **y** are independent, the probabilities in each row may be obtained by multiplying the corresponding probabilities in any other row by the same number, which depends only on the rows involved and not on the values of **y**. This situation is described by saying the rows are all linearly dependent, or that the matrix of probabilities has rank 1: the determinant of each minor of order greater than 1 is 0. Conversely, if each row is a multiple of any other, then it is easy to show that $f(x,y) = f(x)g(y)$, so that **x** and **y** are independent.

▶ A necessary and sufficient condition for the independence of the discrete random variables **x** and **y** is that the matrix of probabilities have rank 1, or that each row be a multiple of each other; or equivalently, that each column be a multiple of each other.

In Example 1, page 57, the two rows are identical; indeed each entry is 1/4. The random variables are accordingly independent. The table for Example 2, page 60, is shown below; we see that neither row is a multiple of the other, and the random variables **x** and **y** are not independent.

$x \backslash y$	-2	-1	1	2
-1	1/4	0	0	1/4
1	0	1/4	1/4	0

PROBLEMS

1. In Problem 1, page 64, find $g(1|1)$, $g(1|2)$, $g(1|3)$, and verify that $g(1) = \sum_x g(1|x)f(x)$.

2. The joint probability function $f(x,y)$ of discrete random variables **x** and **y** is given in the accompanying table.

$x \backslash y$	-1	0	1
-1	1/8	0	1/8
1	1/2	1/4	0

(a) Find the marginal probability function of **x**.

(b) Make a table of values of the conditional probability function of **y**, given $\mathbf{x} = 1$: $g(y|1) = Pr\{\mathbf{y} = y|\mathbf{x} = 1\}$.

3. In Problems 1, 2, 4, and 5, pages 64 and 65, determine whether **x** and **y** are dependent or independent.

4. Given a random variable **x** assuming values 1, 2, 3 with probabilities 1/4, 1/4, 1/2, and a random variable **y** assuming values 1 and 2 with probabilities 1/3 and 2/3; give their joint distribution in a table, if they are independent.

5. A number **x** is chosen at random from among the integers 3, 4, $\cdots$, 10. A number **y** is then chosen at random from among the even positive integers less than **x**.

(a) Find $G(5|x) = Pr\{y < 5|\mathbf{x} = x\}$ for each x.

(b) Find $G(5) = Pr\{\mathbf{y} < 5\}$.

6. A number **x** is chosen at random from among the integers 1, 2, 3, and 4. Another, **y**, is chosen from among those which are at least as large as **x**.

(a) Find the marginal probability function of **x** and the conditional probability function of **y** for each value of **x**.

(b) Determine the joint probability function of **x** and **y** and the marginal probability function of **y**.

(c) Determine the marginal probability function of **y** directly from the conditional probability function of **y** and the marginal probability function of **x**.

7. In Problem 6, (a) find $Pr\{\mathbf{x} + \mathbf{y} \geq 4\}$. (b) Are **x** and **y** independent? Why?

32. Conditional Distributions of Continuous Random Variables. We recall that for discrete random variables **x** and **y** with joint probability function $f(x,y)$ and marginal probability functions $f(x)$ and $g(y)$ respectively, the conditional probability function of **y** given $\{\mathbf{x} = x\}$ is $g(y|x) = Pr\{\mathbf{y} = y|\mathbf{x} = x\} = f(x,y)/f(x)$. Now if **x**,**y** are continuous random variables with joint density function $f(x,y)$ and marginal density functions $f(x)$ and $g(y)$ respectively, on a purely heuristic basis we may think of the probability that **x** will be in a small interval of length dx at x and **y** in a small interval of length dy at y as being given by $f(x,y)\,dx\,dy$, while the probability that **x** will be in a small interval of length dx at x is $f(x)\,dx$; therefore the conditional probability that **y** will be in a small interval of length dy at y given that **x** is in a small interval of length dx at x is given by

$$g(y|x)\,dy = \frac{f(x,y)\,dy\,dx}{f(x)\,dx};$$

or again

$$g(y|x) = \frac{f(x,y)}{f(x)},$$

a formula for the conditional density function of $\mathbf{y}$ given $\mathbf{x} = x$.

In order to discuss the conditional probability density function more precisely, let us consider first, for given numbers a,b with $a < b$, the conditional probability of the event $\{a < \mathbf{y} < b\}$, given that $x < \mathbf{x} < x + \Delta x$ $(\Delta x > 0)$. We have

$$Pr\{a < \mathbf{y} < b | x < \mathbf{x} < x + \Delta x\} = \frac{Pr\{a < \mathbf{y} < b, x < \mathbf{x} < x + \Delta x\}}{Pr\{x < \mathbf{x} < x + \Delta x\}}.$$

The numerator is the integral of the joint density function over the rectangle described by the inequalities:

$$\int_x^{x+\Delta x} du \int_a^b f(u,y)\, dy,$$

while the denominator is

$$\int_x^{x+\Delta x} du \int_{-\infty}^{\infty} f(u,y)\, dy.$$

We shall need the fundamental theorem of the integral calculus, so we recall its content briefly here. If

$$\Phi(x) = \int_c^x \varphi(u)\, du, \quad c \text{ constant, } \varphi \text{ continuous,}$$

then

$$\Phi'(x) = \varphi(x).$$

But

$$\Phi'(x) = \lim_{\Delta x \to 0} \frac{\Phi(x + \Delta x) - \Phi(x)}{\Delta x} = \lim_{\Delta x \to 0} \frac{1}{\Delta x} \int_x^{x+\Delta x} \varphi(u)\, du.$$

Therefore

$$\lim_{\Delta x \to 0} \frac{1}{\Delta x} \int_x^{x+\Delta x} \varphi(u)\, du = \varphi(x).$$

We now apply this to the above situation, first, in replacing $\varphi(u)$ by $\int_a^b f(u,y)\, dy$, a function of u. We find

$$\lim_{\Delta x \to 0} \frac{1}{\Delta x} \int_x^{x+\Delta x} \left[\int_a^b f(u,y)\, dy\right] du = \int_a^b f(x,y)\, dy.$$

Similarly, when we replace $\varphi(u)$ by $\int_{-\infty}^{\infty} f(u,y)\, dy$ we find that

$$\lim_{\Delta x \to 0} \frac{1}{\Delta x} \int_x^{x+\Delta x} \left[\int_{-\infty}^{\infty} f(u,y)\, dy\right] du = \int_{-\infty}^{\infty} f(x,y)\, dx.$$

Finally, then,

$$\lim_{\Delta x\to 0} Pr\{a < \mathbf{y} < b | x < \mathbf{x} < x + \Delta x\} = \lim_{\Delta x\to 0} \frac{\int_x^{x+\Delta x} du \int_a^b f(u,y)\, dy}{\int_x^{x+\Delta x} du \int_{-\infty}^{\infty} f(u,y)\, dy}$$

$$= \lim_{\Delta x\to 0} \frac{\frac{1}{\Delta x}\int_x^{x+\Delta x} du \int_a^b f(u,y)\, dy}{\frac{1}{\Delta x}\int_x^{x+\Delta x} du \int_{-\infty}^{\infty} f(u,y)\, dy} = \frac{\int_a^b f(x,y)\, dy}{\int_{-\infty}^{\infty} f(x,y)\, dy},$$

if the denominator of the last expression is not zero. We recall (page 69) that the denominator is precisely $f(x)$, the marginal density function of $\mathbf{x}$, so that

$$\lim_{\Delta x\to 0} Pr\{a < \mathbf{y} < b | x < \mathbf{x} < x + \Delta x\} = \int_a^b f(x,y)\, dy/f(x)$$

if $f(x) \neq 0$. (We have the same result if $\Delta x < 0$; only certain inequalities must be rewritten.) The left member we define to be the conditional probability that $\mathbf{y}$ will assume a value between a and b for the given value x of $\mathbf{x}$, and observe that it is defined only if $f(x) \neq 0$. This conditional probability is, for every pair a,b with $a < b$, the integral over the interval $[a,b]$ of the function $f(x,y)/f(x)$; this latter is therefore the conditional density function of $\mathbf{y}$:

▶ $$g(y|x) = f(x,y)/f(x).$$

In many problems of interest the conditional probability density function $g(y|x)$ of $\mathbf{y}$ is given for each x, and also the density function $f(x)$ of $\mathbf{x}$; we see now how the joint density function can then be found:

$$f(x,y) = g(y|x)f(x).$$

Hence

▶ $$Pr\{(\mathbf{x},\mathbf{y}) \text{ in } A\} = \iint_A f(x,y)\, dx\, dy = \iint_A f(x)g(y|x)\, dx\, dy$$

if A is any event in the probability space induced on the xy plane by the random variables $\mathbf{x}$ and $\mathbf{y}$.

Similarly the conditional density function of $\mathbf{x}$ for a given value y of $\mathbf{y}$ is given by

▶ $$f(x|y) = f(x,y)/g(y),$$

and we have also

$$f(x,y) = f(x|y)g(y),$$

▶ $$Pr\{(\mathbf{x},\mathbf{y}) \text{ in } A\} = \iint_A f(x|y)g(y)\,dx\,dy:$$

the probability that **x** and **y** will assume a pair of values which are coordinates of a point in A may be found by integrating the conditional density function $f(x|y)$ with respect to x along the line with ordinate y, then integrating the product of $g(y)$ and the result with respect to y over the range of values of y for which this line sweeps out the region A:

$$\int \left[\int f(x|y)\,dx \right] g(y)\,dy,$$

where the limits depend on the region A (Figure 23).

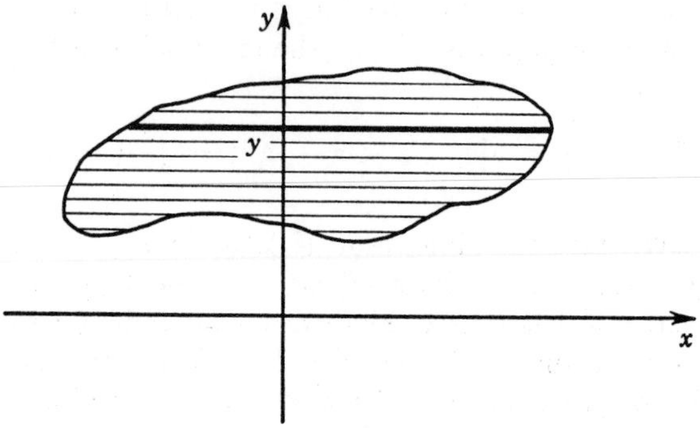

Figure 23

PROBLEMS

1. Given the joint density function $f(x,y) = e^{-(x+y)}$ for $x > 0, y > 0$ $f(x,y) = 0$ elsewhere, find
   (a) $Pr\{0 \le \mathbf{x} \le 1, 0 \le \mathbf{y} \le 1\}$;
   (b) $Pr\{\mathbf{x} > \mathbf{y}\}$;
   (c) The conditional probability density function of **y** for given x.

2. Given the joint density function $f(x,y) = c(x + y)$ for $0 < x < 1$, $0 < y < 1$, $= 0$ elsewhere, find
   (a) The constant c;
   (b) The marginal density functions of **x** and **y**;
   (c) $Pr\{\mathbf{x} > \mathbf{y}\}$;
   (d) The conditional probability density function of **y** for given x.

3. Given the conditional probability density function of **y** for given x, $g(y|x) = 2y/x^2$ for $0 < y < x$ $(0 < x < 1)$, $g(y|x) = 0$ for $y < 0$ or $y > x$ $(0 < x < 1)$, and the density function of **x**, $f(x) = 7x^6$ for $0 < x < 1$, find
   (a) The joint density function of **x**, **y**;
   (b) The marginal density function of **y**;
   (c) $Pr\{\mathbf{x} > 2\mathbf{y}\}$.

√**4.** Let **r**,**s** be two random variables; let **s** have conditional density function $g(s|r)$ for a given value r of **r** given by $g(s|r) = e^{-(s-r)}$ for $s > r$ $(r > 0)$, $= 0$ elsewhere, and let the density function of **r** be $f(r) = 2e^{-2r}$ for $r > 0$. Find

(a) The joint density function of **r**,**s**;

(b) The marginal density function of **s**;

(c) $Pr\{\mathbf{s} < 3\}$.

5. Let $f(x,y) = kxy$ for $0 < x < 1$, $0 < y < 1$, $f = 0$ elsewhere.

(a) Determine k so that $f(x,y)$ is a joint probability density function.

(b) Find the marginal density function and distribution function of **y**.

(c) Find the conditional density function $f(x|y)$ of **x** for a given value y of **y**.

6. A circle is centered at (0,0) in the xy plane and has radius 1. You choose a point at random on its diameter lying on the x axis. Let **x** be its x coordinate. You then choose a point at random on the chord of the circle through this point perpendicular to the x axis. Let **y** be its y coordinate.

(a) What is the joint density function of **x** and **y**?

(b) What is the probability that the point so chosen will lie in the square whose sides are parallel to the coordinate axes and which is inscribed in the circle?

33. Independence of Continuous Random Variables. One way of defining independence of continuous random variables is to require that the conditional probability density functions be equal respectively to the corresponding unconditional probability functions:

$$g(y|x) = g(y), \quad f(x|y) = f(x).$$

Since $g(y|x) = f(x,y)/f(x)$ and $f(x|y) = f(x,y)/g(y)$, we see that if either of the above equations holds then $f(x,y) = f(x)g(y)$, and both are valid.

▶ *Continuous random variables* **x** *and* **y** *are* independent *if and only if their joint density function is the product of their respective marginal density functions*:

$$f(x,y) = f(x)g(y).$$

If A and B are events in the probability spaces induced on R_1 by the random variables **x** and **y** (A and B are sets of real numbers), and if **x** and **y** are independent, then

$$Pr\{\mathbf{x} \text{ in } A, \mathbf{y} \text{ in } B\} = \int_B \int_A f(x,y)\,dx\,dy$$

$$= \int_A f(x)\,dx \int_B g(y)\,dy = Pr\{\mathbf{x} \text{ in } A\}Pr\{\mathbf{y} \text{ in } B\}.$$

Conversely, if for each such A and B we have $Pr\{\mathbf{x} \text{ in } A, \mathbf{y} \text{ in } B\} = Pr\{\mathbf{x} \text{ in } A\}Pr\{\mathbf{y} \text{ in } B\}$, then

$$Pr\{\mathbf{x} \text{ in } A, \mathbf{y} \text{ in } B\} = \int_B \int_A f(x)g(y)\, dx\, dy.$$

It is then possible (but beyond the scope of this text) to show that for every event C in the probability space induced on the xy plane by the random vector $(\mathbf{x},\mathbf{y})$ (C is a set of points or pairs (x,y)), we have

$$Pr\{(\mathbf{x},\mathbf{y}) \text{ in } C\} = \iint_C f(x)g(y)\, dx\, dy.$$

Thus $Pr\{(\mathbf{x},\mathbf{y}) \text{ in } C\}$ is the integral over C of $f(x)g(y)$ for every such event C; but this means that $f(x)g(y)$ is the probability density function of the random vector $(\mathbf{x},\mathbf{y})$.

We have seen then that if

$$f(x,y) = f(x)g(y)$$

then

$$Pr\{\mathbf{x} \text{ in } A, \mathbf{y} \text{ in } B\} = Pr\{\mathbf{x} \text{ in } A\}Pr\{\mathbf{y} \text{ in } B\}$$

for every A and B, and conversely, if the latter equation holds for every A and B then $f(x,y) = f(x)g(y)$. Either equation may then serve as a definition of independence of continuous random variables. (The second may also serve as a definition of independence of discrete random variables.) The second definition makes possible perhaps the simplest proof that functions of independent random variables are independent. Suppose $\mathbf{x}$ and $\mathbf{y}$ are independent random variables, that $h(x)$ and $k(y)$ are functions, and that random variables $\mathbf{w}$ and $\mathbf{z}$ are defined by $\mathbf{w} = h(\mathbf{x})$ and $\mathbf{z} = k(\mathbf{y})$. If C and D are events in the probability spaces induced by $\mathbf{w}$ and $\mathbf{z}$ respectively (sets of real numbers), let A be the event, in the probability space induced by $\mathbf{x}$, consisting of all real numbers x for which $h(x)$ is in C, and B the set of numbers y for which $k(y)$ is in D. (We assume A and B are events; it can be shown they will be if, for example, h and k are continuous functions, or, indeed, any of the functions one might ordinarily expect to encounter in elementary analysis.) Then

$$Pr\{\mathbf{w} \text{ in } C, \mathbf{z} \text{ in } D\} = Pr\{\mathbf{x} \text{ in } A, \mathbf{y} \text{ in } B\}$$
$$= Pr\{\mathbf{x} \text{ in } A\}Pr\{\mathbf{y} \text{ in } B\} = Pr\{\mathbf{w} \text{ in } C\}Pr\{\mathbf{z} \text{ in } D\},$$

so that also $\mathbf{w}$ and $\mathbf{z}$ are independent.

▶ *If* $\mathbf{x}$ *and* $\mathbf{y}$ *are independent random variables, then any random variable which is a function of* $\mathbf{x}$ *and any random variable which is a function of* $\mathbf{y}$ *are independent.*

Continuous random variables $\mathbf{x}_1, \mathbf{x}_2, \cdots, \mathbf{x}_k$ (cf. page 69) are independent if and only if their joint probability density function $f(x_1, x_2, \cdots, x_k)$ is given in terms of their marginal density functions, $f_1(x_1), f_2(x_2), \cdots, f_k(x_k)$, by

$$f(x_1, x_2, \cdots, x_k) = f_1(x_1)f_2(x_2) \cdots f_k(x_k)$$
$$= \prod_{i=1}^{k} f_i(x_i).$$

PROBLEMS

1. Are the random variables in Example 3, page 66, dependent or independent? In Example 4, page 69?

2. Are the random variables in Problems 1, 3, 4, pages 70, 71, dependent or independent?

3. Are the random variables in Problems 2, 3, 4, pages 80, 81, dependent or independent?

4. Random variables $\mathbf{x}$ and $\mathbf{y}$ have joint probability density function $f(x,y) = \frac{\pi^2}{8} \sin \frac{\pi}{2} (x + y)$ for $0 < x < 1, 0 < y < 1, f(x,y) = 0$ elsewhere.

(a) Find the marginal probability density function of $\mathbf{x}$.

(b) What is the conditional density function $g(y|x)$ of $\mathbf{y}$ for a given value x of $\mathbf{x}$?

(c) Are $\mathbf{x}$, $\mathbf{y}$, independent? Why?

(d) Find $Pr\{\mathbf{x} > 2\mathbf{y}\}$.

5. Two numbers $\mathbf{x}$ and $\mathbf{y}$ are chosen independently and at random between 0 and 1. What is the probability that the three segments into which they divide the interval (0,1) will form a triangle?

6. A number $\mathbf{x}$ is chosen at random between 0 and 1. A number $\mathbf{y}$ is then chosen at random in the part of the interval (0,1) to the right of the number $\mathbf{x}$. What is the probability that the three segments into which they divide the interval will form a triangle?

7. Two numbers are to be chosen independently and at random between 0 and 1. What is the probability that both will be less than a specified number y between 0 and 1?

8. You plan to choose independently n numbers at random between 0 and θ, where θ is a given positive number. Find the distribution function of the largest.

Hint. See Problem 7, where $n = 2, \theta = 1$.

9. Given independent random variables $\mathbf{x}_1$ and $\mathbf{x}_2$ with the same density function f, write and evaluate a double integral whose value is $Pr\{\mathbf{x}_2 > \mathbf{x}_1\}$.

34. Summary. A *discrete* random vector $(\mathbf{x},\mathbf{y})$ has a joint probability function

$$f(x,y) = Pr\{\mathbf{x} = x, \mathbf{y} = y\},$$

which is different from zero only when (x,y) is one of the countable number of pairs of values actually assumed by $(\mathbf{x},\mathbf{y})$. If A is any event in the probability space induced on R_2, the xy plane, by $\mathbf{x}$ and $\mathbf{y}$ then

$$Pr\{(\mathbf{x},\mathbf{y}) \text{ in } A\} = \sum_{(x,y) \text{ in } A} f(x,y).$$

In particular, the marginal probability functions of $\mathbf{x}$ and $\mathbf{y}$ are given by

$$f(x) = Pr\{\mathbf{x} = x\} = \sum_y f(x,y)$$

and

$$g(y) = Pr\{\mathbf{y} = y\} = \sum_x f(x,y).$$

The conditional probability function of $\mathbf{y}$ for given x is a probability function defined for all x for which $f(x) \neq 0$:

$$g(y|x) = f(x,y)/f(x) \quad \text{if } f(x) \neq 0;$$

similarly

$$f(x|y) = f(x,y)/g(y) \quad \text{if } g(y) \neq 0.$$

Hence

$$Pr\{(\mathbf{x},\mathbf{y}) \text{ in } A\} = \sum_{(x,y) \text{ in } A} g(y|x)f(x)$$

$$= \sum_{(x,y) \text{ in } A} f(x|y)g(y),$$

and in particular

$$f(x) = \sum_y f(x|y)g(y)$$

and

$$g(y) = \sum_x g(y|x)f(x).$$

The discrete random variables $\mathbf{x},\mathbf{y}$ are *independent* if $f(x,y) = f(x)g(y)$, or if

$$Pr\{\mathbf{x} \text{ in } A, \mathbf{y} \text{ in } B\} = Pr\{\mathbf{x} \text{ in } A\}Pr\{\mathbf{y} \text{ in } B\}$$

for every A, B. Either is equivalent to $f(x|y) = f(x)$ and $g(y|x) = g(y)$.

The random vector $(\mathbf{x},\mathbf{y})$ is *continuous* if there is a function $f(x,y)$ of real variables x and y such that for every event A in the xy plane

$$Pr\{(\mathbf{x},\mathbf{y}) \text{ in } A\} = \iint_A f(x,y)\,dx\,dy.$$

The function $f(x,y)$ is called the *joint density function* or *joint probability density function* of $\mathbf{x}$ and $\mathbf{y}$. The marginal density functions of $\mathbf{x}$ and $\mathbf{y}$ are given respectively by

$$f(x) = \int_{-\infty}^{\infty} f(x,y)\, dy \quad \text{and} \quad g(y) = \int_{-\infty}^{\infty} f(x,y)\, dx.$$

The conditional probability density function of **y** for given x is a probability density function defined for each x for which $f(x) \neq 0$ by

$$g(y|x) = f(x,y)/f(x);$$

similarly

$$f(x|y) = f(x,y)/g(y) \quad \text{if } g(y) \neq 0.$$

We have

$$Pr\{(\mathbf{x},\mathbf{y}) \text{ in } A\} = \iint_A g(y|x)f(x)\, dx\, dy$$

$$= \iint_A f(x|y)g(y)\, dx\, dy;$$

$$f(x) = \int_{-\infty}^{\infty} f(x|y)g(y)\, dy, \; g(y) = \int_{-\infty}^{\infty} g(y|x)f(x)\, dx.$$

The continuous random variables **x** and **y** are *independent* if $f(x,y) = f(x)g(y)$, or if

$$Pr\{\mathbf{x} \text{ in } A, \mathbf{y} \text{ in } B\} = Pr\{\mathbf{x} \text{ in } A\}Pr\{\mathbf{y} \text{ in } B\}$$

for every A,B. Either is equivalent to

$$f(x|y) = f(x) \quad \text{and} \quad g(y|x) = g(y).$$

CHAPTER
5

The Algebra of Expectations

35. Bases for Operations. There are collected in this section certain rules, and their proofs, for operating with expectations, variances, and conditional expectations, which will prove convenient in our later work.

We recall, first, the definition of expectation $E(\mathbf{x})$ of a random variable $\mathbf{x}$: if $\mathbf{x}$ is a discrete random variable with probability function $f(x) = Pr\{\mathbf{x} = x\}$, then

$$E(\mathbf{x}) = \sum_x x\, f(x).$$

If $\mathbf{x}$ is a continuous random variable with probability density function $f(x)$, then

$$E(\mathbf{x}) = \int_{-\infty}^{\infty} x\, f(x)\, dx.$$

▶ ***Theorem A.*** *If $\varphi(x)$ is a function of x, and if $\mathbf{x}$ is a discrete random variable with probability function $f(x)$, then*

$$E[\varphi(\mathbf{x})] = \sum_x \varphi(x)\, f(x).$$

If $\varphi(x)$ is a continuous function of x, and if $\mathbf{x}$ is a continuous random variable with density function $f(x)$, then

$$E[\varphi(\mathbf{x})] = \int_{-\infty}^{\infty} \varphi(x)\, f(x)\, dx.$$

By $\varphi(\mathbf{x})$ we mean, of course, the random variable whose value at each elementary event is the value of the function φ at the number x which is the value of $\mathbf{x}$ at that elementary event. If $\mathbf{x}$ is discrete, then the set of elementary events for which $\varphi(\mathbf{x})$ lies in a specified interval is just the set of elementary events for which $\mathbf{x}$ has one of a certain countable set of values, so that this set of elementary events is an event (Axiom $\mathfrak{F}3$, p. 22), and $\varphi(\mathbf{x})$ is indeed a random variable (p. 34). If $\mathbf{x}$ is a continuous random variable and if φ is a continuous function it can be shown again that the set of elementary events for which $\varphi(\mathbf{x})$ lies in a specified interval is an event, so that $\varphi(\mathbf{x})$ is a random variable.

A hidden hypothesis in Theorem A is that $E[\varphi(\mathbf{x})]$ shall exist, or that the sum (if infinite) or integral shall converge absolutely. This hypothesis will certainly be satisfied if the function φ is bounded.

The proof of the first statement of the theorm is easy, as follows. Consider first the case in which $\mathbf{x}$ has only a finite number of values. Let $\varphi_1, \varphi_2, \cdots, \varphi_N$ denote possible values of $\varphi(\mathbf{x})$. Let $x_{11}, x_{12}, \cdots, x_{1,n_1}$ denote the values of $\mathbf{x}$ such that $\varphi(x_{11}) = \varphi_1$, etc., that is, $\varphi(x_{1j}) = \varphi_1$ for $j = 1, 2, \cdots, n_1$. For each i, $i = 1, 2, \cdots, N$, let $x_{i1}, x_{i2}, \cdots, x_{i,n_i}$ denote the values of $\mathbf{x}$ such that $\varphi(x_{ij}) = \varphi_i$, $j = 1, 2, \cdots, n_i$. Then

$$Pr\{\varphi(\mathbf{x}) = \varphi_i\} = \sum_{j=1}^{n_i} Pr\{\mathbf{x} = x_{ij}\} = \sum_{j=1}^{n_i} f(x_{ij}).$$

Thus $E[\varphi(\mathbf{x})] = \sum_{i=1}^{N} \varphi_i Pr\{\varphi(\mathbf{x}) = \varphi_i\} = \sum_{i=1}^{N} \varphi(x_{ij}) \sum_{j=1}^{n_i} f(x_{ij}) = \sum_{i=1}^{N} \sum_{j=1}^{n_i} \varphi(x_{ij}) f(x_{ij})$; but this is simply another way of writing $\sum_x \varphi(x)f(x)$. If the set of values which $\mathbf{x}$ assumes with positive probability is countable but not finite, properties of absolutely convergent series permit the same conclusion. (Indeed it is for just such reasons that we have required absolute convergence in the definition of expectation.)

The proof of the second statement in the special case where $\varphi(x)$ is strictly increasing is easy with the aid of the theorem on change of variables; but its proof for arbitrary continuous $\varphi(x)$ is beyond the scope of this text. (We note that it is possible for φ to be continuous and for the random variable $\varphi(\mathbf{x})$ to be neither continuous nor discrete, so that our definitions would not cover $E[\varphi(\mathbf{x})]$. The definitions can be extended so as to cover this possibility, and a suitably generalized form of the theorem holds.)

We observe that for the special case $\varphi(x) = x$, each is simply the definition.

▶ ***Theorem B.*** *If $\varphi(x,y)$ is a function of the real variables x and y, and if $(\mathbf{x},\mathbf{y})$ is a discrete random vector with joint probability function $f(x,y)$, then*

$$E[\varphi(\mathbf{x},\mathbf{y})] = \sum_{x,y} \varphi(x,y)f(x,y) \text{ (or } \sum_x \sum_y \varphi(x,y)f(x,y)).$$

If $\varphi(x,y)$ is a continuous function of the real variables x and y, and if $(\mathbf{x},\mathbf{y})$ is a continuous random vector with joint density function $f(x,y)$, then

$$E[\varphi(\mathbf{x},\mathbf{y})] = \int_{-\infty}^{\infty} \int_{-\infty}^{\infty} \varphi(x,y)f(x,y)\, dx\, dy.$$

We have again the hidden hypothesis that $E[\varphi(\mathbf{x},\mathbf{y})]$ shall exist, or that the right-hand member of the equation shall converge absolutely, which will certainly be satisfied if φ is bounded.

Again the proof of the first statement of the theorem is immediate, for by $\varphi(\mathbf{x},\mathbf{y})$ we understand the random variable assuming the value $\varphi(x,y)$ at each elementary event for which $\mathbf{x} = x$ and $\mathbf{y} = y$, or the random variable assuming the value $\varphi(x,y)$ with probability $f(x,y)$, so that the above equation is simply the definition of $E[\varphi(\mathbf{x},\mathbf{y})]$. The proof of the second statement is beyond the scope of this text.

Before stating the next theorem, we note that any constant may be thought of as a random variable taking that constant value with probability 1, or a random variable defined at each elementary event to be that constant.

▶ **Theorem C.** *If a is a constant, then*

$$E(a) = a.$$

You may supply the proof.

▶ **Theorem D.** *If a is a real number (constant) and $\mathbf{x}$ is a random variable with expectation $E(\mathbf{x})$, then $E(a\mathbf{x}) = aE(\mathbf{x})$.*

Proof for discrete $\mathbf{x}$. On setting $\varphi(x) \equiv ax$ in Theorem A, we find that

$$E(a\mathbf{x}) = \textstyle\sum_x ax\, f(x) = a \sum_x x\, f(x) = aE(\mathbf{x}).$$

You may supply the proof for a continuous random variable $\mathbf{x}$.

▶ **Theorem E.** *If $\mathbf{x}$ and $\mathbf{y}$ are random variables with expectations $E(\mathbf{x})$ and $E(\mathbf{y})$, then $E(\mathbf{x} + \mathbf{y}) = E(\mathbf{x}) + E(\mathbf{y})$.*

Proof for a continuous random vector $(\mathbf{x},\mathbf{y})$. By Theorem B, with $\varphi(x,y) \equiv x + y$, we have

$$\begin{aligned}
E(\mathbf{x} + \mathbf{y}) &= \int_{-\infty}^{\infty}\int_{-\infty}^{\infty} (x + y)\, f(x,y)\, dx\, dy \\
&= \int_{-\infty}^{\infty}\int_{-\infty}^{\infty} x\, f(x,y)\, dx\, dy + \int_{-\infty}^{\infty}\int_{-\infty}^{\infty} y\, f(x,y)\, dx\, dy \\
&= \int_{-\infty}^{\infty} x\, dx \int_{-\infty}^{\infty} f(x,y)\, dy + \int_{-\infty}^{\infty} y\, dy \int_{-\infty}^{\infty} f(x,y)\, dx \\
&= \int_{-\infty}^{\infty} x\, f(x)\, dx + \int_{-\infty}^{\infty} y\, g(y)\, dy \\
&= E(\mathbf{x}) + E(\mathbf{y}),
\end{aligned}$$

since

$$f(x) = \int_{-\infty}^{\infty} f(x,y)\, dy \quad \text{and} \quad g(y) = \int_{-\infty}^{\infty} f(x,y)\, dx.$$

We leave the proof for discrete random variables to you. If one of the random variables is continuous and the other discrete, our definitions do not cover $E(\mathbf{x} + \mathbf{y})$; but with appropriately extended definitions the theorem would remain valid.

▶ ***Corollary F.*** *If a is a real number (constant) and if* **x** *is a random variable with expectation $E(\mathbf{x})$, then*

$$E(\mathbf{x} + a) = E(\mathbf{x}) + a.$$

This theorem is easily proved directly, using Theorem A; but it is also a corollary of Theorems E and C, obtained on replacing **y** by a random variable assuming the constant value a with probability 1.

▶ ***Corollary G.*** *The expectation of a finite sum of random variables is the sum of their expectations.*

This follows from Theorem E with the aid of mathematical induction.

▶ ***Theorem H.*** *If* **x**,**y** *are* independent *random variables with expectations $E(\mathbf{x})$ and $E(\mathbf{y})$, then*

$$E(\mathbf{xy}) = E(\mathbf{x})E(\mathbf{y}).$$

Proof for continuous random variables. By Theorem B, with $\varphi(x,y) = xy$, we have

$$E(\mathbf{xy}) = \int_{-\infty}^{\infty} \int_{-\infty}^{\infty} xy\, f(x,y)\, dx\, dy.$$

Since **x** and **y** are independent, $f(x,y) = f(x)g(y)$, so that

$$E(\mathbf{xy}) = \int_{-\infty}^{\infty} \int_{-\infty}^{\infty} xy\, f(x)g(y)\, dx\, dy$$

$$= \int_{-\infty}^{\infty} x\, f(x)\, dx \int_{-\infty}^{\infty} y\, g(y)\, dy = E(\mathbf{x})E(\mathbf{y}).$$

▶ ***Corollary I.*** *The expectation of the product of a finite number of independent random variables is the product of their expectations.*

Again, mathematical induction yields this corollary to Theorem H.

We now recall the definition of variance. If **x** is a discrete random variable with probability function $f(x) = Pr\{\mathbf{x} = x\}$, then

$$V(\mathbf{x}) = \sum_x [x - E(\mathbf{x})]^2 f(x).$$

If $\mathbf{x}$ is a continuous random variable with probability density function $f(x)$, then

$$V(\mathbf{x}) = \int_{-\infty}^{\infty} [x - E(\mathbf{x})]^2 f(x)\, dx.$$

In either case, we see from Theorem A that

$$\blacktriangleright \qquad V(\mathbf{x}) = E[\mathbf{x} - E(\mathbf{x})]^2.$$

▶ ***Theorem J.*** *If a is a real number, and $\mathbf{x}$ a random variable with variance $V(\mathbf{x})$, then $V(a) = 0$ and $V(\mathbf{x} + a) = V(\mathbf{x})$.*

Proof. By Theorem C, $E(a) = a$, so that

$$V(a) = E[a - E(a)]^2 = E(a - a)^2 = 0.$$

Also

$$\begin{aligned} V(\mathbf{x} + a) &= E[\mathbf{x} + a - E(\mathbf{x} + a)]^2, \\ &= E(\mathbf{x} + a - E(\mathbf{x}) - a)^2 \qquad \text{by Corollary F,} \\ &= E[\mathbf{x} - E(\mathbf{x})]^2 = V(\mathbf{x}) \qquad \text{by definition.} \end{aligned}$$

▶ ***Theorem K.*** *If a is a real number and $\mathbf{x}$ a random variable with variance $V(\mathbf{x})$, then $V(a\mathbf{x}) = a^2 V(\mathbf{x})$.*

We leave the proof as an exercise.

We have in the following theorem an alternative formula for the variance which is often more convenient than that given in the definition.

▶ ***Theorem L.***

$$V(\mathbf{x}) = E(\mathbf{x}^2) - [E(\mathbf{x})]^2.$$

Proof. We have

$$\begin{aligned} V(\mathbf{x}) &= E[\mathbf{x} - E(\mathbf{x})]^2 = E(\mathbf{x}^2 - 2\mathbf{x}E(\mathbf{x}) + [E(\mathbf{x})]^2) \\ &= E(\mathbf{x}^2) - E[2\mathbf{x}E(\mathbf{x})] + E([E(\mathbf{x})]^2) \qquad \text{by Corollary G} \\ &= E(\mathbf{x}^2) - 2E(\mathbf{x})E(\mathbf{x}) + [E(\mathbf{x})]^2 \quad \text{by Theorems C and D} \\ &\qquad \text{(note that } E(\mathbf{x}) \text{ is a constant);} \end{aligned}$$

$$V(\mathbf{x}) = E(\mathbf{x}^2) - [E(\mathbf{x})]^2.$$

The formula of Theorem L is often useful in furnishing an expression for $E(\mathbf{x}^2)$:

$$\blacktriangleright \qquad E(\mathbf{x}^2) = V(\mathbf{x}) + [E(\mathbf{x})]^2.$$

▶ ***Theorem M.*** *If* $\mathbf{x},\mathbf{y}$ *are* independent *random variables with variances $V(\mathbf{x})$ and $V(\mathbf{y})$, then*

$$V(\mathbf{x} + \mathbf{y}) = V(\mathbf{x}) + V(\mathbf{y}).$$

Proof.
$$\begin{aligned} V(\mathbf{x} + \mathbf{y}) &= E[(\mathbf{x} + \mathbf{y}) - E(\mathbf{x} + \mathbf{y})]^2 \qquad \text{by definition;} \\ &= E([\mathbf{x} - E(\mathbf{x})] + [\mathbf{y} - E(\mathbf{y})])^2 \\ &= E([\mathbf{x} - E(\mathbf{x})]^2 + 2[\mathbf{x} - E(\mathbf{x})][\mathbf{y} - E(\mathbf{y})] \\ &\qquad + [\mathbf{y} - E(\mathbf{y})]^2) \\ &= E[\mathbf{x} - E(\mathbf{x})]^2 + 2E([\mathbf{x} - E(\mathbf{x})][\mathbf{y} - E(\mathbf{y})]) \\ &\qquad + E[\mathbf{y} - E(\mathbf{y})]^2 \end{aligned}$$

by Corollary G.

Now $\mathbf{x} - E(\mathbf{x})$ is a function of the random variable $\mathbf{x}$, namely, $\mathbf{x}$ minus a constant, and similarly $\mathbf{y} - E(\mathbf{y})$ is a function of the random variable $\mathbf{y}$. By the remark on page 82, $\mathbf{x} - E(\mathbf{x})$ and $\mathbf{y} - E(\mathbf{y})$ are independent, since $\mathbf{x}$ and $\mathbf{y}$ are independent. By Theorem H, then,

$$\begin{aligned} E([\mathbf{x} - E(\mathbf{x})][\mathbf{y} - E(\mathbf{y})]) &= E[\mathbf{x} - E(\mathbf{x})]E[\mathbf{y} - E(\mathbf{y})] \\ &= [E(\mathbf{x}) - E(\mathbf{x})][E(\mathbf{y}) - E(\mathbf{y})] \quad \text{by Corollary F,} \\ &= 0. \end{aligned}$$

Therefore
$$\begin{aligned} V(\mathbf{x} + \mathbf{y}) &= E[\mathbf{x} - E(\mathbf{x})]^2 + E[\mathbf{y} - E(\mathbf{y})]^2 \\ &= V(\mathbf{x}) + V(\mathbf{y}), \qquad \text{by definition.} \end{aligned}$$

Application of the principle of mathematical induction to Theorem M yields the following corollary:

▶ ***Corollary N.*** *The variance of the sum of a finite number of* independent *random variables is the sum of their variances.*

PROBLEMS

1. Let $\mathbf{x}$ be a discrete random variable assuming the value 1 with probability p and the value 0 with probability $q = 1 - p$. Find $E(\mathbf{x})$, $V(\mathbf{x})$.

2. A cube has one spot on each of four sides, two spots on each of the other two sides. Find the mean (expectation) and variance of (a) the number of spots that will show on top when it is tossed to the ground; (b) the total number of spots showing when 6 such cubes are tossed.

3. If $\mathbf{x}$ is the random variable described in Problem 1, what are the values assumed, and with what probabilities, by the random variables $2\mathbf{x}$, $2\mathbf{x} - 1$, $\mathbf{x}^2$? Find the expectation and variance of each.

4. Let $\mathbf{x},\mathbf{y},\mathbf{z}$ be independent random variables with $E(\mathbf{x}) = E(\mathbf{y}) = 2$, $E(\mathbf{z}) = -3$, $V(\mathbf{x}) = 1$, $V(\mathbf{y}) = V(\mathbf{z}) = 2$. Find (a) $E(\mathbf{x} + \mathbf{y} + \mathbf{z})$; (b) $E[\mathbf{x}(\mathbf{y} + \mathbf{z})]$; (c) $V(3\mathbf{y} + \mathbf{z})$. (d) Which, if any, of your answers depend essentially on the independence of the random variables?

5. If n is a positive integer, and if each of the n random variables $\mathbf{x}_1$, $\mathbf{x}_2, \cdots, \mathbf{x}_n$ has the same distribution (same probability function) as the random variable $\mathbf{x}$ in Problem 1, find (a) $E(\sum_{i=1}^n \mathbf{x}_i)$; (b) $E\left(\frac{1}{n}\sum_{i=1}^n \mathbf{x}_i\right)$.

6. If the random variables $\mathbf{x}_1, \mathbf{x}_2, \cdots, \mathbf{x}_n$ in Problem 5 are independent, find (a) $V(\sum_{i=1}^n \mathbf{x}_i)$; (b) $V\left(\frac{1}{n}\sum_{i=1}^n \mathbf{x}_i\right)$.

7. If $(\mathbf{x}_1, \mathbf{x}_2, \cdots, \mathbf{x}_n)$ is any combined random variable, express $E(\sum_{i=1}^n \mathbf{x}_i)$ and $E\left(\frac{1}{n}\sum_{i=1}^n \mathbf{x}_i\right)$ in terms of $E(\mathbf{x}_1)$, $E(\mathbf{x}_2)$, $\cdots$, $E(\mathbf{x}_n)$ (assuming they exist).

8. Express $V(\sum_{i=1}^n \mathbf{x}_i)$ and $V\left(\frac{1}{n}\sum_{i=1}^n \mathbf{x}_i\right)$ in terms of $V(\mathbf{x}_1)$, $V(\mathbf{x}_2)$, $\cdots$, $V(\mathbf{x}_n)$ (assuming they exist) if $\mathbf{x}_1, \mathbf{x}_2, \cdots, \mathbf{x}_n$ are independent.

9. What are the expectation and variance of the sum of the numbers appearing on two dice? on n dice?

10. Prove Theorem C.

11. Prove Theorem D for a continuous random variable $\mathbf{x}$.

12. Prove Theorem E for a discrete random vector $(\mathbf{x},\mathbf{y})$.

13. Carry out the proof by mathematical induction of Corollary G.

14. Prove Theorem H for discrete random variables.

15. Carry out the proof by mathematical induction of Corollary I.

16. Prove Theorem K.

17. Carry out the proof by mathematical induction of Corollary N.

18. Show that if $E(\mathbf{x} - \lambda)^2$ is regarded as a function of the real variable λ, its minimum value is attained for $\lambda = E(\mathbf{x})$; find this minimum value.

36. Conditional Expectation. If $(\mathbf{x},\mathbf{y})$ is a pair of discrete random variables with joint probability function $f(x,y)$, and if $\mathbf{x}$ and $\mathbf{y}$ have probability functions $f(x)$ and $g(y)$, then the conditional probability function of $\mathbf{y}$ for given x,

$$g(y\,|\,x) = f(x,y)/f(x),$$

is, for each x such that $f(x) \neq 0$, a probability function (see page 39); and we may define the conditional expectation of $\mathbf{y}$ for the given value x of $\mathbf{x}$ by

$$\blacktriangleright \qquad E(\mathbf{y}\,|\,x) = \sum_y y\, g(y\,|\,x).$$

Similarly, we may define

▶ $$E(\mathbf{x}\,|\,y) = \textstyle\sum_x x\,f(x\,|\,y),$$

for each value y of $\mathbf{y}$ for which $g(y) \neq 0$.

If $(\mathbf{x},\mathbf{y})$ is a pair of continuous random variables with joint density function $f(x,y)$ and marginal density functions $f(x)$ and $g(y)$ respectively, then for each x for which $f(x) \neq 0$, the conditional probability density function

$$g(y\,|\,x) = f(x,y)/f(x)$$

is a probability density function, and we may define the conditional expectation

▶ $$E(\mathbf{y}\,|\,x) = \int_{-\infty}^{\infty} y\,g(y\,|\,x)\,dy,$$

and similarly

▶ $$E(\mathbf{x}\,|\,y) = \int_{-\infty}^{\infty} x\,f(x\,|\,y)\,dx$$

for each y for which $g(y) \neq 0$.

When x is held fixed, $E(\mathbf{y}\,|\,x)$ is just a number; but when x is allowed to vary over the range of values of $\mathbf{x}$ for which $f(x) \neq 0$, then $E(\mathbf{y}\,|\,x)$ becomes a function of x. We may then define a random variable to have the value $E(\mathbf{y}\,|\,x)$ when $\mathbf{x} = x$; this random variable will be denoted by $E(\mathbf{y}\,|\,\mathbf{x})$; it is a random variable which is a function of the random variable $\mathbf{x}$. (Strictly speaking, $E(\mathbf{y}\,|\,\mathbf{x})$ is defined as a random variable only at those elementary events where $\mathbf{x}$ assumes values x such that $f(x) \neq 0$. However, the elementary events where this is not true form an event of probability 0 which may be neglected.)

▶ ***Theorem O.*** $E[\varphi(\mathbf{x})\mathbf{y}] = E[\varphi(\mathbf{x})E(\mathbf{y}\,|\,\mathbf{x})]$.

Proof for discrete random variables $\mathbf{x},\mathbf{y}$. By definition, the random variable $E(\mathbf{y}\,|\,\mathbf{x})$ is a random variable assuming the value $E(\mathbf{y}\,|\,x)$ at each elementary event where $\mathbf{x}$ assumes the value x, so that $\varphi(\mathbf{x})E(\mathbf{y}\,|\,\mathbf{x})$ assumes the value $\varphi(x)E(\mathbf{y}\,|\,x)$. By Theorem A,

$$E[\varphi(\mathbf{x})E(\mathbf{y}\,|\,\mathbf{x})] = \textstyle\sum_x \varphi(x)E(\mathbf{y}\,|\,x)f(x).$$

But for each x for which $f(x) \neq 0$,

$$E(\mathbf{y}\,|\,x) = \textstyle\sum_y y\,g(y\,|\,x),$$

so that

$$\begin{aligned} E[\varphi(\mathbf{x})E(\mathbf{y}\,|\,\mathbf{x})] &= \textstyle\sum_x \varphi(x)\,f(x)\,\sum_y y\,g(y\,|\,x) \\ &= \textstyle\sum_y y \sum_x \varphi(x)f(x)\,g(y\,|\,x). \end{aligned}$$

But $g(y \mid x) f(x) = f(x,y)$, the joint probability function of $\mathbf{x}$ and $\mathbf{y}$ (page 72), so that

$$\sum_y \sum_x y\varphi(x) f(x) g(y \mid x) = \sum_y \sum_x y\varphi(x) f(x,y) = E[\mathbf{y}\varphi(\mathbf{x})]$$

by Theorem B.

▶ ***Corollary P.*** $$E(\mathbf{y}) = E[E(\mathbf{y} \mid \mathbf{x})].$$

▶ ***Theorem Q.*** *If* $\mathbf{x},\mathbf{y}$ *are independent random variables, then* $E(\mathbf{x} \mid y) = E(\mathbf{x})$ *and* $E(\mathbf{y} \mid x) = E(\mathbf{y})$.

The proof is left as an exercise.

We have the following analogue for conditional expectations of Theorems A and B, which we state without proof:

▶ ***Theorem R.*** *If* $\varphi(x,y)$ *is a function of the real variables* x *and* y, *if* $(\mathbf{x},\mathbf{y})$ *is a discrete random vector, and if* $g(y \mid x)$ *is the conditional probability function of* $\mathbf{y}$ *for given* x, *then*

$$E[\varphi(\mathbf{x},\mathbf{y}) \mid x] = \sum_y \varphi(x,y)\, g(y \mid x).$$

If $\varphi(x,y)$ *is a continuous function of the real variables* x *and* y, *if* $(\mathbf{x},\mathbf{y})$ *is a continuous random vector, and if* $g(y \mid x)$ *is the conditional density function of* $\mathbf{y}$ *for given* x, *then*

$$E[\varphi(\mathbf{x},\mathbf{y}) \mid x] = \int_{-\infty}^{\infty} \varphi(x,y)\, g(y \mid x)\, dy.$$

▶ ***Corollary S.***

$$E[\varphi(\mathbf{x},\mathbf{y}) \mid x] = E[\varphi(x,\mathbf{y}) \mid x].$$

It is assumed again that the sum and integral converge absolutely, as will be the case if, in particular, φ is bounded.

▶ ***Corollary T.*** $$E\{E[\varphi(\mathbf{x},\mathbf{y}) \mid \mathbf{x}]\} = E[\varphi(\mathbf{x},\mathbf{y})].$$

Proof for continuous random variables $\mathbf{x},\mathbf{y}$, *continuous* φ. We have, using Theorem A and the formula in Theorem R,

$$\begin{aligned} E\{E[\varphi(\mathbf{x},\mathbf{y}) \mid \mathbf{x}]\} &= \int_{-\infty}^{\infty} E[\varphi(\mathbf{x},\mathbf{y}) \mid x]\, f(x)\, dx \\ &= \int_{-\infty}^{\infty} f(x)\, dx \int_{-\infty}^{\infty} \varphi(x,y)\, g(y \mid x)\, dy \\ &= \int_{-\infty}^{\infty}\int_{-\infty}^{\infty} \varphi(x,y)\, f(x,y)\, dy\, dx \end{aligned}$$

since $f(x,y) = f(x)\, g(y \mid x)$. But by Theorem B, the latter integral is just $E[\varphi(\mathbf{x},\mathbf{y})]$ (assuming again, of course, that the integral converges absolutely).

PROBLEMS

1. Given the following joint probability function of the random variables $\mathbf{x}$ and $\mathbf{y}$, find the conditional probability function $g(y \mid x)$ and the expectation $E(\mathbf{y} \mid x)$ for each value of x for which they are defined. Use Theorem O to find $E(\mathbf{y})$.

$x \backslash y$	1	2	3
1	1/8	1/8	2/8
2	3/8	0	0
3	0	1/8	0

2. A number $\mathbf{x}$ is chosen at random from among the integers 1, 2, 3, and 4. Another, $\mathbf{y}$, is chosen from among those which are at least as large as $\mathbf{x}$. Find $E(\mathbf{y} \mid x)$ for $x = 1, 2, 3, 4$, and use Theorem O to find $E(\mathbf{y})$.

3. Prove Theorem O for continuous random variables.

4. Let $(\mathbf{x},\mathbf{y})$ have joint density function $f(x,y) = x + y$ for $0 < x < 1$, $0 < y < 1$, $f(x,y) = 0$ elsewhere; find $E(\mathbf{y} \mid x)$ for $0 < x < 1$, and use Theorem O to find $E(\mathbf{y})$.

5. A number $\mathbf{x}$ is chosen at random between 0 and 1. A number $\mathbf{y}$ is then chosen at random in the part of the interval (0,1) to the right of the number $\mathbf{x}$. Find $E(\mathbf{y} \mid x)$ for $0 < x < 1$, and use Theorem O to find $E(\mathbf{y})$.

6. Prove Theorem P for discrete random variables $\mathbf{x}$ and $\mathbf{y}$.

7. Prove Theorem P for continuous random variables $\mathbf{x}$ and $\mathbf{y}$.

8. If $B_1, B_2, \cdots, B_k$ are mutually exclusive events with $\bigcup_{i=1}^{k} B_i = S$ and if $\mathbf{y}$ is a discrete random variable with expectation $E(\mathbf{y})$, then $E(\mathbf{y}) = \sum_{i=1}^{k} E(\mathbf{y} \mid B_i)P(B_i)$. (The theorem is also valid without the restriction to discrete random variables $\mathbf{y}$.)

(Hint: Let $\mathbf{x}$ be a random variable which is equal to i on B_i, $i = 1, 2, \cdots, k$; $E(\mathbf{y} \mid B_i) = E(\mathbf{y} \mid \mathbf{x} = i)$.)

Part Two

STATISTICS

Introduction

"Statistics," like many other words, carries distinct meanings for distinct individuals. For many, it is "what you can prove anything by." No doubt for most of us it evokes a picture of mountainous aggregations of figures, innumerable rows and columns of tabulated numbers. If we are willing to use the term "experiment" to refer to almost any investigation, any planned course of action designed to gather additional information on some subject, then we might be willing to use the word "statistics" to refer to the results of the experiment, the body of information gathered.

Problems of "statistical inference," or of "mathematical statistics," arise primarily after the data have been gathered and the investigator is faced with the problem of drawing conclusions or making decisions on the basis of the data available. How are the data to be interpreted? Studies of the interpretation of data may lead to important suggestions concerning the conduct of future experiments, and to this extent the statistician is concerned with the planning of experiments as well as the analysis of the results. Of course, the definition of a term must always depend upon the context; here we assert that the investigator acts as a statistician when he plans his experiment, and again when he evaluates the results; in between, when he is gathering the data, he may be a scientist, or he may be a man with a brief-case full of forms ringing a doorbell, but he is not a statistician.

From a point of view which is very popular at present, a statistician is a practitioner of the art of making decisions in the absence of complete relevant information. The possible decisions involved may be of many different kinds. The required decision may be to state, after a number of independent observations, that the expected value of a certain random variable is a certain number; it may be to accept as satisfactory a shipment of goods after only partial inspection. The purpose of the theory of statistical inference is to assist the investigator in making his decision. It consists of ideas, methods, theorems, pointing to significant combinations of the experimental data and showing how these "statistics" can be used to provide a rational basis for decision-making. Not all the ideas are appropriate to every situation; those having a wide range of applicability we might refer to as "basic concepts." (For an excellent discussion of various applications of statistics, see [20].)

There seems to be a real danger that the student of formal mathematics will more or less consciously assume that the mathematics he learns in class will be directly useful to him in his later work, in the sense of providing ready-made solutions (called "recipes" in the trade) for his problems. More likely, when he comes to apply his mathematics, he will find there is something new in each situation, something which prevents the particular methods he has learned from being strictly applicable. The function of his formal training has been to supply him with a reservoir of ideas, a knowledge of methods which have worked in somewhat similar situations. The practice of statistics is an art, and the purpose of the student must be to gain an appreciation of general ideas and methods; as the young painter wishes to learn painting in general, and not simply to paint "Great Rockaway," winner of the Stone County Fair trotting race in '04. On the other hand, one becomes adept through practice, and our young painter will paint "Great Rockaway" and many other individual paintings before he is a really capable artist.

CHAPTER

6

Random Sampling

37. Introduction. Our starting point for an investigation of random sampling is the concept of population.

▶ *A* population, *or* parent population, *in (univariate) random sampling, is the probability space induced on the set R of real numbers by a random variable* **x**. *The random variable* **x** *is the* population random variable. *The* distribution *of the population is the distribution of* **x**. *The population is* discrete *or* continuous *according as* **x** *is discrete or continuous.*

EXAMPLE 1. You are head of a small firm whose business utilizes products of other manufacturers. You have just received shipment of a large supply of a certain item, and wish to estimate the fraction which meet certain specifications by testing only a small part of the entire lot.

You would probably choose a certain number of items, test them, and record the fraction of them which met the specifications as an estimate of the fraction of the whole lot which would meet the specifications if tested. It is clear that if, after testing one item, it is not returned to the lot, then the lot from which the second test item is to be drawn differs from the original lot in having one fewer item. The theory, however, is somewhat simpler if each item is to be drawn from the same collection, and if the different drawings are independent, that is, if the probability of finding a defective item in one test is independent of the results of other tests. With this in mind, we shall suppose you draw an item at random (each item has the same probability of being drawn), test it, return it to the lot, mix, and draw again at random. This kind of sampling is sometimes referred to as *sampling with replacement.* In effect, we use a model in which the sampling operation does not change the constitution of the population. We shall become acquainted with a number of situations in which such a model appears more realistic than it does in the present one (cf., for example, Example 2 below, and problems at the end of the chapter).

In constructing a mathematical model appropriate to a discussion of this situation, we shall begin by associating a probability space with the total supply of items. Each item is an elementary event, and if N is the total number of items, then $1/N$ is the probability associated with each elementary event. Each collection of elementary events is an event, and the probability of any event is just $1/N$ multiplied by the number of elementary events in it.

The items in the lot may differ in many respects, but your interest in any one lies solely in the answer to the question: does it meet the specifications? We distinguish between defective and nondefective items by introducing a random variable $\mathbf{x}$ on this probability space which is equal to 1 at each defective item ("the number of defective items at this elementary event is 1") and which is equal to 0 at each nondefective item ("the number of defective items at this elementary event is 0"). This random variable may be regarded as a "counting" random variable: it counts the number of defectives at each item. We may express the definition of the random variable $\mathbf{x}$ alternatively by defining it to be 1 at each elementary event in the event consisting of all defective items and 0 at each other elementary event.

Let p denote the fraction defective. *The probability space induced by the random variable* $\mathbf{x}$ *on the set* R *of all real numbers (page 36) assigns probability* p *to the elementary event which is the real number* 1, *and probability* $q = 1 - p$ *to the elementary event which is the real number* 0. Any event in this induced probability space which contains the number 1 but not the number 0 has probability p; an event containing 0 but not 1 has probability q; an event containing neither has probability 0; and an event containing both has probability 1. *This induced probability space we shall call the population, or the parent population, in a discussion of sampling in the present context.*

Let us begin now with the simplest situation: you plan to draw exactly one item from the lot, and to record the number of defectives you find: it will be either 1 or 0, 1 with probability p and 0 with probability q. Let us denote by $\mathbf{x}_1$ the random variable we might describe verbally as "the number of defectives you will draw": $\mathbf{x}_1$ will assume the value 1 with probability p and the value 0 with probability q. If $f(x)$ is the probability function of $\mathbf{x}$, then $f(x)$ is also the probability function of $\mathbf{x}_1$: $f(x) = Pr\{\mathbf{x} = x\} = Pr\{\mathbf{x}_1 = x\}$, $f(1) = p$, $f(0) = q$, $f(x) = 0$ for all other x. A convenient expression for $f(x)$ is

$$f(x) = p^x q^{1-x} \quad \text{if } x = 0 \text{ or } 1,$$

$$f(x) = 0 \qquad \text{for all other } x.$$

A replica, or copy, of the *population* may be taken as the probability space on which $\mathbf{x}_1$ is defined; the *value of the random variable* $\mathbf{x}_1$ *corresponding to each elementary event or real number in this probability space is just that number*. Since probability p is associated with the elementary event 1, and at this event $\mathbf{x}_1$ has the value 1, we have, as desired, $Pr\{\mathbf{x}_1 = 1\} = p$; and since probability q is associated with the elementary event 0, and at this elementary event $\mathbf{x}_1$ has the value 0, we have $Pr\{\mathbf{x}_1 = 0\} = q$.

Suppose now that you plan to test two items. You require a framework, a context, a mathematical model within which you can consider two random variables: $\mathbf{x}_1$, "the number of defectives in the first test," and $\mathbf{x}_2$, "the number of defectives in the second test." You want these random variables to be independent, and you want each to have the same distribution as the random variable $\mathbf{x}$ which induced the parent population: each should assume the value 1 with probability p and the value 0 with probability q. A way of achieving this is to introduce the *sample space.*

The fundamental set of elementary events for the sample space is the set of all pairs of real numbers. Each pair of real numbers is an elementary event in the sample space, and we may think of the first number of the pair as an elementary event in a replica of the population, and the second number of the pair as an elementary event in another replica of the population. We may define $\mathbf{x}_1$ at an elementary event to have as value the first member of the pair, and $\mathbf{x}_2$ at an elementary event to have as value the second member of the pair. Thus at the elementary event (0,0) in the sample space, $\mathbf{x}_1$ has the value 0 as does also $\mathbf{x}_2$; at the elementary event (3,4), $\mathbf{x}_1$ has the value 3, and $\mathbf{x}_2$ the value 4 (but the probability associated with this elementary event will be 0); at any elementary event (x_1,x_2), $\mathbf{x}_1$ will have the value x_1 and $\mathbf{x}_2$ the value x_2.

You want the random variables $\mathbf{x}_1$ and $\mathbf{x}_2$ to be independent, and each to assume the value 1 with probability p. Then the probability associated with the elementary event (1,1), which is the intersection of the events $\{\mathbf{x}_1 = 1\}$, $\{\mathbf{x}_2 = 1\}$, must be the product of their separate probabilities, p^2. Similarly, the probability associated with the elementary event (0,0) must be q^2, the probability associated with the elementary event (1,0) must be pq, and the probability associated with the elementary event (0,1) must be qp. The sample space is at the same time the probability space on which $\mathbf{x}_1$ and $\mathbf{x}_2$ are defined, and also the probability space induced by $\mathbf{x}_1$ and $\mathbf{x}_2$ on the set R_2 of ordered pairs of real numbers. Its events are described on page 59. We have now described the sample space, the probability space on which $\mathbf{x}_1$ and $\mathbf{x}_2$ are defined, and have defined these random variables on it. Now let us verify that $\mathbf{x}_1$ and $\mathbf{x}_2$ as defined on the sample space are independent, and that each has the same distribution as $\mathbf{x}$. Let $f(x_1,x_2)$ denote the joint probability function of $\mathbf{x}_1$ and $\mathbf{x}_2$:

$$f(x_1,x_2) = Pr\{\mathbf{x}_1 = x_1, \mathbf{x}_2 = x_2\}.$$

We have $f(1,1) = p^2$, $f(1,0) = pq$, $f(0,1) = qp$, and $f(0,0) = q^2$. We can calculate the probability function of $\mathbf{x}_1$:

$$Pr\{\mathbf{x}_1 = 1\} = \sum_{x_2} f(1,x_2) = f(1,1) + f(1,0) = p^2 + pq = p(p + q) = p;$$
$$Pr\{\mathbf{x}_1 = 0\} = \sum_{x_2} f(0,x_2) = f(0,1) + f(0,0) = qp + q^2 = q(p + q) = q.$$

So we see the probability function of $\mathbf{x}_1$ is just $f(x)$, the probability function of $\mathbf{x}$, and similarly the probability function of $\mathbf{x}_2$ is also $f(x)$, the probability function of $\mathbf{x}$. Thus it is true that each of these random variables has the same distribution as $\mathbf{x}$. We observe that

$$f(1,1) = p^2 = f(1)f(1); \quad f(1,0) = pq = f(1)f(0);$$
$$f(0,1) = qp = f(0)f(1); \quad \text{and} \quad f(0,0) = q^2 = f(0)f(0).$$

That is,

$$f(x_1,x_2) = f(x_1)f(x_2).$$

The random variables $\mathbf{x}_1$ and $\mathbf{x}_2$ have the same probability function $f(x)$, that of the random variable $\mathbf{x}$ which induced the parent population, and their joint probability function is the product of their individual probability functions, so that they are indeed independent (pages 74, 75).

As we wrote

$$f(x) = p^x q^{1-x} \quad \text{if } x = 0 \text{ or } 1,$$
$$f(x) = 0 \quad \text{for other } x,$$

we may also write

$$f(x_1,x_2) = p^{x_1+x_2}q^{2-(x_1+x_2)}$$

if each of the numbers x_1 and x_2 is 0 or 1, and

$$f(x_1,x_2) = 0$$

for all other pairs (x_1,x_2). We note that

$$f(x_1)f(x_2) = p^{x_1}q^{1-x_1}p^{x_2}q^{1-x_2} = p^{x_1+x_2}q^{2-(x_1+x_2)} = f(x_1,x_2)$$

if $x_1 = 0, 1, x_2 = 0, 1$.

To summarize, $\mathbf{x}_1$ and $\mathbf{x}_2$, the numbers of defectives which will be found in the first and second tests respectively, are *independent random variables, each with the same probability function as the random variable* $\mathbf{x}$ which induced the probability space which is the *parent population.* The probability space on which $\mathbf{x}_1$ and $\mathbf{x}_2$ are defined is called the *sample space,* and has for the fundamental set of elementary events the set R_2 of all pairs of real numbers. At each elementary event, $\mathbf{x}_1$ has as value the first number of the pair and $\mathbf{x}_2$ has as value the second number of the pair. Probabilities of events are determined so that $\mathbf{x}_1$ and $\mathbf{x}_2$ are independent, and so that each has the same probability function as $\mathbf{x}$.

38. Random Sampling from an Arbitrary Population. The basic ingredient is a random variable $\mathbf{x}$ defined on some probability space idealized from the particular physical situation, as, for example, the probability space in the above example in which the elementary events represented items in the lot. This random variable $\mathbf{x}$ induces on the set R of real numbers a probability space, which is called the *population*, or *parent population*. In the mathematical model we set up to discuss univariate random sampling, then, each population will be a population of real numbers, a probability space in which the probabilities of events are determined by the random variable $\mathbf{x}$: if A (a set of real numbers) is an event in the population, then $P(A) = Pr\{\mathbf{x} \text{ in } A\}$.

If we wish to discuss a random sample of size n (n a positive integer) from this population, we introduce random variables $\mathbf{x}_1$, "the number which will be determined on the first draw," $\mathbf{x}_2$, "the number which will be determined on the second draw," $\cdots$, $\mathbf{x}_n$, "the number which will be found on the nth draw." These random variables are to be *independent*, and *each is to have the same distribution as* $\mathbf{x}$. A random variable must be defined on a probability space; the probability space on which the *sample random variables*, $\mathbf{x}_1, \mathbf{x}_2, \cdots, \mathbf{x}_n$, are defined is called the *sample space*. Each elementary event is an ordered n-tuple of real numbers $(x_1, x_2, \cdots, x_n)$. The family of events is a family of sets of elementary events, including the (n-dimensional) intervals or rectangles as well as the elementary events, which satisfies the axioms for $\mathfrak{F}$ (the class of Borel sets in n-dimensional space R_n, the set of all ordered n-tuples of real numbers). At a particular elementary event or sample point $(x_1, x_2, \cdots, x_n)$, the value of the random variable $\mathbf{x}_1$ is x_1, the value of $\mathbf{x}_2$ is x_2, etc. Probabilities are determined for events in the sample space so that the sample random variables $\mathbf{x}_1, \mathbf{x}_2, \cdots, \mathbf{x}_n$ are independent, and so that each has the same distribution as $\mathbf{x}$.

If $\mathbf{x}$ is a discrete random variable with probability function $f(x) = Pr\{\mathbf{x} = x\}$, this may be accomplished by associating with the sample point $(x_1, x_2, \cdots, x_n)$ the probability $f(x_1)f(x_2) \cdots f(x_n) = \prod_{i=1}^n f(x_i)$. Since this sample point is also the event $\{\mathbf{x}_1 = x_1, \mathbf{x}_2 = x_2, \cdots, \mathbf{x}_n = x_n\}$, we have

$$Pr\{\mathbf{x}_1 = x_1, \mathbf{x}_2 = x_2, \cdots, \mathbf{x}_n = x_n\} = f(x_1)f(x_2) \cdots f(x_n),$$

or

$$\blacktriangleright \qquad f(x_1, x_2, \cdots, x_n) = \prod_{i=1}^n f(x_i),$$

where $f(x_1, x_2, \cdots, x_n)$ is the joint probability function of the random variables $\mathbf{x}_1, \mathbf{x}_2, \cdots, \mathbf{x}_n$. The probability function of the random variable $\mathbf{x}_1$ is then given by

$$Pr\{\mathbf{x}_1 = x_1\} = \sum_{x_2} \sum_{x_3} \cdots \sum_{x_n} f(x_1, x_2, \cdots, x_n)$$

(pages 63, 64)

$$= \sum_{x_2} \sum_{x_3} \cdots \sum_{x_n} f(x_1)f(x_2)\cdots f(x_n)$$

$$= f(x_1) \sum_{x_2} f(x_2) \sum_{x_3} f(x_3) \cdots \sum_{x_n} f(x_n)$$

$$= f(x_1),$$

since $\sum_{x_n} f(x_n) = 1, \cdots, \sum_{x_3} f(x_3) = 1$, and $\sum_{x_2} f(x_2) = 1$. Similarly, $Pr\{\mathbf{x}_i = x_i\} = f(x_i), i = 2, 3, \cdots, n$, and we find that the probability function of each of the sample random variables is just that of the random variable $\mathbf{x}$, and that the sample random variables are independent.

If $\mathbf{x}$ is a continuous random variable with probability density function $f(x)$, then in the sample space we associate with a rectangle, the set of all points $(x_1, x_2, \cdots, x_n)$ satisfying inequalities $a_1 < x_1 < b_1$, $a_2 < x_2 < b_2$, $\cdots, a_n < x_n < b_n$, the probability

$$\int_{a_1}^{b_1} dx_1 \int_{a_2}^{b_2} dx_2 \cdots \int_{an}^{b_n} f(x_1)f(x_2) \cdots f(x_n)\, dx_n.$$

It can then be shown that for each event A (a set of n-tuples of real numbers) in the sample space,

$$Pr\{(\mathbf{x}_1, \mathbf{x}_2, \cdots, \mathbf{x}_n) \text{ in } A\} = \iint \cdots \int_A f(x_1) \cdots f(x_n)\, dx_1 \cdots dx_n,$$

so that the joint density function, $f(x_1, \cdots, x_n)$ of the sample random variables is given by

$$f(x_1, x_2, \cdots, x_n) = \prod_{i=1}^{n} f(x_i).$$

If B is an event (a set of real numbers) in the parent population, then

$$Pr\{\mathbf{x}_1 \text{ in } B\} = \int_B f(x_1)\, dx_1 \int_{-\infty}^{\infty} f(x_2)\, dx_2 \cdots \int_{-\infty}^{\infty} f(x_n)\, dx_n$$

$$= \int_B f(x_1)\, dx_1,$$

since $\int_{-\infty}^{\infty} f(x)\, dx = 1$. Therefore f is the probability density function of $\mathbf{x}_1$, and similarly each of the sample random variables has the same density function, f, as does $\mathbf{x}$. We find then that as defined on the sample space each of the random variables has the same distribution as $\mathbf{x}$, and they are independent:

$$\blacktriangleright \qquad f(x_1, x_2, \cdots, x_n) = \prod_{i=1}^{n} f(x_i).$$

EXAMPLE 2. (*The Binomial Distribution*). We shall begin again with the population of the preceding example. This population may come up for discussion in any of a number of different situations. For example, suppose you have a coin, which may be unbalanced, so that the probability that heads will turn up is a number p between 0 and 1, and the probability that tails will turn up is $q = 1 - p$. Suppose you propose to make n independent tosses of the coin.

You may begin your discussion of your experiment by introducing a probability space with two elementary events H and T with associated probabilities p and q. You may then define a random variable $\mathbf{x}$ on this probability space to have the value 1 (number of heads) at the elementary event H, and the value 0 (number of heads) at the elementary event T. This random variable $\mathbf{x}$ induces on the set R of real numbers the same probability space we discussed in the earlier example, in which the elementary event 1 has probability p and the elementary event 0 has probability q. This probability space will serve as *population* in a discussion in which your n tosses of the coin will yield a random sample of size n from this population.

This same population would be appropriate for a discussion of n repeated, independent trials of any event with probability p of occurring in each trial (such trials are called *Bernoullian trials*).

Every n-tuple of real numbers is an elementary event in the sample space, but only n-tuples in which each number is either 0 or 1 have positive probabilities. Let $\mathbf{x}_1$ denote the number of heads which will turn up at the first toss, $\mathbf{x}_2$ the number of heads which will turn up at the second toss, etc. The random variables $\mathbf{x}_1, \mathbf{x}_2, \cdots, \mathbf{x}_n$ are then the sample random variables of a sample of size n from the population. In the usual language associated with Bernoullian trials, $\mathbf{x}_i$ would be called the *number of successes in the* ith *trial* $(i = 1, 2, \cdots, n)$. The joint probability function $f(x_1, x_2, \cdots, x_n)$ of the random variables $\mathbf{x}_1, \mathbf{x}_2, \cdots, \mathbf{x}_n$ evaluated at the sample point $(x_1, x_2, \cdots, x_n)$ is also the probability associated with the sample point $(x_1, x_2, \cdots, x_n)$.

If each x_i is either 0 or 1,

$$f(x_1, x_2, \cdots, x_n) = \prod_{i=1}^{n} f(x_i) = p^{x_1}q^{1-x_1}p^{x_2}q^{1-x_2} \cdots p^{x_n}q^{1-x_n}$$

$$= p^{\sum_{i=1}^{n} x_i} q^{n-\sum_{i=1}^{n} x_i}$$

Otherwise,

$$f(x_1, x_2, \cdots, x_n) = 0.$$

Since each x_i is either 0 or 1 (if $f(x_1, x_2, \cdots, x_n) \neq 0$), the sum $\sum_{i=1}^n x_i$ is the number of 1's which appear in the sample point $(x_1, x_2, \cdots, x_n)$, or the number of heads in the n tosses represented by the sample point, or the number of successes in the n trial results represented by the sample point.

Since $\mathbf{x}_i$ represents the number of heads which will be thrown in the ith toss, or the number of successes which will occur at the ith trial ($i = 1, 2, \cdots, n$), the random variable $\sum_{i=1}^n \mathbf{x}_i$ is the total number of heads which will be thrown in the n tosses, or the total number of successes which will be observed in the n trials. Let us denote this random variable by $\mathbf{S}$:

$$\mathbf{S} = \sum_{i=1}^n \mathbf{x}_i.$$

The distribution of this random variable $\mathbf{S}$ clearly depends on n and on p, and is known as the *binomial distribution with parameters n and p*. We can find $E(\mathbf{S})$ and $V(\mathbf{S})$ without further discussion of its distribution, using the algebra of expectations. We have

$$E(\mathbf{S}) = E(\sum_{i=1}^n \mathbf{x}_i) = \sum_{i=1}^n E(\mathbf{x}_i) \qquad \text{by Corollary G, page 89.}$$

Also, since each $\mathbf{x}_i$ has the same distribution as the population random variable $\mathbf{x}$, $E(\mathbf{x}_i) = E(\mathbf{x})$ for each i. But

$$E(\mathbf{x}) = \sum_x x f(x) = 1f(1) + 0f(0) = 1 \cdot p + 0 \cdot q = p,$$

so that

▶ $$E(\mathbf{S}) = \sum_{i=1}^n p = np.$$

Also, since the random variables $\mathbf{x}_i$ are independent,

$$V(\mathbf{S}) = V(\sum_{i=1}^n \mathbf{x}_i) = \sum_{i=1}^n V(\mathbf{x}_i) \qquad \text{by Corollary N, page 91.}$$

Again, $V(\mathbf{x}_i) = V(\mathbf{x})$ for each i, and

$$V(\mathbf{x}) = E(\mathbf{x}^2) - [E(\mathbf{x})]^2 \qquad \text{by Theorem L, page 90.}$$

In this particular situation, $\mathbf{x}^2$ is the same random variable as $\mathbf{x}$, so that $E(\mathbf{x}^2) = E(\mathbf{x}) = p$; or, using Theorem A, page 86, we find that

$$E(\mathbf{x}^2) = \sum_x x^2 f(x) = 1f(1) + 0f(0) = 1 \cdot p + 0 \cdot q = p.$$

Therefore

$$V(\mathbf{x}) = E(\mathbf{x}^2) - [E(\mathbf{x})]^2 = p - p^2 = p(1 - p) = pq,$$

and

▶ $$V(\mathbf{S}) = \sum_{i=1}^n pq = npq.$$

The distribution of $\mathbf{S}$ is determined by its probability function, $Pr\{\mathbf{S} = S\}$. Now $Pr\{\mathbf{S} = S\} = Pr\{\sum_{i=1}^{n} \mathbf{x}_i = S\}$. This probability is given by the sum of the values of the joint probability function of $\mathbf{x}_1$, $\mathbf{x}_2, \cdots, \mathbf{x}_n$ at all sample points $(x_1, x_2, \cdots, x_n)$ for which $\sum_{i=1}^{n} x_i = S$ (page 64):

$$Pr\{\mathbf{S} = S\} = \sum_{x_1+x_2+\cdots+x_n=S} f(x_1, x_2, \cdots, x_n).$$

But

$$f(x_1, x_2, \cdots, x_n) = p^{\sum_{i=1}^{n} x_i} q^{n-\sum_{i=1}^{n} x_i},$$

so that at each sample point for which $\sum_{i=1}^{n} x_i = S$ we have

$$f(x_1, x_2, \cdots, x_n) = p^S q^{n-S}.$$

We have yet to determine how many such sample points there are. We may think of this problem in the following way: there are n positions in the ordered n-tuple which is the sample point; if $\sum_{i=1}^{n} x_i$ is to be S, then S of these spaces must be filled with 1's, and the rest with 0's. The number of sample points for which $\sum_{i=1}^{n} x_i = S$ is then just the number of combinations of n things taken S at a time. An often used symbol for this number is $\binom{n}{S}$. We now have

$$Pr\{\mathbf{S} = S\} = \sum_{x_1+x_2+\cdots+x_n=S} p^S q^{n-S},$$

▶ $$Pr\{\mathbf{S} = S\} = \binom{n}{S} p^S q^{n-S} \quad \textit{for } S = 0, 1, 2, \cdots, n$$

$$= 0 \textit{ for all other } S.$$

Any random variable with this probability function is said to have a binomial distribution *with parameters n and p.*

We have

$$Pr\{a < \mathbf{S} < b\} = \sum_{a<S<b} \binom{n}{S} p^S q^{n-S} \quad \text{if } a < b\cdot$$

if a and b are integers, then

$$Pr\{a \leq \mathbf{S} \leq b\} = \sum_{S=a}^{b} \binom{n}{S} p^S q^{n-S}.$$

In particular, the distribution function of $\mathbf{S}$ is given by

$$Pr\{\mathbf{S} < S\} = \sum_{k<S} \binom{n}{k} p^k q^{n-k},$$

or, if S is a non-negative integer not greater than n,

by
$$Pr\{\mathbf{S} < S\} = \sum_{k=0}^{S-1} \binom{n}{k} p^k q^{n-k}.$$

39. Combinations. The number $\binom{n}{k}$ of combinations of n things taken k at a time is equal to the coefficient of x^k in the binomial expansion of $(1 + x)^n$. The reason for this is clear: if $(1 + x)^n$ is written as the product of $(1 + x)$ by itself n times,

$$(1 + x)^n = (1 + x)(1 + x) \cdots (1 + x) \qquad (n \text{ factors}),$$

then the number of times x^k appears in the expanded product is precisely the number of different ways in which k of the x's can be chosen from among the n, that is, the number of combinations of n things taken k at a time. The binomial expansion of $(1 + x)^n$ is

$$(1 + x)^n = \sum_{k=0}^{n} \binom{n}{k} x^k,$$

where

▶
$$\binom{n}{k} = \frac{n!}{k!(n-k)!} \qquad (0! = 1).$$

EXAMPLE 3. Suppose you propose to make 5 tosses of a balanced coin. In applying the above discussion, we have $n = 5, p = q = 1/2$. $\mathbf{S} = \sum_{i=1}^{5} \mathbf{x}_i$ is the total number of heads you will throw. The probability that you will throw exactly 2 heads is

$$Pr\{\mathbf{S} = 2\} = \binom{5}{2}\left(\frac{1}{2}\right)^2\left(\frac{1}{2}\right)^3 = \frac{5!}{2!3!}\left(\frac{1}{2}\right)^5 = \frac{10}{32} = \frac{5}{16}.$$

The probability that you will throw fewer than 3 heads is

$$Pr\{\mathbf{S} < 3\} = \sum_{S<3} \binom{5}{S}\left(\frac{1}{2}\right)^S\left(\frac{1}{2}\right)^{5-S}$$

$$= \frac{5!}{0!5!}\left(\frac{1}{2}\right)^5 + \frac{5!}{1!4!}\left(\frac{1}{2}\right)^5 + \frac{5!}{2!3!}\left(\frac{1}{2}\right)^5 = \frac{16}{32} = \frac{1}{2}.$$

The probability that you will throw at least 4 heads is

$$Pr\{\mathbf{S} \geq 4\} = \sum_{S \geq 4} \binom{5}{S}\left(\frac{1}{2}\right)^S\left(\frac{1}{2}\right)^{5-S} = \binom{5}{4}\left(\frac{1}{2}\right)^4\left(\frac{1}{2}\right) + \binom{5}{5}\left(\frac{1}{2}\right)^5\left(\frac{1}{2}\right)^0$$

$$= \frac{6}{32} = \frac{3}{16}.$$

EXAMPLE 4. You plan to shoot three arrows at a target, and know from past experience you have a probability 0.6 of hitting with each. You set up a probability space with two elementary events, H (hit) and M (miss), with associated probabilities $p = 0.6$ and $q = 0.4$. You define a random variable $\mathbf{x}$, "number of hits," to be 1 at the elementary event H and 0 at the elementary event M. You now introduce as a population the probability space induced on R by $\mathbf{x}$: the elementary event 1 has probability 0.6 and the elementary event 0 has probability 0.4. The numbers $\mathbf{x}_1$, $\mathbf{x}_2$, and $\mathbf{x}_3$ of hits in the first, second, and third shots respectively are sample random variables of a sample of size 3 from this population. $\mathbf{S} = \sum_{i=1}^{3} \mathbf{x}_i$ is the total number of hits; $\mathbf{S}$ has a binomial distribution with parameters $n = 3$ and $p = 0.6$. The probability of 2 hits is $\binom{3}{2}(0.6)^2(0.4) = 0.432$. The probability of getting at least 1 hit is $\sum_{S=1}^{3}\binom{3}{S}(0.6)^S(0.4)^{3-S}$ $= 1 - \binom{3}{0}(0.6)^0(0.4)^3 = 1 - 0.064 = 0.936$.

40. Summary. In a situation where we wish to discuss a *random sample* of size n, we are given to begin with (or we introduce) a probability space, and a random variable $\mathbf{x}$ on the probability space. This random variable induces on the set R of real numbers a probability space, which is the *population*. Thus the population is a probability space in which the elementary events are real numbers, and in which the probability associated with an elementary event a is $Pr\{\mathbf{x} = a\}$, and the probability associated with an event which is an interval is the probability that $\mathbf{x}$ will assume a value in that interval. The *sample random variables* $\mathbf{x}_1, \mathbf{x}_2, \cdots, \mathbf{x}_n$ are random variables defined on the *sample space*. A *sample point* is an elementary event in the sample space, a point in n-space, or an ordered n-tuple of real numbers, the first number being the value of $\mathbf{x}_1$ at that sample point, etc. Each of the sample random variables has the same distribution as $\mathbf{x}$:

$$Pr\{\mathbf{x}_i = x\} = f(x) = Pr\{\mathbf{x} = x\},$$

if $\mathbf{x}$ is discrete with probability function $f(x)$; if $\mathbf{x}$ is continuous with density function $f(x)$, then the value of the density function of $\mathbf{x}_i$ at the real number x is also $f(x)$ $(i = 1, 2, \cdots, n)$. The sample random variables $\mathbf{x}_1, \mathbf{x}_2, \cdots, \mathbf{x}_n$ are independent, having a joint probability function or joint density function

$$f(x_1, x_2, \cdots, x_n) = \prod_{i=1}^{n} f(x_i).$$

If the population random variable, $\mathbf{x}$, assumes the value 1 with probability p, and the value 0 with probability $q = 1 - p$, then

$$f(x) = p^x q^{1-x} \quad \text{if } x = 0 \text{ or } 1,$$

and

$$f(x_1, x_2, \cdots, x_n) = p^{\sum_{i=1}^n x_i} q^{n - \sum_{i=1}^n x_i}$$

if each x_i is either 0 or 1. In this case the probability function of $\mathbf{S} = \sum_{i=1}^n \mathbf{x}_i$ is given by

$$Pr\{\mathbf{S} = S\} = \binom{n}{S} p^S q^{n-S} \qquad (S = 0, 1, 2, \cdots, n)$$

and $\mathbf{S}$ is said to have the *binomial distribution with parameters n and p.* If A is a set of real numbers,

$$Pr\{\mathbf{S} \text{ in } A\} = \sum_{S \text{ in } A} \binom{n}{S} p^S q^{n-S},$$

where the summation is extended over all non-negative integers S not greater than n which are in A.

PROBLEMS

1. Each of four of a battleship's guns trained on an enemy destroyer has probability 0.3 of hitting it.

(a) If the results of the shots, one from each gun, are to be interpreted in terms of a sample of size 4 from a certain population, describe the population, the sample space, and the sample random variables.

(b) Find the probabilities of 0, 1, 2, 3, 4 hits.

(c) Find the probability of at least 2 hits.

2. In a certain city, rain falls on the average one day out of three. If three dates are selected at random, what is the probability that rain will fall on at least one of the three?

3. Suppose you had observed that of 10,000 rats shipped to your psychology laboratory over a period of years only 5 had inner-ear disease. Assuming this proportion of rats with inner-ear disease, find the probability that a shipment of 25 will have 2 or more rats with inner-ear disease.

4. Five dice are tossed. What is the probability that (a) x 6's will turn up; (b) At least y 6's will turn up; (c) At most y 6's will turn up? (d) Find $E(\mathbf{x})$ and $V(\mathbf{x})$ if $\mathbf{x}$ is the number of 6's which will turn up.

5. In a student body of about 8000, opinion is (approximately) two to one in favor of a certain proposal. A student opinion poll takes a random sample of size 100. Write exact expressions for

(a) The probability that at least 60 of those polled will favor the proposal;

(b) The probability that not fewer than 60 nor more than 75 will favor the proposal.

6. The mortality of rats infected with a certain disease is 80%.

(a) Of 100 rats infected, what is the expected number which will succumb?

(b) What is the variance of the number which will succumb?

(c) What is the standard deviation of the fraction that will succumb?

7. Twenty subjects are served, in random order, cooked fresh asparagus and cooked quick-frozen asparagus, and asked to state which is fresh. If in fact each subject is unable to judge, and chooses by chance, what is the exact probability that 15 or more correct choices will be made?

8. An office employs 10 typists. Each requires a new typewriter ribbon about once in 7 weeks. If the stock clerk finds at the beginning of a certain week that he has only 5 ribbons in stock, what is the probability that his supply will be exhausted during that week?

9. Four of six engineers building a computer were hit by spent bullets in the course of a year. If the probability that a given individual in the city where they worked will be hit by a spent bullet during a given year is 10^{-6}, what is the *a priori* probability that at least 4 of the 6 would be hit during the year?

10. Let the random variable $\mathbf{x}$ have a uniform or rectangular distribution over $[0,\theta]$, where θ is a given, positive number.

(a) In the probability space induced on R by $\mathbf{x}$, what is the probability of the event which is the interval $[a,b]$, if $0 \leq a < b \leq \theta$?

(b) Let $\mathbf{x}_1, \mathbf{x}_2, \mathbf{x}_3$ be sample random variables of a random sample of size 3 from the population induced by $\mathbf{x}$. What is an elementary event in the sample space? What is the probability associated in the sample space with the cube $\{0 \leq x_1 \leq a, 0 \leq x_2 \leq a, 0 \leq x_3 \leq a\}$; that is, what is $Pr\{\mathbf{x}_1 \leq a, \mathbf{x}_2 \leq a, \mathbf{x}_3 \leq a\}$?

11. (a) In Problem 10, what is the probability density function of $\mathbf{x}_1$; of $\mathbf{x}_2$; of $\mathbf{x}_3$?

(b) In Problem 10, what is the value at a sample point (x_1, x_2, x_3) of the joint probability density function of $\mathbf{x}_1, \mathbf{x}_2, \mathbf{x}_3$?

12. A random variable $\mathbf{y}$ has probability function $g(y)$ given by $g(0) = 1/2$, $g(1) = 1/3$, $g(2) = 1/6$, $g(y) = 0$ for all other y.

(a) Describe the probability space induced on R by $\mathbf{y}$.

(b) If $\mathbf{y}_1$ and $\mathbf{y}_2$ are sample random variables of a random sample of size 2 from the population induced by $\mathbf{y}$, what are their respective probability functions, and what is their joint probability function?

(c) Find $Pr\{\mathbf{y}_1 + \mathbf{y}_2 < 3\}$.

13. A random variable $\mathbf{z}$ has the probability density function

$$h(z) = \frac{1}{\sqrt{2\pi}} e^{-z^2/2}.$$

(a) If $\mathbf{z}_1, \mathbf{z}_2, \cdots, \mathbf{z}_n$ are sample random variables of a random sample of size n from the population induced on R by $\mathbf{z}$, give their respective density functions and also their joint density function.

(b) Write an integral expression for $Pr\{-1 < \mathbf{z}_3 < 2\}$.

(c) Write an integral expression for $Pr\{0 \leq \mathbf{z}_1 + \mathbf{z}_2 \leq a\}$.

14. A draws from a pinochle deck (48 cards, 8 each of A, K, Q, J, 10, 9); B draws from a standard deck of 52 cards.

(a) What is the probability that A's card will be higher than B's? (Cards of the same rank in different suits are to be regarded as equal in value.)

(b) If they draw 10 times, with replacement and shuffling between draws, what is the probability that A will win 7 times?

(c) What is the most probable number of times A will win? (See Problem 17.)

(d) What is A's expected number of wins?

(e) What is the standard deviation of the number of A's wins?

15. Three machines contribute to a factory's production of a certain small item. Machine A produces items about 3% defective, and accounts for 40% of the production; B produces items about 4% defective, and accounts for 35% of the production, while C produces items 5% defective and 25% of the total production. The items are stored in boxes, each box containing a fixed large number of items produced by a machine. Thus 40% of the boxes contain items produced by A, etc. The boxes are stored together, and not distinguished as to the machine which produced the contents.

(a) A box is to be chosen at random, and an item is to be chosen at random from the box. What is the probability that it will prove defective?

(b) A box is chosen at random, and a random sample of 100 items is taken, of which 4 prove defective. What is the probability that the box came from machine A? from B? from C?

16. Suppose a sample of size n is taken from the population induced by a random variable $\mathbf{x}$ which assumes the values, 1 with probability p, and 0 with probability $q = 1 - p$.

(a) Write an expression for the probability that the sum $\mathbf{S}$ of the sample values will be k.

(b) Use your answer to (a) and the *definition* of expectation to show that

$$E(\mathbf{S}) = \sum_{k=0}^{n} k \binom{n}{k} p^k q^{n-k}.$$

(c) Differentiate the identity $(p+q)^n \equiv \sum_{k=0}^{n} \binom{n}{k} p^k q^{n-k}$ with respect to p, and use the result to prove that $E(\mathbf{S}) = np$.

17. A sequence of n independent trials is to be made of an event with probability p. Let $\mathbf{S}$ denote the number of successes that will be observed.

(a) Show that the ratio $Pr\{\mathbf{S} = k+1\}/Pr\{\mathbf{S} = k\}$ is

$$(n-k)p/(k+1)q.$$

(b) Show that the most probable value of $\mathbf{S}$ is $[(n+1)p]$, the greatest integer not greater than $(n+1)p$. (There may be two most probable values. When?)

Hint. Show that the ratio in part (a) is greater than 1 for $k+1 < (n+1)p$ and less than 1 for $k+1 > (n+1)p$.

(c) Verify this result in Problem 1.

18. Suppose you plan to make independent trials of an event with probability p. Let $\mathbf{y}$ denote the number of trials you will make before a single occurrence of the event. Thus if the event occurs on the first trial, $\mathbf{y}$ will be 0; if the event fails to occur on the first trial but occurs on the second, then $\mathbf{y} = 1$, etc. Find the probability function of $\mathbf{y}$, also $E(\mathbf{y})$, and $V(\mathbf{y})$.

Hint 1. If y is a positive integer, $\mathbf{y}$ will be equal to y if and only if y failures are followed by a success.

Hint 2. $$\sum_{y=0}^{\infty} yq^y = q \sum_{y=0}^{\infty} yq^{y-1} = q \frac{d}{dq} [\sum_{y=0}^{\infty} q^y].$$

★ 41. The Multinomial Distribution. The total number of successes in n independent trials of an event A with probability p has, by definition, a binomial distribution with parameters n and p. In each trial the investigator observes whether the event A or its contrary $\bar{A}$ occurred. Let us now generalize this situation, in supposing that the result of each trial is some one of an exhaustive set of k mutually exclusive events,

$$A_1, A_2, \cdots, A_k, \bigcup_{j=1}^{k} A_j = S,$$

with associated probabilities $p_1, p_2, \cdots, p_k, \sum_{j=1}^{k} p_j = 1$. Let $\mathbf{y}_j$ denote the total number of occurrences of the event A_j, $j = 1, 2, \cdots, k$. Then the random variables $\mathbf{y}_1, \mathbf{y}_2, \cdots, \mathbf{y}_k$ are said to have a *multinomial distribution* (with parameters $n, p_1, p_2, \cdots, p_k$).

Let $f(y_1, y_2, \cdots, y_k)$ denote the value of the probability function of the random variables $\mathbf{y}_1, \mathbf{y}_2, \cdots, \mathbf{y}_k$ at the point $(y_1, y_2, \cdots, y_k)$. Evidently

$f = 0$ unless $y_1, y_2, \cdots, y_k$ are non-negative integers whose sum is n. If they are non-negative integers whose sum is n, the calculation of the joint probability function may be treated as an exercise in the use of the law of compound probability, as follows. We have

$$f(y_1, \cdots, y_k)$$
$$= Pr\{\mathbf{y}_1 = y_1, \mathbf{y}_2 = y_2, \cdots, \mathbf{y}_k = y_k\}$$
$$= Pr\{\mathbf{y}_1 = y_1\}Pr\{\mathbf{y}_2 = y_2 | \mathbf{y}_1 = y_1\}Pr\{\mathbf{y}_3 = y_3 | \mathbf{y}_1 = y_1, \mathbf{y}_2 = y_2\}$$
$$\cdots Pr\{\mathbf{y}_k = y_k | \mathbf{y}_1 = y_1, \cdots, \mathbf{y}_{k-1} = y_{k-1}\}$$

(cf. pages 16, 26). Now $Pr\{\mathbf{y}_1 = y_1\}$ is just the probability of precisely y_1 occurrences in n independent trials of an event A_1 with probability p_1:

$$Pr\{\mathbf{y}_1 = y_1\} = \binom{n}{y_1} p_1^{y_1}(1 - p_1)^{n-y_1}.$$

If there are to be exactly y_1 occurrences of the event A_1, there remain $n - y_1$ trials in which A_2 may occur and in which A_1 is known not to occur. The conditional probability of A_2 in each is $P(A_2 | \bar{A}_1) = P(A_2\bar{A}_1)/P(\bar{A}_1)$. Since A_1 and A_2 are mutually exclusive, we have $A_2 \subset \bar{A}_1$, $A_2\bar{A}_1 = A_2$, and $P(A_2\bar{A}_1) = P(A_2) = p_2$, while $P(\bar{A}_1) = 1 - P(A_1) = 1 - p_1$. Thus the conditional probability of A_2 in each trial remaining is $p_2/(1 - p_1)$. Hence $Pr\{\mathbf{y}_2 = y_2 | \mathbf{y}_1 = y_1\}$ is the probability of precisely y_2 successes in $n - y_1$ independent trials of an event with probability $p_2/(1 - p_1)$, so that

$$Pr\{\mathbf{y}_2 = y_2 | \mathbf{y}_1 = y_1\} = \binom{n - y_1}{y_2}\left(\frac{p_2}{1 - p_1}\right)^{y_2}\left(1 - \frac{p_2}{1 - p_1}\right)^{n-y_1-y_2}.$$

Then

$$Pr\{\mathbf{y}_1 = y_1\}Pr\{\mathbf{y}_2 = y_2 | \mathbf{y}_1 = y_1\}$$
$$= \binom{n}{y_1} p_1^{y_1}(1 - p_1)^{n-y_1}\binom{n - y_1}{y_2}\left(\frac{p_2}{1 - p_1}\right)^{y_2}\left(1 - \frac{p_2}{1 - p_1}\right)^{n-y_1-y_2},$$

which reduces to
$$\frac{n!}{y_1!y_2!(n - y_1 - y_2)!} p_1^{y_1}p_2^{y_2}(1 - p_1 - p_2)^{n-y_1-y_2}.$$

Incidentally, this formula gives the joint probability function of the two random variables $\mathbf{y}_1$ and $\mathbf{y}_2$ at (y_1, y_2) if y_1, y_2 are non-negative integers whose sum is not greater than n. Proceeding in this way (using induction), we find that if $r \leq k$, the joint probability function of the random variables $\mathbf{y}_1, \mathbf{y}_2, \cdots, \mathbf{y}_r$ is

$$\frac{n!}{y_1!y_2! \cdots y_r!(n - y_1 - y_2 - \cdots - y_r)!} p_1^{y_1}p_2^{y_2} \cdots p_r^{y_r} \cdot$$
$$(1 - p_1 - p_2 - \cdots - p_r)^{n-y_1-y_2-\cdots-y_r}$$

if $y_1, y_2, \cdots, y_r$ are non-negative integers whose sum is not greater than n. On setting $r = k$ and noting that $\sum_{j=1}^{k} p_j = 1$, we find that

$$▶ \qquad f(y_1, y_2, \cdots y_k) = n! \prod_{j=1}^{k} \frac{p_j^{y_j}}{y_j!}$$

if $y_1, y_2, \cdots, y_k$ are non-negative integers whose sum is n. (Note that the last factor, $Pr\{\mathbf{y}_k = y_k | \mathbf{y}_1 = y_1, \mathbf{y}_2 = y_2, \cdots, \mathbf{y}_{k-1} = y_{k-1}\}$, is 1.)

EXAMPLE 4. Suppose you are interested in a process for generating random digits. That is, the process produces a random sample from a population whose population random variable $\mathbf{x}$ assumes each of ten values, 0, 1, 2, $\cdots$, 9, with probability 1/10. In other words, the digits produced are the results of independent trials, in each of which any of ten equally likely events can occur. If $\mathbf{y}_0, \mathbf{y}_1, \cdots, \mathbf{y}_9$ represent the numbers of 0's, 1's, $\cdots$, 9's that will occur in 100 trials, then the joint probability function of $\mathbf{y}_0, \mathbf{y}_1, \cdots, \mathbf{y}_9$ is

$$f(y_0, y_1, \cdots, y_9) = 100! \prod_{j=0}^{9} (1/10)^{y_j}/y_j!$$

$$= \frac{100!}{10^{100} \prod_{j=0}^{9} y_j!} \qquad \text{if } \sum_{j=0}^{9} y_j = 100,$$

$$f(y_0, y_1, \cdots, y_9) = 0 \qquad \text{if } \sum_{j=0}^{9} y_j \neq 100.$$

★ 42. The Poisson Distribution.

Suppose you are about to install a telephone switchboard, and are studying the distribution of phone calls. Suppose that the peak period extends from nine o'clock to noon, and that the distribution of calls appears nearly homogeneous over that time interval. You wish to know the probability distribution of the number of calls in a given time interval during that period.

You need first a mathematical model, a probability space, on which "the number of calls in a given time interval of length t" will be a random variable, having a probability distribution. You assume it is possible to set up a probability space in which, for each specified time interval, the following are events:

A: "there will be exactly one call";
B: "there will be no call";
C: "there will be more than one call."

We suppose it seems reasonable to you to assume further that the probability space can be so defined that

(i) These events have probabilities $p(t)$, $q(t)$, and $\epsilon(t)$ respectively, which depend continuously on the length t of the time interval alone, and thus do not depend on when the interval begins or ends.

(ii) Events A, B, C for one time interval are independent of those for another, non-overlapping time interval; that is, the events "no call between 10:00 and 10:01" and "exactly one call between 10:32 and 10:35" are independent events, etc.

(iii) $q(0) = 1$; that is, the probability is 1 that no call will be made during a time interval of length 0; or, the probability that no call will be made in a time interval of length t approaches 1 as $t \to 0$.

(iv) $q(t)$ has a continuous derivative which is negative at $t = 0$: $q'(0) = -a$, where a is a positive number (the probability of "no call" decreases as t increases from 0).

(v) $\dfrac{\epsilon(t)}{t} \to 0$ as $t \to 0$: the probability of *more than one* call in time t approaches 0 as $t \to 0$ faster than does t (for small t this probability is much smaller than t).

Hypotheses (iii) and (iv) are in fact superfluous, as it can be shown they follow from the others.

The actual construction and description of a probability space fulfilling these requirements are beyond the scope of this text.

▶ ***Theorem A.*** *If the above assumptions are satisfied, then the probability of exactly x calls in time t is*

$$(at)^x e^{-at}/x!$$

This theorem will be proved after a preliminary discussion of the Poisson distribution.

▶ ***Definition.*** A random variable $\mathbf{x}$ has a *Poisson distribution with parameter* λ if its probability function is

$$f(x) = Pr\{\mathbf{x} = x\} = e^{-\lambda}\lambda^x/x!$$

for $x = 0, 1, 2, \cdots, f(x) = 0$ for other x.

The conclusion of Theorem A could be stated thus: the number $\mathbf{x}$ of calls in time t has a Poisson distribution with parameter at.

It is easy to verify that the sum of the Poisson probabilities is 1, for Maclaurin's expansion of e^λ is $e^\lambda = \sum_{x=0}^{\infty} \lambda^x/x!$, so that $\sum_{x=0}^{\infty} f(x) = \sum_{x=0}^{\infty} e^{-\lambda}\lambda^x/x! = 1$. If $\mathbf{x}$ has a Poisson distribution with parameter λ, then

$$\begin{aligned} E(\mathbf{x}) &= \sum_{x=0}^{\infty} xe^{-\lambda}\lambda^x/x! = e^{-\lambda}\sum_{x=1}^{\infty} x\lambda^x/x! \\ &= e^{-\lambda}\sum_{x=1}^{\infty} \lambda^x/(x-1)! = \lambda e^{-\lambda}\sum_{x=1}^{\infty} \lambda^{x-1}/(x-1)!. \end{aligned}$$

On making the change of variable $y = x - 1$ in the sum, we find that

$$E(\mathbf{x}) = \lambda e^{-\lambda} \sum_{y=0}^{\infty} \lambda^y/y! = \lambda.$$

Similarly,

$$E(\mathbf{x}^2) = e^{-\lambda} \sum_{x=0}^{\infty} x^2\lambda^x/x! = e^{-\lambda} \left\{\sum_{x=0}^{\infty} x(x-1)\lambda^x/x! + \sum_{x=0}^{\infty} x\lambda^x/x!\right\}$$

$$= e^{-\lambda} \{\lambda^2 \sum_{x=2}^{\infty} \lambda^{x-2}/(x-2)! + \lambda \sum_{x=1}^{\infty} \lambda^{x-1}/(x-1)!\}$$

$$= \lambda^2 + \lambda;$$

hence

$$V(\mathbf{x}) = E(\mathbf{x}^2) - [E(\mathbf{x})]^2 = \lambda^2 + \lambda - \lambda^2 = \lambda.$$

Thus:

▶ Both mean and variance of a Poisson distributed random variable are equal to the parameter.

It will be convenient to precede the proof of Theorem A by the theorem below.

★ *Poisson Approximation to the Binomial Distribution.*

▶ ***Theorem B.*** *If $b_n \to b$ as $n \to \infty$ and if x is a fixed non-negative integer, then the binomial probability,*

$$\binom{n}{x}\left(\frac{b_n}{n}\right)^x\left(1 - \frac{b_n}{n}\right)^{n-x},$$

approaches the Poisson probability,

$$b^x e^{-b}/x!, \text{ as } n \to \infty.$$

Proof. The binomial probability is equal to

$$\frac{n!}{x!(n-x)!}\,\frac{b_n{}^x(1 - b_n/n)^n}{n^x(1 - b_n/n)^x} = \frac{b_n{}^x\, c_n}{x!(1 - b_n/n)^x}$$

where

$$c_n = \frac{n(n-1)(n-2)\cdots(n-x+1)}{n\cdot n\cdot n\cdots n}\,(1 - b_n/n)^n$$

$$= 1\left(1 - \frac{1}{n}\right)\left(1 - \frac{2}{n}\right)\cdots\left(1 - \frac{x-1}{n}\right)\left(1 - \frac{b_n}{n}\right)^n.$$

Each of the first x factors approaches 1 as $n \to \infty$, while $\lim_{n\to\infty} (1 - b_n/n)^n = e^{-b}$. One way to verify this latter is to apply l'Hospital's Rule to $\log \{[1 - b(y)/y]^y\}$, where $b(y)$ is a differentiable function of the continuous variable y which is equal to b_n when y is equal to n. Alternatively, we note first that

$$\frac{d}{dx}[\log(1+x)]\Big|_{x=0} = 1;$$

that is,

$$\lim_{x\to 0} \frac{\log(1+x) - \log 1}{(1+x) - 1} = 1,$$

or

$$\lim_{x\to 0} \frac{\log(1+x)}{x} = 1.$$

Now

$$\log\left(1 - \frac{b_n}{n}\right)^n = n \log\left(1 - \frac{b_n}{n}\right) = -b_n \frac{\log(1 - b_n/n)}{(-b_n/n)} \to -b\cdot 1$$

as $n \to \infty$, since $b_n \to b$ and $b_n/n \to 0$ as $n \to \infty$. We find, then, that $\lim_{n\to\infty} c_n = e^{-b}$; hence

$$\lim_{n\to\infty} \binom{n}{x}\left(\frac{b_n}{n}\right)^x\left(1 - \frac{b_n}{n}\right)^{n-x} = \lim_{n\to\infty} \frac{b_n{}^x c_n}{x!(1 - b_n/n)^x} = \frac{b^x e^{-b}}{x!}.$$

This completes the proof of Theorem B.

Theorem B gives us a means of approximating binomial probabilities by Poisson probabilities. To see this more clearly, let us rephrase Theorem B. Let p_n be a sequence of positive numbers approaching 0 as $n \to \infty$ in such a way that $np_n \to b$. On setting $b_n = np_n$ in Theorem B we find that

► $$\lim_{n\to\infty} \binom{n}{x} p_n{}^x(1 - p_n)^{n-x} = b^x e^{-b}/x!.$$

Thus if p is small and n is large, while np is of moderate size, we shall have

$$\binom{n}{x} p^x(1-p)^{n-x} \doteq (np)^x e^{-np}/x!.$$

Proof of Theorem A. Let $\mathbf{x}$ denote the number of calls in a fixed time interval of length t. We wish to find $f(x) = Pr\{\mathbf{x} = x\}$. For a fixed positive integer n, divide the time interval into n non-overlapping subintervals, each of length t/n. Let E denote the event that in each of exactly x of these subintervals exactly one call will be made. Let F denote the event that in some one of the subintervals two or more calls will be made. Then

$$E\bar{F} \subset \{\mathbf{x} = x\} \subset E \cup F.$$

That is, if the event E occurs, but not F, then the event $\{\mathbf{x} = x\}$ will also occur; while if $\{\mathbf{x} = x\}$ occurs, then either E or F must occur. From properties P9 and P10 (p. 23) it follows that $P(E\bar{F}) \leq Pr\{\mathbf{x} = x\} \leq P(E) + P(F)$. Further, $E = EF \cup E\bar{F}$, so that $P(E) = P(EF) + P(E\bar{F})$, $P(E) \leq P(F) + P(E\bar{F})$, and $P(E\bar{F}) \geq P(E) - P(F)$. Hence

$$P(E) - P(F) \leq Pr\{\mathbf{x} = x\} \leq P(E) + P(F).$$

If F_i denotes the event that two or more calls will be made in the ith subinterval ($i = 1, 2, \cdots, n$), then $F = \bigcup_{i=1}^{n} F_i$, and by Boole's inequality (P10; p. 23),

$$P(F) \leq \sum_{i=1}^{n} P(F_i) = \sum_{i=1}^{n} \epsilon(t/n) = n\epsilon(t/n) = t\left[\frac{\epsilon(t/n)}{(t/n)}\right].$$

By assumption (v), p. 113, $P(F) \to 0$ as $n \to \infty$.

Now let us consider $P(E)$; this is the probability of exactly x successes in n independent trials of an event with probability $p(t/n)$ in each. Therefore

$$P(E) = \binom{n}{x}[p(t/n)]^x[1 - p(t/n)]^{n-x}.$$

We shall use assumptions (iii) and (iv), page 118, to obtain an expression for $p(t/n)$. By the definition of derivative,

$$q'(0) = \lim_{t \to 0} \frac{q(t) - q(0)}{t},$$

so that since $q(0) = 1$ and $q'(0) = -a$, we have

$$\frac{q(t) - 1}{t} + a \to 0 \text{ as } t \to 0.$$

Set

$$\eta(t) = \frac{q(t) - 1}{t} + a;$$

then $\eta(t) \to 0$ as $t \to 0$, and

$$1 - q(t) = at - t\eta(t).$$

For a given time interval of length t, A, B, C are mutually exclusive events whose union is the sure event; hence the sum of their probabilities is 1, and we have $p(t) = 1 - q(t) - \epsilon(t)$, so that

$$p(t/n) = 1 - q(t/n) - \epsilon(t/n)$$

$$= \frac{at}{n} - \frac{t}{n}\eta(t/n) - \epsilon(t/n)$$

$$= \frac{t}{n}\left[a - \eta(t/n) - \frac{\epsilon(t/n)}{(t/n)}\right].$$

Remarking that t is a fixed constant, we set

$$b_n = t\left[a - \eta(t/n) - \frac{\epsilon(t/n)}{(t/n)}\right].$$

Since both $\eta(t)$ and $\epsilon(t)/t$ approach 0 as $t \to 0$, we have $\lim_{n\to\infty} b_n = at$. $P(E)$ now becomes

$$P(E) = \binom{n}{x}\left(\frac{b_n}{n}\right)^x\left(1 - \frac{b_n}{n}\right)^{n-x}.$$

By Theorem B, $P(E) \to e^{-at}(at)^x/x!$ as $n \to \infty$. We recall that

$$P(E) - P(F) \leq Pr\{\mathbf{x} = x\} \leq P(E) + P(F).$$

The center member does not depend on n, though both extremes do. Since we have now shown that as $n \to \infty$ both extremes approach $e^{-at}(at)^x/x!$, the center member, lying between them, must be equal to this number. This completes the proof of Theorem A.

For another derivation, see [17], Section 2.3.

The model we have discussed is appropriate in many other situations as well, for example, in radioactive decay, in which the occurrence of a phone call in the above discussion is to be replaced by the emission of an α-particle. For other examples and a more complete discussion, see [11], Chapter 10, [5], Chapter 6, and [6], page 276.

Let us consider now another model we might set up, in which $\mathbf{x}$, the number of calls made in a specified time interval, would appear as a random variable. Let us suppose that our time measurements are accurate only to the nearest millisecond. If t, the length of the time interval we are considering, is measured in seconds, let us consider the 1000 t separate milliseconds which comprise the interval. Let us observe in each millisecond whether none, one, or more than one call is made, and think of these observations as constituting a series of 1000 t independent trials of an event with probability $p(1/1000)$, the probability of a call in a given millisecond. This is a way-station at which we arrived earlier when starting from another model; what was the number n before is now 1000 t. If we assume that the event F (more than one call in some one millisecond) has negligible probability, then

$$Pr\{\mathbf{x} = x\} = P(E) = \binom{1000\,t}{x}[p(1/1000)]^x[1 - p(1/1000)]^{1000t-x}.$$

Having neglected the event F, that in at least one of the 1000 t milliseconds two or more calls will be made, the above binomial expression is the probability function of the random variable $\mathbf{x}$, the number of calls which will be made in t seconds. If we set $a = 1000p(1/1000)$, and if $n = 1000\,t$ is large, then the Poisson approximation to the binomial (Theorem B) yields

$$Pr\{\mathbf{x} = x\} \doteq (at)^x e^{-at}/x!.$$

Thus what was with the earlier model a precise expression for the probability function of $\mathbf{x}$ becomes with this one an approximate expression valid for time intervals of many milliseconds.

★ PROBL EMS

1. Compute and sketch the graphs of the probability function and distribution function of a Poisson distributed random variable with mean 2.

2. Microscope slides of a certain culture of microorganisms contain "on the average" about 20 per sq. cm. After treatment by a chemical, 1 sq. cm. is found to contain only 10 such microorganisms.

(a) What assumptions do you make in order to conclude that the number per square centimeter has a Poisson distribution?

(b) If the treatment had no effect, what would be the *a priori* probability of finding 10 or fewer of the organisms in a given square centimeter?

3. State and discuss appropriateness of assumptions which lead to a model in which the number of meteorites which will strike Arizona in a certain future month is a random variable with a Poisson distribution. Discuss similarly a model in which this random variable has a binomial distribution.

4. Discuss, as in Problem 3, models in which the number of hurricanes striking the Georgia coast in the first week of next September is a random variable.

5. Discuss, as in Problem 3, models for the random variable "number of two-headed calves to be born in Missouri next June."

6. On the average, the librarian serves 40 borrowers of books during an 8-hour day.

(a) If she leaves for a 15-minute coffee break, what is the expected number of borrowers who will find her gone?

(b) What is the probability that at least one will find her gone?

7. Assume that about 1 of 500 adults has serious loss of hearing. If such persons are not discriminated against as drivers,

(a) What is the expected number of such persons among 5000 drivers?

(b) What is the probability that there will be at least 5?

8. Suppose that a digital computer uses 3000 tubes, and that the expected number failing during 1000 hours of operation is 3. What is the probability that there will be no failures during (a) a 10-hour work period? (b) a 100-hour work period?

9. Assume that the probability of a motor failure on a routine flight between two cities is 0.005. Use the Poisson approximation to the binomial to find approximately the probability of (a) at least one failure in 1000 flights; (b) at least two failures in 1000 flights.

10. What is the probability of throwing three sevens and three elevens in six tosses of a pair of dice?

11. Let A and B denote two genetic characters, and suppose that the probability is 1/2 that an individual chosen at random will exhibit character A, 3/4 that he will exhibit character B. Assume these characters occur independently.

(a) What is the probability that an individual chosen at random will exhibit both? neither? exactly one?

(b) Of four individuals chosen at random, what is the probability that two will exhibit both, one will exhibit only one, and one will exhibit neither?

12. One-tenth of one per cent of the prunes in bins used for packaging have scab. How many can be put in a single package if the probability of finding at least one scabby prune is to be less than 0.05? (Use Poisson approximation.)

13. A certain hospital usually admits about 50 patients per day. On the average, 3 patients in 100 require special facilities found in certain rooms. On the morning of a certain day it is found that there are 3 such rooms available. Assuming that 50 patients will be admitted, find the probability that more than three will require such special rooms.

14. Your typist types again each page on which she has made errors in at least three words. You observe that of 20 pages she has had to recopy 7. Assuming the probability of making errors in at least three words on a page is 7/20, and that there are 200 words on a page, use the Poisson approximation to determine the probability of making an error in one word.

15. Suppose the number of times per year that a group of 6 engineers will have one member struck by a spent bullet has a Poisson distribution with mean $6(10^{-6})$. What is the probability that at least 4 hits will occur in a given year?

16. Show that the Poisson distribution will have a double mode (the probability function $f(x)$ attains its maximum at each of two values of x) if and only if the parameter λ is an integer; and find the most probable values in this case.

17. Carry out the reduction

$$\binom{n}{y_1} p_1^{y_1}(1-p_1)^{n-y_1}\binom{n-y_1}{y_2}\left(\frac{p_2}{1-p_1}\right)^{y_2}\left(1-\frac{p_2}{1-p_1}\right)^{n-y_1-y_2}$$

$$= \frac{n!}{y_1!y_2!(n-y_1-y_2)!} p_1^{y_1}p_2^{y_2}(1-p_1-p_2)^{n-y_1-y_2}.$$

18. Carry out the derivation by mathematical induction of the joint probability function of $\mathbf{y}_1, \mathbf{y}_2, \cdots, \mathbf{y}_r$ on page 116.

19. Prove that if $\mathbf{x}_1, \mathbf{x}_2$ are independent, Poisson distributed random variables with parameters λ_1 and λ_2, then $\mathbf{x}_1 + \mathbf{x}_2$ has a Poisson distribution with parameter $\lambda_1 + \lambda_2$.

20. Suppose λ is the average number of meteorites striking Arizona per month (see Problem 3). Let $\mathbf{t}$ denote the time (in months) between successive meteorites. Find the distribution of $\mathbf{t}$, its mean, and its variance. Hint: If $\mathbf{t} < t$, then at least one meteorite must strike in t months.

21. For large n and moderate values of $np_1 = \lambda_1, np_2 = \lambda_2, \cdots, np_{k-1} = \lambda_{k-1}$, the multinomial joint probability function $f(y_1, \cdots, y_{k-1})$ can be approximated by the *multiple Poisson* probability function,

$$e^{-\sum_{j=1}^{k-1}\lambda_j} \prod_{j=1}^{k-1} \frac{\lambda_j^{y_j}}{y_j!}.$$

Make a precise statement of the limit theorem implied in the above statement, and prove it.

CHAPTER

7

The Law of Large Numbers

43. The Sample Mean. If $\mathbf{x}_1, \mathbf{x}_2, \cdots, \mathbf{x}_n$ are the sample random variables of a sample of size n from a population induced by a random variable $\mathbf{x}$, we define the random variable, the *sample mean*, by

$$\blacktriangleright \qquad \bar{\mathbf{x}} = \frac{1}{n} \sum_{i=1}^{n} \mathbf{x}_i,$$

the arithmetic average of the n sample random variables. A sample point $(x_1, x_2, \cdots, x_n)$ represents the values of the sample random variables for a particular sample, and the sample mean of this particular sample is

$$\bar{x} = \frac{1}{n} \sum_{i=1}^{n} x_i.$$

We can easily compute $E(\bar{\mathbf{x}})$ and $V(\bar{\mathbf{x}})$ using the algebra of expectations. We have

$$E(\bar{\mathbf{x}}) = E\left(\frac{1}{n} \sum_{i=1}^{n} \mathbf{x}_i\right) = \frac{1}{n} E\left(\sum_{i=1}^{n} \mathbf{x}_i\right) = \frac{1}{n} \sum_{i=1}^{n} E(\mathbf{x}_i),$$

by Theorem D and Corollary G, page 88. Since each $\mathbf{x}_i$ has the same distribution as does $\mathbf{x}$, we have $E(\mathbf{x}_i) = E(\mathbf{x})$ for each i, and

$$E(\bar{\mathbf{x}}) = \frac{1}{n} \sum_{i=1}^{n} E(\mathbf{x}) = \frac{1}{n} \cdot nE(\mathbf{x}) = E(\mathbf{x}).$$

We shall often use the symbol μ or μ_x for the mean $E(\mathbf{x})$; then

$$\blacktriangleright \qquad E(\bar{\mathbf{x}}) = \mu, \text{ or } \mu_{\bar{\mathbf{x}}} = \mu_x.$$

Since the random variables $\mathbf{x}_i$ are independent, we have

$$V(\bar{\mathbf{x}}) = V\left(\frac{1}{n} \sum_{i=1}^{n} \mathbf{x}_i\right) = \frac{1}{n^2} V\left(\sum_{i=1}^{n} \mathbf{x}_i\right) = \frac{1}{n^2} \sum_{i=1}^{n} V(\mathbf{x}_i),$$

by Theorem K and Corollary N, pages 90, 91. Again, since each $\mathbf{x}_i$ has the same distribution as $\mathbf{x}$, we have $V(\mathbf{x}_i) = V(\mathbf{x})$ for each i, so that

$$V(\bar{\mathbf{x}}) = \frac{1}{n^2} \sum_{i=1}^{n} V(\mathbf{x}) = \frac{1}{n^2} \cdot nV(\mathbf{x}) = \frac{1}{n} V(\mathbf{x}).$$

We shall often use the symbol σ or σ_x for the standard deviation of $\mathbf{x}$, so that $V(\mathbf{x}) = \sigma^2$ or $\sigma_x{}^2$; then

$$\blacktriangleright \qquad V(\bar{\mathbf{x}}) = \frac{\sigma^2}{n}, \text{ or } \sigma_{\bar{x}} = \frac{\sigma_x}{\sqrt{n}}.$$

We recall that the variance of a random variable in some sense measures the compactness or the dispersion of the probability distribution of the random variable about its mean or expectation: a large variance means at least moderate probabilities associated with values distant from the mean, while a small variance means a high probability that the random variable will assume a value near its mean. We observe that for large n the variance of $\bar{\mathbf{x}}$ is very small, and accordingly suspect that if n is large the probability that $\bar{\mathbf{x}}$ will assume a value near its mean will be high. Essentially, this is the content of the law of large numbers, though we shall state it first in more general form. A theorem which gives us Chebyshev's Inequality will be used in the proof; this inequality is also useful for other purposes.

44. Chebyshev's Inequality. Chebyshev's Inequality applies to any random variable at all, provided its variance, and hence its expectation, exists.

▶ ***Theorem A.*** *Let* $\mathbf{y}$ *be a random variable with expectation* $E(\mathbf{y}) = \mu$ *and variance* $V(\mathbf{y}) = \sigma^2$. *Then if* ϵ *is any positive number,* $Pr\{|\mathbf{y} - \mu| \geq \epsilon\} \leq \sigma^2/\epsilon^2$.

$Pr\{|\mathbf{y} - \mu| \geq \epsilon\}$ may be read: "the probability that $\mathbf{y}$ will differ from μ by at least ϵ."

Proof for a continuous random variable $\mathbf{y}$: By the definition of variance, page 53, we have

$$\sigma^2 = V(\mathbf{y}) = \int_{-\infty}^{\infty} (y - \mu)^2 g(y)\, dy,$$

where $\mu = E(\mathbf{y})$ and where $g(y)$ is the probability density function of $\mathbf{y}$. Further,

$$\sigma^2 = \int_{-\infty}^{\infty} (y - \mu)^2 g(y)\, dy$$

$$= \int_{|y-\mu| \geq \epsilon} (y - \mu)^2 g(y)\, dy + \int_{|y-\mu| < \epsilon} (y - \mu)^2 g(y)\, dy,$$

where $\int_{|y-\mu|\geq\epsilon}$ denotes the integral over the range of values of y for which $|y - \mu| \geq \epsilon$, and $\int_{|y-\mu|<\epsilon}$ denotes the integral over the remainder of the range of y. (The last equation could also have been written

$$\int_{-\infty}^{\infty} (y - \mu)^2 g(y)\, dy$$

$$= \int_{\mu+\epsilon}^{\infty} (y - \mu)^2 g(y)\, dy + \int_{-\infty}^{\mu-\epsilon} (y - \mu)^2 g(y)\, dy + \int_{\mu-\epsilon}^{\mu+\epsilon} (y - \mu)^2 g(y)\, dy.)$$

Since the integrand is non-negative, the last integral is non-negative, and we have

$$\sigma^2 \geq \int_{|y-\mu|\geq\epsilon} (y - \mu)^2 g(y)\, dy.$$

In the integral in the right member, the integrand is always at least as large as $\epsilon^2 g(y)$ over the indicated range of integration, so that

$$\sigma^2 \geq \epsilon^2 \int_{|y-\mu|\geq\epsilon} g(y)\, dy.$$

But the integral of the probability density function of a random variable over a range of values is just the probability that the random variable will assume a value in that range (page 40). Therefore

$$\int_{|y-\mu|\geq\epsilon} g(y)\, dy = Pr\{|\mathbf{y} - \mu| \geq \epsilon\},$$

and the last inequality gives us

$$\sigma^2 \geq \epsilon^2 Pr\{|\mathbf{y} - \mu| \geq \epsilon\},$$

or

$$Pr\{|\mathbf{y} - \mu| \geq \epsilon\} \leq \sigma^2/\epsilon^2.$$

EXAMPLE 1. In the example on page 101 you have a large lot of items and wish, by random sampling, to estimate the fraction which are defective. We can use Chebyshev's inequality to find a number N with the property that if you take a sample of size N or larger, the probability will be at least, say, 0.95 that the average number of defectives in your sample will differ from the true proportion in the lot by less than, say, 0.1. If we set up the population as we did earlier (pp. 102 ff.), the random variable $\mathbf{x}$, "number of defectives at an elementary event," induces on R a probability space in which the elementary event 1 has probability p, the probability of a defective, and the elementary event 0 has probability $q = 1 - p$. If $\mathbf{x}_i$ is the ith sample random variable of a sample of size n from this population, then $\mathbf{x}_i$ may be described as "the number of defectives in the ith sample." The sum

$$\mathbf{S} = \sum_{i=1}^{n} \mathbf{x}_i$$

is the total number of defectives in the sample, and the sample mean

$$\bar{\mathbf{x}} = \frac{1}{n} \sum_{i=1}^{n} \mathbf{x}_i$$

is the average number of defectives in the sample. To use the terminology of Bernoullian trials, $\mathbf{x}_i$ is the number of successes (defectives) in the ith trial, $\mathbf{S}$ is the total number of successes, and $\bar{\mathbf{x}}$ is the average number of successes, in n independent trials of an event with probability p. In this problem we are concerned with the probability that the average number of defectives will differ from p by less than 0.1:

$$Pr\{|\bar{\mathbf{x}} - p| < 0.1\} = 1 - Pr\{|\bar{\mathbf{x}} - p| \geq 0.1\}.$$

Since $\bar{\mathbf{x}} = \mathbf{S}/n$, the inequality

$$|\bar{\mathbf{x}} - p| < 0.1$$

is equivalent to (multiply both sides by n)

$$|\mathbf{S} - np| < 0.1n,$$

so that we have to consider

$$Pr\{|\mathbf{S} - np| < 0.1n\} = 1 - Pr\{|\mathbf{S} - np| \geq 0.1n\}.$$

We saw earlier (cf. pages 108 ff.) that the random variable $\mathbf{S}$ has a binomial distribution with parameters n and p; so that

$$Pr\{|\mathbf{S} - np| < 0.1n\} = \sum_{|S-np|<0.1n} \binom{n}{S} p^S q^{n-S},$$

where the summation is extended over the values S of $\mathbf{S}$ for which $|S - np| < 0.1n$ (page 112). You can see the difficulty involved in trying to determine a positive integer n so that no matter what p is we shall have

$$\sum_{|S-np|<0.1n} \binom{n}{S} p^S q^{n-S} \geq 0.95.$$

Chebyshev's inequality permits us to do exactly this. Applying Chebyshev's inequality to the random variable $\mathbf{S}$, we have

$$Pr\{|\mathbf{S} - E(\mathbf{S})| \geq 0.1n\} \leq V(\mathbf{S})/(0.1n)^2.$$

We found (page 108) that $E(\mathbf{S}) = np$ and $V(\mathbf{S}) = npq$, so that

$$Pr\{|\mathbf{S} - np| \geq 0.1n\} \leq npq/(0.1n)^2.$$

The right-hand member depends on the unknown p, but an upper bound independent of p can easily be determined, for the largest value of pq for $0 \leq p \leq 1$ is achieved for $p = 1/2$. This can be seen as follows. We have $q = 1 - p$, and $0 < p < 1$; we have $pq = p(1 - p) = p - p^2 = 1/4 - (1/2 - p)^2 \leq 1/4$, since $(1/2 - p)^2 \geq 0$. Therefore

$$\frac{npq}{(0.1n)^2} \leq \frac{1/4}{(0.1)^2 n} = \frac{25}{n}.$$

We find then that

$$Pr\{|\mathbf{S} - np| \geq 0.1n\} \leq \frac{25}{n}.$$

We wish to determine n so that

$$Pr\{|\mathbf{S} - np| < 0.1n\} \geq 0.95,$$

or so that

$$Pr\{|\mathbf{S} - np| \geq 0.1n\} \leq 0.05.$$

This will be achieved if

$$\frac{25}{n} \leq 0.05,$$

or if

$$n \geq \frac{25}{0.05} = 500.$$

Thus if we make at least 500 trials, or take a sample of size at least 500, we shall have a probability at least 0.95 that the average number of successes (defectives) will differ from the (unknown) true proportion by less than 0.1. We shall see later that we can use our knowledge of the distribution of $\mathbf{S}$ to show that many fewer trials, or a much smaller sample size, would also suffice. Chebyshev's inequality has the advantage, however, that it does not depend at all on the distribution of the random variable involved (except that it requires the random variable to have an expectation and a variance).

45. The Law of Large Numbers. Suppose $\mathbf{y}_1, \mathbf{y}_2, \cdots$ is an arbitrary sequence of random variables, with expectations $E(\mathbf{y}_1), E(\mathbf{y}_2), \cdots$. Suppose further that the random variable $\sum_{i=1}^n \mathbf{y}_i$ has a variance for each positive integer n.

▶ ***Theorem B.*** *If* $V\left(\frac{1}{n}\sum_{i=1}^n \mathbf{y}_i\right) \to 0$ *as* $n \to \infty$, *and if* ϵ *is a positive number, then*

$$Pr\left\{\left|\frac{1}{n}\sum_{i=1}^n [\mathbf{y}_i - E(\mathbf{y}_i)]\right| \geq \epsilon\right\} \to 0 \text{ as } n \to \infty,$$

or equivalently,

$$Pr\left\{\left|\frac{1}{n}\sum_{i=1}^{n}[\mathbf{y}_i - E(\mathbf{y}_i)]\right| < \epsilon\right\} \to 1 \text{ as } n \to \infty.$$

In view of the definition of limit, Theorem B could be restated as follows: *if* $V\left(\frac{1}{n}\sum_{i=1}^{n}\mathbf{y}_i\right) \to 0$ *as* $n \to \infty$, *and if* ϵ, η *are any two positive numbers, then there is a positive integer* N *(depending on* ϵ *and* η*) such that*

$$Pr\left\{\left|\frac{1}{n}\sum_{i=1}^{n}[\mathbf{y}_i - E(\mathbf{y}_i)]\right| \geq \epsilon\right\} \leq \eta \text{ if } n \geq N,$$

or

$$Pr\left\{\left|\frac{1}{n}\sum_{i=1}^{n}[\mathbf{y}_i - E(\mathbf{y}_i)]\right| < \epsilon\right\} \geq 1 - \eta \text{ if } n \geq N.$$

Proof. Let $\mathbf{y}$ denote the random variable $\frac{1}{n}\sum_{i=1}^{n}[\mathbf{y}_i - E(\mathbf{y}_i)]$. Then $E(\mathbf{y}) = \frac{1}{n}\sum_{i=1}^{n}E[\mathbf{y}_i - E(\mathbf{y}_i)] = 0$. Chebyshev's inequality applied to this random variable states that $Pr\{|\mathbf{y}| \geq \epsilon\} \leq V(\mathbf{y})/\epsilon^2$; but since $V(\mathbf{y}) = V\left(\frac{1}{n}\sum_{i=1}^{n}[\mathbf{y}_i - E(\mathbf{y}_i)]\right) = V\left(\frac{1}{n}\sum_{i=1}^{n}\mathbf{y}_i\right)$ (Theorem J, p. 90), the hypothesis of the theorem is that $V(\mathbf{y}) \to 0$ as $n \to \infty$. Therefore whatever positive number ϵ may be,

$$Pr\{|\mathbf{y}| \geq \epsilon\} \to 0 \text{ as } n \to \infty,$$

or

$$Pr\{|\mathbf{y}| < \epsilon\} \to 1 \text{ as } n \to \infty.$$

This is precisely the conclusion of Theorem B.

▶ ***Definition.*** *A sequence* $\mathbf{z}_n$ *of random variables is said to* converge in probability, *or to* converge stochastically, *to a constant* a, *if for every positive number* ϵ, $Pr\{|\mathbf{z}_n - a| \geq \epsilon\} \to 0$ *as* $n \to \infty$ *(or equivalently,* $Pr\{|\mathbf{z}_n - a| < \epsilon\} \to 1$ *as* $n \to \infty$*).* For this kind of convergence we shall use the symbol $\xrightarrow{P}$: $\mathbf{z}_n \xrightarrow{P} a$. In view of this definition, the conclusion of Theorem B can be restated as follows: *the sequence*

$$\left\{\frac{1}{n}\sum_{i=1}^{n}[\mathbf{y}_i - E(\mathbf{y}_i)]\right\} \xrightarrow{P} 0 \text{ as } n \to \infty.$$

The conclusion of this theorem is known as the law of large numbers, or the weak law of large numbers, to distinguish it from a stronger statement of a similar kind, known as the strong law of large numbers ([5], pages 189, 243; [11], pages 143, 204; [6], Section 6.12); this latter is beyond the scope of this text.

Corollary C below gives the application of Theorem B to the sampling situation. Let $\mathbf{x}$ be a random variable with mean $\mu = E(\mathbf{x})$ and variance $V(\mathbf{x}) = \sigma^2$, and let $\mathbf{x}_1, \mathbf{x}_2, \cdots, \mathbf{x}_n$ be the sample random variables of a sample of size n from the population induced by $\mathbf{x}$. We shall let the sample random variables play the roles of the random variables $\mathbf{y}_1, \mathbf{y}_2, \cdots$ in Theorem B. The random variable $(1/n)\sum_{i=1}^{n}\mathbf{y}_i$ then becomes $(1/n)\sum_{i=1}^{n}\mathbf{x}_i$, which is just the sample mean $\bar{\mathbf{x}}$. Since, as we have seen, $V(\bar{\mathbf{x}}) = \sigma^2/n$ (page 127), the hypothesis $V[(1/n)\sum_{i=1}^{n}\mathbf{y}_i] \to 0$ as $n \to \infty$ is indeed satisfied in this special case. Also, $E(\mathbf{x}_i) = \mu$ for each i, so that

$$(1/n)\sum_{i=1}^{n}[\mathbf{y}_i - E(\mathbf{y}_i)]$$

becomes

$$(1/n)\sum_{i=1}^{n}(\mathbf{x}_i - \mu) \text{ or } (1/n)\sum_{i=1}^{n}\mathbf{x}_i - (1/n)\sum_{i=1}^{n}\mu, \text{ or } \bar{\mathbf{x}} - \mu.$$

On making these substitutions in Theorem B we have Corollary C:

▶ ***Corollary C.*** *If $\bar{\mathbf{x}}$ is the sample mean of a random sample of size n from the population induced by a random variable $\mathbf{x}$ with mean μ and standard deviation σ, and if $\epsilon > 0$, then*

$$Pr\{|\bar{\mathbf{x}} - \mu| \geq \epsilon\} \to 0 \text{ as } n \to \infty,$$

or

$$Pr\{|\bar{\mathbf{x}} - \mu| < \epsilon\} \to 1 \text{ as } n \to \infty,$$

or again,

$$\bar{\mathbf{x}} \xrightarrow{P} \mu \text{ as } n \to \infty.$$

Although the notation used does not show it, we must bear in mind that the random variable $\bar{\mathbf{x}}$ depends on n.

Let us now apply Corollary C to the special (binomial) situation where $\mathbf{x}$ has the value 1 with probability p and the value 0 with probability $q = 1 - p$. The sample mean $\bar{\mathbf{x}}$ may be thought of as the average number of successes in n independent trials with probability p:

$$\bar{\mathbf{x}} = \frac{\mathbf{S}_n}{n},$$

where $\mathbf{S}_n$ is the total number of successes in n trials.

▶ ***Corollary D.*** (Bernoulli's Theorem). *If* $\mathbf{S}_n$ *represents the number of successes in n independent trials of an event with probability p, and if* $\epsilon > 0$, *then*

$$Pr\left\{\left|\frac{\mathbf{S}_n}{n} - p\right| \geq \epsilon\right\} \to 0 \text{ as } n \to \infty,$$

or

$$Pr\left\{\left|\frac{\mathbf{S}_n}{n} - p\right| < \epsilon\right\} \to 1 \text{ as } n \to \infty,$$

or again,

$$\mathbf{S}_n/n \xrightarrow{P} p \text{ as } n \to \infty.$$

The conclusion of Corollary C may be stated somewhat loosely as follows: If the sample size is large, the probability is high that the sample mean $\bar{\mathbf{x}}$ will be near the population mean μ. Or again, by choosing a sufficiently large sample size, we can make the probability as near 1 as we wish that the sample mean we shall obtain will be as near as we wish to the population mean. In the example above (pages 129, 130), we found that $Pr\{|(\mathbf{S}_n/n) - p| < 0.1\} \geq 0.95$ if $n \geq 500$. Clearly, the same technique would provide a positive integer N in place of 500 for whatever ϵ we might choose instead of 0.1, and η instead of 0.05 ($1 - \eta$ instead of 0.95).

▶ ***Theorem E.*** (Khintchine's Theorem). *If* $\bar{\mathbf{x}}$ *is the sample mean of a random sample of size n from the population induced by a random variable* $\mathbf{x}$ *with mean* μ, *and if* $\epsilon > 0$, *then*

$$Pr\{|\bar{\mathbf{x}} - \mu| \geq \epsilon\} \to 0 \text{ as } n \to \infty\text{; i.e.,}$$

$$\bar{\mathbf{x}} \xrightarrow{P} \mu \text{ as } n \to \infty.$$

A proof of this theorem is given in [6], page 219. We note that it is a stronger form of Corollary C; the conclusion is the same, but one hypothesis is omitted: the variance of $\mathbf{x}$ is not assumed to exist.

PROBLEMS

√**1.** On the average, 2/3 of the seeds of a certain variety germinate.

(a) If 100 seeds are planted, what is the expected number that will germinate, and what is the variance of the number that will germinate?

(b) Use Chebyshev's inequality to obtain an upper bound on the probability that the number germinating will differ from the expected number by more than 10.

(c) Interpret the experiment of choosing 100 seeds at random and observing each to see whether or not it germinates, in terms of taking a random sample of size 100 from a population. What is the distribution of the random variable which induces the population? Describe the population.

2. You are given a large box full of numbered slips. You are permitted to draw one slip at a time from the box, to note the number, then to replace it and mix the slips before drawing another. You are not told the mean of the numbers nor their distribution, but are told that their variance is 10.

(a) If you draw 100 numbers in this way, you are taking a random sample of size 100 from the population induced by what random variable? Describe the population.

(b) What is the variance of the mean of a sample of size 100?

(c) Use Chebyshev's inequality to obtain an upper bound on the probability that the mean of a sample of size 100 will differ from the population mean by more than 1.

(d) Find a number ϵ such that the probability that the sample mean will differ from the population mean by at least ϵ is certainly not greater than 0.05, if the sample size is 100.

3. The will of an eccentric uncle requires you to ascertain the average distance between the eyes of cats in New Guinea. After 25 measurements, you are willing to accept the sample standard deviation, 2 cm., in lieu of the unknown population standard deviation.

(a) Use Chebyshev's inequality to obtain a lower bound on the *a priori* probability that the sample mean will differ from the population mean by less than 1 cm., given that the population standard deviation is 2 cm.

(b) How many measurements would suffice to give a probability at least 0.95 that the sample mean will differ from the population mean by less than 0.5 cm., if the population standard deviation is 2 cm.?

4. Ten shots are fired from a gun which has probability 1/4 of hitting the target with any one shot.

(a) Write an exact expression for the probability that exactly 9 will hit.

(b) Write an exact expression for the probability that at least 5 will hit.

(c) If n shots are to be fired, use Chebyshev's inequality to find an upper bound for the number n of shots required to have a probability at least 1/2 that the average number of hits will differ from 1/4 by less than 1/4.

5. Fifty practice bomb drops are made, with 30 hits.

(a) Write an exact expression for the probability that the average number of hits will differ from the true probability p of a hit by not more than ϵ if 50 drops are made.

(b) If the probability of a hit is about 0.6 and if 50 drops are made, use Chebyshev's inequality to determine a number ϵ such that the probability is at least 0.9 that the ratio, number of hits divided by number of drops, will differ from the true probability of a hit by not more than ϵ.

6. You throw a single die, winning two dollars if an odd number of spots turns up, six dollars if the six spot turns up, otherwise nothing.

(a) What is a fair price for the privilege of playing the game; i.e., what is the expectation of your winnings, $\mathbf{x}$ dollars?

(b) What is the variance of $\mathbf{x}$?

(c) Suppose you play the game 10 times. Let $\bar{\mathbf{x}}$ denote your average winnings, i.e., one-tenth of the total amount won (before subtracting what you pay to play). Use Chebyshev's inequality to obtain an upper bound on the probability that your average winnings will differ from $E(\bar{\mathbf{x}})$ by at least two dollars.

7. Let $1/\sigma_{\bar{x}}$ be considered as a measure of the *precision* of the sample mean $\bar{\mathbf{x}}$ as an estimator of the population mean. Sketch the graph of precision vs. sample size, if the population standard deviation is 1.

8. Prove that if $\mathbf{y}_n$ is a sequence of random variables, and if $F_n(y)$ is the distribution function of $\mathbf{y}_n$, then the following two statements are equivalent (in any particular situation, both are true, or both are false):

(1) For each $\epsilon > 0$,

$$Pr\{|\mathbf{y}_n - \mu| > \epsilon\} \to 0 \text{ as } n \to \infty.$$

(2) $F_n(y) \to 0$ as $n \to \infty$ if $y < \mu$,
$F_n(y) \to 1$ as $n \to \infty$ if $y > \mu$.

CHAPTER

8

Estimation of Parameters

46. Introduction. If independent trials are made of an event with unknown probability p in each, it seems natural to use the average number of successes as an estimate of p. More generally, the sample mean of a random sample from a population seems the natural function of the sample values to use as an estimate of the population mean, if that is unknown. We emphasize that the sample mean $\bar{x}$ is a function of the sample values, or the sample point $(x_1, x_2, \cdots, x_n)$:

$$\bar{x} = \frac{1}{n} \sum_{i=1}^{n} x_i.$$

This function of the sample point furnishes an *estimate* of the population mean. By contrast, before the sample is actually taken, the sample values are thought of as random variables, the sample random variables, and the sample mean is also a random variable:

$$\bar{\mathbf{x}} = \frac{1}{n} \sum_{i=1}^{n} \mathbf{x}_i;$$

$\bar{\mathbf{x}}$ is an *estimator* of the population mean. In general, a function of the sample random variables is called a *statistic.*

We can approach the sample mean, as well as other statistics, from another point of view. Suppose we have at hand the sample values, $x_1, x_2, \cdots, x_n$ of a random sample of size n from the population of the random variable $\mathbf{x}$. Let us ask ourselves, What information about $\mathbf{x}$ is furnished by the sample values? Or perhaps better, What is the best estimate of the distribution of $\mathbf{x}$ that we can make on the basis of the sample values alone? This is not really a mathematically meaningful question, since "best estimate" remains undefined. Yet you will perhaps feel impelled toward consideration of a random variable $\tilde{\mathbf{x}}$ which takes each of the sample values with probability $1/n$ as the most reasonable approximation to the population random variable which you can make on the basis of the sample values alone. This random variable $\tilde{\mathbf{x}}$ might be called an *empiric* random variable corresponding to the particular set of sample values observed. Its distribution function, $\tilde{F}(x) = Pr\{\tilde{\mathbf{x}} < x\}$, has a jump of magnitude $1/n$ at each sample value. This step-function is called the *empiric distribution function.* Its graph is sketched below for a possible situation in which $n = 4$. We emphasize that a different set of sample values would lead to a different empiric random variable $\tilde{\mathbf{x}}$ and a different empiric distribution function $\tilde{F}(x)$, though the notations $\tilde{\mathbf{x}}$, $\tilde{F}(x)$ do not indicate explicitly the dependence on the sample values.

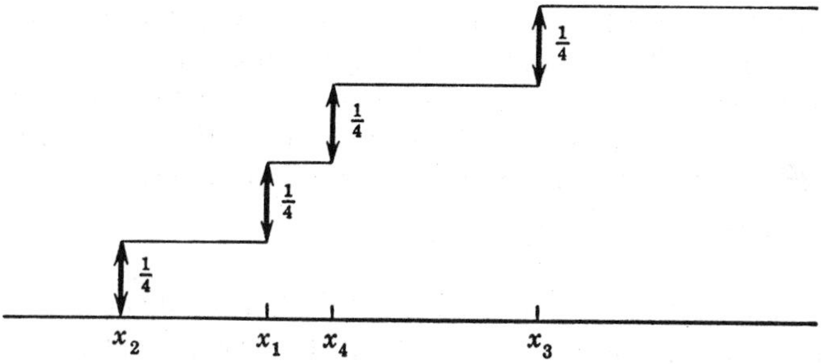

Figure 24

One may think of the empiric distribution as that estimate of the population distribution in which the influence of the sample values actually observed is maximized at the expense of other possible values of the population random variable (and which is symmetric as a function of the sample values; that is, interchanging sample values does not affect the empiric distribution). It is in this sense that the empiric distribution is the "best" estimate of the population distribution based on the sample values as the sole source of available information.

Now let us compute the expectation of the empiric random variable, $E(\tilde{\mathbf{x}})$. We have

$$E(\tilde{\mathbf{x}}) = \sum_{i=1}^{n} x_i(1/n) = \frac{1}{n}\sum_{i=1}^{n} x_i,$$

which is just the sample mean, $\bar{x}$. Its variance,

$$V(\tilde{\mathbf{x}}) = \frac{1}{n}\sum_{i=1}^{n} (x_i - \bar{x})^2 = \frac{1}{n}\sum_{i=1}^{n} x_i^2 - \bar{x}^2$$

(p. 90, Theorem L), is called the *sample variance.* When the sample values x_i are replaced by the sample random variables $\mathbf{x}_i$, the sample variance becomes a random variable,

$$\blacktriangleright \quad \mathbf{s}^2 = \frac{1}{n}\sum_{i=1}^{n}(\mathbf{x}_i - \bar{\mathbf{x}})^2 = \frac{1}{n}\sum_{i=1}^{n}\mathbf{x}_i^2 - \bar{\mathbf{x}}^2.$$

If we adopt the point of view that the empiric distribution is an acceptable estimate of the population distribution, then the sample mean, $E(\hat{\mathbf{x}}) = \bar{x}$, and the sample variance, $V(\hat{\mathbf{x}}) = s^2$, appear as reasonable estimates of the population mean and variance respectively. The random variables $\bar{\mathbf{x}}$ and $\mathbf{s}^2$ may be used as *estimators* of the population mean μ and population variance σ^2 respectively.

In the general sampling situation, suppose you are sampling from a population induced by a random variable whose distribution is completely unknown, or concerning which you have only partial information, not sufficient to specify it completely. Let θ represent an unknown parameter of the distribution. This might be the population mean, the population standard deviation, or some other number which, if known, would either specify the distribution completely, or provide further information about it. An *estimate*, $\hat{\theta}$, of θ, is a function of the sample values, or of the sample point $(x_1, x_2, \cdots, x_n)$,

$$\hat{\theta} = \hat{\theta}(x_1, x_2, \cdots, x_n),$$

which you are willing to use in guessing the unknown value of θ. The corresponding *estimator* of θ is the same function, evaluated at the sample random variables:

$$\hat{\boldsymbol{\theta}} = \hat{\theta}(\mathbf{x}_1, \mathbf{x}_2, \cdots, \mathbf{x}_n).$$

The estimator is itself a random variable.

47. Unbiased Estimators.

▶ ***Definition.*** *The estimator* $\hat{\boldsymbol{\theta}}$ *is* unbiased *if* $E(\hat{\boldsymbol{\theta}}) = \theta$.

For example, the sample mean is an unbiased estimator of the population mean, since $E(\bar{\mathbf{x}}) = \mu$ (page 126). *The sample variance is not an unbiased estimator of the population variance.*

We have

$$E(\mathbf{s}^2) = E\left[\left(\frac{1}{n}\sum_{i=1}^{n}\mathbf{x}_i^2\right) - \bar{\mathbf{x}}^2\right]$$

$$= \frac{1}{n}\sum_{i=1}^{n}E(\mathbf{x}_i^2) - E(\bar{\mathbf{x}}^2). \qquad \text{(Corollary G, page 89)}$$

Now for any random variable $\mathbf{y}$, we have

$$E(\mathbf{y}^2) = V(\mathbf{y}) + [E(\mathbf{y})]^2. \qquad \text{(page 90)}$$

In particular, for each i,

$$E(\mathbf{x}_i^2) = V(\mathbf{x}_i) + [E(\mathbf{x}_i)]^2 = V(\mathbf{x}) + [E(\mathbf{x})]^2 = \sigma^2 + \mu^2,$$

since each sample random variable has the same distribution as the random variable $\mathbf{x}$ which induced the population. Also

$$E(\bar{\mathbf{x}}^2) = V(\bar{\mathbf{x}}) + [E(\bar{\mathbf{x}})]^2 = \frac{\sigma^2}{n} + \mu^2. \qquad \text{(page 127)}$$

Therefore

$$E(\mathbf{s}^2) = \frac{1}{n}\sum_{i=1}^{n} (\sigma^2 + \mu^2) - \left(\frac{\sigma^2}{n} + \mu^2\right)$$

$$= \sigma^2 + \mu^2 - \frac{\sigma^2}{n} - \mu^2 = \frac{n-1}{n}\sigma^2,$$

so that $E(\mathbf{s}^2) \neq \sigma^2$, and the sample variance is not an unbiased estimator of the population variance σ^2. On the other hand,

$$E\left(\frac{n}{n-1}\mathbf{s}^2\right) = \frac{n}{n-1}E(\mathbf{s}^2) = \left(\frac{n}{n-1}\right)\left(\frac{n-1}{n}\right)\sigma^2 = \sigma^2,$$

so that the statistic

$$\frac{n}{n-1}\mathbf{s}^2 = \frac{1}{n-1}\sum_{i=1}^{n} [\mathbf{x}_i - \bar{\mathbf{x}}]^2$$

is an unbiased estimator of the population variance.

It would be natural to expect some divergence of opinion as to the importance of such a concept as "unbiasedness." We list here some of the desirable properties an estimator possesses by virtue of being unbiased.

1. To state that an estimator is unbiased is to state that there is a measure of central tendency, the mean, of the distribution of the estimator, which is equal to the population parameter. This is simply the definition of unbiasedness. An equally appealing property, however, from this point of view, might, for example, be that the *median* (page 348) of the estimator be equal to the population parameter.

2. For many unbiased estimators one can conclude, by applying the law of large numbers, that when the sample size is large the estimator is likely to be near the population parameter. However, this is the property of consistency, discussed below; and the argument here is not primarily in favor of unbiasedness, but in favor of consistency. For example, the unbiased estimator, $\frac{n}{n-1}\mathbf{s}^2$, of the population variance has this property; but so also does the sample variance $\mathbf{s}^2$ itself.

3. An important advantage from the point of view of the development of the theory of statistical inference is that in many respects unbiased estimators are simpler to deal with. The linear properties of the expectation are particularly convenient in dealing with unbiased estimators. If, for example θ is a parameter having $\hat{\boldsymbol{\theta}}_1$ and $\hat{\boldsymbol{\theta}}_2$ as unbiased estimators in two

different experiments, every weighted mean $\alpha\hat{\boldsymbol{\theta}}_1 + \beta\hat{\boldsymbol{\theta}}_2$ with $\alpha + \beta = 1$ is also an unbiased estimator of θ. We note, however, that non-linear transformations do not in general preserve unbiasedness. For example, if $\hat{\boldsymbol{\theta}}$ is an unbiased estimator of θ, then $\hat{\boldsymbol{\theta}}^2$ is not an unbiased estimator of θ^2.

One point of view is that the class of all possible estimators of a particular parameter is unmanageably large. A way of approaching the problem is to restrict attention to an important subclass, such as the class of unbiased estimators. For detailed discussion and references see [8].

48. Consistent Estimators. An estimator is *consistent* if for a large sample there is a high probability that the estimator will be near the parameter it is intended to estimate. More precisely,

▶ ***Definition.*** $\hat{\boldsymbol{\theta}} = \hat{\theta}(\mathbf{x}_1, \mathbf{x}_2, \cdots, \mathbf{x}_n)$ *is a* consistent estimator of θ *if for each positive number* ϵ,

$$Pr\{|\hat{\boldsymbol{\theta}} - \theta| \geq \epsilon\} \to 0 \text{ as } n \to \infty,$$

or equivalently,

$$Pr\{|\hat{\boldsymbol{\theta}} - \theta| < \epsilon\} \to 1 \text{ as } n \to \infty$$

or again,

$$\hat{\boldsymbol{\theta}} \xrightarrow{P} \theta \text{ as } n \to \infty.$$

Corollary C, page 132, the application of the law of large numbers to the sampling situation, thus states simply that *the sample mean is a consistent estimator of the population mean.* It is also possible to use the law of large numbers to prove that the *sample variance is a consistent estimator of the population variance* (see starred section below).

It is of interest also to observe that for each fixed real number x, the empiric distribution function $\tilde{F}(x)$ is a consistent estimator of the value $F(x)$ of the population distribution function at x. This too follows from the law of large numbers, indeed, from Bernoulli's Theorem. To see this, let us regard the observation of successive sample random variables as independent trials of an event "the sample value will be less than x." The event will occur on the first trial if $\mathbf{x}_1 < x$, on the second trial if $\mathbf{x}_2 < x$, etc. The probability of success at the ith trial is $Pr\{\mathbf{x}_i < x\} = Pr\{\mathbf{x} < x\} = F(x)$, $i = 1, 2, \cdots, n$. The number, $\mathbf{S}_n$, of successes in n trials will be just the number of sample random variables which will be found to be less than x, and the average number, $\mathbf{S}_n/n$, of successes is just the fraction of the sample random variables which will be observed to be less than x: $\mathbf{S}_n/n = \tilde{F}(x)$. By Bernoulli's Theorem $\tilde{F}(x) = \mathbf{S}_n/n \xrightarrow{P} F(x)$; in other words, $\tilde{F}(x)$ is a consistent estimator of $F(x)$ for each real number x.

★ **49. Consistency of Sample Moments.** In this section we shall show that sample moments, and polynomial functions of the sample moments, are consistent estimators of the corresponding population parameters, in particular, that the sample variance is a consistent estimator of the population variance.

▶ ***Theorem A.*** $\frac{1}{n}\sum_{i=1}^{n} \mathbf{x}_i^k$ *is a consistent estimator of* $E(\mathbf{x}^k)$, *if* $E(\mathbf{x}^k)$ *exists.*

Proof. Set $\mathbf{y} = \mathbf{x}^k$, and $\mathbf{y}_i = \mathbf{x}_i^k$, $i = 1, 2, \cdots, n$. The random variables $\mathbf{y}_1, \mathbf{y}_2, \cdots, \mathbf{y}_n$ are independent, and each has the same distribution as $\mathbf{y}$; that is, they are sample random variables of a random sample from the population of values of $\mathbf{y}$. We have $E(\mathbf{y}) = E(\mathbf{x}^k)$, and from Theorem E (Khintchine's Theorem), page 133, we conclude that for positive ϵ, $Pr\left\{\left|\frac{1}{n}\sum_{i=1}^{n} \mathbf{y}_i - E(\mathbf{y})\right| \geq \epsilon\right\} \to 0$ as $n \to \infty$. That is, $(1/n)\sum_{i=1}^{n} \mathbf{y}_i = (1/n)\sum_{i=1}^{n} \mathbf{x}_i^k$ is a consistent estimator of $E(\mathbf{x}^k)$.

In order to apply Theorem A to the problem of the consistency of other sample moments, we require Theorem B below. To begin, we recall the definition of continuity of a function of several arguments.

▶ ***Definition.*** *A function g of r arguments is* continuous *at the point $(a_1, \cdots, a_r)$ of r-dimensional space R_r if to each $\epsilon > 0$ corresponds $\delta > 0$ such that $|g(w_1, \cdots, w_r) - g(a_1, \cdots, a_r)| < \epsilon$ for every point $(w_1, \cdots, w_r)$ such that $|w_1 - a_1| < \delta$, $|w_2 - a_2| < \delta, \cdots, |w_r - a_r| < \delta$.*

▶ ***Theorem B.*** *If g is continuous at $(a_1, \cdots, a_r)$, if $\{\mathbf{w}_{1,n}\}, \cdots, \{\mathbf{w}_{r,n}\}$ are r sequences of random variables, if $\mathbf{w}_{1,n} \xrightarrow{P} a_1$ as $n \to \infty, \cdots, \mathbf{w}_{r,n} \xrightarrow{P} a_r$ as $n \to \infty$, then $g(\mathbf{w}_{1,n}, \cdots, \mathbf{w}_{rn}) \xrightarrow{P} g(a_1, \cdots, a_r)$ as $n \to \infty$.*

Proof. Let ϵ denote an arbitrary positive number. We have to show that for every positive number η, there is a positive integer N, possibly depending on ϵ and on η, such that if $n > N$ then $Pr\{|g(\mathbf{w}_{1,n}, \cdots, \mathbf{w}_{r,n}) - g(a_1, \cdots, a_r)| \geq \epsilon\} \leq \eta$. According to the definition above, there is a positive number δ, possibly depending on ϵ, such that $|g(w_1, \cdots, w_r) - g(a_1, \cdots, a_r)| < \epsilon$ for every set of numbers $(w_1, \cdots, w_r)$ satisfying $|w_1 - a_1| < \delta, \cdots, |w_r - a_r| < \delta$. Also, by the definition of convergence in probability (page 131), there is a positive integer N_1 (possibly depending on δ and on η) such that $Pr\{|\mathbf{w}_{1,n} - a_1| \geq \delta\} < \eta/r$ if $n > N_1$; there is a positive integer N_2 such that $Pr\{|\mathbf{w}_{2,n} - a_2| \geq \delta\} < \eta/r$ if $n > N_2$; $\cdots$; and there is a positive integer N_r such that $Pr\{|\mathbf{w}_{r,n} - a_r|$

$\geq \delta\} < \eta/r$ if $n > N_r$. Let N denote a positive integer larger than the greatest of the positive integers $N_1, \cdots, N_r$. Let $A_{i,n}$ denote the event $\{|\mathbf{w}_{i,n} - a_i| < \delta\}$, $i = 1, 2, \cdots, r$. Then if $n > N$, we shall have $P(\bar{A}_{i,n}) < \eta/r, i = 1, 2, \cdots, r$. Let B_n denote the event $\{|\mathbf{w}_{1,n} - a_1| < \delta, |\mathbf{w}_{2,n} - a_2| < \delta, \cdots, |\mathbf{w}_{r,n} - a_r| < \delta\} = A_{1,n} \cap A_{2,n} \cap \cdots \cap A_{r,n}$. Then $\bar{B}_n = \bigcup_{i=1}^{r} \bar{A}_{i,n}$, and by Boole's inequality, $P(\bar{B}_n) \leq \sum_{i=1}^{r} P(\bar{A}_{i,n}) < \sum_{i=1}^{r} \eta/r = \eta$, if $n > N$. The positive number δ was chosen so that at every elementary event in B_n we should have

$$|g(\mathbf{w}_{1,n}, \cdots, \mathbf{w}_{r,n}) - g(a_1, \cdots, a_r)| < \epsilon.$$

That is,

$$B_n \subset \{|g(\mathbf{w}_{1,n}, \cdots, \mathbf{w}_{r,n}) - g(a_1, \cdots, a_r)| < \epsilon\},$$

hence

$$\bar{B}_n \supset \{|g(\mathbf{w}_{1,n}, \cdots, \mathbf{w}_{r,n}) - g(a_1, \cdots, a_r)| \geq \epsilon\},$$

so that also

$$Pr\{|g(\mathbf{w}_{1,n}, \cdots, \mathbf{w}_{r,n}) - g(a_1, \cdots, a_r)| \geq \epsilon\} \leq P(\bar{B}_n) < \eta$$

if $n > N$. Having shown that for every pair ϵ, η of positive numbers there is a positive integer N such that the above inequality is satisfied when $n > N$, we have completed the proof of Theorem B.

▶ **Corollary C.** *If* $\mathbf{z}_n$ *and* $\mathbf{w}_n$ *are statistics which are consistent estimators of parameters a and b respectively, then* (i) $\mathbf{z}_n + \mathbf{w}_n$ *is a consistent estimator of* $a + b$, *and* (ii) $\mathbf{z}_n\mathbf{w}_n$ *is a consistent estimator of* ab.

Proof. In Theorem B, set $r = 2$, $\mathbf{w}_{1,n} = \mathbf{z}_n$, $\mathbf{w}_{2,n} = \mathbf{w}_n$ and $g(z,w) = z + w$. Being given $\mathbf{z}_n \xrightarrow{P} a$ and $\mathbf{w}_n \xrightarrow{P} b$, we conclude that $\mathbf{z}_n + \mathbf{w}_n = g(\mathbf{z}_n,\mathbf{w}_n) \xrightarrow{P} g(a,b) = a + b$. In other words, $\mathbf{z}_n + \mathbf{w}_n$ is a consistent estimator of $a + b$. The verification of the second conclusion is similar.

▶ **Corollary D.** *Any finite sum or finite product of consistent estimators is a consistent estimator of the sum or product of the corresponding parameters.*

Proof. The proof proceeds from Corollary C by mathematical induction.

▶ **Corollary E.** *Any polynomial in the sample moments is a consistent estimator of the same polynomial in the population moments provided the population moments exist.*

Proof. This follows from Theorem A and Corollary D, since a polynomial is a finite sum of finite products.

▶ **Corollary F.** *The average,* $\frac{1}{n}\sum_{i=1}^{n}(\mathbf{x}_i - \bar{\mathbf{x}})^k$, *is a consistent estimator of* $E(\mathbf{x} - \mu)^k$, *provided* $E(\mathbf{x}^k)$ *exists.*

Proof. It can be shown that if $E(\mathbf{x}^k)$ exists, then also $E(\mathbf{x}^j)$ exists for every positive integer j less than k. The statistic $\frac{1}{n}\sum_{i=1}^{n}(\mathbf{x}_i - \bar{\mathbf{x}})^k$ (called the kth *central* sample moment) may be written as follows:

$$\frac{1}{n}\sum_{i=1}^{n}(\mathbf{x}_i - \bar{\mathbf{x}})^k = \frac{1}{n}\sum_{i=1}^{n}\sum_{j=1}^{k}\binom{k}{j}\mathbf{x}_i^j\bar{\mathbf{x}}^{k-j}$$
$$= \sum_{j=1}^{k}\binom{k}{j}\bar{\mathbf{x}}^{k-j}\left[\frac{1}{n}\sum_{i=1}^{n}\mathbf{x}_i^j\right]$$

The application of Corollary E yields

$$\frac{1}{n}\sum_{i=1}^{n}(\mathbf{x}_i - \bar{\mathbf{x}})^k \xrightarrow{P} \sum_{j=1}^{k}\binom{k}{j}\mu^{k-j}E(\mathbf{x}^j) = E\left[\sum_{j=1}^{k}\binom{k}{j}\mathbf{x}^j\mu^{k-j}\right]$$
$$= E[(\mathbf{x} - \mu)^k]$$

50. Maximum Likelihood Estimators. The principle of maximum likelihood provides a general method which, under conditions often satisfied in random sampling, furnishes estimators which are consistent and have other desirable properties ([3], Chapters 32 and 33; [22], Chapter 12). (See Problem 25, page 161 for an instance in which the maximum likelihood estimator is not consistent.) The essential feature of the principle of maximum likelihood as it applies to the problem of estimation is that it requires one to choose as estimate of a parameter that value of the parameter for which the *a priori* probability of obtaining the sample point actually observed, or of obtaining a sample point near it, is as large as possible. That is, having performed the sampling experiment and observed sample values, one "looks back" and computes the probability, from the point of view of one about to perform the experiment, that these sample values will be observed. This probability will in general depend on the parameter, which is then given that value for which this probability is as large as possible.

Suppose first that the population random variable $\mathbf{x}$ has a probability function which depends on some parameter θ: $Pr\{\mathbf{x} = x\} = f(x;\theta)$. We suppose that the form of the function f is known, but not the value of θ. The joint probability function of the sample random variables, evaluated at the sample point $(x_1, x_2, \cdots, x_n)$, is

$$L(\theta) = f(x_1, x_2, \cdots, x_n; \theta) = \prod_{i=1}^{n} f(x_i; \theta). \qquad \text{(page 105)}$$

This function is also known as the *likelihood function* of the sample; we are here particularly interested in it as a function of θ when the sample values $x_1, x_2, \cdots, x_n$ are fixed. The principle of maximum likelihood requires us to choose as an estimate of the unknown parameter that value of θ for which the likelihood function assumes its maximum value.

If the parent distribution will be completely determined only when values of two or more unknown parameters, $\theta_1, \theta_2, \cdots, \theta_k$ are specified, then the likelihood function will be a function of them all:

$$L(\theta_1, \theta_2, \cdots, \theta_k) = f(x_1, \cdots, x_n; \theta_1, \cdots, \theta_k)$$

$$= \prod_{i=1}^{n} f(x_i; \theta_1, \cdots, \theta_k).$$

The maximum likelihood estimators of $\theta_1, \cdots, \theta_k$ will be those numbers which render the likelihood function a maximum. (In special cases, maximum likelihood estimates may not exist: the maximum likelihood may not be attained; and if they exist they may not be unique.)

We observe a maximum likelihood estimator depends on the observed values: it is a statistic.

EXAMPLE 1. You are given a coin, and told that it is biased, with one side 4 times as likely to turn up as the other; you are allowed three tosses, and must then guess whether it is biased in favor of heads or in favor of tails.

Here we may take the probability of heads on a single toss as the parameter θ. The random variable $\mathbf{x}$, number of heads in a single toss, has two values, 0 and 1, with respective probabilities 1/5 and 4/5 if $\theta = 4/5$, and 4/5 and 1/5 if $\theta = 1/5$. Its probability function $f(x;\theta)$ is then given by

$$f(0; 4/5) = 1/5, \quad f(1; 4/5) = 4/5;$$
$$f(0; 1/5) = 4/5, \quad f(1; 1/5) = 1/5.$$

Suppose you throw HTH. The sample values are $x_1 = 1$, $x_2 = 0$, $x_3 = 1$. The likelihood function is

$$L(\theta) = f(x_1, x_2, x_3; \theta) = f(1,0,1; \theta) = f(1; \theta)f(0; \theta)f(1; \theta),$$

or

$$L(4/5) = (4/5)(1/5)(4/5) = 16/125, \qquad (\theta = 4/5)$$

and

$$L(1/5) = (1/5)(4/5)(1/5) = 4/125. \qquad (\theta = 1/5)$$

Of the two admissible values of θ, $\theta = 4/5$ and $\theta = 1/5$, the former yields the larger value, 16/125, of the likelihood function at the sample point (1,0,1) and is thus the maximum likelihood estimate of θ. That is, if the coin is biased in favor of heads ($\theta = 4/5$), the probability of getting HTH is 16/125; if the coin is biased in favor of tails ($\theta = 1/5$), the probability of getting HTH is only 4/125. The maximum likelihood estimate of θ is then

4/5 rather than 1/5, since the parameter value $\theta = 4/5$ yields the larger *a priori* probability of the event actually observed.

51. Maximum Likelihood; Continuous Distribution. Suppose now that the population random variable is continuous and has a probability density function $f(x;\theta)$ which depends on some parameter θ. The joint probability density function of the sample random variables, evaluated at the sample point $(x_1, x_2, \cdots, x_n)$, is given by

$$L(\theta) = f(x_1, x_2, \cdots, x_n; \theta) = \prod_{i=1}^{n} f(x_i; \theta). \qquad \text{(page 107)}$$

For small $dx_1, dx_2, \cdots, dx_n$, $f(x_1, x_2, \cdots, x_n;\theta)\, dx_1\, dx_2 \cdots dx_n$ represents approximately the probability that a sample will be chosen for which the sample point lies within an n-dimensional rectangle at $(x_1, x_2, \cdots, x_n)$ with sides $dx_1, dx_2, \cdots, dx_n$. We may consider, somewhat imprecisely, that the maximum likelihood estimate of θ is that which maximizes this *a priori* probability of obtaining a sample point "near" the one actually observed. The above joint density function is called the likelihood function, and our interest in it here is as a function of θ, the sample values $x_1, x_2, \cdots, x_n$ being fixed. *The maximum likelihood estimate of θ is that value of θ for which $L(\theta)$ assumes its maximum value.*

EXAMPLE 2. Suppose you are given n numbers, and the information that they have been chosen independently and at random from the interval $[0,\theta]$; you know that θ is positive, but otherwise nothing about it. Let $x_1, x_2, \cdots, x_n$ denote the actual numbers you were given. What is the maximum likelihood estimate of θ?

The numbers $x_1, x_2, \cdots, x_n$ are the values of n sample random variables, $\mathbf{x}_1, \mathbf{x}_2, \cdots, \mathbf{x}_n$, a sample of size n from the population induced by a random variable $\mathbf{x}$ having a uniform distribution over the interval $[0,\theta]$. The probability density function of $\mathbf{x}$ is given by

$$f(x; \theta) = \frac{1}{\theta} \text{ if } 0 < x < \theta,$$

$$f(x; \theta) = 0 \text{ if } x > \theta.$$

Each of the random variables $\mathbf{x}_1, \mathbf{x}_2, \cdots, \mathbf{x}_n$ has this same density function, and they are independent, so that their joint density function at the sample point $(x_1, x_2, \cdots, x_n)$ is given by

$$L(\theta) = f(x_1, x_2, \cdots, x_n; \theta) = \prod_{i=1}^{n} f(x_i; \theta);$$

$$L(\theta) = \left(\frac{1}{\theta}\right)^n$$

if no x_i is greater than θ;

$$L(\theta) = 0$$

if some x_i is greater than θ (for then one of the factors will be 0).

Thus the joint density function is 0 if θ is less than some x_i, and is $(1/\theta)^n$ if θ is greater than all x_i. The largest value of $(1/\theta)^n$ is attained for the smallest admissible θ, so that the maximum likelihood estimate of θ is the largest of the n sample values, max $(x_1, x_2, \cdots, x_n)$.

It is of interest to note that, in the spirit of this section, the empiric distribution (page 137) may be regarded as the maximum likelihood estimate of the population distribution. If $(x_1, x_2, \cdots, x_n)$ is the sample point actually observed, then in applying the maximum likelihood principle to estimate the population distribution, we require the distribution assigning the greatest possible probability to the event

$$\{\mathbf{x}_1 = x_1, \mathbf{x}_2 = x_2, \cdots, \mathbf{x}_n = x_n\} = \bigcap_{i=1}^n \{\mathbf{x}_i = x_i\}.$$

The probability of this event is

$$\prod_{i=1}^n Pr\{\mathbf{x}_i = x_i\} = \prod_{i=1}^n Pr\{\mathbf{x} = x_i\}.$$

Set $p_i = Pr\{\mathbf{x} = x_i\}$, $i = 1, 2, \cdots, n$; our problem is to choose the numbers p_i subject to the condition $\sum_{i=1}^n p_i \leq 1$ so as to maximize the product $\prod_{i=1}^n p_i$. Evidently the maximum value of the product will be assumed for values p_i such that $\sum_{i=1}^n p_i = 1$, for if $\sum_{i=1}^n p_i < 1$ the product could be increased by increasing one factor so as to bring their sum up to 1. You can use the methods of the calculus to show that the maximum is attained when all p_i are equal; in which case each must be $1/n$, since their sum is 1. It also follows from the famous inequality relating the geometric and arithmetic means. The geometric mean of the numbers $p_1, p_2, \cdots, p_n$ is defined to be $(\prod_{i=1}^n p_i)^{1/n}$, and the arithmetic mean is $\frac{1}{n}\sum_{i=1}^n p_i$. The inequality states that whatever the positive numbers p_i may be, we shall have

$$\left(\prod_{i=1}^n p_i\right)^{1/n} \leq \frac{1}{n}\sum_{i=1}^n p_i.$$

In our case, $\sum_{i=1}^n p_i \leq 1$, so that

$$\left(\prod_{i=1}^n p_i\right)^{1/n} \leq 1/n,$$

$$\prod_{i=1}^n p_i \leq (1/n)^n.$$

Thus no choice of $p_1, p_2, \cdots, p_n$ subject to $\sum_{i=1}^{n} p_i \leq 1$ will give a larger value to $\prod_{i=1}^{n} p_i$ than the value $(1/n)^n$; but this value is attained when $p_1 = p_2 = \cdots = p_n = 1/n$, so that $(1/n)^n$ is actually the maximum value of $\prod_{i=1}^{n} p_i$. The maximum likelihood estimates of the numbers $p_i = Pr\{\mathbf{x} = x_i\}$ are each $1/n$, and the maximum likelihood estimate of the population distribution is the empiric distribution, which assigns probability $1/n$ to each of the sample values actually observed.

Usually, of course, our problem is not simply to estimate the unknown population distribution function, given the empiric distribution function; rather, we are given also (or assume) that the population distribution function belongs to a certain class or family of distribution functions. Thus, for example, the problem of estimating a single parameter may be regarded as the problem of estimating the distribution function when it is given that it belongs to the one-parameter family of distribution functions obtained when the parameter is allowed to vary. As a particular illustration, suppose we wish to estimate the mean p of an elementary binomial distribution. The population distribution function has, by assumption, the form

$$F(x) = 0(x \leq 0), F(x) = 1 - p(0 < x \leq 1), F(x) = 1(x > 1).$$

The problem of choosing (estimating) a particular value of the population mean p is equivalent to the problem of choosing a particular one of this one-parameter family of distributions; for with this assumption the mean p determines and is determined by the distribution function.

However, the empiric distribution is in fact very often used descriptively; in the absence of other knowledge or reasonable assumptions as to the nature of the population distribution, one feels that the empiric distribution represents the unknown population distribution as accurately as is possible.

Example 3. (*The Normal Distribution*). The normal distribution, defined below, is perhaps the most useful single distribution. The reason for this lies partly in the fact that the distributions of many populations studied are approximately normal or may be reduced to approximately normal distributions by simple transformations, and partly in the approximation to the distribution of $\bar{\mathbf{x}}$ and other sample statistics furnished, for large sample sizes, by the normal distribution, under very general hypotheses. Further, there are available tables and an extensively developed theory of sampling from normal populations.

► ***Definition.*** *A random variable* $\mathbf{z}$ *has a* standardized normal distribution *if it has a probability density function* $\varphi(z)$ *given by*

$$\varphi(z) = \frac{1}{\sqrt{2\pi}} e^{-z^2/2}. \qquad \text{(see Fig. 25)}$$

The mean of such a random variable is

$$E(\mathbf{z}) = \frac{1}{\sqrt{2\pi}} \int_{-\infty}^{\infty} ze^{-z^2/2}\, dz = 0,$$

and its variance is

$$V(\mathbf{z}) = \frac{1}{\sqrt{2\pi}} \int_{-\infty}^{\infty} z^2 e^{-z^2/2}\, dz = 1.$$

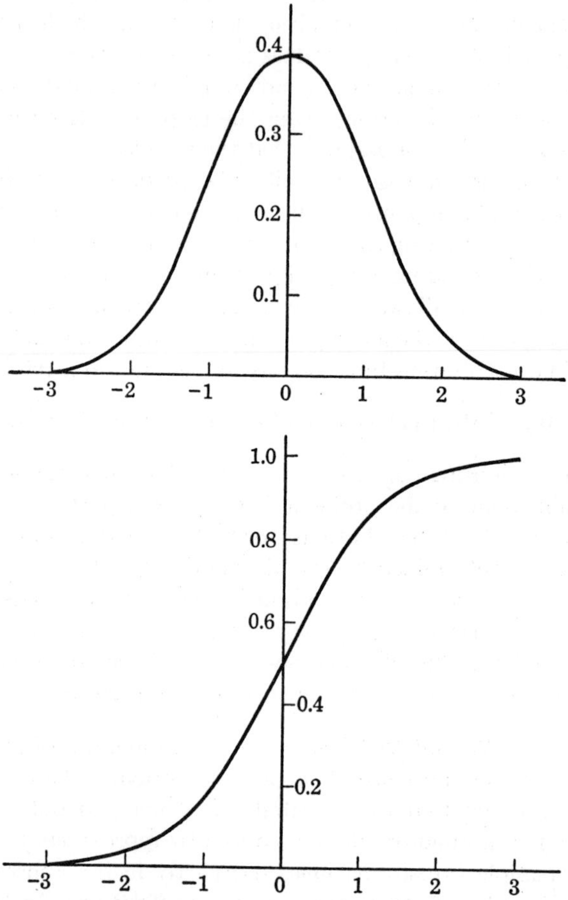

Figure 25. Graphs of standardized normal density and distribution functions.

Its standard deviation is then

$$\sigma = \sqrt{V(\mathbf{z})} = 1.$$

A random variable with this density function is therefore also said to have a normal distribution with mean 0 and standard deviation 1, *or simply to be* normal (0,1). (Cf. Problem 4, page 71.)

Any random variable $\mathbf{x}$ having a mean $E(\mathbf{x}) = \mu$ and a variance $V(\mathbf{x}) = \sigma^2$ can be reduced by a translation and a change of scale to a random variable with mean 0 and standard deviation 1, as follows:
Let

$$\mathbf{z} = \frac{\mathbf{x} - \mu}{\sigma}.$$

Then

$$E(\mathbf{z}) = E\left(\frac{\mathbf{x} - \mu}{\sigma}\right) = \frac{1}{\sigma}[E(\mathbf{x}) - \mu] = 0,$$

by Theorem D and Corollary F, page 86. Also,

$$V(\mathbf{z}) = \frac{1}{\sigma^2} V(\mathbf{x} - \mu) = \frac{1}{\sigma^2} V(\mathbf{x}) = 1,$$

by Theorem J and Theorem K, page 90. Thus if $\mathbf{x}$ is a random variable with mean μ and standard deviation σ, the random variable obtained by subtracting μ from $\mathbf{x}$ and dividing by σ has mean 0 and standard deviation 1. We say that $\mathbf{x}$ *is normal* (μ,σ), *or has a normal distribution with mean* μ *and standard deviation* σ, *if the reduced random variable*, $(\mathbf{x} - \mu)/\sigma$, *has a normal distribution with mean* 0 *and standard deviation* 1, *a standardized normal distribution.*

If $\mathbf{z}$ is normal (0,1), let $\Phi(z)$ be its distribution function:

$$\Phi(z) = Pr\{\mathbf{z} < z\} = \frac{1}{\sqrt{2\pi}} \int_{-\infty}^{z} e^{-u^2/2}\, du.$$

If $\mathbf{x}$ is normal (μ,σ), let

$$\mathbf{z} = (\mathbf{x} - \mu)/\sigma, \quad \mathbf{x} = \sigma\mathbf{z} + \mu,$$

and let $F(x)$ be the distribution function of $\mathbf{x}$. Then

$$F(x) = Pr\{\mathbf{x} < x\} = Pr\{\sigma\mathbf{z} + \mu < x\} = Pr\left\{\mathbf{z} < \frac{x - \mu}{\sigma}\right\} = \Phi\left(\frac{x - \mu}{\sigma}\right),$$

the distribution function of $\mathbf{z}$, evaluated at $(x - \mu)/\sigma$. We recall that the density function is the derivative of the distribution function (page 44): $f(x) = F'(x)$ is the density function of $\mathbf{x}$, and $\varphi(z) = \Phi'(z)$ is the density function of $\mathbf{z}$. We have

$$f(x) = F'(x) = \frac{d}{dx}\Phi\left(\frac{x - \mu}{\sigma}\right) = \frac{1}{\sigma}\Phi'\left(\frac{x - \mu}{\sigma}\right) = \frac{1}{\sigma}\varphi\left(\frac{x - \mu}{\sigma}\right),$$

or

$$f(x) = \frac{1}{\sqrt{2\pi}\,\sigma} e^{-[(x-\mu)/\sigma]^2/2} = \frac{1}{\sqrt{2\pi}\,\sigma} e^{-(x-\mu)^2/2\sigma^2}.$$

▶ *If* **x** *is normal* (μ,σ), *its density function is given by*

$$f(x) = \frac{1}{\sqrt{2\pi}\,\sigma} e^{-(x-\mu)^2/2\sigma^2},$$

and its distribution function by

$$F(x) = \frac{1}{\sqrt{2\pi}\,\sigma}\int_{-\infty}^{x} e^{-(t-\mu)^2/2\sigma^2}\,dt$$

$$= \frac{1}{\sqrt{2\pi}}\int_{-\infty}^{\frac{x-\mu}{\sigma}} e^{-t^2/2}\,dt.$$

52. Maximum Likelihood Estimation of the Variance of a Normal Population. Suppose you have at hand a sample of size n from a normally distributed population whose mean μ is known, but whose variance θ is unknown; you are required to determine the maximum likelihood estimate of θ. The sample values $x_1, x_2, \cdots, x_n$ are values of sample random variables of a sample of size n from a population induced by a random variable **x** whose probability density function is

$$f(x;\theta) = \frac{1}{\sqrt{2\pi\theta}} e^{-(x-\mu)^2/2\theta}.$$

Here we think of μ as known, and of $\theta(=\sigma^2)$ as the parameter you wish to estimate. The likelihood function is given by

$$L(\theta) = f(x_1, x_2, \cdots, x_n;\theta) = \prod_{i=1}^{n} f(x_i;\theta)$$

$$= \left(\frac{1}{\sqrt{2\pi\theta}}\right)^n \prod_{i=1}^{n} e^{-(x_i-\mu)^2/2\theta}$$

$$= \left(\frac{1}{2\pi\theta}\right)^{n/2} e^{-\sum_{i=1}^{n}(x_i-\mu)^2/2\theta}.$$

The maximum likelihood estimate of θ is that value of θ for which L, regarded as a function of θ for fixed $x_1, x_2, \cdots, x_n$ (and given μ), attains its maximum value. In order to facilitate the computations, let us begin by observing that the same value of θ which maximizes L will maximize $\log L$ (natural logarithm). We have

$$\log L = -\frac{n}{2}\log(2\pi\theta) - \sum_{i=1}^{n}(x_i-\mu)^2/2\theta.$$

This function of θ has a derivative for every positive θ, and hence can attain a maximum only where its derivative is 0 (note that $L \to 0$ as $\theta \to 0$). We set, then,

$$\frac{d}{d\theta} \log L = -\frac{n}{2\theta} + \frac{\sum_{i=1}^{n} (x_i - \mu)^2}{2\theta^2} = 0.$$

On solving this equation for θ we find

$$\theta = \frac{1}{n} \sum_{i=1}^{n} (x_i - \mu)^2.$$

The usual tests show that for this value of θ, where $d(\log L)/d\theta = 0$, $\log L$ (and therefore also L) does actually attain its maximum value. The maximum likelihood estimate of the variance, in sampling from a normal population with known mean μ, is thus given by

$$\theta = \frac{1}{n} \sum_{i=1}^{n} (x_i - \mu)^2.$$

This is the formula for the sample variance, except that the sample mean $\bar{x}$ is replaced by the population mean μ.

If we were to reformulate the above problem so that both μ and σ^2 were unknown, we should find that the values of μ and σ^2 which maximize L are the sample mean and the sample variance: the maximum likelihood estimates of population mean and population variance, in sampling from a normal population, are the sample mean and the sample variance. (We note, however, that a "restricted" maximum likelihood estimator of σ^2, obtained by maximizing the density of $\mathbf{s}^2$, is the unbiased estimator $n\mathbf{s}^2/(n-1)$; cf. W. A. Thompson, Jr., Ann. Math. Stat. 33(1962), pp. 273–289.)

★ **53. The Method of Moments.** If there are k parameters to be estimated, you will in general obtain k equations involving these parameters if you equate the first k of the population moments depending on these parameters to the corresponding sample moments actually observed. The estimates given by the method of moments are found by solving these equations for the unknown parameters. It is assumed, of course, that the population moments are known functions of the parameters. When the parameters are themselves population moments, this method leads to sample moments as estimators of population moments. The sample mean, for example, the first moment about the origin of the sample, is the estimator of the population mean, which is the first moment about the origin of the population.

As an especially simple example, suppose you wish to use the method of moments to estimate the mean and variance of a population. If $\mathbf{x}$ is the population random variable, then the unknown parameters are $\mu = E(\mathbf{x})$ and $\sigma^2 = E(\mathbf{x} - \mu)^2 = E(\mathbf{x}^2) - \mu^2$. The first two sample moments are

$$\frac{1}{n}\sum_{i=1}^{n} x_i = \bar{x}$$

and

$$\frac{1}{n}\sum_{i=1}^{n} x_i^2 = s^2 + \bar{x}^2.$$

The first two population moments are $E(\mathbf{x}) = \mu$ and $E(\mathbf{x}^2) = \sigma^2 + \mu^2$. We have then to solve the equations

$$\mu = \bar{x},$$

$$\sigma^2 + \mu^2 = s^2 + \bar{x}^2$$

for μ and σ^2 in terms of $\bar{x}$ and s; the solutions are obviously $\bar{x}$ and s^2.

In general, it is desirable that the equations admit unique solutions for the parameters in terms of the sample moments. This will be possible if and only if the parameters could (theoretically) at first have been expressed as functions of the corresponding population moments. The method of moments could then alternatively be explained as requiring that the (unknown) population parameters be expressed in terms of the (unknown) population moments, which are then to be replaced by the sample moments in order to yield estimates of the parameters. In the special example above, the expressions for the parameters μ and σ^2 were independent of the particular form of the population distribution; but in general the functions giving the parameters in terms of the population moments will depend on the form of the distribution.

We note that the population moments are functionals of the population distribution; that is, they are defined for distributions in general, and to obtain the moments of a particular population one simply puts its distribution in place of the general distribution in the expressions defining the moments. The same expressions, with the general distribution replaced by the empiric distribution, yield the sample moments. This suggests a generalization of the method of moments as described above. If the (unknown) population parameter can be expressed in terms of the population distribution, then an estimate of it is obtained by replacing the population distribution by the empiric distribution. It may occur to you that a given parameter may be expressible in several different ways in terms of the population distribution; this comment is also appropriate to a moment method. For example, the variance (a parameter) can be written

$$\sigma^2 = \alpha_2 - \mu^2$$

where μ and α_2 are respectively first and second moments about the origin of the population distribution. But the variance can also, if the population is normal, be written

$$\sigma^2 = \sqrt{6\mu^4 + 3\alpha_4} - 3\mu^2$$

where μ, α_4 are respectively first and fourth moments about the origin. Thus one application of a moment method would lead to the estimate

$$\frac{1}{n}\sum_{i=1}^{n} x_i^2 - \bar{x}^2 = s^2$$

of the population variance σ^2, while another would lead to the estimate

$$\sqrt{6\bar{x}^2 + \frac{3}{n}\sum_{i=1}^{n} x_i^4} - 3\bar{x}^2.$$

The (somewhat arbitrary) principle of restricting consideration to moments of the lowest usable order yields the first estimate.

★54. Bayes Estimates. If the parameter θ, while unknown, can be regarded as having been determined by chance as a sample value of a random variable $\boldsymbol{\theta}$ having a known probability distribution, then one method of estimating θ is to choose its expected value according to the posterior distribution; another would be to choose the most probable value. In order to clarify this statement, let $L(x_1, x_2, \cdots, x_n \mid \theta)$ denote the joint probability function (or probability density function) of the sample random variables, evaluated at the sample point $(x_1, x_2, \cdots, x_n)$ which was actually observed, conditioned by the value θ of the parameter random variable $\boldsymbol{\theta}$. Then the joint probability (density) function of the sample random variables and the random variable $\boldsymbol{\theta}$ is

$$L(x_1, x_2, \cdots, x_n \mid \theta)h(\theta),$$

where $h(\theta)$ is the probability function (or probability density function) of $\boldsymbol{\theta}$. The conditional probability function of $\boldsymbol{\theta}$ for given values $x_1, x_2, \cdots, x_n$ of the sample random variables, $x_1, x_2, \cdots, x_n$, is the quotient,

$$\frac{L(x_1, x_2, \cdots, x_n \mid \theta)h(\theta)}{f(x_1, x_2, \cdots, x_n)},$$

where $f(x_1, x_2, \cdots, x_n)$ is the (marginal) joint probability function (probability density function) of the sample random variables. The *Bayes estimate* of θ is the expected value of $\boldsymbol{\theta}$, computed from this posterior conditional probability function of $\boldsymbol{\theta}$, given the observed sample values.

In some situations in which θ could not properly be regarded as a random variable, or in which its probability distribution was unknown, some investigators assumed $h(\theta)$ constant, or equivalently, that the distribution of θ was uniform. This practice drew much criticism.

We see that if $h(\theta)$ is constant, that is, independent of θ, then the "most probable" value of θ is that value which maximizes the likelihood function, $L(x_1, x_2, \cdots, x_n \mid \theta)$. Thus in this case this estimate and the maximum likelihood estimate coincide.

For further discussion of Bayes estimates see [3], pages 507–509, [22], pages 508–511, [2], [4], [7], [8], [9], [13], [14], [19], [21].

★**55. Estimation As Decision-Making.** From the point of view of Wald, who was largely responsible for what many regard as one of the most significant of recent advances in mathematical statistics, the function of the statistician is to make decisions on the basis of incomplete data. This is a very general point of view: the decision may be to reject a shipment of goods on the basis of a sample; it may be to continue a sampling experiment; it may be to state that a parameter value is a certain number.

The investigator plans to perform an experiment, all of whose possible results he can foresee. A *decision rule* makes a decision correspond to each possible result; that is, the investigator's decision rule tells him what decision to make when he is given any one of the possible results of the experiment.

In order to apply this concept to the problem of parameter estimation, let us suppose there is at hand a population of unknown distribution, and that the investigator plans to take a random sample of fixed size from this population. The distribution is assumed to be one of a certain restricted class of possible distributions; with each is associated a value of the parameter to be estimated. For example, he may wish to estimate the population standard deviation, and may know or assume that the population distribution is normal with mean 0; in this case, with each distribution is associated its standard deviation, a value of the parameter to be estimated. As another, extreme example, he may again wish to estimate the population standard deviation, but be willing to assume nothing at all about the form of the distribution. Still, to each distribution corresponds a value of the parameter σ to be estimated. A *decision rule* yields an estimate of the parameter corresponding to each set of observed sample values. Thus an *estimator* provides a decision rule.

A basic assumption in Wald's approach is that the investigator is able to assign a definite numerical *loss* to each erroneous decision. In the case of parameter estimation, he is able to specify numerically what loss he suffers when his estimate is a number $\hat{\theta}$ and the true parameter value is a number θ. That is, with every pair θ, $\hat{\theta}$ of possible parameter values, he is able to associate a numerical value $L(\hat{\theta};\theta)$ which measures his "loss" if he states that the parameter value is $\hat{\theta}$ when in fact it is θ.

To complete the description of a method for determining a unique estimator, a criterion is required. The best known was proposed by Wald, and is called the *minimax principle.* For each particular estimator (decision rule) and each possible distribution of the population, the investigator computes the *expected loss:* when the population distribution is fixed, the loss is a random variable, a function of the estimator, itself a function of the sample random variables; its expectation is the expected loss. When the investigator considers different possible population distributions, he arrives at different expected losses; he determines the largest, the *maximum expected loss* (for simplicity, we assume there *is* a largest expected loss). When he considers different estimators, each will have a maximum expected loss; the *minimax principle* requires him to use that estimator for which the maximum expected loss is as small as possible (again we assume this smallest maximum expected loss exists). Thus in accordance with the minimax principle he chooses the estimator which minimizes the maximum expected loss.

For further discussion of this topic and references to the literature, see Chapter 11.

As applied to the estimation problem, the minimax principle has been criticized as unduly pessimistic. From the point of view of game theory, it is as if the investigator regards nature as a hostile opponent, who deliberately adopts a strategy for choosing a population distribution which is designed to render the investigator's loss as large as possible. In effect, in applying this principle the investigator minimizes the worst nature can do.

★56. Efficiency and Sufficiency. In defining the concept, *efficient estimator,* we restrict ourselves to unbiased estimators. We recall that if $\hat{\boldsymbol{\theta}}$ is an unbiased estimator of a parameter θ, we have $E(\hat{\boldsymbol{\theta}}) = \theta$. The variance of such an estimator, $V(\hat{\boldsymbol{\theta}}) = E(\hat{\boldsymbol{\theta}} - \theta)^2$, is then a measure of the dispersion of the distribution of $\hat{\boldsymbol{\theta}}$ about θ; it is desirable to have an unbiased estimator with small variance. It is possible to show, under certain regularity conditions, that the variance of an unbiased estimator can never be less than a certain number depending on the population distribution and the sample size. If the variance of an unbiased estimator $\hat{\boldsymbol{\theta}}$ is equal to this number, then $\hat{\boldsymbol{\theta}}$ has the smallest possible variance, and is called *efficient* (we adopt here the terminology of Cramér; cf. [3], Chapter (32). The term "efficiency" is, however, often used for the concept "asymptotic efficiency" discussed in a later section.

An estimator $\hat{\boldsymbol{\theta}}$ is *sufficient* if, roughly, all information pertinent to the problem of estimating the parameter is summarized in its value, that is, if the precise knowledge of all the sample values affords no more information as to the parameter value than did the value of $\hat{\boldsymbol{\theta}}$ alone. More precisely, $\hat{\theta}$ is sufficient if the conditional distribution of the sample random variables for a given value of $\hat{\theta}$ is *independent* of the parameter θ. That is, *when the value of* $\hat{\theta}$ *is given*, the conditional probability distribution of the sample random variables is the *same* for all values of the parameter, so that complete knowledge of the sample values is of no further aid in guessing at the parameter value.

It can be shown that when the range of the population distribution is the same for all parameter values, and when certain regularity conditions are satisfied, sufficient estimators and efficient estimators exist only when the population distribution changes in a certain way with the parameter; the population distribution must range over what is called an *exponential family* or a Laplacian family as the parameter varies. After possibly making a change of parameter and a change of variable, in such a situation the parameter is the mean of the population, and the maximum likelihood method and the method of moments, both yield the sample mean as estimator. In these situations the sample mean is unbiased, efficient, and sufficient.

Another interpretation of sufficient statistic will be found in Halmos and Savage, *Application of the Radon-Nikodym Theorem to the theory of sufficient statistics*, Annals of Mathematical Statistics, vol. 20 (1949), pp. 225–241.

For further discussion, and references on efficient and sufficient estimators, see [3], Chapter 32, [8], [9], [22].

PROBLEMS ON MAXIMUM LIKELIHOOD

1. A sample of size n is taken from a normal population with mean μ and standard deviation 1. Find the maximum likelihood estimate of μ.

2. A sample of size n is taken from a normal population with mean 0 and standard deviation σ. Find the maximum likelihood estimate of σ.

3. A random variable $\mathbf{x}$ has a *Poisson distribution* with parameter λ if its probability function $f(x)$ is given by

$$f(x) = Pr\{\mathbf{x} = x\} = \lambda^x e^{-\lambda}/x!, \quad \text{for } x = 0, 1, 2, \cdots.$$

A sample of size n is taken from a population induced by such a random variable. Find the maximum likelihood estimate of λ.

4. If n independent trials are made of an event with unknown probability p, prove that the maximum likelihood estimate of p is the average number of successes. To state the same problem in other words, if the parent population is induced by a random variable assuming the value 1 with probability p and the value 0 with probability $q = 1 - p$, show that the sample mean of a random sample of size n is the maximum likelihood estimate of the population mean p.

5. You are given n numbers which have been chosen independently and at random from an interval $[a,b]$. Find the maximum likelihood estimates of a and b.

6. (a) Jones has 4 sacks of marbles; each of 3 has a fraction $p = 1/2$ of red marbles, $q = 1/2$ of white, while the other has fraction $p = 1/3$ of red and $q = 2/3$ of white. He chooses one sack at random. From this sack he then chooses, with replacement and mixing, a random sample of size 5, obtaining 2 red and 3 white. Use Bayes Theorem to find the *a posteriori* probability that $p = 1/3$ and the *a posteriori* probability that $p = 1/2$. Which is the more probable value of p?

(b) Jones hands you a sack of red marbles and white marbles, and tells you the fraction p of red marbles is either $1/3$ or $1/2$. You take a random sample (with replacement and mixing) of size 5, obtaining 2 red and 3 white. Determine the maximum likelihood estimate of p (it must be $1/3$ or $1/2$!).

7. The time interval $\mathbf{x}$ between successive feedings of a certain type of insect has a probability density function $f(x) = \theta e^{-\theta x}$ for $x > 0$, $f(x) = 0$ for $x < 0$. Observations are made on n insects, obtaining intervals between feedings $x_1, x_2, \cdots, x_n$. What is the maximum likelihood estimator of θ?

8. (a) Show that if $\hat{\boldsymbol{\theta}}$ is an unbiased estimator of θ and if $V(\hat{\boldsymbol{\theta}}) > 0$, then $\hat{\boldsymbol{\theta}}^2$ is not an unbiased estimator of θ^2.

(b) If the *bias* of an estimator $\hat{\boldsymbol{\lambda}}$ of a parameter λ is defined as $E(\hat{\boldsymbol{\lambda}}) - \lambda$, is the bias of $\hat{\boldsymbol{\theta}}^2$ positive or negative?

9. A random variable $\mathbf{x}$ is known to have a uniform distribution over an interval of length 2, but its center point θ is unknown. If $x_1, x_2, \cdots,$ are the results of n independent observations on $\mathbf{x}$, find the maximum likelihood estimate of θ.

10. In order to determine the acute angles A and B of a right triangle, both were measured. Assuming the measurements equally accurate, find maximum likelihood estimates of the angles. (Assume the measurements come from normal populations with equal standard deviations; note the sum of the means is $\pi/2$.)

11. In Problem 10, assume n measurements, $A_1, A_2, \cdots, A_n$, were made of angle A, and m measurements, $B_1, B_2, \cdots, B_m$, of angle B. With the same assumptions as in Problem 10, what are the maximum likelihood estimates of the angles (the means)? Discuss for n large in comparison to m.

12. In each of N independent repetitions of an experiment, mutually exclusive events A and B will occur with probabilities α and β, the event $\bar{A}\bar{B}$ occurring with probability $1 - \alpha - \beta$. The probabilities α and β are known to be related by the relation $\alpha = 2\beta$. Given that event A occurred in N_1 of the experiments, event B in N_2 of them, and event $\bar{A}\bar{B}$ in $N - N_1 - N_2$ of them, determine the maximum likelihood estimates of α and β.

Hint. Use multinomial distribution.

13. Let $\mathbf{y}_n$ denote the maximum likelihood estimator of θ in a random sample of size n from the uniform distribution over $(0,\theta)$. Find the limiting distribution of $\mathbf{t}_n = n(\theta - \mathbf{y}_n)$ (as $n \to \infty$).

14. In Problem 9, suppose $\theta = 0$ and let y_1, y_n denote respectively the smallest and largest sample values:

$$y_1 = \min (x_1, x_2, \cdots, x_n), \; y_n = \max (x_1, x_2, \cdots, x_n).$$

It can be shown that the joint probability density function of $\mathbf{y}_1$ and $\mathbf{y}_n$ is

$$(1/2^n)\, n(n-1)(y_n - y_1)^{n-2}, \; -1 < y_1 < y_n < 1.$$

(a) Show that the distribution function of $\mathbf{w} = \frac{1}{2}(\mathbf{y}_1 + \mathbf{y}_n)$ is

$$\tfrac{1}{2}(w+1)^n \; (-1 < w < 0), \; 1 - \tfrac{1}{2}(1-w)^n \; (0 < w < 1).$$

(b) Set $\mathbf{t}_n = n\mathbf{w}$, and find the limiting distribution of $\mathbf{t}_n$ as $n \to \infty$.

15. Assume that the probability of death of an insect dosed by an insecticide is a known function of the dosage and a quantity R, the "resistance of the species." That is, when an insect chosen at random from the species is subjected to a known dosage t, its probability of death is a known function $p(R;t)$ of the unknown resistance R. Suppose n_1 insects chosen independently and at random are subjected to dosage t_1, and a_1 succumb; n_2 are given dosage t_2, and a_2 succumb, etc.; n_k are given dosage t_k and a_k succumb. Show that the maximum likelihood estimate of R is a solution of the equation

$$\sum_{i=1}^{k} \left[\frac{a_1}{p(R;t_i)} - n_i\right]\left[\frac{1}{1 - p(R;t_i)}\right] \frac{d}{dR}[p(R;t_i)] = 0.$$

16. (a) Suppose $\mathbf{x}$ has a binomial distribution with parameters m and p. Given a sample of n observations on $\mathbf{x}$, find the maximum likelihood estimator of p (assume m known).

(b) A geologist was studying the lithologic composition of a small Lake Michigan beach area. One hundred sub-samples of 10 pebbles each were drawn at random from the area, and the number of limestone pebbles in each sub-sample was observed. The geologist assumes these 100 observations are independent and knows from past experience (see Problem 14, p. 283) that they are binomially distributed with parameters $m = 10$ and p. Obtain the maximum likelihood estimate of the probability, p, that a pebble in this area is limestone, using the following data:

Number of limestone pebbles per sub-sample:	0	1	2	3	4	5	6	7	8	9	10
Observed:	0	1	6	7	23	26	21	12	3	1	0

(*Source:* KRUMBEIN, W. C., "Applications of Statistical Methods to Sedimentary Rocks," *Journal of the American Statistical Association,* Vol. 49 (1954), pp. 51–66.)

17. (a) A sample of size n is taken from a Poisson population (as defined in Problem 3, p. 156). Find the maximum likelihood estimator of $Pr(\mathbf{x} = 0)$.

(b) A South African railroad company has established that the number of serious accidents incurred by a shunter in a five-year period has a Poisson distribution. Find the maximum likelihood estimate of the probability that a shunter has no serious accident during a five-year period, using the following sample of size 122:

Number of serious accidents incurred by a shunter	0	1	2	3	4	5
Observed:	44	42	21	9	4	2

(*Source:* MARITZ, J. S., "On the Validity of Inferences Drawn from the Fitting of Poisson and Negative Binomial Distributions from Accident Data," *Psychological Bulletin,* Vol. 47 (1950), pp. 437–438.)

18. (a) Suppose that $\mathbf{z} = \log_{10} \mathbf{y}$ and that $\mathbf{z}$ is normally distributed with mean μ and variance σ^2, i.e. $\mathbf{y}$ has a log-normal distribution (see Problem 8, p. 162). Find $E(\mathbf{y})$.

(b) A sample of size n is taken from the log-normal population defined in (a). Obtain the maximum likelihood estimator of $E(\mathbf{y})$, assuming μ and σ^2 unknown.

(c) It is known that the number of words in a sentence in George Bernard Shaw's *An Intelligent Woman's Guide to Socialism* has a log-normal distribution (approximately). A sample of 20 sentences from the latter book was obtained, the numbers of words in the 20 sentences being:

52, 24, 15, 67, 15, 22, 63, 26, 16, 32, 7, 33, 28, 14, 7, 29, 10, 6, 59, 30.

Assuming μ and σ^2 unknown, what is the maximum likelihood estimate of the mean number of words in a sentence in G. B. S.'s book?
(*Source:* WILLIAMS, C. B., "A Note on the Statistical Analysis of Sentence-Length as a Criterion of Literary Style," *Biometrika,* Vol. 31 (1939–40), pp. 356–361.)

19. (a) Given the n numbers of Problem 5, find the maximum likelihood estimator of the length $b - a$ of the interval $[a,b]$. Find the unbiased estimator of $b - a$ which is a constant multiple of the maximum likelihood estimator of $b - a$.

(b) A large organization has been using office equipment (desks, bookcases, etc.) upon which serial numbers had been placed. The question was raised as to how many such pieces of equipment were there. This equipment had been purchased many years ago and no records were immediately available to determine the total purchase. The serial numbers used are the consecutive integers from s to $s + p$, but s and $s + p$ are unknown. The serial numbers on 31 pieces of equipment were observed, obtaining the following:

83, 135, 274, 380, 668, 895, 955, 964, 1113, 1174, 1210, 1344, 1387, 1414, 1610, 1668, 1689, 1756, 1865, 1874, 1880, 1936, 2005, 2006, 2065, 2157, 2220, 2224, 2396, 2543, 2787.

The total number p of pieces of equipment is known *a priori* to be large, so as an approximation to the exact results suppose these serial numbers are a sample from the uniform distribution on the interval $[s,s + p]$. Using the estimators of (a), obtain the maximum likelihood and unbiased estimates of $(s + p) - s = p$.
(*Source:* Goodman, L. A., "Some Practical Techniques in Serial Number Analysis," *Journal of the American Statistical Association*, Vol. 49 (1954), pp. 97–112.)

20. (a) A sample of size n from a $N(\mu,\sigma)$ population is given, μ and σ being unknown. Obtain the maximum likelihood estimator of $Pr(\mathbf{X} < t)$.

(b) It is known that the probability distribution of the lifetime (in hours) of forty-watt 110-volt internally frosted incandescent light bulbs is normal. A sample of ten light bulbs from one week's total production was obtained, and each bulb was used until it burnt out (a "forced-life" test). The lifetimes (in hours) of the ten bulbs were:

1067, 919, 1196, 785, 1126, 936, 918, 1156, 920, 948.

Assuming μ and σ unknown, obtain the maximum likelihood estimate of the probability that a bulb produced during the given week lasts more than 1300 hours.
(*Source:* Davis, D. J., "An Analysis of Some Failure Data," *Journal of the American Statistical Association*, Vol. 47 (1952), pp. 141–144.)

Note. Problems 21–24 depend on Section 56.

21. In Problem 1, show that the maximum likelihood estimator is sufficient.

22. As in Problem 21, for Problem 3.

23. As in Problem 21, for Problem 6.

24. You are stationed at the midpoint of a cross-country race. You know that the runners are numbered consecutively from 1 to an integer k, unknown to you. Show that the highest number among the first n to pass you is a sufficient estimator of k. (The definition of sufficiency given in the text covered only random sampling (with replacement) and will require an obvious modification to be applicable here.)

25. Let N, n be positive integers. For $i = 1, 2, \cdots, N$, let there be given a normal population with unknown mean μ_i, which may vary with i, and unknown variance σ^2, the same for all i. Take independent random samples of size n from the N populations. Let $\mathbf{x}_{ij}$ denote the jth sample random variable in the sample from the ith population, $j = 1, 2, \cdots, n$, and $\bar{\mathbf{x}}_i$ the mean of the sample from the ith population, $i = 1, 2, \cdots, N$.

(a) Show that the maximum likelihood estimator of σ^2 is given by the formula

$$S_1{}^2 = \frac{1}{n} \sum_{j=1}^{n} \left[\frac{1}{N} \sum_{i=1}^{N} (\mathbf{x}_{ij} - \bar{\mathbf{x}}_i)^2 \right].$$

(b) Show that $S_2{}^2 = nS_1{}^2/(n - 1)$ is unbiased and consistent (as $N \to \infty$), so that $S_1{}^2$ is neither unbiased nor consistent. (Cf., J. Neyman and E. L. Scott, *Econometrica*, Vol. 16 (1948), pp. 1–32.)

PROBLEMS ON THE NORMAL DISTRIBUTION

1. If $\mathbf{x}$ is normally distributed with mean $\mu = 1$ and standard deviation $\sigma = 2$, use tables to find

(a) $Pr\{-1 < \mathbf{x} < 3\}$;

(b) a number c such that $Pr\{|\mathbf{x} - 1| < c\} = 0.90$;

(c) a number d such that $Pr\{\mathbf{x} > d\} = 0.90$.

2. (a) Let $\mathbf{x}$ be normal $(-3,1)$. Use tables to find the area under the graph of the density function of $\mathbf{x}$ over the interval $(-5,-4)$.

(b) Use tables to find an extreme right interval (a,∞) over which the area under the graph of the density function is 0.05.

3. (a) Use tables to determine a number c such that the probability is 0.8 that a normally distributed random variable with mean 0 and standard deviation 1 will assume a value between $-c$ and c.

(b) Find the probability that a normally distributed random variable with mean 3 and standard deviation 2 will assume a negative value.

4. If $\mathbf{x}$ and $\mathbf{y}$ are independent random variables, if $\mathbf{x}$ is normal (0,2), and if $\mathbf{y}$ is normal (0,3), write exact integral expressions for

(a) the probability that the larger of $\mathbf{x}$ and $\mathbf{y}$ will be less than 3;

(b) the probability that the smaller of $\mathbf{x}$ and $\mathbf{y}$ will be less than 3.

(c) Use tables to obtain numerical answers to (a) and (b).

5. A sample of size n is to be taken from a normally distributed population with mean μ and standard deviation σ. Write expressions involving integrals for the following; also use tables:

(a) the probability that all sample values will be less than $\mu + 3\sigma$;

(b) the probability that the smallest sample value will be less than $\mu - 3\sigma$;

(c) the probability that all sample values will lie between $\mu - 3\sigma$ and $\mu + 3\sigma$.

(d) Determine n so that the probability that at least one sample value will lie outside the range $(\mu - 3\sigma, \mu + 3\sigma)$ is at least 1/3.

6. You wish to determine the percentage of lime in the soil from a certain field. You take 10 samples at random and determine the percentage of lime in each. Suppose the population is (approximately) normally distributed with mean μ and standard deviation σ. What is an elementary event in the sample space? Write the probability density function of any one of the sample random variables, and also their joint density function.

7. Let $\mathbf{x}$ be the logarithm of the intensity of illumination at a given fixed distance of a light bulb chosen at random from a stock of bulbs. Assume $\mathbf{x}$ is normally distributed with mean μ and standard deviation σ.

(a) You select n light bulbs at random, with replacement (so as to have random sampling), from the stock of light bulbs, and measure their intensities at the given fixed distance. Let $\mathbf{x}_i$ be the logarithm of intensity of the ith bulb chosen ($i = 1, 2, \cdots, n$). The random variables $\mathbf{x}_i$ are sample random variables from what parent population? What is the sample space?

(b) What kind of probability distribution does $\mathbf{x}_i$ have, for each i? What is the probability density function of $\mathbf{x}_i$? What can you say about the relationships among the sample random variables, that is, about their joint distribution? What is their joint density function?

8. A random variable $\mathbf{y}$ has a *log-normal distribution* if $\mathbf{z} = \log \mathbf{y}$ (logarithm to the base e) is normally distributed. If $E(\mathbf{z}) = 0$, $V(\mathbf{z}) = 1$, find the distribution function and density function of $\mathbf{y}$.

9. Let $\mathbf{x}$ be normal $(\mu,2)$.

(a) What is $Pr\{|\mathbf{x} - \mu| > 3\}$? (Use tables.)

(b) Use Chebyshev's inequality to obtain an upper bound on $Pr\{|\mathbf{x} - \mu| > 3\}$, and compare with the answer to (a).

10. If $\mathbf{x}$ is normal (μ,σ), find the points of inflection of the density function of $\mathbf{x}$.

11. Assume that the life of a fuse of a certain kind is normally distributed with mean 800 hours and standard deviation 200 hours. Given 10,000 fuses, what are the distribution, the expectation, and the variance of the number which will still be in operation after 1000 hours?

12. Assume that the IQ's of elementary school children as measured by a certain test have mean 100 and standard deviation 12. (a) In a class of 30, how many would you expect to have IQ 120 or higher? (b) You have selected 10 who do well in music. If the distribution of IQ scores is independent of ability in music, what is the probability that at least 8 of the 10 will have IQ's 110 or higher? (c) How large a class must you have in order to have a probability of 0.10 that the class will have at least one member with an IQ above 130?

13. Two California growers pool their production of peaches; A furnishes 40% of the total number. The distributions of diameters of peaches from the two growers are approximately normal; A's peaches have mean diameter 3.5 inches with standard deviation 0.5 inch, B's have mean diameter 3 inches with standard deviation 0.3 inch. Find the density function of the diameter of a peach drawn at random from the mixture, and its mean and standard deviation.

14. From a stock of peas whose diameter is normally distributed with mean μ cm. and standard deviation σ cm., all those of diameter less than x_0 cm. are separated. Find the distribution of those remaining, and its mean.

CHAPTER

9

Central Limit Theorem

57. Central Limit Theorem. We considered very briefly above certain properties of estimators, and a general method of estimation. We turn now to the question you have probably already been asking: "What confidence can I have that the estimate I make will be near the 'true' parameter value?" More precisely: if you use the estimator $\hat{\boldsymbol{\theta}} = \hat{\theta}(\mathbf{x}_1, \mathbf{x}_2, \cdots, \mathbf{x}_n)$, of the parameter θ, what is the probability that your error, $|\hat{\boldsymbol{\theta}} - \theta|$, will not be more than a specified number? Or, if you specify the probability, what error will you not exceed, with at least that probability? You can answer these questions, if you know the probability distribution of the estimator for each value of the parameter. For the special situation (which arises often in practice) of estimating the population mean using a sample of large size, the *Central Limit Theorem* gives approximately the distribution of the sample mean.

In essence, the Central Limit Theorem states that the sample mean has an approximately normal distribution with mean μ, the population mean, and variance σ^2/n, where σ is the population standard deviation. This is in apparent contradiction to the law of large numbers, which states that the distribution of the sample mean tends to that of a random variable which assumes the value μ with probability 1. If $\bar{\mathbf{x}}_n$ is the sample mean of a sample of size n from a population with mean μ and standard deviation σ, then it follows from the law of large numbers that

$$Pr\{a < \bar{\mathbf{x}}_n < b\} \to 1 \quad \text{as} \quad n \to \infty \quad \text{if} \quad a < \mu < b,$$

and

$$Pr\{a < \bar{\mathbf{x}}_n < b\} \to 0 \quad \text{as} \quad n \to \infty \quad \text{if} \quad \mu < a \quad \text{or if} \quad \mu > b.$$

It would perhaps then be misleading to say that the distribution of $\bar{\mathbf{x}}_n$ tends to normality as $n \to \infty$. The fact is that if we reduce $\bar{\mathbf{x}}_n$ by a translation and change of scale so as to produce a random variable with mean 0 and standard deviation 1 (page 149), the distribution of this reduced random variable tends to normality as $n \to \infty$. We have seen (page 126) that

$E(\bar{\mathbf{x}}_n) = \mu$, and $V(\bar{\mathbf{x}}_n) = \sigma^2/n$; therefore the reduced random variable

$$\frac{(\bar{\mathbf{x}}_n - \mu)}{\sigma/\sqrt{n}}$$

has mean 0 and standard deviation 1. The Central Limit Theorem states that for each interval (a,b), the probability that this reduced random variable will assume a value between a and b tends, as $n \to \infty$, to the probability that a random variable which is normal (0,1) will assume a value between a and b. This statement is really a special case of a theorem (or theorems) of probability theory known under the name, Central Limit Theorem; however, we shall not prove here even this special case (see p. 236). For more general discussions, cf. [3], Chapter 17, page 367; [5], Chapter 10; [6], Chapter 6; [11], Chapter 9.

▶ ***Theorem A.*** (Central Limit Theorem). *If $\bar{\mathbf{x}}_n$ is the sample mean of a sample of size n from a population with mean μ and standard deviation σ, then for any real numbers a and b with $a < b$,*

$$Pr\left\{a < \frac{\bar{\mathbf{x}}_n - \mu}{\sigma/\sqrt{n}} < b\right\} \to \frac{1}{\sqrt{2\pi}} \int_a^b e^{-z^2/2}\,dz \text{ as } n \to \infty,$$

or

$$Pr\left\{\mu + \frac{a\sigma}{\sqrt{n}} < \bar{\mathbf{x}}_n < \mu + \frac{b\sigma}{\sqrt{n}}\right\} \to \frac{1}{\sqrt{2\pi}} \int_a^b e^{-z^2/2}\,dz$$

as $n \to \infty$.

▶ ***Corollary B.*** (De Moivre's Theorem). *If $\mathbf{S}_n$ is the total number of successes in n independent trials of an event with probability p, and if a and b are real numbers with $a < b$, then*

$$Pr\{np + a\sqrt{npq} < \mathbf{S}_n < np + b\sqrt{npq}\} \to \frac{1}{\sqrt{2\pi}} \int_a^b e^{-z^2/2}\,dz$$

as $n \to \infty$, where $q = 1 - p$.

Proof of Corollary B. We have already seen (page 107 ff.) that the average number of successes in n independent trials of an event with probability p may be regarded as the sample mean of a sample of size n from the population induced by a random variable which assumes the value 1 with probability p and the value 0 with probability $q = 1 - p$. The mean of such a population is $\mu = E(\mathbf{x}) = p$, and its variance is $\sigma^2 = V(\mathbf{x}) = pq$. We have $E(\bar{\mathbf{x}}_n) = \mu = p$ and $V(\bar{\mathbf{x}}_n) = \sigma^2/n = pq/n$. The last statement in Theorem A becomes, in this special case,

$$Pr\left\{p + a\sqrt{\frac{pq}{n}} < \bar{\mathbf{x}}_n < p + b\sqrt{\frac{pq}{n}}\right\} \to \frac{1}{\sqrt{2\pi}} \int_a^b e^{-z^2/2}\,dz.$$

When we observe that $\bar{\mathbf{x}}_n = \mathbf{S}_n/n$, and multiply both sides of each inequality by n, we obtain the statement of Corollary B.

EXAMPLE 1. You have been furnished, by an electrical supply house, a resistor to be used in an experiment. You wish to determine its resistance very accurately, and you make 36 measurements by a method which previous experience indicates involves a variance of 10 ohms^2. The average of your measurements is 52 ohms.

(a) What is the probability that your average, 52 ohms, is in error by more than 1 ohm? Here 52 represents the sample mean determined from a particular sample of size 36 from a population with unknown mean μ and variance 10. The question as stated is, what is the probability that μ lies between 51 and 53, or what is

$$Pr\{|\mu - 52| < 1\}?$$

This is not an appropriate question (but cf. Chapter 11). The population mean μ, while unknown, is just a constant, and not a random variable; also, the particular sample mean 52 is a constant, and probability statements about them are not appropriate. Either μ lies between 51 and 53, in which case one might perhaps say the probability is 1; or it does not, and the probability is 0; which is true cannot be determined surely from the given data.

(b) What is the *a priori* probability—the probability before you have made your measurements—that you will obtain sample values for which the sample mean $\bar{\mathbf{x}}$ will differ from the population mean μ by less than 1? The Central Limit Theorem permits an approximate solution of this problem, since it specifies, approximately, the distribution of the difference $\bar{\mathbf{x}} - \mu$. You have to determine

$$Pr\{|\bar{\mathbf{x}} - \mu| < 1\} \quad \text{or} \quad Pr\{-1 < \bar{\mathbf{x}} - \mu < 1\}.$$

In order to use the Central Limit Theorem, rewrite the inequalities by dividing each member of the inequalities by the standard deviation of $\bar{\mathbf{x}}$, $\sigma/\sqrt{n} = \sqrt{10}/\sqrt{36} = \dfrac{\sqrt{10}}{6}$:

$$Pr\{|\bar{\mathbf{x}} - \mu| < 1\} = Pr\left\{-\frac{6}{\sqrt{10}} < \frac{\bar{\mathbf{x}} - \mu}{\sigma/\sqrt{n}} < \frac{6}{\sqrt{10}}\right\}.$$

We have

$$Pr\left\{-\frac{6}{\sqrt{10}} < \frac{\bar{\mathbf{x}} - \mu}{\sigma/\sqrt{n}} < \frac{6}{\sqrt{10}}\right\} \doteq \frac{1}{\sqrt{2\pi}} \int_{-6/\sqrt{10}}^{6/\sqrt{10}} e^{-z^2/2}\, dz.$$

The right member represents the area under the standardized normal density curve from -1.90 to 1.90, or twice the area from 0 to 1.90, and is found from tables to be 0.943.

Experience appears to indicate ([3], page 454) that a sample size of 30 or more is often sufficient for the Central Limit Theorem to yield an adequate approximation; of course this depends on the accuracy required as well as on the population distribution. As we shall see later, the distribution of the sample mean is precisely normal if the parent population is normal; so that in this case the conclusion of the Central Limit Theorem is not merely an approximation, but exact. One might expect, then, that if the distribution of the population does not differ markedly from normality, the Central Limit Theorem will give good approximations for fairly small sample sizes. In fact, even when the distribution of the population does differ very noticeably from normality, the approximation given by the Central Limit Theorem may still be good for moderate sample size. For example, suppose the population is binomial with parameter $p = 1/2$; that is, the population random variable $\mathbf{x}$ is capable of assuming only two values, 0 and 1, each with probability 1/2. If the sample size n is 30, then the greatest error given by the Central Limit Theorem approximation to the distribution function of the sample mean is about 0.07 (or even less, if the simple correction mentioned on page 169 is made).

(c) The probability is 0.95 that the error will be less than what number? That is, what is a number ϵ, such that the *a priori* probability that a sample will be taken for which the sample mean will differ from the population mean by less than ϵ is 0.95? We have to determine ϵ so that

$$Pr\{|\bar{\mathbf{x}} - \mu| < \epsilon\} = 0.95,$$

or

$$Pr\{-\epsilon < \bar{\mathbf{x}} - \mu < \epsilon\} = 0.95.$$

In order to use the Central Limit Theorem, again we rewrite the inequality by dividing both sides by $\sqrt{V(\bar{\mathbf{x}})} = \sigma_{\bar{x}} = \sqrt{10}/6$, so that $(\bar{\mathbf{x}} - \mu)/\sigma_{\bar{x}}$ stands in the center; we wish then to choose ϵ so that

$$Pr\left\{-\frac{6\epsilon}{\sqrt{10}} < \frac{\bar{\mathbf{x}} - \mu}{\sigma_{\bar{x}}} < \frac{6\epsilon}{\sqrt{10}}\right\} = 0.95.$$

Since by the Central Limit Theorem the left member is approximately equal to

$$\frac{1}{\sqrt{2\pi}}\int_{-6\epsilon/\sqrt{10}}^{6\epsilon/\sqrt{10}} e^{-z^2/2}\,dz \quad \text{or to} \quad \frac{2}{\sqrt{2\pi}}\int_0^{6\epsilon/\sqrt{10}} e^{-z^2/2}\,dz,$$

we enter the normal probability tables and find that the area from 0 to 1.96 under the normal density curve is 0.475:

$$\frac{1}{\sqrt{2\pi}}\int_0^{1.96} e^{-z^2/2}\,dz = 0.475, \quad \frac{1}{\sqrt{2\pi}}\int_{-1.96}^{1.96} e^{-z^2/2}\,dz = 0.95,$$

$$6\epsilon/\sqrt{10} = 1.96, \quad \epsilon = \frac{1.96\sqrt{10}}{6} = 1.03.$$

Thus the probability is only 0.05 that you will make 36 measurements such that the average of your measurements will differ from the "true" resistance by more than 1.03 ohms.

(d) How many measurements should you make in order to have an *a priori* probability of only 0.05 that the average of your measurements will differ from the "true" resistance by more than 1? You have to determine n so that

$$Pr\{|\bar{\mathbf{x}} - \mu| > 1\} = 0.05,$$

or so that

$$Pr\{-1 < \bar{\mathbf{x}} - \mu < 1\} = 0.95,$$

or

$$Pr\left\{-\frac{\sqrt{n}}{\sigma} < \frac{\bar{\mathbf{x}} - \mu}{\sigma_{\bar{x}}} < \frac{\sqrt{n}}{\sigma}\right\} = 0.95,$$

since $\sigma_{\bar{x}} = \sigma/\sqrt{n}$. Since $\sigma = \sqrt{10}$, you want

$$Pr\left\{\frac{-\sqrt{n}}{\sqrt{10}} < \frac{\bar{\mathbf{x}} - \mu}{\sigma_{\bar{x}}} < \frac{\sqrt{n}}{\sqrt{10}}\right\} = 0.95.$$

As in (c), this requires

$$\frac{\sqrt{n}}{\sqrt{10}} \doteq 1.96,$$

or

$$n \doteq (1.96)^2 \cdot 10 \doteq 39.$$

Example 2. Let us consider again the example discussed on page 101 and on page 128. You have a large lot of items, and wish, by random sampling, to estimate the fraction which are defective. Let us use the Central Limit Theorem now, to find a number N with the property that if you take a sample of size N or larger, the probability will be at least 0.95 that the average number, $\bar{\mathbf{x}}$, of defectives will differ from the true proportion by less than 0.1. We wish to have

$$Pr\{|\bar{\mathbf{x}} - p| < 0.1\} \geq 0.95$$

or

$$Pr\{-0.1 < \bar{\mathbf{x}} - p < 0.1\} \geq 0.95.$$

Now $E(\bar{\mathbf{x}}) = p$, $\sqrt{V(\bar{\mathbf{x}})} = \sigma_{\bar{x}} = \sqrt{pq/n}$. On dividing both sides of each inequality by $\sigma_{\bar{x}}$ we obtain

$$Pr\left\{-0.1\sqrt{\frac{n}{pq}} < \frac{\bar{\mathbf{x}} - p}{\sigma_{\bar{x}}} < 0.1\sqrt{\frac{n}{pq}}\right\} \geq 0.95.$$

According to De Moivre's Theorem (Corollary B, page 165), the probability on the left is given approximately for large n by

$$\frac{1}{\sqrt{2\pi}} \int_{-0.1\sqrt{n/pq}}^{0.1\sqrt{n/pq}} e^{-z^2/2}\, dz.$$

We find again from the tables that this will be at least 0.95 if

$$0.1 \sqrt{\frac{n}{pq}} \geq 1.96,$$

or if

$$n \geq (19.6)^2 pq.$$

Since $pq = p(1 - p) \leq 1/4$ for all p between 0 and 1, n will be at least $(19.6)^2 pq$, no matter what p may be, if

$$n \geq (19.6)^2(1/4) \doteq 96.$$

Thus whatever the unknown proportion of defectives, the probability will be at least 0.95 that the average number found in a sample of size about 100 will differ from the true proportion by less than 0.1. We contrast this result with the number 500 found on page 130 with the aid of Chebyshev's inequality. Chebyshev's inequality applies to a random variable with any distribution (so long as it has a mean and a standard deviation). Here we have made use of additional information to the effect that the distribution of the sample mean is approximately normal; this added information has resulted in a better estimate of the sample size required for a given precision.

★58. Normal and Poisson Approximations to the Binomial Distribution. Let $\mathbf{S}_n$ denote the total number of successes in n independent trials of an event with probability p in each. De Moivre's Theorem (given on page 165) states that the limiting distribution of a reduced random variable $(\mathbf{S}_n - np)/\sqrt{npq}$ is that of the normally distributed random variable with mean 0 and standard deviation 1. Thus when n is appropriately large we may use the distribution function of a normal $(np, \sqrt{npq})$ random variable as an approximation to that of $\mathbf{S}_n$. If we do so, we shall be approximating the distribution function of $\mathbf{S}_n$ by a normal distribution function fitted to that of $\mathbf{S}_n$ by making its mean and variance coincide with those of $\mathbf{S}_n$. The approximation is improved if the value of the binomial distribution function at an integer k is approximated by the value of the normal distribution function at $k - 1/2$. (Cf. [5], Chapter 7.)

It is interesting to fit the binomial distribution function by a Poisson distribution function, which is also a step function. Let $\mathbf{z}$ have a Poisson distribution with parameter λ. Its mean and variance are then both λ (see page 118). If β is an integer, then the distribution function of the random variable $\mathbf{w} = \mathbf{z} + \beta$ also has its jumps at integers. Since $E(\mathbf{z}) = \lambda$, we have $E(\mathbf{w}) = \lambda + \beta$. Since $V(\mathbf{z}) = \lambda$, also $V(\mathbf{w}) = \lambda$. If these are to coincide respectively with the mean np and the variance npq of the binomial distribution, we must have

$$\lambda + \beta = np,$$

$$\lambda = npq,$$

whence it follows that

$$\beta = np - \lambda = np(1 - q) = np^2.$$

However, we want β to be an integer; therefore we choose as β the nearest integer to np^2 and set $\lambda = np - \beta$.

If in particular p is small, $p < \sqrt{1/2n}$, this approximation coincides with the one given earlier, on page 120; for then $\beta = 0$ and $\lambda = np$.

★**59. Asymptotically Efficient Estimators.** These estimators are also called simply "efficient" by many. Let us first define the term *asymptotically normal and unbiased* estimator. Such an estimator of a parameter θ is asymptotically normally distributed, with (asymptotic) mean value θ, and (asymptotic) standard deviation inversely proportional to $\sqrt{n}$ (n is the sample size). That is, we now restrict our attention to estimators $\hat{\boldsymbol{\theta}}$, for each of which there is a constant c (which may depend on θ) such that

$$Pr\left\{a < \frac{\hat{\boldsymbol{\theta}} - \theta}{c/\sqrt{n}} < b\right\} \to \frac{1}{\sqrt{2\pi}} \int_a^b e^{-t^2/2}\, dt \text{ as } n \to \infty$$

for every pair a,b of real numbers ($a < b$) whatever θ may be (on some interval). For example, the central limit theorem states that the sample mean is an asymptotically normal and unbiased estimator of the population mean. We note that for any fixed sample size n, the estimator $\hat{\boldsymbol{\theta}}$ need not be unbiased nor have standard deviation $c/\sqrt{n}$; but that the distribution of the reduced random variable $[\hat{\boldsymbol{\theta}} - \theta]/(c/\sqrt{n})$ must approach the standardized normal distribution. If $\hat{\boldsymbol{\theta}}$ is an asymptotically normal and unbiased estimator for which the associated constant c is (for almost all θ) at least as small as that for any other asymptotically normal and unbiased estimator, then $\hat{\boldsymbol{\theta}}$ is *asymptotically efficient.*

We note in passing that an asymptotically normal and unbiased estimator is necessarily consistent. To prove this, we have to show that whatever positive numbers ϵ and η may be given, however small, a positive integer N can be found so that

$$Pr\{-\epsilon < \hat{\boldsymbol{\theta}} - \theta < \epsilon\} > 1 - \eta$$

for all $n > N$. Given two positive numbers ϵ and η, choose real numbers a and b so that

$$\frac{1}{\sqrt{2\pi}} \int_a^b e^{-t^2/2}\, dt > 1 - \eta/2$$

(b, large and positive; a, large and negative). Choose N_1 so large that

$$\left| Pr\left\{\frac{ac}{\sqrt{n}} < \hat{\theta} - \theta < \frac{bc}{\sqrt{n}}\right\} - \frac{1}{\sqrt{2\pi}} \int_a^b e^{-t^2/2}\, dt\right| < \eta/2$$

for $n > N_1$; then

$$Pr\left\{\frac{ac}{\sqrt{n}} < \hat{\theta} - \theta < \frac{bc}{\sqrt{n}}\right\} > \frac{1}{\sqrt{2\pi}} \int_a^b e^{-t^2/2}\, dt - \eta/2$$

$$> 1 - \eta/2 - \eta/2 = 1 - \eta$$

for all $n > N_1$. Now choose N_2 so large that

$$-\epsilon < ac/\sqrt{N_2} \quad \text{and} \quad bc/\sqrt{N_2} < \epsilon.$$

If $n > N_2$, the event $\{ac/\sqrt{n} < \hat{\theta} - \theta < bc/\sqrt{n}\}$ can then occur only if $\{-\epsilon < \hat{\theta} - \theta < \epsilon\}$ occurs; that is,

$$\{-\epsilon < \hat{\theta} - \theta < \epsilon\} \supset \left\{\frac{ac}{\sqrt{n}} < \hat{\theta} - \theta < \frac{bc}{\sqrt{n}}\right\},$$

so that

$$Pr\{-\epsilon < \hat{\theta} - \theta < \epsilon\} \geq Pr\left\{\frac{ac}{\sqrt{n}} < \hat{\theta} - \theta < \frac{bc}{\sqrt{n}}\right\} \quad \text{for } n > N_2.$$

Let N now be the larger of the two numbers N_1 and N_2; if $n > N$ we have

$$Pr\{-\epsilon < \hat{\theta} - \theta < \epsilon\} \geq Pr\left\{\frac{ac}{\sqrt{n}} < \hat{\theta} - \theta < \frac{bc}{\sqrt{n}}\right\} > 1 - \eta.$$

Thus given ϵ and η we have been able to find a number N satisfying the desired conditions, and $\hat{\theta}$ is consistent.

Under fairly general conditions, the method of maximum likelihood leads to asymptotically efficient estimators. For further discussion and references, see [3], Chapters 32 and 33, [8], [9], and [22].

PROBLEMS

1. In sampling from a population with standard deviation 2, what, approximately, is the probability that the sample mean will differ from the population mean by not more than 0.2, if the sample size is 50?

2. If the standard deviation of a population is 2, what is the sample size required in order to assure a probability approximately 0.90 that the sample mean will differ from the population mean by not more than 0.2?

3. If the sample size is 50 and if $\sigma = 2$, the probability will be approximately 0.90 that the sample mean will differ from the population mean by how little?

4. In preparing a complaint against her neighbors for disturbing her peace, Miss T. has made 49 measurements of the noise volume in decibels produced when young T. A. pulls the tail of Tabby. She finds the sample mean is 50, with a sample standard deviation of 7.

(a) Assuming the standard deviation of the population is 7, find the *a priori* probability that the sample mean will be at least 2 decibels above the population mean; at least 1 decibel; 1 decibel below the population mean or higher.

(b) How many measurements should she make to be 99% certain that the sample mean will be not more than 1/2 decibel above the population mean (assuming that the population standard deviation is 7)?

5. In Problem 3, page 134, assume the sample size is large enough to justify the use of the Central Limit Theorem, and use it instead of Chebyshev's inequality to answer (a) and (b).

6. Suppose the length of left ear of rabbits in Australia has a standard deviation 1 inch. About how many rabbits must be caught (at random) to determine the mean length of left ear to within 0.1 inch with probability 0.99; that is, how many left ears must be measured in order that the sample mean may differ from the population mean by less than 0.1 inch with probability 0.99?

7. You plan an experiment to determine the mean yield per acre of a new hybrid corn. You will plant n plots of one acre each with the new seed. In similar, previous experiments, the standard deviation in yield has been about 10 bushels per acre, and you are willing to assume that 10 bushels per acre is the population standard deviation.

(a) Use Chebyshev's inequality to determine a sample size n sufficient to insure a probability at least 0.80 that the sample mean (average yield of the sample plots) will not differ from the population mean by more than 2 bushels per acre.

(b) Use the normal approximation (Central Limit Theorem) in (a) instead of Chebyshev's inequality.

8. One thousand rounds are fired from a gun at a target, the probability of a hit on each round being 0.7. Use the Central Limit Theorem (or de Moivre's Theorem) to determine the probability that the number of hits will be (a) between 675 and 725; (b) more than 730; (c) fewer than 680. (d) You can be 95% sure that there will be at least how many hits?

9. A student opinion poll takes a random sample of size 100 in an attempt to estimate the fraction p of students who favor a certain proposal.

(a) Write in terms of p the expectation and variance of the number of those among the 100 who will favor the proposal.

(b) Write in terms of p an exact expression for the probability that the number among the 100 favoring the proposal will differ from the expected number by more than 10.

(c) Use Chebyshev's inequality to find an upper bound on the probability in (b), if $p = 2/3$; without assuming $p = 2/3$.

(d) Use the Central Limit Theorem to estimate the probability in (b), if $p = 2/3$.

(e) Use the Central Limit Theorem to find an upper bound on the probability in (b), *without assuming* $p = 2/3$.

(f) Use the Central Limit Theorem, without assuming $p = 2/3$, to determine a sample size large enough to have a probability at least 0.95 that the fraction favoring the proposal will differ from p by less than 0.05.

10. Find three pairs of numbers a,b, depending on μ, σ, and n, such that $Pr\{a < \bar{\mathbf{x}} < b\} \doteq 0.90$, if $\bar{\mathbf{x}}$ is the sample mean of a sample of size n from a population with mean μ and standard deviation σ, assuming n large enough for the Central Limit Theorem to yield an adequate approximation.

11. The mortality of rats infected with a certain disease is 80%. Suppose 100 are infected.

(a) Use the normal approximation to find approximately the probability that fewer than 75 will succumb.

★(b) Use the Poisson approximation (with summed Poisson tables) to find approximately the probability in (a).

12. (a) A blindfolded person is given several sips of each of 3 cups of cola, two of brand A and one of brand B, and he is asked to state the brand of each cup. If in fact his answers are determined by chance alone, what is the probability that his answers will all be correct?

★(b) If the above test is given to 100 persons, what is the probability that at least 10 will be found who give all correct answers? (Use both normal and Poisson approximations.)

CHAPTER

10

Confidence Intervals and Tests of Hypotheses

60. Confidence Interval for the Mean. This topic is introduced by the following example.

EXAMPLE 1. Let us consider again the example on page 166. Thirty-six measurements of a resistor by a method yielding a variance of 10 ohms^2 have given a sample mean of 52 ohms. We saw in (a) on page 166 that it would not be correct to say $Pr\{|\mu - 52| < 1.03\} = 0.95$, since μ, the population mean, is not a random variable. However, we found in (c) that the probability, *before the sample is taken*, that sample values will be obtained for which $|\bar{\mathbf{x}} - \mu| < 1.03$, is 0.95. Therefore, if you make the statement that the population mean lies between $52 + 1.03$ and $52 - 1.03$, you may feel a certain confidence in your statement. The interval (50.97,53.03) is called a 95% *confidence interval* for μ, and the numbers 50.97, 53.03 are 95% *confidence limits* for μ.

Consider your situation before you made the measurements. You might have determined before making any measurements that the probability was 0.95 that you would obtain sample values for which the sample mean would differ from the population mean by less than 1.03. Suppose you then decided that after making the measurements you would assert that the population mean was between the sample mean less 1.03 and the sample mean plus 1.03. You would realize that this procedure could lead you to make a false statement; *but you would also realize that there was a probability of only* 0.05 *that you would be led to a false statement.* In other words, the *a priori* probability that you will finally make a true statement about the location of the population mean is 0.95.

You may think of the entire course of action as a single trial of an event with probability 0.95. Suppose that in dealing with possibly an entirely different situation, estimating a different parameter altogether, you were to choose again a course of action leading to a true statement with probability 0.95, to a false statement with probability 0.05. "*In the long run,*" *about* 95% *of such statements would be correct;* the law of large numbers (Corollary D, page 133) asserts that with high probability the average number of successes in n independent trials with probability 0.95 of success in each will be near 0.95 if n is large; more precisely, the probability that the average number of successes will differ from 0.95 by less than an arbitrary preassigned positive number tends to 1 as $n \to \infty$. It is in this sense that you may say you have 95% confidence in each individual statement.

61. Test of a Hypothesis. It is convenient to introduce this test by way of an example.

EXAMPLE 2. In the example we were considering above (and on page 166), you made 36 measurements of a resistance using a method giving a variance of 10 ohms^2, and obtained a sample mean of 52 ohms. Suppose the supply house had represented the resistor as one with a resistance of 50 ohms. Are you justified in claiming they have made an error, and the resistance is not in fact 50 ohms?

The question at issue is not whether or not it is possible to manufacture a resistor of *exactly* 50 ohms resistance, but whether your sample data (the measurements) could "reasonably" have been made on a resistor with resistance (about) 50 ohms. We can of course conceive the possibility that enough of the measurements may have been enough in error so that the sample mean is at least two ohms different from the population mean. However, this is unlikely; before deciding whether or not to charge your supplier with having issued faulty equipment, you may wish to determine how unlikely it is. If the *a priori* probability of obtaining sample values for which the sample mean is as much as 2 ohms different from the population mean is very small you may *reject the hypothesis that the population mean is* 50 *in favor of the alternative that the population mean is not* 50.

You must exercise your judgment in deciding how small the probability should be before you will reject the hypothesis. If serious consequences are attendant upon your rejection of the hypothesis when it is in fact true, you may insist on a very small probability, or a very small *level of significance.* Suppose you decide you will declare the resistor faulty (resistance not 50 ohms) if the probability, based on the assumption $\mu = 50$, is less than 0.05 that the sample mean will differ from 50 by 2 or more. *You are then testing, at the* 5% *significance level, the hypothesis that the population mean is* 50 *against the alternative that it is not.*

We found above that

$$Pr\{|\bar{\mathbf{x}} - \mu| \leq 1.03\} = 0.95,$$

so that

$$Pr\{|\bar{\mathbf{x}} - \mu| > 1.03\} = 0.05,$$

and

$$Pr\{|\bar{\mathbf{x}} - \mu| > 2\} < 0.05.$$

Since the probability of drawing a sample for which the sample mean differs from the population mean by more than 2 is less than 0.05 (indeed, much less than 0.05), *you will reject, at the 5% significance level, the hypothesis* $\mu = 50$, *in favor of the alternative* $\mu \neq 50$.

Indeed, you would reject at the 5% significance level the hypothesis $\mu = 50$ if the sample mean differed from 50 by more than 1.03; and this suggests an alternative way of looking at this test of significance. You will reject, at the 5% significance level, the hypothesis $\mu = 50$ if the number 50 falls outside a 95% confidence interval for the population mean.

62. Confidence Intervals for Population Mean. Testing a Hypothesis on the Sample Mean. We have seen in the preceding examples how to use the Central Limit Theorem to determine confidence limits for the population mean, or to test a hypothesis of the form $\mu = \mu_0$ when the sample size is large enough for the Central Limit Theorem to give an adequate approximation. Let μ denote the unknown mean of the population, a population induced by a random variable $\mathbf{x}$: $\mu = E(\mathbf{x})$; and let $\sigma^2 = V(\mathbf{x})$ be the variance of the population. Then according to the Central Limit Theorem (page 165) the probability distribution of $(\bar{\mathbf{x}} - \mu)/(\sigma/\sqrt{n})$ tends to normality as $n \to \infty$.

We begin by finding from the tables of the normal distribution two numbers a and b such that

$$Pr\{a < \mathbf{z} < b\} = 1 - \alpha,$$

where $\mathbf{z}$ is normal (0,1), and where $100\alpha\%$ is the significance level we have decided on, or where we wish $100(1 - \alpha)\%$ confidence limits for μ. There are infinitely many choices we might make of a and b so as to have $Pr\{a < \mathbf{z} < b\} = 1 - \alpha$; we will obtain the shortest confidence interval if we choose $a = -b$, so that

$$Pr\{\mathbf{z} > b\} = \alpha/2$$

and

$$Pr\{\mathbf{z} < a\} = Pr\{\mathbf{z} < -b\} = \alpha/2.$$

Since $(\bar{\mathbf{x}} - \mu)/(\sigma/\sqrt{n})$ is (approximately) normal (0,1) (if n is large), we have

$$Pr\left\{-b < \frac{\bar{\mathbf{x}} - \mu}{\sigma/\sqrt{n}} < b\right\} \doteq 1 - \alpha.$$

The right inequality may be rewritten after multiplying both sides by $\sigma/\sqrt{n}$ and subtracting $\bar{\mathbf{x}}$:

$$-\mu < -\bar{\mathbf{x}} + \frac{b\sigma}{\sqrt{n}};$$

and on multiplying both sides by -1 (changing the sense of the inequality),

$$\mu > \bar{\mathbf{x}} - \frac{b\sigma}{\sqrt{n}}.$$

Similarly, the left inequality may be rewritten

$$\mu < \bar{\mathbf{x}} + \frac{b\sigma}{\sqrt{n}}.$$

We have, therefore,

$$Pr\left\{\bar{\mathbf{x}} - \frac{b\sigma}{\sqrt{n}} < \mu < \bar{\mathbf{x}} + \frac{b\sigma}{\sqrt{n}}\right\} = 1 - \alpha.$$

Now on taking a particular sample of size n and computing the sample mean $\bar{x}$, we have as a $100(1 - \alpha)\%$ *confidence interval* for μ:

$$\bar{x} - \frac{b\sigma}{\sqrt{n}} < \mu < \bar{x} + \frac{b\sigma}{\sqrt{n}}.$$

Further, *we shall reject at the* $100\alpha\%$ *significance level the hypothesis* $\mu = \mu_0$ *in favor of the alternative* $\mu \neq \mu_0$, *if* $|(\bar{x} - \mu_0)/(\sigma/\sqrt{n})| \geq b$, *or if* $\bar{x} - (b\sigma/\sqrt{n}) < \mu_0 < \bar{x} + (b\sigma/\sqrt{n})$ *is a false statement; that is, if* $\mu = \mu_0$ *does not lie in the above determined* $100(1 - \alpha)\%$ *confidence interval for* μ. *If* $\bar{x} - (b\sigma/\sqrt{n}) < \mu_0 < \bar{x} + (b\sigma/\sqrt{n})$ *is a true statement, we fail to reject the hypothesis* $\mu = \mu_0$ *at the* $100\alpha\%$ *significance level.*

In the above discussion, the population standard deviation σ was assumed known. If in fact σ is not known, another statistic, depending only on the unknown population mean μ, is required. It can be shown that

▶ *the asymptotic distribution of* $(\bar{\mathbf{x}} - \mu)/(\mathbf{s}/\sqrt{n})$ *is normal* (0,1): *if* $a < b$, *then* $Pr\{a < (\bar{\mathbf{x}} - \mu)/(\mathbf{s}/\sqrt{n}) < b\} \to \frac{1}{\sqrt{2\pi}}\int_a^b e^{-t^2/2}\,dt$ *as* $n \to \infty$.

The reason is essentially that the sample standard deviation $\mathbf{s}$ is a consistent estimator of the population standard deviation σ (Corollary F, page 143). That is, for large sample sizes there is a high probability that a sample will be chosen for which $\mathbf{s}$ differs very little from σ. For two numbers a and b, $a < b$, consider the two events: "$(\bar{\mathbf{x}} - \mu)/(\sigma/\sqrt{n})$ lies between a and b" and " $\mathbf{s}$ is very near σ." If both events occur, then $(\bar{\mathbf{x}} - \mu)/(\mathbf{s}/\sqrt{n})$ will lie between numbers very near a and b. If the probability of the first event is approximately equal to a number p, and the probability of the second is nearly 1, then the probability that both will occur is approximately equal to p. A careful proof that

$$\left|Pr\left\{a < \frac{\bar{\mathbf{x}} - \mu}{\sigma/\sqrt{n}} < b\right\} - Pr\left\{a < \frac{\bar{\mathbf{x}} - \mu}{\mathbf{s}/\sqrt{n}} < b\right\}\right| \to 0 \text{ as } n \to \infty$$

can be given along the lines of the arguments in pages 141–142.

63. A General Method for Determining Confidence Intervals and Testing Hypotheses of the Form $\theta = \theta_0$. In general you can obtain a confidence interval for a parameter θ of the parent population if you can find a statistic

z, a function of the sample random variables, whose distribution is known for each value of the parameter θ. If you are seeking a $100(1 - \alpha)\%$ confidence interval for θ you determine two numbers a and b, which will generally depend on θ, $a = a(\theta)$, $b = b(\theta)$, such that

$$Pr\{a(\theta) < \mathbf{z} < b(\theta)\} = 1 - \alpha.$$

After performing an experiment (taking a sample) to determine particular sample values and thus a particular value z of **z**, you find the interval (if it is an interval) in which θ must lie in order that the inequalitites

$$a(\theta) < z < b(\theta)$$

shall be satisfied. *That interval is then a* $100(1 - \alpha)\%$ *confidence interval for* θ. If you reject the hypothesis $\theta = \theta_0$ provided

$$a(\theta_0) < z < b(\theta_0)$$

is a false statement, and otherwise fail to reject it, you have a test of the hypothesis $\theta = \theta_0$ at the $100\alpha\%$ significance level.

The special case discussed above provides an example of the use of this method. Suppose you wish to determine $100(1 - \alpha)\%$ confidence limits for the population mean μ, or to test a hypothesis $\mu = \mu_0$ at the $100\alpha\%$ significance level. You seek a statistic **z** whose distribution is known for each value of the parameter μ. If the population standard deviation σ is known, and if the sample size is sufficiently large, the sample mean $\bar{\mathbf{x}}$ is such a statistic; for according to the Central Limit Theorem, $\bar{\mathbf{x}}$ is approximately normally distributed with mean μ and standard deviation σ. Thus two functions of μ, $a = a(\mu)$ and $b = b(\mu)$, can be found from the normal tables so that

$$Pr\{a(\mu) < \bar{\mathbf{x}} < b(\mu)\} = 1 - \alpha.$$

Suppose, for example, $\alpha = 0.05$ and $\sigma = 2$. Then from the normal tables we find that $Pr\{\bar{\mathbf{x}} \leq \mu - 4\} \doteq 0.025$, and $Pr\{\bar{\mathbf{x}} \geq \mu + 4\} \doteq 0.025$, so that

$$Pr\{\mu - 4 < \bar{\mathbf{x}} < \mu + 4\} \doteq 0.95;$$

that is, we may take $a(\mu) = \mu - 4$, $b(\mu) = \mu + 4$. If, in the inequality $\mu - 4 < \bar{\mathbf{x}} < \mu + 4$, the symbol $\bar{\mathbf{x}}$ is replaced by the sample mean actually observed (a number), and the resulting inequalities solved for μ, we obtain 95% confidence limits for μ. If, after replacing in the inequalities $\mu - 4 < \bar{\mathbf{x}} < \mu + 4$ both $\bar{\mathbf{x}}$ by the observed sample mean and μ by μ_0, we reject the hypothesis $\mu = \mu_0$ when and only when the inequality fails, we have a test at the $100\alpha\%$ significance level of the hypothesis $\mu = \mu_0$ against the alternative $\mu \neq \mu_0$.

There is an alternative way of describing what is essentially the same method for determining confidence intervals or testing hypotheses. Suppose you are able to find a random variable **y**, whose distribution is known precisely, and which is a function of the sample random variables and of the unknown parameter θ. If you are seeking a $100(1 - \alpha)\%$ confidence interval for θ, you determine two numbers a and b such that

$$Pr\{a < \mathbf{y} < b\} = 1 - \alpha.$$

After performing an experiment (taking a sample) to determine particular sample values, you find the interval (if it is an interval) in which θ must lie in order for y, the value of $\mathbf{y}$ at the sample values and at θ, to satisfy the inequalities

$$a < y < b.$$

That interval is then a $100(1 - \alpha)\%$ *confidence interval for* θ. If you reject the hypothesis $\theta = \theta_0$ provided

$$a < y < b$$

becomes a false statement when the sample values and θ_0 are substituted in the expression for y, and otherwise fail to reject it, you have a *test of the hypothesis* $\theta = \theta_0$ *at the* $100\alpha\%$ *significance level.*

Let us consider the problem of determining confidence intervals for the population mean μ or testing the hypothesis $\mu = \mu_0$ from this point of view. We seek a random variable $\mathbf{y}$ depending on μ and the sample random variables, whose distribution is known. If the sample size is sufficiently large and if the population standard deviation σ is known, then

$$\mathbf{y} = \frac{\bar{\mathbf{x}} - \mu}{\sigma/\sqrt{n}}$$

is such a random variable, having (approximately) a normal (0,1) distribution. If the sample size is sufficiently large and if the population standard deviation σ is not known, then

$$\mathbf{y} = \frac{\bar{\mathbf{x}} - \mu}{\mathbf{s}/\sqrt{n}}$$

is such a random variable, having (approximately) a normal (0,1) distribution; here $\mathbf{s}$ is the sample standard deviation (cf. p. 177). From the normal tables we find that

$$Pr\{-2 < \mathbf{y} < 2\} \doteq 0.95,$$

or

$$Pr\left\{-2 < \frac{\bar{\mathbf{x}} - \mu}{\mathbf{s}/\sqrt{n}} < 2\right\} \doteq 0.95.$$

If in the inequality $-2 < (\bar{\mathbf{x}} - \mu)/(\mathbf{s}/\sqrt{n}) < 2$ we replace $\bar{\mathbf{x}}$ and $\mathbf{s}$ by the observed sample mean and sample standard deviation respectively, and then solve the resulting inequalities for μ, we have 95% confidence limits for μ. If in the inequality $-2 < (\bar{\mathbf{x}} - \mu)/(\mathbf{s}/\sqrt{n}) < 2$ we replace $\bar{\mathbf{x}}$ and $\mathbf{s}$

by the observed sample mean and sample standard deviation respectively, and further replace the symbol μ by the number μ_0, rejecting the hypothesis $\mu = \mu_0$ if the resulting inequality is false, we have a test of the hypothesis $\mu = \mu_0$ at the 5% significance level.

This second way of describing the method of determining confidence intervals or of testing a hypothesis is in fact more general than the first. The reason is that whenever a statistic **z**, a function of the sample random variables alone, not depending on θ, can be found whose distribution is known for each value of the parameter θ, it is also possible to find a random variable **y** which is a function of the sample random variables and the parameter θ, and whose distribution is precisely known. The converse is not true. However, it is sometimes more convenient to think of the method from the first point of view, as in the following example.

EXAMPLE 3. You are given a coin. In 100 tosses, heads comes up 65 times. Are you justified in claiming the coin is unbalanced?

You may rephrase the question, asking whether you should reject the hypothesis that the coin is balanced, in favor of the alternative that it is unbalanced. But first you must decide on a level of significance. Suppose you choose the 5% significance level: $\alpha = 0.05$. To apply the general method discussed above, you require a statistic whose distribution depends on the population mean, p, alone; here p is the probability of throwing heads. Such a statistic is, say, the total number of successes, **S**: its mean is $np = 100p$ (page 108, its variance is $npq = 100p(1 - p)$ (page 108). Its probability function is

$$Pr\{\mathbf{S} = S\} = \binom{100}{S} p^S (1-p)^{100-S}, \quad S = 0, 1, 2, \cdots, 100.$$

If $p = 1/2$, then $E(\mathbf{S}) = 50$, $V(\mathbf{S}) = 25$; and to test the hypothesis $p = 1/2$ at the 5% significance level, we ask: if $p = 1/2$, is the probability that **S** will differ from its mean by as much as 15 smaller than or greater than 0.05? If smaller, we reject the hypothesis $p = 1/2$; if larger, we fail to reject it. We have

$$\begin{aligned} Pr\{|\mathbf{S} - 50| \geq 15\} &= \sum_{|S-50|\geq 15} \binom{100}{S} \left(\frac{1}{2}\right)^S \left(\frac{1}{2}\right)^{100-S} \\ &= \sum_{S=65}^{100} \binom{100}{S} \left(\frac{1}{2}\right)^S \left(\frac{1}{2}\right)^{100-S} \\ &\quad + \sum_{S=0}^{35} \binom{100}{S} \left(\frac{1}{2}\right)^S \left(\frac{1}{2}\right)^{100-S}, \end{aligned}$$

or

$$Pr\{|\mathbf{S} - 50| < 15\} = \sum_{S=36}^{64} \binom{100}{S} \left(\frac{1}{2}\right)^S \left(\frac{1}{2}\right)^{100-S}, \quad \text{if } p = \frac{1}{2}.$$

A direct calculation will now give us the probability we desire, but this calculation is quite tedious to perform; so we use instead the approximation given by De Moivre's Theorem (Corollary B, page 165):

$$Pr\{|\mathbf{S} - np| < 15\} = Pr\left\{\left|\frac{\mathbf{S} - np}{\sqrt{npq}}\right| < \frac{15}{5}\right\} \quad \text{(since } npq = 25\text{)}$$

$$= Pr\left\{-3 < \frac{\mathbf{S} - np}{\sqrt{npq}} < 3\right\} \doteq \frac{1}{\sqrt{2\pi}} \int_{-3}^{3} e^{-z^2/2}\, dz.$$

According to the normal tables, this latter probability is about 0.9974, so that

$$Pr\{|\mathbf{S} - np| \geq 15\} \doteq 0.0026$$

if $p = 1/2$. (The normal approximation with the correction mentioned on page 169 gives 0.0038 for this probability, which you will find is very nearly exact if you have sufficiently extensive binomial tables—0.0035.) Clearly then, you would reject the hypothesis $p = 1/2$ at the 5% significance level, or even at the 1% significance level.

Suppose you wish also to determine a 95% confidence interval for p. We let $\mathbf{S}$ play the role of $\mathbf{z}$ in the above discussion, p the role of θ, and wish to determine $a(\theta)$ and $b(\theta)$. By De Moivre's Theorem, $(\mathbf{S} - np)/\sqrt{npq}$ is approximately normal (0,1), and we find, using the normal tables, that

$$Pr\left\{-1.96 < \frac{\mathbf{S} - np}{\sqrt{npq}} < 1.96\right\} \doteq 0.95.$$

We shall then have 95% confidence limits for p if we replace $\mathbf{S}$ by 65 in the inequalities:

$$-1.96 < \frac{65 - 100p}{10\sqrt{p(1 - p)}} < 1.96,$$

and solve for p. The computations will be easier if we use 2 instead of 1.96:

$$-2 < \frac{65 - 100p}{10\sqrt{p(1 - p)}} < 2,$$

$$\left|\frac{65 - 100p}{10\sqrt{p(1 - p)}}\right| < 2,$$

$$(65 - 100p)^2 < 4 \cdot 100p(1 - p),$$

$$10{,}400p^2 - 13{,}400p + 4225 < 0.$$

From the quadratic formula we find that the left member is 0 for $p = 0.55$ and $p = 0.74$. It is positive for large positive p and for large negative p, so that the solutions of the inequality are values of p between 0.55 and 0.74: (0.55,0.74) is a 95% confidence interval for p. We note that the value

$p = 1/2$ is not contained in this confidence interval, and thus verify what we found above, that this test rejects, at the 5% significance level, the hypothesis $p = 1/2$ in favor of the alternative $p \neq 1/2$.

64. Testing the Difference between Two Means. One of the most frequently occurring situations in which statistical analysis is to be applied is that in which the means of two populations are to be compared. When a difference is observed between two sample means, the question arises: "Is the difference small enough so that it could reasonably have occurred by chance if the population means were the same, or is it so large that a difference that large or larger would be very unlikely to occur if the population means were the same?" Thus the investigator may wish to know whether or not the application of nitrogen has increased his corn yield significantly; whether or not the results of an achievement test indicate a significant difference between two groups of students; whether or not distinct manufacturing processes yield products of substantially the same quality, etc. The hypothesis to be tested is that the population means are the same, or that their difference is zero: a "null" hypothesis. In other situations as well, the hypothesis to be tested is frequently referred to as the *null hypothesis*.

65. Standard Deviations Known. If the populations have unknown means μ_1 and μ_2 and known standard deviations σ_1 and σ_2, then an appropriate statistic for use in testing the hypothesis $H_0: \mu_1 = \mu_2$ against the alternative $\mu_1 \neq \mu_2$ is

$$\frac{\bar{\mathbf{x}}_1 - \bar{\mathbf{x}}_2}{\sqrt{\dfrac{\sigma_1^2}{n_1} + \dfrac{\sigma_2^2}{n_2}}};$$

here n_1, n_2 are the sample sizes, $\bar{\mathbf{x}}_1$, $\bar{\mathbf{x}}_2$ the sample means. To see this we observe that since $\bar{\mathbf{x}}_1$ and $\bar{\mathbf{x}}_2$ are independent,

$$V(\bar{\mathbf{x}}_1 - \bar{\mathbf{x}}_2) = V(\bar{\mathbf{x}}_1) + V(\bar{\mathbf{x}}_2) = \frac{\sigma_1^2}{n_1} + \frac{\sigma_2^2}{n_2}.$$

Further, if H_0 is true, then $E(\bar{\mathbf{x}}_1 - \bar{\mathbf{x}}_2) = 0$. Thus this statistic has mean 0 and standard deviation 1. Both $\bar{\mathbf{x}}_1$ and $\bar{\mathbf{x}}_2$ are approximately normally distributed for large n_1 and n_2, by the Central Limit Theorem; it can be shown that their difference is also, and

▶ the statistic $(\bar{\mathbf{x}}_1 - \bar{\mathbf{x}}_2) \Big/ \sqrt{\dfrac{\sigma_1^2}{n_1} + \dfrac{\sigma_2^2}{n_2}}$ is for large sample sizes approximately normal (0,1).

Standard Deviations Unknown. Let σ_1, σ_2 denote the unknown standard deviations of the two populations, and let s_1^2, s_2^2 denote sample variances of the two samples. These sample variances are consistent estimators of the corresponding population variances (page 143); it can be shown to follow (cf. also page 177) that

▶ the statistic $(\bar{x}_1 - \bar{x}_2) \Big/ \sqrt{\dfrac{s_1^2}{n_1} + \dfrac{s_2^2}{n_2}}$ is, for large sample sizes, approximately normal (0,1).

66. Standard Deviations Unknown, but Assumed Equal. We assume here that σ_1 and σ_2 are not known, but are known to be equal: $\sigma_1 = \sigma_2 = \sigma$. The sum of the squared deviations of the sample random variables from the sample mean of the sample from the first population is $n_1 s_1^2$, and the corresponding sum for the other is $n_2 s_2^2$. The assumption that the standard deviations σ_1 and σ_2 are equal suggests pooling the sums of squares and using the overall mean square,

$$\frac{n_1 s_1^2 + n_2 s_2^2}{n_1 + n_2}$$

as an estimator of the common variance σ^2. In fact, we have already observed that s_1^2 and s_2^2 are consistent estimators of σ^2; it can be shown to follow (cf. Corollary C, page 142) that $(n_1 s_1^2 + n_2 s_2^2)/(n_1 + n_2)$ is also a consistent estimator of σ^2. Now

$$V(\bar{x}_1 - \bar{x}_2) = \frac{\sigma_1^2}{n_1} + \frac{\sigma_2^2}{n_2} = \frac{(n_1 + n_2)\sigma^2}{n_1 n_2};$$

hence $(\bar{x}_1 - \bar{x}_2)/\sqrt{(n_1 + n_2)\sigma^2/n_1 n_2}$ is asymptotically normal (0,1). But $(n_1 s_1^2 + n_2 s_2^2)/n_1 n_2$ is a consistent estimator of $(n_1 + n_2)\sigma^2/n_1 n_2$, so that

▶ the statistic

$$\frac{(\bar{x}_1 - \bar{x}_2)\sqrt{n_1 n_2}}{\sqrt{n_1 s_1^2 + n_2 s_2^2}} = \frac{(\bar{x}_1 - \bar{x}_2)}{\sqrt{\dfrac{s_1^2}{n_2} + \dfrac{s_2^2}{n_1}}}$$

is asymptotically normal (0,1), as $n_1, n_2 \to \infty$.

Cf. also p. 258 and following.

(Straightforward computation shows that if the populations have equal second and fourth moments about the mean, then at least for large n_1 and n_2 the variance of $s_1^2/n_2 + s_2^2/n_1$ is at least as small as that of $s_1^2/n_1 + s_2^2/n_2$.)

EXAMPLE 4. On the same achievement test, 100 students from the West Side School had a mean score 60 with sample standard deviation 18, while 200 students from the East Side School had mean score 64 with sample standard deviation 15. We ask: Is the difference significant at the 5% level?

We have in mind the following assumptions:

(1) Each group of students may be thought of as selected at random from a (somewhat hypothetical) group of all students taught at the appropriate school over an indefinite period of time.

(2) The sample sizes are not so small, and the populations not so pathological, as to render doubtful the approximate normality of the appropriate statistic.

We find

$$\frac{\bar{x}_2 - \bar{x}_1}{\sqrt{\dfrac{s_1{}^2}{n_1} + \dfrac{s_2{}^2}{n_2}}} = 1.91.$$

Referring to the normal tables, we find that a random variable which is normal (0,1) has probability 0.056 of assuming a value this far from 0. The difference between means is therefore not quite significant at the 5% level.

Now suppose that past experience with similar achievement tests justifies the following further assumption:

(3) The two populations have the same variance.

We find now

$$\frac{\bar{x}_2 - \bar{x}_1}{\sqrt{s_1{}^2/n_2 + s_2{}^2/n_1}} = 2.03.$$

A normal (0,1) random variable has a probability 0.042 of assuming a value this far from 0, and the difference is significant at the 5% level.

PROBLEMS

1. Suppose you have sufficient reason to believe that the standard deviation in height in a certain large group is 15 cm., and you find the average height of 100 individuals selected at random is 175. Determine a 95% confidence interval for the mean height of the group.

2. Suppose the volume of noise in decibels produced when T. A. pulls Tabby's tail has a standard deviation of 7 decibels. Miss T. makes 49 measurements and finds a sample mean of 50.

(a) Determine 90% confidence limits for the mean noise level.

(b) Test at the 5% significance level the hypothesis that the mean noise level is 48.2 against the alternative that it is not; test at the 10% significance level.

3. A random sample of size 100 is drawn from a population with standard deviation 40. The sample mean is found to be 7.

(a) Set up 95% confidence limits for the population mean.

(b) Test at the 5% significance level the hypothesis that the population mean is 0 against the alternative that it is not.

4. In Deepest Africa you select at random 100 men from among the adults of a large pigmy tribe, and find they have average height 4 feet with sample standard deviation 1/2 foot. Assume that the sample is large enough for the sample mean to be approximately normally distributed, with population variance approximately equal to sample variance. Find 90% confidence limits for the average height of men of the tribe.

5. In 49 tosses of two dice, 7 spots turned up 15 times. Test at the 5% significance level the hypothesis that the probability of 7 is 1/6 against the hypothesis that it is not.

6. Principal T. of Davis Heights High School (DHHS) believes that, partly because of the financial status of their parents, the percentage of his graduates attending college is larger than the city-wide average. Over the preceding 5 years, 20% of all high-school graduates in the city had attended college, while in the same period 350 of his 1500 graduates attended college. Is the principal justified in saying that the percentage of graduates of DHHS attending college is significantly higher than 20%, at the 1% significance level?

7. Suppose your experience indicates that wire rods purchased from a certain company have a mean breaking strength of 400 lb. and a standard deviation of 15 lb. Assuming that those in a new lot come from a population of standard deviation 15 lb., find how many rods you should test in order to have a probability 0.95 that the resulting mean strength would not be in error by more than 2 lb.

8. If the difference between means is found to be significant at the 5% level, does it follow that it is also significant at the 1% level? at the 10% level?

9. From a student body of 8000, a student opinion group takes a random sample of size 100, asking each person selected his (her) opinion on a certain proposal. They find that 75 favor the proposal, while 25 do not. Test the hypothesis that the proportion favoring the proposal is 2/3 against the alternative that it is not, at the 5% significance level. What role does the Central Limit Theorem play in your solution?

10. Two hundred army recruits have an average pulse rate 72 beats per minute with a sample variance of 100. Find 95% confidence limits for the mean pulse rate of recruits.

11. Thirty students in a physics laboratory make determinations of the speed of sound. The average of their determinations is 11,000 ft./sec., and the sample standard deviation is 200 ft./sec. Find a 90% confidence interval and a 50% confidence interval for the "true" speed of sound in the laboratory at the time.

12. Test at the 5% significance level the hypothesis that a certain genetic character has a probability 1/4 of appearing in an individual selected at random from a second generation group of plants, if 25 out of 125 exhibited it.

13. Suppose you have given a class of engineering students and a class of arts students a test in the basic skills of English. The mean score of one group, of size 50, was 75 with standard deviation 10; the mean score of the other group, of size 40, was 69 with standard deviation 15. Assuming the population standard deviations equal, would you say the difference in means is significant at the 5% level? at the 1% level?

14. In a certain state election 52% of the 10,000 who voted in City A voted for candidate C, while in City B (20,000 votes) 54% voted for candidate C. Is the difference significant at the 1% level?

15. Suppose you find that 80 students coming from rural communities have a mean absolute visual threshold 2.01 in appropriate units, with standard deviation 0.31, while 120 students from urban communities have a mean absolute visual threshold 1.89 with standard deviation 0.29. Assuming the population variances the same, tell whether the difference is significant at the 1% level.

16. In a random sample of 100 frogs, the average life span was 10 years with standard deviation 3 years, while in a random sample of 200 dogs the average life span was 11 years with standard deviation 4 years. At what level of significance is one justified in concluding that the mean life spans of frogs and dogs differ?

17. Of 50 rounds fired at a target, 35 were hits.

(a) Determine 80% confidence limits for the probability of a hit.

(b) Test at the 10% significance level the hypothesis that the probability of a hit is 0.8, against the alternative that it is not.

18. Of 64 dates selected at random, there was a measurable amount of precipitation in the form of rain on 18 of them. (a) Determine 90% confidence limits for the probability that it will rain on a date selected at random. (b) Test, at the 10% level, the hypothesis that it rains on the average one day out of three, against the alternative that it does not.

19. How large a sample would you require to determine a 95% confidence interval of length not more than 0.05 for the proportion of people in a given large group who prefer steak well-done to rare?

20. Suppose a continuous population random variable $\mathbf{x}$ has a density function $f(x)$ which is increasing for $x < m$, decreasing for $x > m$, and thus has a single maximum (the *mode* of $\mathbf{x}$) at $x = m$.

(a) Show that if α is a given number, $0 < \alpha < 1$, and if R is defined by

$$1 - \alpha = \int_u^{u+R} f(x)\, dx$$

for each u, then R is minimized for a choice of u, $u < m$, for which $f(u) = f(u + R)$.

(b) Use your result in (a) to show how to determine the shortest confidence interval for the mean in sampling from a normally distributed population with known standard deviation.

21. Suppose it is asked whether there is any significant difference between the National and the American (Baseball) Leagues in winning (7-game) World Series. The National League has won 20 out of the 55 seven-game World Series which have been played (up to and including 1958).

(a) Test at the .05 level the hypothesis that the probability, p, of the National League winning a (7-game) World Series is 1/2 against the alternative that it is not.

(b) Obtain a 95% confidence interval for p.

(c) Of what population are the 55 observations a sample?

(*Source:* Mosteller, F., "The World Series Competition," *Journal of the American Statistical Association*, Vol. 47 (1952), p. 360.)

22. Consider two populations of identical twin pairs, one population (I) in which every pair of twins is separated soon after birth (reared apart) and one population (II) in which every pair of twins is reared together. A pair of twins may be either "alike" or "unalike" in smoking habits. Let p_1 be the proportion of "alike" twin pairs in population I and let p_2 be the proportion of "alike" pairs in population II. In a sample of 27 pairs of twins from population I, 23 pairs were "alike" in smoking habits; in a sample of 26 pairs of twins from population II, 21 pairs were "alike."

(a) Obtain a 95% confidence interval for $p_1 - p_2$.

(b) Test the hypothesis $p_1 = p_2$ against the alternative hypothesis $p_1 \neq p_2$ at the .05 significance level.

(c) Does this test provide evidence that (identical) twins reared apart are no different than (identical) twins reared together with respect to similarity of smoking habits?

(*Source:* Fisher, R. A. As reported in the *Chicago Sun-Times* article "Rolls Cigaret Data; Calls 'Em Helpful" on p. 24, Wednesday, Sept. 17, 1958.)

★CHAPTER

11

Decision Theory and Bayesian Inference

67. Introduction. Throughout most of the text we work with methods and concepts that have been used very widely for some time. Of course these ideas are by no means old when compared with those of many other fields of applied mathematics; many of these developments have their main roots in work of R. A. Fisher (1890–1962) and in work of E. S. Pearson, J. Neyman, and others who continue to participate actively in the further development of the field.

We emphasize again that one can not (and would not) hope to find in a textbook ready-made solutions ("recipes") of more than a small fraction of the problems he will meet in his working lifetime. New problems have features distinguishing them from problems already solved; one can only hope or believe that some of the techniques and ideas proved useful in the past will also be helpful in the future.

The concepts of statistical tests and confidence limits play very important roles in current applications of statistical method. But recent years have witnessed the introduction of other concepts intended to replace or to supplement these now "classical" ideas; it is the purpose of this chapter to provide a very brief introduction to some of them.

We have seen in Chapter 10 that there are in general many tests at, say, the 5% significance level of a null hypothesis: $\mu = \mu_0$. In Example 2 of that chapter we selected a test which rejects the hypothesis $\mu = 50$ if the inequalities $-1.03 < \bar{x} - \mu < 1.03$ are not satisfied. Another test at the 5% level would reject the hypothesis if inequalities $-0.99 = -1.88\sqrt{10}/6 < \bar{x} - \mu < 2.05\sqrt{10}/6 = 1.08$ are not satisfied. It is true that the first test possesses a certain attractive symmetry the second does not. While it may be shown to have other desirable properties as well, it appears impossible, both in this case and in general, to avoid the subjective element in the choice of a test. This applies in particular to the choice of a significance level. It has been suggested (cf. F. J. Anscombe, Bayesian Statistics, American Statistician, Vol. 15 (1961), pp. 21–24) that an approach via statistical decision theory or Bayesian inference makes it possible to formalize, at least in part, the subjective element inherent in applying statistical theory. Recent interest in statistical decision theory was stimulated largely by the work of Wald in a series of papers beginning in 1939 and in his book [19]. We shall be able here only to introduce some of the basic concepts, with a few simple (simplified!) examples.

From the point of view of statistical decision theory, the statistician uses the result of an experiment as an aid in arriving at a decision to take one or another of alternative possible actions. He may have to decide between the two alternatives of rejecting or failing to reject a null hypothesis. Or the action required may be that he assert that the population mean is a certain number or lies in a certain interval; here the alternative actions are infinite in number. The problems of testing hypotheses and of estimation of parameters are thus subsumed under general decision theory. In sequential testing situations, a possible action at a certain stage of the experiment might be to continue testing. Statistical decision theory is very general in character, and has given new and penetrating insights into many phases of statistical activity.

Let us denote by $\mathcal{A}$ the set of possible *actions*. If one is testing a null hypothesis H_0, $\mathcal{A}$ may have two members: a_1, reject H_0; a_2, fail to reject H_0. If one is estimating a wave length from physical observations, $\mathcal{A}$ may have infinitely many members, one corresponding to each possible wave length. Here an "action" would be an assertion that the wave length is a certain number.

Let $\mathcal{S}$ denote the *sample space*. In general, each element of the sample space represents one possible outcome of the experiment the statistician performs as an aid in arriving at a decision. If the experiment should consist of n independent observations on a random variable $\mathbf{x}$ (i.e., a random sample of size n from the population whose random variable is $\mathbf{x}$), then $\mathcal{S}$ would consist of all sample points $s = (x_1, x_2, \cdots, x_n)$, where x_i is the result of the ith observation, a value of the ith sample random variable, $i = 1, 2, \cdots, n$.

A *decision function d* is a function whose domain is $\mathcal{S}$ and whose range is included in $\mathcal{A}$. That is, a decision function is a rule associating with each member s of the sample space a possible action a in $\mathcal{A}$: $d(s) = a$; d is the name of the function, s is an element of the sample space, and $d(s)$, or a, is the action prescribed by the decision function when the result s of the experiment is observed.

For example, suppose one wishes to estimate the unknown mean μ of a population, using a random sample of size n from the population. A possible action is represented by a real number, which one will assert is the estimate of the population mean. One possible decision rule makes correspond to each point $s = (x_1, x_2, \cdots, x_n)$ in the sample space the mean $\bar{x} = (1/n) \sum_{i=1}^{n} x_i$, an element in $\mathcal{A}$, a possible action. For this decision rule d, $d(s) = \bar{x}$ when $s = (x_1, x_2, \cdots, x_n)$.

Again, suppose you plan to use a test of the null hypothesis $H_0: \mu = 3$ which requires you to reject H_0 if $\bar{x} > 4$, and to fail to reject H_0 if $\bar{x} \leq 4$. There would then be two elements in $\mathcal{A}$, a_1: reject H_0, and a_2: fail to reject H_0. Your test is prescribed by a decision function d for which $d(s) = a_1$ if $s = (x_1, x_2, \cdots, x_n)$ and $\frac{1}{n}\sum_{i=1}^{n} x_i > 4$, while $d(s) = a_2$ if $s = (x_1, x_2, \cdots, x_n)$ and $\frac{1}{n} \sum_{i=1}^{n} x_i \leq 4$.

An essential part of the picture is the probability distribution on the sample space. In any nontrivial situation this is unknown to the statistician, for if he knew with exactly what probabilities he might expect the various possible results s, it would be unnecessary for him to perform the experiment.

For example, suppose 10 observations are to be made on the wave length of light from a monochromatic source, using a certain apparatus. Suppose it is known or assumed that the result of a single observation is a normally distributed random variable whose mean is the unknown true wave length λ, and whose standard deviation is 1 unit. The sample space consists of all 10-tuples $s = (x_1, x_2, \cdots, x_{10})$ of real numbers. The distribution on the sample space, the joint distribution of the sample random variables, is unknown since λ is unknown, but is completely determined when λ is specified. Indeed, the joint density function of the sample random variables is the product

$$\prod_{i=1}^{10} f(x_i;\lambda) \quad \text{where } f(x;\lambda) = \frac{1}{\sqrt{2\pi}} e^{-\frac{1}{2}(x-\lambda)^2}.$$

Thus to each λ corresponds a probability distribution on $\mathcal{S}$. If both mean λ and standard deviation σ of the normal parent population were unknown, then to each pair (λ,σ) would correspond a probability distribution on $\mathcal{S}$.

In general, we suppose there is in any particular situation a *parameter space* Ω consisting of elements ω, associated with each of which is a probability distribution on $\mathcal{S}$. In the above illustration, Ω might be the set of all possible wave lengths, and $\omega = \lambda$ a particular one. Or if σ were unknown, each ω would represent a pair (λ,σ). More generally, ω need not be a parameter or finite set of parameters at all. For example, the "parameter" space might even consist of all possible probability distributions on $\mathcal{S}$.

In the above illustration, the statistician would know what action to take if he knew λ. But he doesn't; and he may think of himself as involved in a game with nature, in which nature chooses a value of λ and in which the statistician, after a little spying (the experiment!) chooses an action. In fact, there is a very intimate relationship between statistical decision theory and game theory (cf. [2]). One of the most obvious differences is that often in game theory one deals with an intelligent, antagonistically motivated opponent, while most of us are not willing to cast nature in such a role.

68. Principles of Choice. The essential question which the statistician must answer is: how to choose between alternative decision functions? Attention has been devoted for the most part to an approach involving two steps.

(1) Associate in some way with each possible ω in the parameter space a *utility* of each possible decision function d: $U(d;\omega)$.

(2) Base the ultimate choice of a decision function on the application of some appealing *principle of choice*, or criterion, using the utility function determined in (1).

We illustrate (2) first. Suppose in a given situation you have been successful in assigning a utility $U(d;\omega)$ to each decision function d for each ω in Ω. A most conservative principle of choice is the *minimax principle:* choose that decision function d for which $\min_{\omega} U(d;\omega)$ is as large as possible. (We neglect questions of existence and uniqueness.)
If you were playing against an antagonistic opponent who had it in his power to choose ω, and if after you chose d he would choose ω so as to minimize your utility, then with this principle you would salvage as much as possible from the situation. If we introduce "inutility" as the negative of utility, $I(d;\omega) = -U(d;\omega)$, then to minimize U is to maximize I, and to maximize $\min_{\omega} U(d;\omega)$ is equivalent to minimizing $\max_{\omega} I(d;\omega)$. Thus the minimax principle is to choose d so as to *minimize* the *maximum* for all ω of $I(d;\omega)$; this accounts for the name.

When the "opponent" is nature, such an attitude seems unnecessarily pessimistic. Indeed, the application of this principle may lead to most unreasonable decisions. Suppose you are offered for purchase a quantity of ore at such a price that you will make a profit only if at least a certain fraction, p_0, of it is gold. Two actions are possible: a_1, to buy; and a_2, to refuse to buy. You plan to take samples and to base your decision on the fraction $\bar{p}$ of gold in the samples. Your decision function d is then a function of the observed fraction $\bar{p}$ of gold in the samples. It has only two "values," either a_1 or a_2, for each $\bar{p}$. Let p denote the unknown true fraction of gold in the entire quantity of ore. The number p here plays the role of ω, and Ω consists of all numbers p between 0 and 1 inclusive. The value of p determines the probability distribution on the sample space. Suppose you use as utility, $U(d;p)$, your expected profit if the true fraction is p and if you use decision function d. Your profit is negative if $p < p_0$ and if you choose action a_1, while it is 0 if $p < p_0$ and if you choose action a_2. Therefore $\min_p U(d;p) < 0$ for *every* decision function d, *except* the one decision function which assigns action a_2 to every outcome of the experiment. (We assume every decision function which yields a positive probability of buying for some $p > p_0$ also yields a positive probability of buying for some $p < p_0$.) For this last decision function, the utility is 0, whatever p may be. Using the minimax principle then, you would refuse to buy the ore, whatever the result of your tests.

A modification of the minimax principle is the *minimax loss* or *minimax regret* principle: choose d so as to maximize $\min_\omega [U(d;\omega) - \max_d U(d;\omega)]$; see [2], page 114.

Let us now consider another principle of choice applicable to a situation in which you may think of $\boldsymbol{\omega}$ as a random variable (or combined random variable), chosen according to some chance process, and in which you know its probability distribution. You may then use the *Bayes principle:* choose that decision function d_0 which maximizes your expected utility; d_0 is a decision function chosen so that

$$E[U(d_0;\boldsymbol{\omega})] = \max_d E[U(d;\boldsymbol{\omega})].$$

Here $\boldsymbol{\omega}$ is the random variable involved, and $E[U(d;\boldsymbol{\omega})]$ is computed according to the probability distribution of $\boldsymbol{\omega}$, assumed known.

In the illustration above, if you knew where the ore came from, you might be able to form an estimated probability distribution for $\mathbf{p}$, the unknown fraction of gold in the ore. Using the Bayes principle, you would first compute, for a given decision function and a fixed p, your expected profit (utility), using the sample space probability distribution determined by p. You would then compute the expected value of this result, still holding the decision function fixed, and using the probability distribution of $\mathbf{p}$. Finally, you would choose the decision function for which this expected value is as large as possible. An alternative way of describing the Bayes method is discussed on pages 198–199.

There is a close relationship between the Bayes principle and the minimax principle. Indeed, it is often the case that the minimax decision function coincides with the Bayes decision function for a "least favorable" *a priori* distribution. Let us denote by $f(\omega)$ a frequency function (or density function) of $\boldsymbol{\omega}$. Let $E[U(d;\boldsymbol{\omega});f]$ denote the expected utility using decision function d if $\boldsymbol{\omega}$ has frequency function f. Then $f_0(\omega)$ is the frequency function of a *least favorable a priori distribution of* $\boldsymbol{\omega}$ if for every possible frequency function f,

$$\max_d E[U(d;\boldsymbol{\omega});f_0] \leq \max_d E[U(d;\boldsymbol{\omega});f].$$

That is, *an a priori frequency function f_0 is least favorable if the Bayes decision function for every other a priori distribution gives at least as large an expected utility as does the Bayes decision function for f_0.*

An observation which is sometimes useful in finding a minimax decision function is that *if a decision function d_0 is Bayes for an a priori frequency function* (*or density function*) *f_0 of $\boldsymbol{\omega}$ and if*

$$E[U(d_0;\boldsymbol{\omega});f_0] = \min_{\omega} U(d_0;\omega),$$

then d_0 is a minimax decision function, and f_0 gives a least favorable a priori distribution of $\boldsymbol{\omega}$. To prove this we note first that to say that d_0 is Bayes for f_0 means that $E[U(d_0;\boldsymbol{\omega});f_0] = \max_{d} E[U(d;\boldsymbol{\omega});f_0]$; that is, for every decision function d we have

$$E[U(d_0;\boldsymbol{\omega});f_0] \geq E[U(d;\boldsymbol{\omega});f_0].$$

Also, if m is the minimum value of a random variable $\mathbf{x}$, we have $E(\mathbf{x}) \geq m$. In particular, $E[U(d,\boldsymbol{\omega});\, f_0] \geq \min_{\omega} U(d;\omega)$. Thus if d is any decision function, we have the chain of inequalities,

$$\begin{aligned}\min_{\omega} U(d_0;\omega) = E[U(d_0;\boldsymbol{\omega});\, f_0] &\geq E[U(d;\boldsymbol{\omega});f_0]\\ &\geq \min_{\omega} U(d;\omega).\end{aligned}$$

Hence for every decision function d,

$$\min_{\omega} U(d_0;\omega) \geq \min_{\omega} U(d;\omega).$$

But this states simply that d_0 is a minimax decision function, a decision function for which the minimum possible utility is as large as possible.

Furthermore, since d_0 is a particular decision function, we have for every *a priori* frequency function f,

$$\max_{d} E[U(d;\boldsymbol{\omega});f] \geq E[U(d_0;\boldsymbol{\omega});f].$$

Also,

$$E[U(d_0;\boldsymbol{\omega});f] \geq \min_{\omega} U(d_0;\omega) = E[U(d_0;\boldsymbol{\omega});f_0].$$

Therefore, for every frequency function f,

$$\max_{d} E[U(d;\boldsymbol{\omega});f] \geq E[U(d_0;\boldsymbol{\omega});f_0],$$

or

$$\max_{d} E[U(d;\boldsymbol{\omega});f] \geq \max_{d} E[U(d;\boldsymbol{\omega});f_0].$$

But this states that f_0 is a least favorable *a priori* frequency function for $\boldsymbol{\omega}$, and completes the proof.

We may replace utility by inutility in the above discussion, at the same time reversing all inequalities, and replacing max by min, min by max.

69. Utility, Loss, and Risk. Suppose the statistician is able to determine a precise, numerical *loss* L which will result from action a if ω is the true element of the parameter space: $L = L(a;\omega)$. Then if he uses decision function d and if the result of the experiment is s, his loss will be $L[d(s);\ \omega]$. Before the experiment is conducted, his *expected loss* is $E[L(d(\mathbf{s});\omega)]$, the expected value being computed using the probability distribution, determined by ω, over the sample space. This expected loss is called the *risk*, r:

$$r(d;\omega) = E[L(d(\mathbf{s});\omega)].$$

Suppose, for example, the experiment consists of taking a random sample of size n from a discrete population with probability function $f(x;\omega)$. An element of the sample space is $s = (x_1, x_2, \cdots, x_n)$. The joint density function of the sample random variables is $\prod_{i=1}^{n} f(x_i;\omega)$. If $d(x_1, x_2, \cdots, x_n)$ denotes the action prescribed by decision function d when the sample point $(x_1, x_2, \cdots, x_n)$ is observed, then the risk is

$$r = r(d;\omega) = \sum_{x_1, x_2, \cdots, x_n} L[d(x_1, x_2, \cdots, x_n);\omega] f(x_1;\omega) \cdots f(x_n;\omega).$$

This risk, an expected loss, can be taken as the negative of utility, or inutility, in the above discussions:

$$I(d;\omega) = r(d;\omega), \text{ or } U(d;\omega) = -r(d;\omega).$$

Again, one is often at a loss as to what loss function should be assigned. However, a more or less satisfactory situation will obtain if it can be ascertained that essentially the same conclusion can be drawn if any of a wide class of "reasonable" loss functions is used—and this is sometimes the case.

EXAMPLE 1. To illustrate these concepts, we consider the following situation, simplified in an admittedly unreasonable way. You are preparing to ship 1000 items of your manufacture to a customer. You guarantee them non-defective, under an arrangement whereby you furnish a new one for each one found defective and also refund its purchase price, at a total cost to you of mc (including, perhaps, an estimated monetary equivalent of loss of good will), where m is the total number defective and c is the loss per defective item. Suppose you plan to test 20, and, depending on the number of defectives found, either

(i) replace the defectives found with non-defective items at a cost h each, or

(ii) test all 1000 at an additional testing cost of C, and replace each defective at a cost h. Suppose you will follow (i) if the number of defectives among the 20 tested is k or fewer, (ii) if the number of defectives is greater than k. The specification of k then determines the decision rule you are using.

Involved under (i) are actually 21 possible actions: a_0, no defective is found, and you replace none; a_1, one defective is found, and you replace it, etc. Thus the space $\mathcal{A}$ of actions has 22 elements: 21 under (i), and 1, which we shall call a_{21}, under (ii).

The sample space $\mathcal{S}$ can be set up in any of a variety of ways. An element s of $\mathcal{S}$ might be taken to be an ordered set of 20 1's and 0's; 1 would appear in the first place if the first item tested were defective, otherwise 0; 1 would appear in the second place if the second item tested were defective, otherwise 0, etc. However, since each decision function to be considered is based on the total number of defectives alone, it will be simpler to let the sample space consist of the integers $0, 1, 2, \cdots, 20$, possible numbers of defectives.

We assume the total lot large enough that we make a negligible error in treating the tests of the 20 items as independent trials of an event whose unknown probability is $p = N/1000$, where N is the number of defectives in the total lot, and p the probability that an item chosen at random will prove to be defective.

With each possible value of p: $0, 0.001, 0.002, \cdots, 1.000$, is associated a sample space probability distribution. If $\mathbf{s}$ is the number of defectives to be found among the 20, then $Pr\{\mathbf{s} = s\} = \binom{20}{s} p^s(1 - p)^{20-s}$, for $s = 0, 1, 2, \cdots, 20$. Here p plays the role of ω in the above general discussion, and Ω consists of the 1001 possible values of p.

Suppose that action a_0 is taken, and that $N = 1000p$ is the true number of defectives. The customer will find N defectives, so that your loss is $L(p,a_0) = Nc$. If action a_1 is taken, the customer will find $N - 1$ defectives, and your loss is $L(p,a_1) = (N - 1)c + h$. In general, if action a_i is taken, $i = 0, 1, 2, \cdots, 20$, your loss is $L(p,a_i) = (N - i)c + ih$. If action a_{21} is taken, your loss is $L(p,a_{21}) = C + Nh$.

Suppose you are using the decision rule d determined by a number k of defectives among the 20 tested items. Then $d(s) = a_0$ if $s = 0$; that is, $d(0) = a_0$. Similarly, $d(1) = a_1$, $d(2) = a_2, \cdots, d(i) = a_i$ if $i = 0, 1, 2, \cdots, k$. But $d(s) = a_{21}$ if $s > k$. The risk is given by

$$r = r(d; p) = \sum_{s=0}^{20} L[d(s); p] \binom{20}{s} p^s(1 - p)^{20-s}.$$

We have

$$r = L(a_0;p)\, Pr\{\mathbf{s} = 0\} + L(a_1;p)\, Pr\{\mathbf{s} = 1\} + \cdots + L(a_k;p)\, Pr\{\mathbf{s} = k\} + L(a_{21};p)\, Pr\{\mathbf{s} = k + 1\} + \cdots + L(a_{21};p)\, Pr\{\mathbf{s} = 20\},$$

or

$$r = \sum_{s=0}^{k} [(N - s)c + sh] \binom{20}{s} p^s(1 - p)^{20-s} + (C + Nh) \sum_{s=k+1}^{20} \binom{20}{s} p^s(1 - p)^{20-s},$$

where $N = 1000p$.

70. Mixed Strategies, Admissible Strategies, and Complete Classes. We shall here simply introduce these terms, which you will meet in other reading. Using game-theoretic terminology, we may say that the choice by the statistician of a decision function constitutes a *pure strategy*. A *mixed strategy* is a chance process he uses to choose possible alternative decision functions with specified probabilities. Suppose decision functions $d_1(s), d_2(s), \cdots$ are available to the statistician. If he then chooses positive numbers $\lambda_1, \lambda_2, \cdots$, whose sum is 1, and if he will use decision function d_1 with probability λ_1, decision function d_2 with probability λ_2, etc., he has chosen a mixed strategy; the numbers $\lambda_1, \lambda_2, \cdots$ determine his mixed strategy.

We shall illustrate in a simple if somewhat inadequate way the possibilities of mixed strategies, by considering a coin-matching game. Players I and II simultaneously place coins on a table. If they match, Player II wins a dollar; if not, he loses a dollar. Suppose Player II bases his choice of strategy on the minimax principle. If he places his coin heads up, his maximum possible loss is a dollar; his maximum possible loss is also a dollar if he chooses tails. But now suppose he uses a random device (such as tossing the coin) to choose heads with probability 1/2 and tails with probability 1/2. His maximum expected loss is now 0, whereas it was 1 with either pure strategy.

Suppose we denote by $\lambda = (\lambda_1, \lambda_2, \cdots)$ a possible mixed strategy for the statistician: with this strategy there is a probability λ_1 that he will use decision function d_1, a probability λ_2 that he will use decision function d_2, etc. Let $L(a;\omega)$ be a loss function, and $p(s|\omega)$ the probability of outcome s (assumed discrete) of the experiment for a given ω in Ω. Then the risk or expected loss is given by

$$\rho = \rho(\lambda;\omega) = \sum_s p(s|\omega) \sum_i \lambda_i L[d_i(s);\omega].$$

We should say that a mixed strategy λ^* is *better* than a mixed strategy λ for a given ω if $\rho(\lambda^*;\omega) < \rho(\lambda;\omega)$, and *at least as good* for ω if $\rho(\lambda^*;\omega) \leq \rho(\lambda;\omega)$. We say a mixed strategy λ is an *admissible* strategy if there is no strategy λ^* which is at least as good as λ for every ω, and better for at least one ω. A class of strategies is a *complete* class if for every strategy not in the class there is a strategy in the class which is at least as good for all and better for at least one ω.

For further discussion of these concepts, the student is referred to [2], [4], [7], [9], [19], and [21]. However, we cite an illustrative result. Let us consider the problem of estimating a real parameter θ. An "action" here is the assertion that a certain real number a is the estimated value of θ; $\mathcal{A}$ is the set of all real numbers. A decision function is thus a real valued function $d(s)$ of the result s of the experiment: that is, an *estimator*, as defined on page 138. Suppose we use a loss function $L(a;\omega)$ which for each fixed ω is a convex function of a (has a nondecreasing derivative with respect to a). It can then be shown that the class of pure strategies, or estimators, is complete. That is, given any mixed strategy, which will use at least two different estimators with non-zero probabilities, there is one estimator which is at least as good for all ω and better for some.

71. Existence of Utility. The discussion in Section 68 was based on an assumed utility associated with each decision function d and each state ω of nature. In Section 69 one way was indicated of assigning such utilities, based on an assumed numerical loss $L(a,\omega)$ associated with action a in the presence of the state ω of nature: the utility of d given ω was just the negative of the expected loss, or risk. One might imagine that only in rather special circumstances will it be at all clear how such losses $L(a,\omega)$, or more generally, utilities $U(d,\omega)$, can be assigned. However, it can be shown that a utility is determined, at least in principle, in very general circumstances indeed.

Suppose that when ω is fixed, a specified action a will yield an end result $e = e(a,\omega)$. Let $\mathcal{E}$ denote the set of all possible end results, one corresponding to each pair (a,ω) (of course, different pairs (a,ω) may yield the same end result). Further, a given ω in Ω determines the probability distribution of the outcome s of the experiment, and hence the probability distribution of a specified decision function $d(s)$. If result s of the experiment is observed and decision function d is used, the end result is $e[d(s);\omega]$. From the point of view of the experimenter before the experiment, $\mathbf{s}$ is a random variable (or random vector); hence also $\mathbf{e} = e[d(\mathbf{s});\omega]$ is random (not necessarily real-valued, since the end results may not be numbers), and its probability distribution is determined when d and ω are fixed. That is, if d and ω are given, and if e is an end result in $\mathcal{E}$, then $Pr\{e[d(\mathbf{s});\omega] = e\}$ is determined; or if A is an "event" in the space of end results, then $Pr\{e[d(\mathbf{s});\omega] \text{ in } A\}$ is determined. In still other words, ω and d together determine a probability distribution on $\mathcal{E}$. We shall discuss the introduction of a "utility" on the class of probability distributions on $\mathcal{E}$.

We remark first that the assignment of a utility to each probability distribution over $\mathcal{E}$ gives a utility $U(d,\omega)$ to a decision function d in the presence of state ω of nature: $U(d,\omega)$ is just the utility of the probability distribution over $\mathcal{E}$ to which d and ω give rise. This in turn determines a utility $U(a,\omega)$ for each action a in the presence of state ω of nature: it is just the utility of the decision to take action a regardless of the result of the experiment.

Some discussion of the class $\mathcal{P}$ of probability distributions over $\mathcal{E}$ is in order. If p denotes a probability distribution over $\mathcal{E}$, then $p(e)$ will denote the corresponding probability of result e in $\mathcal{E}$; if p_1 and p_2 are probability distributions over $\mathcal{E}$, and if λ_1 and λ_2 are non-negative real numbers whose sum is 1, then another probability distribution p over $\mathcal{E}$ is determined by

$$p(e) = \lambda_1 p_1(e) + \lambda_2 p_2(e)$$

for e in $\mathcal{E}$. Suppose the experimenter is able to specify a preference relation over $\mathcal{P}$; we write $p_1 \geq p_2$ if p_1 is preferred or indifferent to p_2. (One might expect the experimenter to prefer p_1 to p_2 if, for example, p_1 assigns higher probabilities than does p_2 to the more "desirable" end results.) We now use the term "utility" in a more restricted, technical sense than heretofore. A real-valued function U on $\mathcal{P}$ is a "utility" for $\mathcal{P}$ if:

(i) $U(p_1) \geq U(p_2)$ whenever $p_1 \geq p_2$; that is, U is an "order-preserving" function;

(ii) $U(p) = \lambda_1 U(p_1) + \lambda_2 U(p_2)$ whenever $p = \lambda_1 p_1 + \lambda_2 p_2$, $0 \leq \lambda_1 \leq \lambda_1 + \lambda_2 = 1$; that is, U is linear.

There are several known sets of axioms for $\mathcal{P}$ from which it can be deduced that a utility for $\mathcal{P}$ exists. The following is given by Blackwell and Girshick ([2], Section 4.2):

Axiom I. The relation "$\geq$" provides a complete ordering for $\mathcal{P}$; that is,
(i) for every pair p_1, p_2 in $\mathcal{P}$, either $p_1 \geq p_2$ or $p_2 \geq p_1$ (or both), and
(ii) if $p_1 \geq p_2$ and $p_2 \geq p_3$ then $p_1 \geq p_3$.

Axiom II. If $\lambda_1 + \lambda_2 = 1$, $\lambda_1 \geq 0$, $\lambda_2 \geq 0$, and if $p_1 \geq q_1$, $p_2 \geq q_2$ then $\lambda_1 p_1 + \lambda_2 p_2 \geq \lambda_1 q_1 + \lambda_2 q_2$. If $p_1 > q_1$ and $\lambda_1 > 0$ then $\lambda_1 p_1 + \lambda_2 p_2 > \lambda_1 q_1 + \lambda_2 q_2$.

Axiom III. If $p_1 \geq p_2 \geq p_3$ then there are positive numbers λ_1, λ_2, μ_1, μ_2 with $\lambda_1 + \lambda_2 = \mu_1 + \mu_2 = 1$ such that $\lambda_1 p_1 + \lambda_2 p_3 \leq p_2$, $\mu_1 p_1 + \mu_2 p_3 \geq p_2$.

72. Bayes Principle. Let us suppose first that $\boldsymbol{\omega}$ is a discrete random variable, with *a priori* probability function $f(\omega)$. Suppose the outcome $\mathbf{s}$ of the experiment is also a discrete random variable (or a discrete combined random variable), and for fixed ω let $p(s|\omega) = Pr\{\mathbf{s} = s|\boldsymbol{\omega} = \omega\}$. Let $L(a;\omega)$ denote the loss resulting from action a if ω is the true element of Ω. For given ω, the risk is

$$r(d;\omega) = \sum_s L[d(s);\omega]p(s|\omega).$$

In applying Bayes principle as described above, we calculate the expected risk according to the *a priori* distribution of $\boldsymbol{\omega}$:

$$E[r(d;\boldsymbol{\omega})] = \sum_{\omega} f(\omega) \sum_{s} L[d(s);\omega]p(s|\omega);$$

we then choose the decision function d which makes this expected risk (or inutility) as small as possible. We shall develop now another way of thinking of the application of the Bayes principle, in terms of *a posteriori* probabilities of the various parameter points ω. Changing the order of summation, we find that

$$E[r(d;\boldsymbol{\omega})] = \sum_{s} \sum_{\omega} L[d(s);\omega]p(s|\omega)f(\omega).$$

Now for a fixed observed sample point s, let us develop a formula for the *a posteriori* probability of a parameter point ω, to be denoted by $p^*(\omega|s)$. We have

$$p^*(\omega|s) = Pr\{\boldsymbol{\omega} = \omega|\mathbf{s} = s\} = Pr\{\boldsymbol{\omega} = \omega,\mathbf{s} = s\}/Pr\{\mathbf{s} = s\}$$
$$= Pr\{\mathbf{s} = s|\boldsymbol{\omega} = \omega\}\ Pr\{\boldsymbol{\omega} = \omega\}/Pr\{\mathbf{s} = s\}.$$

Now

$$Pr\{\mathbf{s} = s\} = \sum_{\omega} Pr\{\mathbf{s} = s|\boldsymbol{\omega} = \omega\}Pr\{\boldsymbol{\omega} = \omega\},$$

or

$$Pr\{\mathbf{s} = s\} = \sum_{\omega} p(s|\omega)f(\omega),$$

so that

$$p^*(\omega|s) = p(s|\omega)f(\omega)/\sum_{\omega} p(s|\omega)f(\omega).$$

This is Bayes formula, which we met before (page 28). Again,

$$p(s|\omega)f(\omega) = p^*(\omega|s) \sum_{\omega} p(s|\omega)f(\omega)$$

(note that $\sum_{\omega} p(s|\omega)f(\omega)$ is a function of s alone; ω is the dummy summation index). Making this replacement in the expression above for $E[r(d;\boldsymbol{\omega})]$, we have

$$E[r(d;\boldsymbol{\omega})] = \sum_{s} \left\{\left[\sum_{\omega} p(s|\omega)f(\omega)\right] \sum_{\omega} L[d(s);\omega]p^*(\omega|s)\right\}.$$

According to the Bayes principle, we have to choose d so as to minimize this expected risk. To do so, for each s we choose $d(s)$ so as to make the expression in braces as small as possible. That is, we choose $d(s)$ so as to minimize, for each s,

$$\sum_{\omega} L[d(s);\omega]p^*(\omega|s).$$

But this is simply an expression for the *a posteriori* expected loss: thus we have proved that for this case (discrete s, ω), when we apply the Bayes principle we choose the *decision function which, for each observed outcome of the experiment, minimizes the a posteriori expected loss.*

EXAMPLE 2. (*Testing a simple hypothesis against a simple alternative; a classification problem.*) Let us suppose ourselves in a situation where we have to decide between two possible alternatives, H_0 and H_1, which have *a priori* probabilities h_0 and h_1. Our action space has two elements: a_0, to assert that H_0 holds, and a_1, to assert that H_1 holds. The parameter space Ω has likewise just two elements: ω_0 corresponding to H_0, and ω_1 corresponding to H_1. Let $p_0(s)$ denote the probability that the result s of the experiment will be observed if H_0 holds, $p_1(s)$ the corresponding probability if H_1 holds. Let the loss sustained be L_0 if action a_1 is taken when in fact H_0 holds: $L(a_1;\omega_0) = L_0$, L_1 if action a_0 is taken when H_1 holds: $L(a_0;\omega_1) = L_1$, and otherwise 0: $L(a_0;\omega_0) = L(a_1;\omega_1) = 0$.

Suppose outcome s is observed. The *a posteriori* probability $p^*(\omega|s)$ is given by

$$p^*(\omega_0|s) = h_0p_0(s)/[h_0p_0(s) + h_1p_1(s)],$$

$$p^*(\omega_1|s) = h_1p_1(s)/[h_0p_0(s) + h_1p_1(s)].$$

The *a posteriori* expected loss for decision function d is

$$\{L[d(s);\omega_0]h_0p_0(s) + L[d(s);\omega_1]h_1p_1(s)\}/[h_0p_0(s) + h_1p_1(s)].$$

If $d(s) = a_0$, then the *a posteriori* expected loss is

$$L_1h_1p_1(s)/[h_0p_0(s) + h_1p_1(s)],$$

while if $d(s) = a_1$, it is

$$L_0h_0p_0(s)/[h_0p_0(s) + h_1p_1(s)].$$

We therefore minimize the *a posteriori* expected loss by setting $d(s) = a_0$ if $L_0h_0p_0(s) \geq L_1h_1p_1(s)$; otherwise $d(s) = a_1$. In other words, we choose a_1 if

$$p_0(s)/p_1(s) \leq L_1h_1/L_0h_0,$$

and choose a_0 if the reverse inequality obtains.

In a situation where it is desired to test a simple hypothesis H_0 against a simple alternative H_1, it may seem unreasonable to postulate the existence of *a priori* probabilities of H_0 and H_1. Yet it is interesting to note that the test obtained above, in which H_0 is rejected (a_1 chosen) if the likelihood ratio is less than a certain constant, is the test shown to be most powerful on page 264 and following. There, of course, the constant was determined by the specified probability of a Type I error.

A classification problem, in which an individual is to be classified as belonging to one or the other of two groups, H_0 or H_1, is a problem of the above type (cf. [2], Chapter 6). Suppose the individual comes from a population in which fraction h_0 belong to group H_0 and fraction $h_1 = 1 - h_0$ to group H_1. Suppose **s** represents the result of observations to be made on the individual: scores of tests or physical measurements, etc.

As an illustrative example, suppose the population under consideration is that of freshmen entering a certain college. On the average, about 2 out of 3 entering freshmen successfully complete a college career. Scores on an entrance examination of those who failed are approximately normally distributed with mean 35 and standard deviation 15, while scores of those who succeeded are approximately normally distributed with mean 55 and standard deviation 15. For what scores s would you predict success? Let H_0 denote the "success" group, H_1 the other. Here again the specification of loss is a difficult problem; let us just assume loss $L(a_1;\omega_0) = L_0$ if failure is predicted for one who will succeed, and $L(a_0;\omega_1) = L_1$ if success is predicted for one who will fail. (If students are to be assigned to different classes according to the prediction of success or failure, this might play a role in assessing losses.) We have assumed discrete random variables in the above discussion, but analogous results would be obtained for continuous random variables. In this case we should have

$$p_0(s) = \frac{1}{15\sqrt{2\pi}} e^{-(1/450)(s-55)^2},$$

and

$$p_1(s) = \frac{1}{15\sqrt{2\pi}} e^{-(1/450)(s-35)^2},$$

the density functions of the score s under hypotheses H_0 and H_1. We have then

$$p_0(s)/p_1(s) = e^{-(1/450)[-40s+1800]}.$$

We then predict success (a_0) if

$$p_0(s)/p_1(s) = e^{-(1/450)[-40s+1800]} > L_1h_1/L_0h_0,$$

otherwise failure (a_1). That is, we predict success if

$$s > (1/40)[1800 + 450(\log L_1h_1 - \log L_0h_0)]$$

(logarithms to base e). Since $h_0 = 2/3$ and $h_1 = 1/3$, if $L_0 = L_1$, we predict success if

$$s > (1/40)[1800 + 450 \log (1/2)] \doteq 37.$$

According to the theory we developed above, this decision rule would minimize the expected risk.

There is a sense in which it can be said that only the Bayes method is "consistent"; a sense in which one might say: "if a man knows what he wants, and is consistent about it, he must behave as if he assigned prior probabilities to the various states of nature"; or again, if one is able to establish preference relations among the various courses of action, subject to "reasonable" conditions, it is as if one's preferences were determined by a prior probability distribution on the space Ω of states of nature. The following discussion is based largely on the last part of Section 4.3 in [2].

Suppose the use of decision function d in the presence of state ω of nature has utility $U(d,\omega)$ (the existence of such a utility was discussed in Section 71). If the experimenter knew the state of nature was, say, ω_0, he would then choose a decision function d for which $U(d,\omega_0)$ is as large as possible. Lacking precise knowledge as to the state of nature, if he were able to assign prior probabilities $f(\omega)$ to the various states ω of nature, he could use the Bayes principle and choose d to maximize the expected utility $\sum_{\omega\epsilon\Omega} U(d,\omega)f(\omega)$ (we assume, for simplicity, that the set Ω of states of nature is finite). Suppose, however, that such prior probabilities are not obviously available, and that the experimenter uses some other "principle of choice." Of primary interest to him as a result of choosing a decision function d_0 is the function $U(d_0,\omega)$ of ω which associates a utility with each state ω of nature. Let us suppose his principle of choice imposes a preference relation on the class of all numerical functions on Ω (utility as a function of ω), allowing him to choose that d for which the function $U(d,\omega)$ on Ω is "best." We use the following notation for the preference relation: we write $U_1 \geq U_2$ if the function U_1 on Ω is preferred to U_2, or rather, if U_2 is not preferred to U_1. If both $U_1 \geq U_2$ and $U_2 \geq U_1$ (neither is preferred to the other), we say they are indifferent. Suppose the preference relation has the following properties.

1. The preference relation yields a complete ordering on the set of all bounded functions U on Ω: for every pair U_1, U_2 either $U_1 \geq U_2$ or $U_2 \geq U_1$ or both; and if $U_1 \geq U_2$ and $U_2 \geq U_3$ then $U_1 \geq U_3$.
2. If $U_1(\omega) \geq U_2(\omega)$ for all $\omega\epsilon\Omega$ then $U_1 \geq U_2$.
3. If $U_1 \geq U_2$ then $U_1 + U \geq U_2 + U$ for every U.
4. Not all functions are indifferent; i.e., there is at least one pair U_1, U_2 such that $U_1 > U_2$ ($U_1 \geq U_2$ but not $U_2 \geq U_1$). It can be shown ([2], Section 4.3) that there is then a prior distribution on Ω such that $U_1 > U_2$ if $\sum_\omega U_1(\omega)f(\omega) > \sum_\omega U_2(\omega)f(\omega)$, where f is the probability function of the prior distribution. That is, there is a prior distribution on Ω such that if the expected value of U_1 is greater than that of U_2 then U_1 is preferred to U_2.

The above hypotheses are not sufficient to assure that the linear form $\sum_\omega U(\omega)f(\omega)$ will determine the preference relation completely: it is possible to have $U_1 > U_2$ while $\sum_\omega U_1(\omega)f(\omega) = \sum_\omega U_2(\omega)f(\omega)$. This possibility is illustrated in [2] as follows. Suppose there are only two possible states of nature, ω_1 and ω_2, in Ω. Suppose also that of two functions U_1 and U_2 on Ω, $U_1 > U_2$ if $U_1(\omega_1) > U_2(\omega_1)$ or if $U_1(\omega_1) =$

$U_2(\omega_1)$ and $U_1(\omega_2) > U_2(\omega_2)$. You can verify that the above hypotheses on the preference relation are satisfied. The associated prior distribution turns out to be $f(\omega_1) = 1$, $f(\omega_2) = 0$, and if $U_1(\omega_1) = U_2(\omega_1)$, $U_1(\omega_2) > U_2(\omega_2)$ then $U_1 > U_2$ but $\sum_\omega U_1(\omega)f(\omega) = \sum_\omega U_2(\omega)f(\omega)$. This possibility is denied by an additional "continuity" hypothesis:

5. If $U_1, U_2, \cdots$ is a sequence of functions on Ω, if U_0 and V are functions on Ω, if $U_1 \geq U_0$, $U_2 \geq U_0, \cdots$, and if $\lim_{n\to\infty} U_n(\omega) = V(\omega)$ for each $\omega \epsilon \Omega$, then also $V \geq U_0$.

This hypothesis is not satisfied in the above example, in which $U(\omega_1)$ and $U(\omega_2)$ are, so to speak, not of comparable "power" in determining the preference relation. In that example, if $U_n(\omega_1) = 1 + 1/n$, $U_n(\omega_2) = 0$, $n = 1, 2, \cdots$, if $U_0(\omega_1) = 1$, $U_0(\omega_2) = 1$, $V(\omega_1) = 1$, $V(\omega_2) = 0$, then $U_1 \geq U_0$, $U_2 \geq U_0, \cdots$, $\lim_{n\to\infty} U_n(\omega) = V(\omega)$ for $\omega \epsilon \Omega$, but $U_0 > V$.

Under hypotheses 1–5 inclusive, the linear form $\sum_\omega U(\omega)f(\omega)$ does determine the preference relation completely: $U_1 \leq U_2$ if and only if $\sum_\omega U_1(\omega)f(\omega) \leq \sum_\omega U_2(\omega)f(\omega)$, $U_1 < U_2$ if and only if $\sum_\omega U_1(\omega)f(\omega) < \sum_\omega U_2(\omega)f(\omega)$, and U_1 and U_2 are indifferent if and only if $\sum_\omega U_1(\omega)f(\omega) = \sum_\omega U_2(\omega)f(\omega)$. We shall see that it follows that *no randomized decision function is best.* If k is a positive integer and if $d_1, d_2, \cdots, d_k$ are any k available decision functions, one could use an independent random device to select decision function d_1 with probability λ_1, d_2 with probability $\lambda_2, \cdots$, d_k with probability λ_k, where $\lambda_1, \lambda_2, \cdots, \lambda_k$ are arbitrary prescribed non-negative numbers whose sum is 1. From the linear property of the utility (see Section 71), the utility function U associated with this *randomized* decision function would be $\lambda_1 U_1 + \cdots + \lambda_k U_k$, where U_i is the utility function associated with decision function d_i, $i = 1, 2, \cdots, k$. For this randomized utility function $U_0 = \lambda_1 U_1 + \cdots + \lambda_k U_k$ we have $\sum_\omega f(\omega)U_0(\omega) = \sum_\omega f(\omega) \sum_{i=1}^k \lambda_i U_i(\omega) = \sum_{i=1}^k \lambda_i \sum_\omega f(\omega)U_i(\omega) \leq \max_{1\leq i\leq k} \sum_\omega f(\omega)U_i(\omega)$ since $\lambda_1, \cdots, \lambda_k$ are non-negative numbers whose sum is 1. This shows that U_0 is not preferred to the best among the k utilities $U_1, U_2, \cdots, U_k$, and accordingly the randomized decision is not better than the best of the decisions $d_1, \cdots, d_k$.

73. Precise Measurement. A criticism sometimes leveled against Bayesian inference is that conclusions lose objectivity through the introduction of prior probability distributions which must differ from person to person, if indeed the individual can even specify his own prior probability distribution. One might reply that there is undeniably an important subjective element in inference—in hypothesis testing it is evident in the necessity of making a personal choice of test or of significance level, for example—and that Bayesian inference provides a means of formalizing this inescapable subjective element. It is reassuring to realize that with Bayesian methods as well, conclusive experiments lead to "objective" conclusions: conclusions with which most "reasonable" persons would agree. In effect, a "conclusive" experiment leads to a conclusion nearly the same for all "reasonable" prior distributions. The following discussion is based on an illustrative example in [14].

Imagine you hold in your hand a potato, and wish to know its weight, w. In principle, if you are willing to answer, in a consistent way, appropriate questions about how you would bet on different weights, it would be possible to elicit a prior distribution for the weight, personal to you. In practice, all must admit that it would be at best exceedingly difficult for you to settle on a precise prior distribution, with density, say, $p(w)$ for the weight, $\mathbf{w}$. On the other hand, you would no doubt be willing to agree that such a prior density should not change sharply, say, between 120 gm. and 130 gm., or over any other 10 gm. interval. Suppose then you weigh the potato on a balance known to have an error normally distributed with mean 0 and standard deviation 1 gm., and find the balance gives the weight as 214.4 gm. What can you now conclude about the weight?

Let $\mathbf{x}$ denote the random variable representing the reading of the balance, and $\mathbf{w}$ the random variable, weight of the potato. The marginal, or prior, density of $\mathbf{w}$ we denote by $p(w)$. The conditional density, $f(x \mid w)$ of $\mathbf{x}$ given $\mathbf{w} = w$ is given by

$$f(x \mid w) = \frac{1}{\sqrt{2\pi}} e^{-(x-w)^2/2}.$$

The joint density $f(x,w)$ is $f(x \mid w)p(w)$ and the conditional density $g(w \mid x)$ of $\mathbf{w}$ given $\mathbf{x} = x$ is $f(x,w)/f(x)$, where $f(x)$ is the marginal density of $\mathbf{x}$. We have

$$g(w \mid x) = \frac{1}{\sqrt{2\pi}} e^{-(x-w)^2/2} p(w)/f(x),$$

where

$$f(x) = \frac{1}{\sqrt{2\pi}} \int_{-\infty}^{\infty} e^{-(x-w)^2/2} p(w)\, dw.$$

Thus the posterior density of $\mathbf{w}$ given $\mathbf{x} = 214.4$ is

$$g(w \mid 214.4) = \frac{1}{\sqrt{2\pi}} e^{-(w-214.4)^2/2} p(w)/f(214.4).$$

The factor $e^{-(w-214.4)^2/2}$ is less than 0.0001 for $w < 210$ and for $w > 219$ and decreases very rapidly for w even farther from 214.4. By contrast, $p(w)$ is, as agreed above, nearly constant between $w = 210$ and $w = 220$. Since

$$\frac{1}{\sqrt{2\pi}} \int_{-\infty}^{\infty} e^{-(w-214.4)^2/2}\, dw = 1,$$

in order to have $\int_{-\infty}^{\infty} g(w \mid 214.4)\, dw = 1$ the (approximate) constant value of $p(w)$ over (210, 220) must be nearly equal to $f(214.4)$. We then have approximately

$$g(w \mid 214.4) \doteq \frac{1}{\sqrt{2\pi}} e^{-(w-214.4)^2/2}.$$

That is, *whatever "reasonable" prior distribution is assigned to* **w**, *its posterior distribution is nearly normal with mean* 214.4 *and standard deviation* 1.

We see that when the conditional density of **w** given **x** is sharply peaked in contrast to a prior density which is relatively flat in the neighborhood of the peak, the posterior density is effectively independent of the prior. The relatively flat prior seems an appropriate reflection of comparative uncertainty before the measurement, and the conclusion a correspondingly appropriate reflection of the agreement which could be reached after the measurement.

PROBLEMS

1. Suppose you intend to take a sample of size n from a normal population, and wish to estimate the population standard deviation. Describe the action space $\mathcal{A}$, the sample space $\mathcal{S}$, the parameter space Ω. Describe also two decision functions one might consider.

2. A farmer considers Diets A and B for his hogs. He estimates loss 0 if he uses A and A is better, loss 0 if he uses B and B is better, loss 2 units if he uses A but B is better, loss 3 units if he uses B but A is better (B is more expensive). Assuming no experimenting, what mixed strategy is called for by the minimax principle?

3. You have three items for sale at $10 each, and three purchasers. If a purchaser finds his item defective, he is entitled to $15 refund and penalty. You are to choose one of two actions: to sell all three, or to discard them. Which action is prescribed by the minimax principle? (Note: No experiment is involved, so that loss and risk coincide.)

4. In Problem 3, suppose each item has *a priori* probability 1/3 of being defective. Suppose you have thoroughly tested one chosen at random, and have convinced yourself it is non-defective. Which action is prescribed by the Bayes principle, and what is its *a posteriori* expected loss?

5. Suppose you are classifying certain beetles in Genus 1 or Genus 2 depending on the result **s** of a certain measurement. Suppose the loss due to misclassification is assumed constant, and that beetles of Genus 1 and Genus 2 are in the general population in the ratio 5 to 1. If **s** is normal (4,1) in Genus 1 and normal (7,1.5) in Genus 2, what is the Bayes decision function?

6. Prove the result expressing the Bayes principle in terms of an *a posteriori* expected risk for the case where **s** is discrete but $\boldsymbol{\omega}$ is a continuous random variable.

7. Let a single trial be made of an event with probability p. Let $\mathbf{x}$ denote the number of successes, $\mathbf{x} = 0$ or 1. If the loss function is $(p - \hat{p})^2/p(1 - p)$, where $\hat{p}$ represents an estimate of p, show that the minimax estimator is $d_0(x) \equiv x$.

Hint. Show first that with a uniform *a priori* distribution of $\mathbf{p}$ over $0 \leq p \leq 1$ ($f_0(p) = 1$ for $0 \leq p \leq 1$), $d_0(x) \equiv x$ is the only estimator with a finite expected risk; hence it is Bayes for f_0. Then show that $\max_p r(d_0;p) = E[r(d_0;\mathbf{p});f_0]$.

8. Suppose you are classifying into Class I or Class II depending on the results **x** and **y** of two observations whose joint distribution is bivariate normal (cf. p. 216) and whose correlation coefficient is ρ. Let **x** be normal (μ_{x1},σ) if the individual is in Class I, otherwise normal (μ_{x2},σ), while **y** is normal (μ_{y1},σ) if the individual is in Class I, otherwise normal (μ_{y2},σ). Suppose individuals of the two classes appear in the general population in equal proportions, and that equal losses are assigned to the two possibilities for misclassification. Show that the Bayes decision rule classifies into I if $2x[(\mu_{x2} - \mu_{x1}) - \rho(\mu_{y2} - \mu_{y1})] + 2y[(\mu_{y2} - \mu_{y1}) - \rho(\mu_{x2} - \mu_{x1})] + \mu_{x1}^2 - \mu_{x2}^2 + \mu_{y1}^2 - \mu_{y2}^2 - 2\rho(\mu_{x1}\mu_{y1} - \mu_{x2}\mu_{y2}) < 0$.

9. Suppose you are trying to distinguish among three kinds of radioactive substance, A, B, and C by counting radioactive emissions in a certain time. The number of particles emitted has a Poisson distribution, with mean a if the substance is A, $b > a$ if the substance is B, and $c > b$ if the substance is C. Assume constant loss for misclassification, zero loss for proper classification, and *a priori* probabilities h_1, h_2, and h_3 for A, B, and C. Let $s_{12} = [(b - a) + \ln(h_1/h_2)]/\ln(b/a)$, $s_{13} = [(c - a) + \ln(h_1/h_3)]/\ln(c/a)$, and $s_{23} = [(c - b) + \ln(h_2/h_3)]/\ln(c/b)$. Show that the Bayes decision rule chooses A if $s < s_{12}$, $s < s_{13}$; B if $s > s_{12}$, $s < s_{23}$; and C if $s > s_{13}$, $s > s_{23}$.

10. In the problem of testing a hypothesis H_0 against an alternative H_1, let Ω consist of the two elements H_0 and H_1, and let $\mathcal{A}$ also consist of two elements, a_0: accept H_0, and a_1: accept H_1. Let $\mathcal{E}$ consist of four elements:

e_{00}, H_0 is accepted, and H_0 is true; e_{10}, H_1 is accepted, but H_0 is true; e_{01}, H_0 is accepted, but H_1 is true; and e_{11}, H_1 is accepted, and H_1 is true. Show that the following two methods of defining an inutility are equivalent. (1) The inutility of any probability distribution on $\mathcal{E}$ is defined to be $Pr\{e_{01}\} + Pr\{e_{10}\}$. The inutility of a given decision function d and a given element ω of Ω is defined to be the inutility of the probability distribution on $\mathcal{E}$ to which they give rise. (2) $L(a_1;H_0) = L(a_0;H_1) = 1$, $L(a_0;H_0) = L(a_1;H_1) = 0$, inutility is expected loss.

CHAPTER

12

Regression

74. Central Problem. The central problem of the theory of regre sion for bivariate populations is to find a line or curve which represen the joint probability distribution best in an appropriate sense, usually the sense of least squares. (For a discussion of the "regression" ph nomenon see [20], especially page 261.)

Suppose $\mathbf{x}$ and $\mathbf{y}$ are a pair of random variables; we assume they are de fined on the same probability space, so that we can refer to their joint dis tribution. (In particular, they may be independent.) For fixed constant λ and β, consider a random variable $\mathbf{y}'$ which is the linear function of $\mathbf{x}$,

$$\mathbf{y}' = \lambda\mathbf{x} + \beta.$$

The linear regression problem is to determine the constants λ and β so tha $\mathbf{y}'$ will be as close as possible to $\mathbf{y}$ in an appropriate sense. The criterio usually applied, perhaps largely because of the simplicity of the associate theory, and ease of computation, is a least-squares criterion. Let $\mathbf{d}^2$ denot the squared difference between $\mathbf{y}$ and $\mathbf{y}'$:

$$\mathbf{d}^2 = (\mathbf{y} - \mathbf{y}')^2 = (\mathbf{y} - \lambda\mathbf{x} - \beta)^2.$$

The linear regression problem is to determine λ and β so as to minimize th expectation of $\mathbf{d}^2$. The distribution of the random variable $\mathbf{d}$ depends o λ and β, so that $E(\mathbf{d}^2)$ is a function of λ and β, and the problem is to choos λ and β so as to obtain the smallest possible value of this function. Suc values of λ and β having been found, the line in the xy plane whose equatic is

$$y = \lambda x + \beta$$

is called *the regression line of* $\mathbf{y}$ *on* $\mathbf{x}$.

▶ ***Definition.*** *The* regression line *of* $\mathbf{y}$ *on* $\mathbf{x}$ *is the line whose equation is* $y = \lambda x + \beta$, *where* λ *and* β *are determined so as to minimize*

$$E[(\mathbf{y} - \lambda\mathbf{x} - \beta)^2].$$

Suppose $\mathbf{x}$ and $\mathbf{y}$ are random variables having means μ_x and μ_y respectively, and standard deviations σ_x and σ_y respectively. We have

$$E(\mathbf{d}^2) = E[(\mathbf{y} - \mu_y) - \lambda(\mathbf{x} - \mu_x) - (\beta - \mu_y + \lambda\mu_x)]^2,$$

$$E(\mathbf{d}^2) = E(\mathbf{y} - \mu_y)^2 + \lambda^2 E(\mathbf{x} - \mu_x)^2 + (\beta - \mu_y + \lambda\mu_x)^2$$
$$-2\lambda E[(\mathbf{y} - \mu_y)(\mathbf{x} - \mu_x)] - 2(\beta - \mu_y + \lambda\mu_x)E(\mathbf{y} - \mu_y)$$
$$+ 2\lambda(\beta - \mu_y + \lambda\mu_x)E(\mathbf{x} - \mu_x).$$

But $E(\mathbf{y} - \mu_y) = 0$, $E(\mathbf{y} - \mu_y)^2 = \sigma_y^2$, $E(\mathbf{x} - \mu_x) = 0$, and $E(\mathbf{x} - \mu_x)^2 = \sigma_x^2$. Thus we have

$$E(\mathbf{d}^2) = \sigma_y^2 + \lambda^2\sigma_x^2 + (\beta - \mu_y + \lambda\mu_x)^2 - 2\lambda E[(\mathbf{y} - \mu_y)(\mathbf{x} - \mu_x)].$$

We note that the third term is the only one which involves β, and it is the square of $\beta - \mu_y + \lambda\mu_x$. Whatever λ may be, $E(\mathbf{d}^2)$ will be smaller for $\beta = \mu_y - \lambda\mu_x$ than for any other value of β. For this value of β (which depends on λ)

$$E(\mathbf{d}^2) = \lambda^2\sigma_x^2 - 2\rho\lambda\sigma_x\sigma_y + \sigma_y^2$$

where

$$\rho = \frac{1}{\sigma_x\sigma_y} E[(\mathbf{y} - \mu_y)(\mathbf{x} - \mu_x)].$$

Then

$$E(\mathbf{d}^2) = \lambda^2\sigma_x^2 - 2\rho\lambda\sigma_x\sigma_y + \rho^2\sigma_y^2 + (1 - \rho^2)\sigma_y^2,$$

or

$$E(\mathbf{d}^2) = (\lambda\sigma_x - \rho\sigma_y)^2 + (1 - \rho^2)\sigma_y^2.$$

Only the first term involves λ, and it is clear that $E(\mathbf{d}^2)$ assumes its minimum value for

$$\lambda = \frac{\rho\sigma_y}{\sigma_x},$$

$$\beta = \mu_y - \lambda\mu_x = \mu_y - \frac{\rho\sigma_y}{\sigma_x}\mu_x.$$

The minimum value of $E(\mathbf{d}^2)$ is

$$(1 - \rho^2)\sigma_y^2.$$

The equation of the least-squares regression line of $\mathbf{y}$ on $\mathbf{x}$ is

$$y = \lambda x + \beta = \frac{\rho\sigma_y}{\sigma_x} x + \mu_y - \frac{\rho\sigma_y}{\sigma_x}\mu_x,$$

or

▶ $$\frac{y - \mu_y}{\sigma_y} = \rho\,\frac{x - \mu_x}{\sigma_x},$$

a nearly symmetric form easy to remember. If $\boldsymbol{\xi}$ and $\boldsymbol{\eta}$ are the reduced random variables associated with **x** and **y**,

$$\boldsymbol{\xi} = \frac{\mathbf{x} - \mu_x}{\sigma_x}, \quad \boldsymbol{\eta} = \frac{\mathbf{y} - \mu_y}{\sigma_y},$$

then the regression line of $\boldsymbol{\eta}$ on $\boldsymbol{\xi}$ is

$$\eta = \rho\xi,$$

where

$$\rho = E(\boldsymbol{\xi}\boldsymbol{\eta}) = E\left(\frac{\mathbf{x} - \mu_x}{\sigma_x} \cdot \frac{\mathbf{y} - \mu_y}{\sigma_y}\right).$$

The numerator of this latter expression is called the *covariance* of **x** and **y**:

▶ $$\mathrm{Cov}(\mathbf{x},\mathbf{y}) = E[(\mathbf{x} - \mu_x)(\mathbf{y} - \mu_y)].$$

The number ρ itself is the *correlation coefficient* of **x** and **y**:

▶ $$\rho = \frac{\mathrm{Cov}\ (\mathbf{x},\mathbf{y})}{\sigma_x\sigma_y} = E\left[\frac{\mathbf{x} - \mu_x}{\sigma_x} \cdot \frac{\mathbf{y} - \mu_y}{\sigma_y}\right].$$

75. The Correlation Coefficient. Since $E(\mathbf{d}^2) \geq 0$ and $E(\mathbf{d}^2) = (1 - \rho^2)\sigma_y^2$, $1 - \rho^2$ must be non-negative, and

▶ $$-1 \leq \rho \leq 1.$$

If $\rho = -1$ or if $\rho = 1$, then $E(\mathbf{d}^2) = 0$. This can happen only if the random variable **d** is 0 with probability 1; since $\mathbf{d} = \mathbf{y} - \lambda\mathbf{x} - \beta$, this means that for each elementary event (except possibly for those favorable to an event of probability 0), the value of the random variable **y** is given by the formula

$$\mathbf{y} = \lambda\mathbf{x} + \beta \quad \text{or} \quad \frac{\mathbf{y} - \mu_y}{\sigma_y} = \rho\frac{\mathbf{x} - \mu_x}{\sigma_x}$$

in terms of the value of the random variable **x**. In terms of the joint distribution of **x** and **y** this means that the entire probability mass is concentrated on the regression line

$$y = \lambda x + \beta \quad \text{or} \quad \frac{y - \mu_y}{\sigma_y} = \rho\frac{x - \mu_x}{\sigma_x}.$$

In this case **y** and **x** are completely dependent, and further, the *dependence is linear.*

▶ *If $\rho^2 = 1$, the random variables* **x** *and* **y** *are linearly dependent; each is a linear function of the other. If $\rho = 1$ there is a perfect positive correlation between* **x** *and* **y**; *if $\rho = -1$, there is a perfect negative correlation between them.*

Since, for the minimizing values of λ and β,

$$E(\mathbf{d}^2) = (1 - \rho^2)\sigma_y^2,$$

we have

$$\sigma_y^2 = \rho^2\sigma_y^2 + E(\mathbf{d}^2).$$

In accord with this formula, $\rho^2\sigma_y^2$ is often interpreted as the part of the variance of $\mathbf{y}$, and ρ^2 as the fraction of the variance of $\mathbf{y}$, which is *attributable to a linear relationship* between $\mathbf{y}$ and $\mathbf{x}$. With this interpretation, $E(\mathbf{d}^2) = (1 - \rho^2)\sigma_y^2$ is the *residual variance*, that part of the variance of $\mathbf{y}$ which cannot be "explained" on the basis of a linear relationship. Of course the roles of $\mathbf{x}$ and $\mathbf{y}$ may be interchanged; which points up the need for caution in drawing conclusions about causal relationships.

If $\mathbf{x}$ and $\mathbf{y}$ are independent, then

$$E[(\mathbf{x} - \mu_x)(\mathbf{y} - \mu_y)] = E(\mathbf{x} - \mu_x)E(\mathbf{y} - \mu_y) = 0,$$

so that $\rho = 0$ if $\mathbf{x}$ and $\mathbf{y}$ are independent. On the other hand, ρ may be 0 when $\mathbf{x}$ and $\mathbf{y}$ are not independent, even when they are completely dependent. For example, suppose $\mathbf{x}$ has a uniform distribution over $(-1,1)$, and that $\mathbf{y} = \mathbf{x}^2$; then $\mathbf{y}$ is completely dependent on $\mathbf{x}$. The density function of $\mathbf{x}$ is

$$f(x) = 1/2 \quad \text{for } -1 < x < 1,$$

$$f(x) = 0 \qquad \text{for } x < -1, x > 1.$$

We have

$$\mu_x = E(\mathbf{x}) = \int_{-1}^{1} \frac{1}{2} x \, dx = 0,$$

$$\mu_y = E(\mathbf{y}) = E(\mathbf{x}^2) = \int_{-1}^{1} \frac{1}{2} x^2 \, dx = \frac{1}{3},$$

$$\operatorname{cov}(\mathbf{x},\mathbf{y}) = E\left[(\mathbf{x} - 0)\left(\mathbf{y} - \frac{1}{3}\right)\right] = E\left[\mathbf{x}\left(\mathbf{x}^2 - \frac{1}{3}\right)\right]$$

$$= E\left[\mathbf{x}^3 - \frac{1}{3}\mathbf{x}\right] = 0.$$

Therefore $\rho = 0$ even though $\mathbf{x}$ and $\mathbf{y}$ are completely dependent.

When the correlation coefficient of two random variables is 0, they are said to be *uncorrelated*. We have seen then that independent random variables are uncorrelated, but that uncorrelated random variables need not be independent.

PROBLEM

If $\mathbf{x}$ and $\mathbf{y}$ are uncorrelated, then $V(\mathbf{x} + \mathbf{y}) = V(\mathbf{x}) + V(\mathbf{y})$.

76. The Regression Curve. If $E(\mathbf{d}^2)$ is not 0, that is, if ρ^2 is not 1, then there is not a complete linear dependence between $\mathbf{y}$ and $\mathbf{x}$. There may or may not be complete dependence; for example, if $\mathbf{y} = \mathbf{x}^2$, the value of $\mathbf{y}$ is determined when that of $\mathbf{x}$ is given, yet ρ is neither 1 nor -1. However, in this case the *regression curve* is $y = x^2$.

▶ ***Definition.*** *A* regression curve *of* $\mathbf{y}$ *on* $\mathbf{x}$ *is the graph of a function* $R(x)$ *for which*

$$E([\mathbf{y} - R(\mathbf{x})]^2)$$

is minimized.

We shall show that if φ is a function and if $R(x) = E(\mathbf{y} \mid x)$ then

$$E[\mathbf{y} - \varphi(\mathbf{x})]^2 = E[\mathbf{y} - R(\mathbf{x})]^2 + E[R(\mathbf{x}) - \varphi(\mathbf{x})]^2.$$

Since $E[R(\mathbf{x}) - \varphi(\mathbf{x})]^2 \geq 0$, it will follow that $E[\mathbf{y} - R(\mathbf{x})]^2 \leq E[\mathbf{y} - \varphi(\mathbf{x})]^2$ for every function φ for which this expectation exists. Thus $R(x) = E(\mathbf{y} \mid x)$ is the required minimizing function. In order to verify this equation, we recall that by Theorem O in Chapter 5,

$$E[\varphi(\mathbf{x})\mathbf{y}] = E[\varphi(\mathbf{x})E(\mathbf{y} \mid \mathbf{x})] = E[\varphi(\mathbf{x})R(\mathbf{x})],$$

so that $E\{[\mathbf{y} - R(\mathbf{x})]\varphi(\mathbf{x})\} = 0$; in particular $E\{[\mathbf{y} - R(\mathbf{x})]R(\mathbf{x})\} = 0$. Therefore also $E\{[\mathbf{y} - R(\mathbf{x})][R(\mathbf{x}) - \varphi(\mathbf{x})]\} = 0$. But

$$\begin{aligned}[\mathbf{y} - \varphi(\mathbf{x})]^2 &= \{[\mathbf{y} - R(\mathbf{x})] + [R(\mathbf{x}) - \varphi(\mathbf{x})]\}^2 \\ &= [\mathbf{y} - R(\mathbf{x})]^2 + [R(\mathbf{x}) - \varphi(\mathbf{x})]^2 + 2[\mathbf{y} - R(\mathbf{x})][R(\mathbf{x}) - \varphi(\mathbf{x})].\end{aligned}$$

Taking expectations yields

$$E[\mathbf{y} - \varphi(\mathbf{x})]^2 = E[\mathbf{y} - R(\mathbf{x})]^2 + E[R(\mathbf{x}) - \varphi(\mathbf{x})]^2,$$

since the expectation of the last term above is zero. We have thus proved the following theorem.

▶ ***Theorem.*** *If* $\mathbf{x}$ *and* $\mathbf{y}$ *are random variables possessing finite variances, then a regression curve of* $\mathbf{y}$ *on* $\mathbf{x}$ *is the graph of the function of* x, $E[\mathbf{y} \mid x]$.

77. Least Squares Linear Fit of Data. Suppose you make n measurements of a quantity x, obtaining values $x_1, x_2, \cdots, x_n$, and for each of these values of x measure a corresponding value y_i of a quantity y ($i = 1, 2, \cdots, n$). The result of your measurements is a set of n pairs (x_i,y_i) ($i = 1, 2, \cdots, n$). If when plotted on coordinate paper the points (x_i,y_i) appear to lie nearly on a straight line, you may wish to determine the equation of the line which represents them best, the line of closest fit to the data. Clearly there are many possible criteria to use in choosing the "best" line. You may prefer simply to draw with a rule the line which appears to your eye to lie closest to the plotted points. Such a criterion would have the disadvantage of being highly subjective as well as that of yielding results not susceptible of analysis. Again, you may try to determine that line for which the greatest distance to a plotted point is as small as possible. However, the criterion which generally leads to the simplest calculations is the least-squares criterion, according to which you choose slope m and y-intercept b so as to minimize the sum of the squares of the vertical distances from plotted points to the line:

$$\sum_{i=1}^{n} (y_i - mx_i - b)^2.$$

Imagine a pair of random variables $\tilde{\mathbf{x}}$ and $\tilde{\mathbf{y}}$ having a joint probability distribution with a probability mass $1/n$ at each point (x_i,y_i) $(i = 1, 2, \cdots, n)$; the regression line of $\tilde{\mathbf{y}}$ on $\tilde{\mathbf{x}}$ is the graph of the linear function $mx + b$ for which

$$E(\tilde{\mathbf{y}} - m\tilde{\mathbf{x}} - b)^2$$

is minimized. But

$$E(\tilde{\mathbf{y}} - m\tilde{\mathbf{x}} - b)^2 = \frac{1}{n} \sum_{i=1}^{n} (y_i - mx_i - b)^2$$

so that the same values of m and b which minimize $\sum_{i=1}^{n} (y_i - mx_i - b)^2$ also minimize $E(\tilde{\mathbf{y}} - m\tilde{\mathbf{x}} - b)^2$. The original problem may not have involved probability considerations at all; but we see now that the problem of finding the line of best fit to the points (x_i,y_i) in the sense of least squares is precisely that of finding the regression line of the "fictitious" random variable $\tilde{\mathbf{y}}$ on the "fictitious" random variable $\tilde{\mathbf{x}}$, where the joint distribution of $\tilde{\mathbf{x}}$ and $\tilde{\mathbf{y}}$ has probability $1/n$ situated at each of the points (x_i,y_i) $(i = 1, 2, \cdots, n)$. This problem has already been solved; the regression line of $\tilde{\mathbf{y}}$ on $\tilde{\mathbf{x}}$ is

$$\frac{y - \mu_{\tilde{y}}}{\sigma_{\tilde{y}}} = \tilde{\rho} \left(\frac{x - \mu_{\tilde{x}}}{\sigma_{\tilde{x}}} \right),$$

where

$$\mu_{\tilde{x}} = E(\tilde{\mathbf{x}}) = \frac{1}{n} \sum_{i=1}^{n} x_i = \bar{x},\ \mu_{\tilde{y}} = E(\tilde{\mathbf{y}}) = \frac{1}{n} \sum_{i=1}^{n} y_i = \bar{y},$$

$$\sigma_{\tilde{x}}^2 = V(\tilde{\mathbf{x}}) = \frac{1}{n} \sum_{i=1}^{n} (x_i - \bar{x})^2 = \left(\frac{1}{n} \sum_{i=1}^{n} x_i^2 \right) - \bar{x}^2 = s_x^2,$$

$$\sigma_{\tilde{y}}^2 = V(\tilde{\mathbf{y}}) = \frac{1}{n} \sum_{i=1}^{n} (y_i - \bar{y})^2 = \left(\frac{1}{n} \sum_{i=1}^{n} y_i^2 \right) - \bar{y}^2 = s_y^2,$$

$$\tilde{\rho} = \frac{E[(\tilde{\mathbf{x}} - \mu_{\tilde{x}})(\tilde{\mathbf{y}} - \mu_{\tilde{y}})]}{\sigma_{\tilde{x}}\sigma_{\tilde{y}}} = \frac{1}{n}\sum_{i=1}^{n}(x_i - \bar{x})(y_i - \bar{y})/s_x s_y,$$

$$\tilde{\rho} = \left[\left(\frac{1}{n}\sum_{i=1}^{n} x_i y_i\right) - \bar{x}\bar{y}\right]/s_x s_y = r,$$

and where the above equations define the quantities $\bar{x}$, $\bar{y}$, s_x^2, s_y^2, and r. The similarity of these formulas to those defining sample mean and sample variance is obvious; however, here x_i, y_i $(i = 1, 2, \cdots, n)$ are not sample values but simply measured numbers.

After simplifying, the equation of the least-squares line of best fit can be rewritten

$$\frac{y - \bar{y}}{s_y} = r\frac{x - \bar{x}}{s_x},$$

or

$$y - \bar{y} = \frac{\left(\sum_{i=1}^{n} x_i y_i\right) - n\bar{x}\bar{y}}{\left(\sum_{i=1}^{n} x_i^2\right) - n\bar{x}^2}(x - \bar{x}).$$

The number $\tilde{\rho}$ is the correlation coefficient of $\tilde{\mathbf{x}}$ and $\tilde{\mathbf{y}}$, and is also called the *correlation coefficient* r of x and y from the original data. As was seen above, r^2 will be 1 if and only if all the points (x_i, y_i) lie on the regression line; $r = 1$ if it has positive slope, $r = -1$ if it has negative slope.

Probability considerations may enter into a least-squares linear fit of data in the following way: For each i, $i = 1, 2, \cdots, n$, the value x_i may be a known, accurate measurement of a certain quantity, while the corresponding value y_i is the value of a random variable drawn from a population whose distribution depends on x_i. For example, suppose 10 children are drawn at random from a group of children aged 60 months, and their average weight found to be 45 lb.; $x_1 = 60$, $y_1 = 45$. The number x_1 is a constant, the number y_1 is a value of a random variable: the sample mean of a sample of size 10 from a population of weights of children aged 60 months. On successively choosing children from groups aged 61 months, 62 months, etc., and weighing them, we should have a set of numbers, $x_1 = 60$, $x_2 = 61$, $x_3 = 62$, $\cdots$, x_n, and corresponding to each x_i a value of a random variable $\mathbf{y}_i$ whose distribution depends on x_i $(i = 1, 2, \cdots, n)$. We might believe that, at least in a certain age range, the mean weight increases linearly with age, and that for fixed x_i, $\mathbf{y}_i$ is approximately normally distributed about $\lambda x_i + \beta$ for certain constants λ and β. If the $\mathbf{y}_i$ all have the same variance, the regression line of y on x from the data (x_i, y_i) $(i = 1, 2, \cdots, n)$ would serve as a convenient estimate of the linear mean weight function $\lambda x + \beta$. (If the $\mathbf{y}_i$ do not have equal variances, some observations should perhaps carry more weight than others. However, you can verify that, whether or not the $\mathbf{y}_i$ have equal variances, the coefficient of x and the constant term in the equation of the regression line computed from the sample data are unbiased estimators of λ and β respectively.)

78. Regression Line in Sampling from a Bivariate Population. We consider now a sampling situation in which the parent population is induced not by a single random variable $\mathbf{x}$ but by a pair of random variables $\mathbf{x}$ and $\mathbf{y}$. Each elementary event in the population is not a single number, but a pair of real numbers. For example, consider a probability space in which each elementary event represents a man aged 30 years in Missouri. The probability associated with each elementary event is $1/N$, where N is the number of men aged 30 years in Missouri. If we are interested in studying weight and height, we may associate with each elementary event a pair of numbers, x, the height of the man represented by that elementary event, and y, the weight of that man. Thus we have associated with each elementary event a value of a random variable $\mathbf{x}$ and a value of a random variable $\mathbf{y}$. In the probability space induced by $\mathbf{x}$ and $\mathbf{y}$ (pages 59–60), a probability $1/N$ is associated with each number pair which is the pair of values of $\mathbf{x}$ and $\mathbf{y}$ corresponding to an elementary event in the original probability space. We can obtain a random sample of size n from this population by choosing successively, at random, and with replacement, n men from the group and measuring the height and weight of each, obtaining n pairs (x_i,y_i) $(i = 1, 2, \cdots, n)$. Before actual sample values are obtained, the pairs $(\mathbf{x}_1,\mathbf{y}_1)$, $(\mathbf{x}_2,\mathbf{y}_2)$, $\cdots$, $(\mathbf{x}_n,\mathbf{y}_n)$ must be considered n independent pairs of random variables having identical joint distributions.

In considering sampling from bivariate populations, we shall restrict our attention to those possessing first and second moments: the first moments, $E(\mathbf{x}) = \mu_x$ and $E(\mathbf{y}) = \mu_y$; the second moments, $E(\mathbf{x} - \mu_x)^2 = \sigma_x^2$, $E(\mathbf{y} - \mu_y)^2 = \sigma_y^2$, and $E[(\mathbf{x} - \mu_x)(\mathbf{y} - \mu_y)] = \text{cov}(\mathbf{x},\mathbf{y}) = \rho\sigma_x\sigma_y$. Suppose we take a sample of size n, and obtain pairs (x_i,y_i) $(i = 1, 2, \cdots, n)$. If we are interested in the correlation coefficient ρ between the random variables $\mathbf{x}$ and $\mathbf{y}$, it seems natural to determine the *sample correlation coefficient* r from the formulas developed above, as an estimate of ρ:

$$▶ \quad r = \frac{[(\sum_{i=1}^{n} x_i y_i) - n\bar{x}\bar{y}]}{n s_x s_y},$$

where

$$\bar{x} = \frac{1}{n}\sum_{i=1}^{n} x_i, \quad \bar{y} = \frac{1}{n}\sum_{i=1}^{n} y_i,$$

$$s_x^2 = \left(\frac{1}{n}\sum_{i=1}^{n} x_i^2\right) - \bar{x}^2,$$

$$s_y^2 = \left(\frac{1}{n}\sum_{i=1}^{n} y_i^2\right) - \bar{y}^2.$$

79. Normal Bivariate Population. A (non-singular) *normal bivariate population* is the probability space induced by a pair of random variables **x**, **y** having a joint density function $f(x,y)$ given by

$$f(x,y) = \frac{1}{2\pi\sigma_x\sigma_y\sqrt{1-\rho^2}} e^{-\frac{1}{2(1-\rho^2)}\left[\left(\frac{x-\mu_x}{\sigma_x}\right)^2 - 2\rho\left(\frac{x-\mu_x}{\sigma_x}\right)\left(\frac{y-\mu_y}{\sigma_y}\right) + \left(\frac{y-\mu_y}{\sigma_y}\right)^2\right]}$$

for certain constants μ_x, μ_y, ρ, and positive constants σ_x and σ_y. If you carry out the required integration, you will find that the marginal density function $f(x)$ of **x** is given by

$$f(x) = \frac{1}{\sqrt{2\pi}\,\sigma_x} e^{-(x-\mu_x)^2/2\sigma_x^2},$$

and that of **y** by

$$g(y) = \frac{1}{\sqrt{2\pi}\,\sigma_y} e^{-(y-\mu_y)^2/2\sigma_y^2}.$$

Thus **x** and **y** are normally distributed random variables with means μ_x and μ_y, standard deviations σ_x and σ_y. If you compute the expectation

$$E\left[\left(\frac{\mathbf{x}-\mu_x}{\sigma_x}\right)\left(\frac{\mathbf{y}-\mu_y}{\sigma_y}\right)\right]$$

you will find it is just the constant ρ appearing in the expression for $f(x,y)$, so that this constant is the correlation coefficient of **x** and **y**.

If $\rho = 1$ or $\rho = -1$, the above expression for $f(x,y)$ is meaningless. In this case **x**, **y** are said to have a *singular normal distribution*, the entire probability mass being concentrated on the line

$$\frac{y-\mu_y}{\sigma_y} = \pm\frac{x-\mu_x}{\sigma_x}$$

($+$ if $\rho = 1$, $-$ if $\rho = -1$); **x** and **y** are normal, and there is a complete linear dependence between them:

$$\mathbf{y} = \frac{\sigma_y}{\sigma_x}(\mathbf{x} - \mu_x) + \mu_y.$$

If **x** and **y** are independent, then $\rho = 0$, and the joint density function is the product of the marginal density functions

$$f(x,y) = f(x)g(y) = \frac{1}{\sqrt{2\pi}\,\sigma_x} e^{-\frac{1}{2}\left(\frac{x-\mu_x}{\sigma_x}\right)^2} \cdot \frac{1}{\sqrt{2\pi}\,\sigma_y} e^{-\frac{1}{2}\left(\frac{y-\mu_y}{\sigma_y}\right)^2}.$$

We notice also that if **x** and **y** are only uncorrelated, so that $\rho = 0$, then the expression for $f(x,y)$ becomes precisely that in the right member above, so that the joint density function is the product of the marginal density functions, and **x** and **y** are independent. We saw earlier that two uncorrelated random variables need not be independent; but it is clear now that

▶ *in the special case where the joint density function of* **x** *and* **y** *is normal, they are* independent *if and only if they are uncorrelated.*

In this connection we remark also that it can be shown ([22], Chapter 7) that if **u** and **v** are linear combinations, $\mathbf{u} = a\mathbf{x} + b\mathbf{y}$, $\mathbf{v} = c\mathbf{x} + d\mathbf{y}$, of random variables **x** and **y** having a joint normal distribution, then **u** and **v** also have a joint normal distribution (cf. also page 229).

Let us determine the regression curve (page 212) of **y** on **x**, where **x** and **y** have a normal joint distribution. The regression curve is the graph of the function of x:

$$R(x) = E(\mathbf{y}\,|\,x) = \int_{-\infty}^{\infty} y\, g(y\,|\,x)\, dy,$$

where

$$g(y\,|\,x) = f(x,y)/f(x)$$

$$= \frac{1}{\sqrt{2\pi}\,\sigma_y\sqrt{1-\rho^2}}\, e^{-\frac{1}{2(1-\rho^2)}\left\{\left(\frac{x-\mu_x}{\sigma_x}\right)^2 - 2\rho\left(\frac{x-\mu_x}{\sigma_x}\right)\left(\frac{y-\mu_y}{\sigma_y}\right) + \left(\frac{y-\mu_y}{\sigma_y}\right)^2\right\} + \frac{1}{2}\left\{\frac{x-\mu_x}{\sigma_x}\right\}^2}$$

$$= \frac{1}{\sqrt{2\pi}\,\sigma_y\sqrt{1-\rho^2}}\, e^{-\frac{1}{2(1-\rho^2)}\left\{\rho^2\left(\frac{x-\mu_x}{\sigma_x}\right)^2 - 2\rho\left(\frac{x-\mu_x}{\sigma_x}\right)\left(\frac{y-\mu_y}{\sigma_y}\right) + \left(\frac{y-\mu_y}{\sigma_y}\right)^2\right\}}$$

$$= \frac{1}{\sqrt{2\pi}\,\sigma_y\sqrt{1-\rho^2}}\, e^{-\frac{1}{2(1-\rho^2)}\left[\frac{y-\mu_y}{\sigma_y} - \frac{\rho(x-\mu_x)}{\sigma_x}\right]^2}$$

$$= \frac{1}{\sqrt{2\pi}\,\sigma_y\sqrt{1-\rho^2}}\, e^{-\frac{1}{2(1-\rho^2)\sigma_y^2}\left\{y - \left[\mu_y + \frac{\rho\sigma_y}{\sigma_x}(x-\mu_x)\right]\right\}^2}$$

But for fixed x this is just the density function (in y) of a normally distributed random variable with mean $\mu_y + \dfrac{\rho\sigma_y}{\sigma_x}(x - \mu_x)$ and standard deviation $\sigma_y\sqrt{1-\rho^2}$. Therefore

$$E(\mathbf{y}\,|\,x) = \mu_y + \frac{\rho\sigma_y}{\sigma_x}(x - \mu_x).$$

But this is just the formula for the ordinate of the regression line of **y** on **x**:

▶ *when* **x** *and* **y** *have a normal joint distribution, the regression curve of* **y** *on* **x** *coincides with the regression line.*

PROBLEMS

1. When **x** and **y** are independent and have a normal joint distribution with $\sigma_x = \sigma_y$, their joint distribution is called *circular normal.*

(a) Write as an integral in polar coordinates, and evaluate, the probability that (**x**,**y**) will lie in a circle of radius a centered at (μ_x,μ_y).

(b) The CEP (circular probable error), C, is the radius of a circle centered at (μ_x,μ_y) such that the probability is 1/2 that (**x**,**y**) will lie in that circle. Express C in terms of σ, where $\sigma = \sigma_x = \sigma_y$.

2. A number **x** is chosen at random from among the integers 1, 2, 3, 4. Another, **y**, is chosen from among those at least as large as **x**. Find (a) $E(\mathbf{x})$, $V(\mathbf{x})$; (b) $E(\mathbf{y})$, $V(\mathbf{y})$; (c) cov (**x**,**y**); (d) the correlation coefficient of **x** and **y**; (e) the regression line of **y** on **x**; (f) the regression line of **x** on **y**.

3. In Problem 2, find a regression curve of **y** on **x**.

4. Let **x**, **y** be two continuous random variables with joint density function $f(x,y) = x + y$ for $0 < x < 1$, $0 < y < 1$, $f(x,y) = 0$ elsewhere. Find (a) $E(\mathbf{x})$, $V(\mathbf{x})$, $E(\mathbf{y})$, $V(\mathbf{y})$; (b) cov (**x**,**y**), and the correlation coefficient of **x** and **y**; (c) the regression line of **y** on **x**; (d) the regression line of **x** on **y**.

5. In Problem 4, find (a) the conditional density function of **y** given $\mathbf{x} = 1/2$; (b) the regression curve of **y** on **x**.

6. Let **x** be chosen at random between -1 and 1, and let **y** then be chosen at random between $-\sqrt{1-\mathbf{x}^2}$ and $\sqrt{1-\mathbf{x}^2}$. The point (**x**,**y**) is then the point obtained by first choosing a point at random on the diameter on the x axis of the unit circle, and then a point at random on the chord through this point perpendicular to the x axis.

(a) What is the regression curve of **y** on **x**?

(b) What are $E(\mathbf{x})$, $V(\mathbf{x})$, $E(\mathbf{y})$, $V(\mathbf{y})$?

(c) What is the correlation coefficient of **x** and **y**? What is the regression line of **y** on **x**?

(d) Are **x**, **y** independent?

7. A student employment bureau asked applicants their weekly wages on jobs last held. The actual wages were obtained for 54 of them, and are recorded in the table below to the nearest \$5; x represents reported wage, y actual wage, and the entry in the table represents frequency. Find the correlation coefficient.

x/y	15	20	25	30	35	40
40						2
35				3	5	
30			4	15		
25			20			
20		3	1			
15	1					

8. Suppose 100 students are given an IQ test on entering college; their scores are $x_1, x_2, \cdots, x_{100}$. At the end of the first year they are given an achievement test; their scores are $y_1, y_2, \cdots, y_{100}$.

(a) Compute the correlation between scores on the two tests, given that $\sum_{i=1}^{100} x_i = 10{,}500$, $\sum_{i=1}^{100} y_i = 8{,}000$, $\sum_{i=1}^{100} x_i^2 = 1{,}125{,}000$, $\sum_{i=1}^{100} y_i^2 = 680{,}000$, $\sum_{i=1}^{100} x_iy_i = 862{,}500$.

(b) What is the regression line of y on x from the data?

(c) If Mr. A had an IQ score of 110, what would be your estimate of his expected score on the achievement test? (Assume the scores are from a bivariate normal population; how do you use this assumption?)

9. Suppose height h and weight w of a group of people are approximately normally distributed with mean weight 140 lb., standard deviation 12 lb., mean height 68 in., standard deviation 4 in., and correlation coefficient 2/3. Given that an individual is 66 in. tall, what is his expected weight?

10. The accompanying table is a partial listing of measured boiling points in degrees C at various pressures of water and of a 63.23% aqueous solution of dextrose. Each pair of figures represents simultaneous measurements using a twin ebulliometer. Find the regression line of the boiling point of the dextrose solution on the boiling point of water.

Water	Dextrose	Water	Dextrose
100.06	105.39	65.09	76.69
100.07	101.16	86.49	105.29
93.71	96.58	99.88	110.64
86.46	91.39	106.36	115.15
76.49	84.84	112.15	119.27

(*Source:* TORGESEN, J. L., BOWES, V. E., SMITH, E. R. "Boiling Points of Aqueous Solutions of Dextrose within the Pressure Range of 200 to 1500 Millimeters," *Journal of Research of National Bureau of Standards*, Vol. 45 (1950), pp. 458–462.)

11. If $\mu_x = \mu_y = 0$, $\sigma_x = \sigma_y = 1$, and if $\mathbf{x}$ and $\mathbf{y} - \rho\mathbf{x}$ are independent random variables, then the regression curve of $\mathbf{y}$ on $\mathbf{x}$ is the regression line.

Hint: $E(\mathbf{y}|x) = E(\mathbf{y} - \rho\mathbf{x}|x) + E(\rho\mathbf{x}|x) = E(\mathbf{y} - \rho\mathbf{x}) + \rho x$.

12. If $\mu_x = \mu_y = 0$, $\sigma_x = \sigma_y = 1$, and if $\mathbf{x}$, $\mathbf{y}$ have a (non-singular) normal joint distribution, then $\mathbf{x}$ and $\mathbf{y} - \rho\mathbf{x}$ are independent.
Hint: Show that $\mathbf{x}$ and $\mathbf{y} - \rho\mathbf{x}$ are uncorrelated.

13. Let $\mathbf{x}_1, \mathbf{x}_2, \cdots, \mathbf{x}_n$ be sample random variables of a sample of size n from a population whose random variable is $\mathbf{x}$, and let $\bar{\mathbf{x}}$ and $\mathbf{s}^2$ denote the sample mean and sample variance. Then (a) for each i, $i = 1, 2, \cdots, n$, $\mathbf{x}_i - \bar{\mathbf{x}}$ and $\bar{\mathbf{x}}$ are uncorrelated; (b) $\mathbf{s}^2$ and $\bar{\mathbf{x}}$ are uncorrelated if $E[(\mathbf{x} - \mu)^3] = 0$.

14. Let $x_1, x_2, \cdots, x_n$ be given numbers (*not* random variables). For $i = 1, 2, \cdots, n$, let $\mathbf{y}_i$ be a random variable with $E(\mathbf{y}_i) = \lambda x_i + \beta$, where λ and β are fixed, but unknown. Independent observations are to be made on the random variables $\mathbf{y}_i$; let y_i denote the resulting observed value, $i = 1, 2, \cdots, n$. In the formula for the linear regression function $lx + b$ of y on x from the data (x_i,y_i) $(i = 1, 2, \cdots, n)$, replace the observed values y_i by the random variables $\mathbf{y}_i$, so that $\mathbf{l}$ and $\mathbf{b}$ become functions of the random variables $\mathbf{y}_i$.
(a) What functions of the random variables $\mathbf{y}_i$ are $\mathbf{l}$ and $\mathbf{b}$?
(b) Show that $\mathbf{l}$ and $\mathbf{b}$ are unbiased estimators of λ and β respectively.

15. Let $\mathbf{x}$, $\mathbf{y}$ be independent and normally distributed, and let $\mathbf{u} = \mathbf{x} + \mathbf{y}$, $\mathbf{v} = \mathbf{x} - \mathbf{y}$. Show that the correlation coefficient of $\mathbf{u}$ and $\mathbf{v}$ is $\dfrac{\sigma_x^2 - \sigma_y^2}{\sigma_x^2 + \sigma_y^2}$.

16. Let $\mathbf{x}$, $\mathbf{y}$ have a (not necessarily normal) bivariate distribution with $E(\mathbf{x}) = E(\mathbf{y}) = 0$, $V(\mathbf{x}) = V(\mathbf{y}) = 1$, cov $(\mathbf{x},\mathbf{y}) = \rho$. Let $\tilde{\mathbf{x}}$, $\tilde{\mathbf{y}}$ have the uniform distribution over the *ellipse of concentration*

$$x^2 - 2\rho xy + y^2 = 4(1 - \rho^2).$$

Show that $E(\tilde{\mathbf{x}}) = E(\tilde{\mathbf{y}}) = 0$, $V(\tilde{\mathbf{x}}) = V(\tilde{\mathbf{y}}) = 1$, and cov $(\tilde{\mathbf{x}},\tilde{\mathbf{y}}) = \rho$. (Cf. [3], Section 21.10.)

17. (a) Show that if $\mathbf{x}$, $\mathbf{y}$ have a bivariate normal joint distribution with means μ_x, μ_y, standard deviations σ_x, σ_y, correlation coefficient ρ, and if a, b are any real numbers, then $\mathbf{u} = a\mathbf{x} + b\mathbf{y}$ is normally distributed.
(b) What are $E(\mathbf{u})$ and $V(\mathbf{u})$?

18. Let $\mathbf{x}$, $\mathbf{y}$ have a bivariate normal joint distribution, with $\sigma_x^2 = \sigma_y^2 = \sigma^2$, and correlation coefficient ρ. Show that $\mathbf{u} = \mathbf{x} + \mathbf{y}$, and $\mathbf{v} = \mathbf{x} - \mathbf{y}$ are independent. (Cf. comments, pages 217, 229.)

80. Correlation Coefficient in Sampling from Normal Bivariate Population. Once you have computed the sample correlation coefficient from the sample data, you may wish to consider what confidence you can have that the sample correlation coefficient is near the unknown population correlation coefficient ρ. A means of determining approximate confidence limits for ρ is given by the following theorem, stated here without proof. (Cf. [3], page 361.)

▶ ***Theorem.*** *If* $\mathbf{r}$ *is the sample correlation coefficient of a sample of size n from a normal bivariate population, then the statistic*

$$\mathbf{z} = \frac{1}{2} \log \frac{1 + \mathbf{r}}{1 - \mathbf{r}}$$

(the logarithm is the logarithm to the base e, the natural logarithm) is asymptotically normally distributed with

$$E(\mathbf{z}) \doteq \frac{1}{2} \log \frac{1 + \rho}{1 - \rho} + \frac{\rho}{2n - 1}$$

$$\doteq \frac{1}{2} \log \frac{1 + \rho}{1 - \rho}, \quad \textit{and}$$

$$V(\mathbf{z}) \doteq \frac{1}{n - 3}.$$

The approximation appears adequate for most purposes even for sample sizes as small as 10.

EXAMPLE. You select 50 rats at random from a population of rats, and record weight and time to traverse a maze for each. You find a sample correlation coefficient $r = -0.20$. Is this result significant?

Suppose you are willing to assume that weight $\mathbf{x}$ and traversal time $\mathbf{y}$ are normally distributed random variables with unknown correlation coefficient ρ, and that the 50 recorded pairs, weight and time, form a sample of size 50 from the normal bivariate population induced by $\mathbf{x}$ and $\mathbf{y}$. You now have to decide on a significance level; suppose you choose 5%. You will consider the correlation coefficient $r = -0.20$ significant at the 5% level if you are able to reject, at the 5% significance level, the hypothesis $\rho = 0$ in favor of the alternative $\rho \neq 0$. By the above theorem,

$$V(\mathbf{z}) \doteq \frac{1}{47}, \quad E(\mathbf{z}) \doteq \frac{1}{2} \log \frac{1 + \rho}{1 - \rho},$$

where

$$\mathbf{z} = \frac{1}{2} \log \frac{1 + \mathbf{r}}{1 - \mathbf{r}},$$

and $\mathbf{z}$ is approximately normally distributed. Therefore

$$Pr\left\{-1.96 < \frac{\mathbf{z} - E(\mathbf{z})}{\sqrt{V(\mathbf{z})}} < 1.96\right\} \doteq 0.95.$$

For the particular sample, $r = -0.20$, so that the sample value of $\mathbf{z}$ is

$$z = \frac{1}{2}\log\frac{0.8}{1.2} = -0.203.$$

In order to test the hypothesis $\rho = 0$, you set $\rho = 0$, and find $E(\mathbf{z}) = (\log 1)/2 = 0$. On substituting these values in the inequality you find

$$-1.96 < -1.39 < 1.96.$$

Since this is a correct inequality, you are not justified in rejecting the hypothesis $\rho = 0$ at the 5% significance level in favor of the alternative $\rho \neq 0$.

You will obtain 95% confidence limits for ρ if you replace $\mathbf{z}$ in the inequality

$$-1.96 < \frac{\mathbf{z} - E(\mathbf{z})}{\sqrt{V(\mathbf{z})}} < 1.96$$

by the observed value, -0.203, of $\mathbf{z}$. After multiplying by $1/\sqrt{47} = \sqrt{V(\mathbf{z})}$, you find

$$-0.286 < -0.203 - \frac{1}{2}\log\left(\frac{1+\rho}{1-\rho}\right) < 0.286,$$

$$-0.489 < \frac{1}{2}\log\left(\frac{1+\rho}{1-\rho}\right) < 0.083,$$

$$-0.978 < \log\left(\frac{1+\rho}{1-\rho}\right) < 0.166,$$

or

$$e^{-0.978} < \frac{1+\rho}{1-\rho} < e^{0.166}.$$

On solving these two linear inequalities, you find

$$-\frac{1-e^{-0.978}}{1+e^{-0.978}} < \rho < \frac{e^{0.166}-1}{e^{0.166}+1},$$

or

$$-0.45 < \rho < 0.08.$$

These are 95% confidence limits for ρ; the value $\rho = 0$ is included between them.

PROBLEMS

1. In sampling from a bivariate normal population, is a sample correlation coefficient $r = 0.35$ significant at the 5% significance level in testing the hypothesis $\rho = 0$ against the alternative $\rho \neq 0$, if $n = 40$?

2. Suppose a correlation coefficient $r = 0.12$ is reported between percentage of gray hairs and years of married life. If the sample size is $n = 103$, is the correlation significant at the 5% level? (Assume distribution of percentage of gray hairs and years of married life approximately bivariate normal.)

3. You choose 28 rabbits from a large group and measure the length of tail **x** and the length of left ear **y** of each. You find that the sample correlation coefficient r is 1/3. Assume that **x** and **y** have a joint normal distribution.

(a) Test at the 5% significance level the hypothesis that the population correlation coefficient is 0, against the alternative that it is not.

(b) Determine 90% confidence limits for the population correlation coefficient. $\left(\text{Use the approximation } E(\mathbf{z}) \doteq \frac{1}{2}\log\frac{1+\rho}{1-\rho}.\right)$

4. Professor A claims there is a correlation 0.8 between scores on "intelligence" test T which he devised, and a standard "intelligence" test S. You have given members of a class of 103 both tests, and find a sample correlation coefficient $r = 0.7$. At what level does your result appear significantly different from that reported by Professor A?

5. The accompanying table is a portion of a larger table giving two measures, A* and ΔE, of color for each of various solutions (identified by number) of filtered raw sugars. (a) Find the correlation coefficient of the two measures. (b) Discuss the possibility of using the z-statistic in a test of the hypothesis $\rho = 1$.

Sugar	A*	ΔE	Sugar	A*	ΔE
18	0.0232	7	87	0.0905	31
73	.0477	19	102	.1092	38
86	.0625	23	80	.1352	43
32	.0705	21	9	.1013	30
46	.0780	25	101	.0748	30

(*Source:* DEITZ, V. R., "Color Evaluation in the Sugar Cane Industry," *Journal of Research of National Bureau of Standards*, Vol. 57 (1956), pp. 159–170.)

CHAPTER

13

Sampling from a Normal Population

The Central Limit Theorem gives the *approximate* distribution of the sample mean when the sample size is large, regardless of what the population may be, provided it has a mean and variance. But when the distribution of the population is specified, the distribution of the sample mean and other statistics are determined *exactly*. It has been found that in many cases of interest the parent population has an approximately normal distribution. Examples which come to mind of population random variables whose distributions are nearly normal are: the weight of a person chosen at random from a large, more or less homogeneous group; the yield of a plot chosen at random from a large number planted to a certain grain; the result of a typical one of a series of similar physical measurements (in some or all of these cases the logarithm of the random variable might be even more nearly normally distributed). Consequently, the experimenter is often willing to assume that the parent population is normally distributed, and a vast body of literature has grown up around the general problem of sampling from a normal population. In this section we shall study the distributions of certain sample statistics in sampling from a normal population, and their use in determining confidence limits for population means and standard deviations, and in testing hypotheses specifying the population mean or standard deviation.

81. Moment Generating Function. A very useful tool for determining the distributions and limiting distributions of sample statistics is furnished by the *characteristic function.* The characteristic function of a random variable $\mathbf{x}$ is defined as $E(e^{i\mathbf{x}t})$, where $i = \sqrt{-1}$; it is a function of the real variable t. However, to discuss the characteristic function requires a familiarity with elementary properties of complex numbers, which is not prerequisite for this text, and we shall adopt the practice of other elementary texts in mathematical statistics of substituting the moment generating function for the characteristic function. The moment generating function of a random variable **x** is

$$▶ \qquad M_x(t) = E(e^{\mathbf{x}t}).$$

If **x** is a discrete random variable, with probability function $f(x) = Pr\{\mathbf{x} = x\}$, then by Theorem A, page 84,

$$M_x(t) = E(e^{\mathbf{x}t}) = \sum_x e^{xt} f(x).$$

If **x** is a continuous random variable with density function $f(x)$, then by the same theorem,

$$M_x(t) = \int_{-\infty}^{\infty} e^{xt} f(x)\, dx.$$

One advantage of the characteristic function shows up immediately; every random variable has a characteristic function defined for all t; but since, if $t > 0$, e^{xt} grows rapidly as $x \to \infty$, the density function $f(x)$ must tend to 0 rapidly as $x \to \infty$ in order that the integral may converge for positive t; also $f(x)$ must tend to 0 rapidly as $x \to -\infty$ in order for the integral to converge for negative t.

The reason for the name, moment generating function, is that its derivatives, evaluated at $t = 0$, give, formally, the moments of the distribution of **x**. Assuming that the function $f(x)$ is such as to justify repeated differentiation under the integral sign, we have

$$M_x'(t) = \frac{d}{dt} M_x(t) = \int_{-\infty}^{\infty} x\, e^{xt} f(x)\, dx,$$

$$M_x''(t) = \frac{d^2}{dt^2} M_x(t) = \int_{-\infty}^{\infty} x^2\, e^{xt} f(x)\, dx,$$

and for each positive integer n,

$$M_x^{(n)}(t) = \frac{d^n}{dt^n} M_x(t) = \int_{-\infty}^{\infty} x^n\, e^{xt} f(x)\, dx.$$

On setting $t = 0$ we find that

$$M_x'(0) = \int_{-\infty}^{\infty} x f(x)\, dx = E(\mathbf{x}),$$

$$M_x''(0) = \int_{-\infty}^{\infty} x^2 f(x)\, dx = E(\mathbf{x}^2),$$

and for each positive integer n,

$$M_x^{(n)}(0) = \int_{-\infty}^{\infty} x^n f(x)\, dx = E(\mathbf{x}^n).$$

We have carried out these formal operations for a continuous random variable **x**, but you can easily verify that also for a discrete random variable we have for each positive integer n,

$$M_x^{(n)}(0) = E(\mathbf{x}^n).$$

Since $E(\mathbf{x}^n)$ is by definition the nth moment about the origin of the distribution of **x**, the reason for the name, moment generating function, is clear. We observe further (without proof) that if the moment generating function exists for values of t near 0, both positive and negative, then it is represented for such values of t by its Maclaurin's series:

$$M_x(t) \equiv \sum_{n=0}^{\infty} \frac{M_x^{(n)}(0)}{n!} t^n.$$

Thus if the Maclaurin's series expansion of $M_x(t)$ can be found, the moments of **x** about the origin can easily be determined from the coefficients: for each positive integer n, the nth moment about the origin is the coefficient of t^n, multiplied by $n!$.

Our chief interest in the moment generating function lies not in the fact that its derivatives at $t = 0$ are the moments about the origin, but rather in its use in determining the distributions of sample statistics. To this end we require a theorem which we shall state without proof.

▶ ***Theorem A.*** *Two random variables having identical moment generating functions are identically distributed. That is, if* **x** *and* **y** *have the same moment generating function, then for every pair* a, b *of real numbers, with* $a < b$, $Pr\{a < \mathbf{x} < b\} = Pr\{a < \mathbf{y} < b\}$. *In particular,* **x** *and* **y** *have the same distribution function; and the same probability function if discrete, the same probability density function if continuous.*

(We understand that two probability density functions are "the same" if they agree except possibly at points of discontinuity.) We shall see how this theorem is used in the proofs of Corollary D and Theorem F below. But first, in order to use the moment generating function to determine the distribution of the mean of a sample from a normal population, we need to know the moment generating function of a normally distributed random variable.

▶ ***Theorem B.*** *If* **z** *is a normally distributed random variable with mean* 0 *and standard deviation* 1, *then its moment generating function is*

$$M_z(t) = e^{t^2/2}.$$

Proof. The proof consists of calculating the moment generating function of **z**, $M_z(t) = E(e^{\mathbf{z}t})$. The density function of **z** is

$$\varphi(z) = \frac{1}{\sqrt{2\pi}} e^{-z^2/2}. \qquad \text{(page 147)}$$

By Theorem A, page 86, we then have

$$E(e^{\mathbf{z}t}) = \int_{-\infty}^{\infty} e^{zt}\varphi(z)\,dz = \frac{1}{\sqrt{2\pi}}\int_{-\infty}^{\infty} e^{zt}e^{-z^2/2}\,dz$$

$$= \frac{1}{\sqrt{2\pi}}\int_{-\infty}^{\infty} e^{-z^2/2+zt-t^2/2}e^{t^2/2}\,dz$$

$$= \frac{1}{\sqrt{2\pi}}e^{t^2/2}\int_{-\infty}^{\infty} e^{-\frac{1}{2}(z-t)^2}\,dz.$$

On making the change of variable $u = z - t$ we have

$$E(e^{\mathbf{z}t}) = e^{t^2/2}\left[\frac{1}{\sqrt{2\pi}}\int_{-\infty}^{\infty} e^{-u^2/2}\,du\right];$$

but the expression in brackets is just 1, since it is the integral of a density function, so that

$$M_z(t) = E(e^{\mathbf{z}t}) = e^{t^2/2}.$$

▶ ***Theorem C.*** *If* $\mathbf{x}$ *is a random variable having a moment generating function* $M_x(t)$, *and if* $\mathbf{y} = a\mathbf{x} + b$, *then*

$$M_y(t) = e^{bt}M_x(at).$$

Proof. By definition of moment generating function (page 225), the moment generating function of $\mathbf{y}$ is

$$M_y(t) = E(e^{\mathbf{y}t}) = E(e^{[a\mathbf{x}+b]\,t}) = E(e^{bt}e^{at\mathbf{x}}).$$

But e^{bt} is a number, not a random variable, so that by Theorem D, page 88,

$$E(e^{bt}e^{a\mathbf{x}t}) = e^{bt}E(e^{a\mathbf{x}t}).$$

But $E(e^{at\mathbf{x}})$ is just the moment generating function of $\mathbf{x}$, evaluated at at instead of at t:

$$E(e^{at\mathbf{x}}) = M_x(at).$$

Therefore

$$M_y(t) = e^{bt}M_x(at).$$

▶ ***Corollary D.*** *The random variable* $\mathbf{x}$ *is normal* (μ,σ) *if and only if*

$$M_x(t) = e^{\mu t+\sigma^2t^2/2}.$$

Proof. By definition, page 149, $\mathbf{x}$ is normal (μ,σ) if and only if $\mathbf{z}$ is normal $(0,1)$ where $\mathbf{z} = (\mathbf{x} - \mu)/\sigma$,

$$\mathbf{x} = \sigma\mathbf{z} + \mu.$$

By Theorem C,

$$M_x(t) = e^{\mu t} M_z(\sigma t),$$

and by Theorem B,

$$M_z(t) = e^{t^2/2},$$

so that

$$M_z(\sigma t) = e^{\sigma^2 t^2/2}.$$

Therefore

$$M_x(t) = e^{\mu t} e^{\sigma^2 t^2/2} = e^{\mu t + \sigma^2 t^2/2}.$$

We see then that if $\mathbf{x}$ is normal (μ,σ), its moment generating function is $e^{\mu t+\sigma^2 t^2/2}$. By Theorem A, any random variable having the same moment generating function is also normal (μ,σ); this completes the proof of Corollary D.

▶ ***Theorem E.*** *The moment generating function of the sum of a finite number of independent random variables is the product of their moment generating functions.*

Proof. We shall prove Theorem E in the case of two independent random variables:

$$\mathbf{S} = \mathbf{x} + \mathbf{y}.$$

You may complete the proof by using the principle of mathematical induction, or by rewriting it for the sum of an arbitrary finite number of independent random variables. Let $M_x(t), M_y(t), M_S(t)$ denote the moment generating functions of $\mathbf{x}, \mathbf{y}, \mathbf{S}$ respectively:

$$M_x(t) = E(e^{\mathbf{x}t}), \quad M_y(t) = E(e^{\mathbf{y}t}), \quad M_S(t) = E(e^{\mathbf{S}t}).$$

Then

$$M_S(t) = E(e^{[\mathbf{x}+\mathbf{y}]t}) = E(e^{\mathbf{x}t}e^{\mathbf{y}t}).$$

Since the random variables $\mathbf{x}$ and $\mathbf{y}$ are independent, so also are the random variables $e^{\mathbf{x}t}$ and $e^{\mathbf{y}t}$, for every t (page 82). By Theorem H, page 89,

$$E(e^{\mathbf{x}t}e^{\mathbf{y}t}) = E(e^{\mathbf{x}t})E(e^{\mathbf{y}t}),$$

so that

$$M_S(t) = M_x(t)M_y(t).$$

▶ ***Theorem F.*** *The sum of a finite number of independent normally distributed random variables is normally distributed.*

Proof. Let the random variables $\mathbf{y}_i$ be normally distributed (μ_i,σ_i), $i = 1, 2, \cdots, n$. By Corollary D, the moment generating function of $\mathbf{y}_i$ is

$$M_{y_i}(t) = e^{\mu_i t + \sigma_i^2 t^2/2}.$$

By Theorem E, if $\mathbf{S} = \sum_{i=1}^{n} \mathbf{y}_i$, then its moment generating function is

$$M_S(t) = \prod_{i=1}^{n} M_{y_i}(t) = \prod_{i=1}^{n} e^{\mu_i t + \sigma_i^2 t^2/2}$$

$$= e^{\sum_{i=1}^{n} (\mu_i t + \sigma_i^2 t^2/2)} = e^{(\sum_{i=1}^{n} \mu_i)t + (\sum_{i=1}^{n} \sigma_i^2)t^2/2}.$$

By Corollary D again, $\mathbf{S}$ is a normally distributed random variable with mean $\sum_{i=1}^{n} \mu_i$ and variance $\sum_{i=1}^{n} \sigma_i^2$.

More generally, it can be shown that any linear combination $\sum_{i=1}^{n} a_i \mathbf{x}_i$ of random variables $\mathbf{x}_1, \mathbf{x}_2, \cdots, \mathbf{x}_n$ whose joint distribution is (multivariate) normal is normally distributed, whether or not the random variables $\mathbf{x}_1, \mathbf{x}_2, \cdots, \mathbf{x}_n$ are independent. Further, the joint distribution of several linear combinations of $\mathbf{x}_1, \mathbf{x}_2, \cdots, \mathbf{x}_n$ will also be multivariate normal (cf. [3], p. 313; [22], p. 168; Problem 17, p. 220).

▶ ***Corollary G.*** *The mean of a sample of size n from a normally distributed population of mean μ and standard deviation σ is normally distributed with mean μ and standard deviation $\sigma/\sqrt{n}$.*

Proof. Let the sample random variables $\mathbf{x}_1, \mathbf{x}_2, \cdots, \mathbf{x}_n$ play the roles of the random variables $\mathbf{y}_i$ $(i = 1, 2, \cdots, n)$ in Theorem F; the random variables $\mathbf{x}_i$ are independent, and each is normal (μ,σ), so that $\mu_i = \mu$ and $\sigma_i = \sigma$ $(i = 1, 2, \cdots, n)$. Let $\mathbf{S} = \sum_{i=1}^{n} \mathbf{x}_i$, so that $\bar{\mathbf{x}} = \mathbf{S}/n$. By Theorem F,

$$M_S(t) = e^{(\sum_{i=1}^{n} \mu_i)t + (\sum_{i=1}^{n} \sigma_i^2)t^2/2} = e^{n\mu t + n\sigma^2 t^2/2},$$

so that by Theorem C

$$M_{\bar{x}}(t) = M_S\left(\frac{1}{n} t\right) = e^{n\mu\left(\frac{t}{n}\right) + n\sigma^2\left(\frac{t}{n}\right)^2 / 2} = e^{\mu t + \left(\frac{\sigma^2}{n}\right) t^2 / 2}.$$

It now follows from Corollary D that $\bar{\mathbf{x}}$ is normal $(\mu,\sigma/\sqrt{n})$.

EXAMPLE 1. You are conducting a study of memory. You choose five people at random from among a certain group and give each a list of meaningless combinations of letters to memorize. On the basis of other experience, you are willing to assume that the number of "words" learned is approximately normally distributed with standard deviation 4 "words." You find that the average number of words learned by your five subjects is 15, and you wish to determine 90% confidence limits for the expected number of words learned.

Your model consists of a population whose random variable $\mathbf{x}$ may be described as "number of words which will be learned by a person chosen at random from the group"; $\mathbf{x}$ has standard deviation 4, unknown mean μ. You have a sample of size 5 from this population, with a sample mean 15, and wish to determine 90% confidence limits for μ.

If the sample size were large, you might use the Central Limit Theorem and the method discussed in the example on pp. 174 ff. without making an assumption as to the distribution of the population; if the sample size were large enough you might even be willing to use the sample standard deviation in place of the population standard deviation in applying the Central Limit Theorem, without assuming that you know the population standard deviation. Here the sample size is not large, but in your mathematical model the distribution of the population is known to be normal with standard deviation 4; only the mean μ is unknown. The method of pages 177–179 is available, provided you can find a random variable whose distribution depends only on μ. Corollary G states that the sample mean $\bar{\mathbf{x}}$ itself is such a random variable, being normally distributed with mean μ and standard deviation $\sigma/\sqrt{n} = 4/\sqrt{5}$. From tables of the normal distribution you then find that

$$Pr\left\{-1.64 < \frac{\bar{\mathbf{x}} - \mu}{4/\sqrt{5}} < 1.64\right\} = 0.90;$$

you find a 90% confidence interval for μ by replacing $\bar{\mathbf{x}}$ in the inequalities by 15 and solving for μ:

$$-1.64 < \frac{15 - \mu}{4/\sqrt{5}} < 1.64,$$

$$12.1 = 15 - \frac{1.64(4)}{\sqrt{5}} < \mu < 15 + \frac{1.64(4)}{\sqrt{5}} = 17.9.$$

82. The χ^2 Distribution. To find confidence limits for the population standard deviation σ by the method of pages 177–179, we need a statistic whose distribution depends only on σ. When the population is normal, the sample variance is such a random variable; its distribution is essentially a χ^2 distribution.

▶ ***Definition.*** *A random variable has a* χ^2 distribution with n degrees of freedom *if it has the same distribution as the sum of the squares of n independent, normally distributed random variables, each with mean* 0 *and standard deviation* 1.

We recall that two random variables have the same distribution if the probability of assuming a value in any specified interval is the same for each; they have the same distribution function; if discrete, they have the same probability function; if continuous, the same density function.

▶ ***Theorem H.*** *The moment generating function of a χ^2 distributed random variable with n degrees of freedom is, for t < 1/2,*

$$(1 - 2t)^{-n/2}.$$

Proof. Let $\mathbf{z}_1, \mathbf{z}_2, \cdots, \mathbf{z}_n$ be independent random variables, each normal (0,1). By definition, the distribution of the sum of their squares,

$$\chi^2 = \sum_{i=1}^{n} \mathbf{z}_i^2,$$

is a χ^2 distribution. By Theorem E its moment generating function is given by

$$M_{\chi^2}(t) = \prod_{i=1}^{n} E(e^{\mathbf{z}_i^2 t}).$$

But for each i, $\mathbf{z}_i$ is normal (0,1), so that by Theorem A, page 86, and by the definition on page 147,

$$E(e^{\mathbf{z}_i^2 t}) = \frac{1}{\sqrt{2\pi}} \int_{-\infty}^{\infty} e^{z^2 t} e^{-z^2/2}\, dz$$

$$= \frac{1}{\sqrt{2\pi}} \int_{-\infty}^{\infty} e^{-\frac{z^2}{2}(1-2t)}\, dz.$$

Let us make the change of variable $u = z\sqrt{1 - 2t}$ (if $t < 1/2$), $du = dz\sqrt{1 - 2t}$; t is fixed. (If $t \geq 1/2$ the integral does not converge.) We find that

$$E(e^{\mathbf{z}_i^2 t}) = \frac{1}{\sqrt{2\pi}\,\sqrt{1 - 2t}} \int_{-\infty}^{\infty} e^{-u^2/2}\, du = \frac{1}{\sqrt{1 - 2t}},$$

if $t < 1/2$, since $\frac{1}{\sqrt{2\pi}} \int_{-\infty}^{\infty} e^{-u^2/2}\, du = 1$. Therefore

$$M_{\chi^2}(t) = \prod_{i=1}^{n} E(e^{\mathbf{z}_i^2 t}) = \left(\frac{1}{\sqrt{1 - 2t}}\right)^n = (1 - 2t)^{-n/2}$$

if $t < 1/2$.

You can easily prove the following theorem:

▶ ***Theorem I.*** *The sum of independent random variables having χ^2 distributions has a χ^2 distribution with a number of degrees of freedom equal to the sum of their numbers of degrees of freedom.*

Perhaps a word should be said about the term *degrees of freedom.* Possibly the aptness of the phrase would be more evident if we were to observe its use in the context in which it was originally used. For our purposes we may think of it as the number of free variables involved; a random variable having a χ^2 distribution with n degrees of freedom is the sum of the squares of exactly n independent random variables, each normal (0,1).

In determining the distribution of the sample variance, we shall require a further theorem.

▶ ***Theorem J.*** *In sampling from a normal population, the sample mean and sample variance are independent random variables.*

A proof of this theorem as a consequence of Fisher's Lemma is sketched on page 295. We show here only that $\bar{\mathbf{x}}$ and $\mathbf{s}^2$ are uncorrelated. Let $\mathbf{x}_1, \mathbf{x}_2, \cdots, \mathbf{x}_n$ denote the sample random variables, $\bar{\mathbf{x}}$ the sample mean, and $\mathbf{s}^2 = (1/n) \sum_{i=1}^n (\mathbf{x}_i - \bar{\mathbf{x}})^2$ the sample variance. Consider first, for fixed i, the covariance of $(\mathbf{x}_i - \bar{\mathbf{x}})$ and $\bar{\mathbf{x}}$ (see Problem 13(a), page 220 Let $\boldsymbol{\xi}_i = \mathbf{x}_i - \mu$, $i = 1, 2, \cdots, n$, and $\bar{\boldsymbol{\xi}} = \bar{\mathbf{x}} - \mu = (1/n) \sum_{j=1}^n \boldsymbol{\xi}_j$. Then

$$\text{cov}\,(\mathbf{x}_i - \bar{\mathbf{x}}, \bar{\mathbf{x}}) = E[(\boldsymbol{\xi}_i - \bar{\boldsymbol{\xi}})\bar{\boldsymbol{\xi}}] = E(\boldsymbol{\xi}_i\bar{\boldsymbol{\xi}}) - E(\bar{\boldsymbol{\xi}})^2.$$

Now $\boldsymbol{\xi}_i\bar{\boldsymbol{\xi}} = (1/n) \sum_{j=1}^n \boldsymbol{\xi}_i\boldsymbol{\xi}_j$, while since the sample random variables are independent, $E(\boldsymbol{\xi}_i\boldsymbol{\xi}_j) = E(\boldsymbol{\xi}_i)E(\boldsymbol{\xi}_j) = 0$ unless $j = i$. Therefore $E(\boldsymbol{\xi}_i\bar{\boldsymbol{\xi}}) = (1/n)E(\boldsymbol{\xi}_i^2) = \sigma^2/n$. Also $E(\bar{\boldsymbol{\xi}}^2) = V(\bar{\mathbf{x}}) = \sigma^2/n$, so that cov $(\mathbf{x}_i - \bar{\mathbf{x}}, \bar{\mathbf{x}}) = 0$. That is, $\mathbf{x}_i - \bar{\mathbf{x}}$ and $\bar{\mathbf{x}}$ are uncorrelated.

From the remark on page 229 above the statement of Corollary G, we conclude that $\mathbf{x}_i - \bar{\mathbf{x}}$ and $\bar{\mathbf{x}}$ have a bivariate normal joint distribution. From the remark on page 217 it follows that $\mathbf{x}_i - \bar{\mathbf{x}}$ and $\bar{\mathbf{x}}$ are independent. We conclude from the remark on page 82 that $(\mathbf{x}_i - \bar{\mathbf{x}})^2$ and $\bar{\mathbf{x}} - \mu$ are independent for each i. From this alone it does not follow that $\mathbf{s}^2$ and $\bar{\mathbf{x}}$ are independent, but it does follow that

$$\begin{aligned} E[\mathbf{s}^2(\bar{\mathbf{x}} - \mu)] &= \frac{1}{n} \sum_{i=1}^n E[(\mathbf{x}_i - \bar{\mathbf{x}})^2(\bar{\mathbf{x}} - \mu)] \\ &= \frac{1}{n} \sum_{i=1}^n E[(\mathbf{x}_i - \bar{\mathbf{x}})^2]E[\bar{\mathbf{x}} - \mu] = 0. \end{aligned}$$

Thus

$$\begin{aligned} \text{cov}\,(\mathbf{s}^2, \bar{\mathbf{x}}) &= E\{[\mathbf{s}^2 - E(\mathbf{s}^2)](\bar{\mathbf{x}} - \mu)\} \\ &= E[\mathbf{s}^2(\bar{\mathbf{x}} - \mu)] = 0, \text{ and} \end{aligned}$$

$\mathbf{s}^2$ and $\bar{\mathbf{x}}$ are uncorrelated.

▶ ***Theorem K.*** *If $\mathbf{s}^2$ is the sample variance of a sample of size n from a normal population with mean μ and standard deviation σ, then the random variable $n\mathbf{s}^2/\sigma^2$ has a χ^2 distribution with $n - 1$ degrees of freedom.*

Proof. We begin by writing $n\mathbf{s}^2/\sigma^2$ in terms of squares of random variables which are normal (0,1). By definition, page 138,

$$\mathbf{s}^2 = \frac{1}{n}\sum_{i=1}^n (\mathbf{x}_i - \bar{\mathbf{x}})^2,$$

where $\mathbf{x}_1, \mathbf{x}_2, \cdots, \mathbf{x}_n$ are the sample random variables, and $\bar{\mathbf{x}}$ is the sample mean. Then

$$\mathbf{s}^2 = \frac{1}{n}\sum_{i=1}^n [(\mathbf{x}_i - \mu) - (\bar{\mathbf{x}} - \mu)]^2$$

$$= \frac{1}{n}\sum_{i=1}^n [(\mathbf{x}_i - \mu)^2 - 2(\mathbf{x}_i - \mu)(\bar{\mathbf{x}} - \mu) + (\bar{\mathbf{x}} - \mu)^2].$$

Since $\bar{\mathbf{x}} - \mu$ does not involve the summation index i, we have

$$\mathbf{s}^2 = \frac{1}{n}\sum_{i=1}^n (\mathbf{x}_i - \mu)^2 - \frac{2}{n}(\bar{\mathbf{x}} - \mu)\sum_{i=1}^n (\mathbf{x}_i - \mu) + (\bar{\mathbf{x}} - \mu)^2.$$

But

$$\frac{1}{n}\sum_{i=1}^n (\mathbf{x}_i - \mu) = \frac{1}{n}\sum_{i=1}^n \mathbf{x}_i - \frac{1}{n}\sum_{i=1}^n \mu = \bar{\mathbf{x}} - \mu,$$

so that

$$\mathbf{s}^2 = \frac{1}{n}\sum_{i=1}^n (\mathbf{x}_i - \mu)^2 - (\bar{\mathbf{x}} - \mu)^2.$$

On multiplying both sides by n/σ^2 we have

$$\frac{n\mathbf{s}^2}{\sigma^2} = \sum_{i=1}^n \left(\frac{\mathbf{x}_i - \mu}{\sigma}\right)^2 - \left(\frac{\bar{\mathbf{x}} - \mu}{\sigma/\sqrt{n}}\right)^2.$$

Now for each i, $\mathbf{x}_i$ is normal (μ,σ), so that $(\mathbf{x}_i - \mu)/\sigma$ is normal (0,1) (page 149). Also, by Corollary G, page 229, $\bar{\mathbf{x}}$ is normal $(\mu,\sigma/\sqrt{n})$, and $(\bar{\mathbf{x}} - \mu)/(\sigma/\sqrt{n})$ is normal (0,1). We have

$$\frac{n\mathbf{s}^2}{\sigma^2} + \left(\frac{\bar{\mathbf{x}} - \mu}{\sigma/\sqrt{n}}\right)^2 = \sum_{i=1}^n \left(\frac{\mathbf{x}_i - \mu}{\sigma}\right)^2.$$

For the moment, let us denote the random variable $n\mathbf{s}^2/\sigma^2$ by $\mathbf{w}$, and the random variable $[(\bar{\mathbf{x}} - \mu)/(\sigma/\sqrt{n})]^2$ by $\mathbf{z}$. According to Theorem J, page 232 (and the remark on page 82), $\mathbf{w}$ and $\mathbf{z}$ are independent random variables. We have

$$\mathbf{w} + \mathbf{z} = \sum_{i=1}^n \left(\frac{\mathbf{x}_i - \mu}{\sigma}\right)^2.$$

The right member is the sum of the squares of n independent random variables, each normal (0,1). By definition (page 230), it has a χ^2 distribution with n degrees of freedom, and by Theorem H its moment generating function is

$$(1 - 2t)^{-n/2} \quad (\text{for } t < 1/2).$$

The moment generating function of the left member is

$$M_{w+z}(t) = M_w(t)M_z(t)$$

by Theorem E, page 228, so that

$$M_w(t)M_z(t) = (1 - 2t)^{-n/2}.$$

Now $\mathbf{z}$ is itself the square of a random variable whose distribution is normal (0,1), so that by definition $\mathbf{z}$ has a χ^2 distribution with 1 degree of freedom, and by Theorem H its moment generating function is

$$M_z(t) = (1 - 2t)^{-\frac{1}{2}}.$$

Therefore

$$M_w(t) = (1 - 2t)^{-(n-1)/2}.$$

By Theorem H this is the moment generating function of a random variable having a χ^2 distribution with $n - 1$ degrees of freedom, so that by Theorem A, page 226, $\mathbf{w} = n\mathbf{s}^2/\sigma^2$ has a χ^2 distribution with $n - 1$ degrees of freedom. It is indeed possible to write $n\mathbf{s}^2/\sigma^2$ as the sum of the squares of $n - 1$ independent random variables, each normal (0,1) (cf. [3], Chapter 29). Some prefer to think of $n\mathbf{s}^2/\sigma^2$ as involving $n - 1$ free random variables, the n sample random variables $\mathbf{x}_1, \mathbf{x}_2, \cdots, \mathbf{x}_n$ being bound by the condition that their sum is $n\bar{x}$.

Example 2. Suppose you have introduced into a process for manufacturing tuning forks an innovation which you hope will yield forks having a smaller variance about the true pitch. In a sample of 20 forks produced by the new process the sample standard deviation is 0.7 cycles per second. You believe the distribution of the random variable, "pitch of a fork produced by the new process," is normal, and wish to determine 90% confidence limits for the standard deviation. By Theorem K the statistic $n\mathbf{s}^2/\sigma^2$ has a χ^2 distribution with $n - 1 = 19$ degrees of freedom. You find from tables of the χ^2 distribution numbers a and b such that

$$Pr\{\chi^2 < a\} = 0.05$$

and

$$Pr\{\chi^2 > b\} = 0.05;$$

such numbers are $a = 10.12$ and $b = 30.14$. Hence

$$Pr\{10.12 < 20\mathbf{s}^2/\sigma^2 < 30.14\} = 1 - 0.05 - 0.05 = 0.90.$$

On substituting $s^2 = (0.7)^2$, you find

$$10.12 < \frac{20(0.7)^2}{\sigma^2} < 30.14,$$

$$0.33 < \sigma^2 < 0.97,$$

or

$$0.57 < \sigma < 0.98.$$

83. Student's t-distribution. An advantage of the statistic ns^2/σ^2 as used in estimating σ in sampling from a normal population, which is not enjoyed by the statistic $\bar{\mathbf{x}}$ as used in estimating μ, is that the random variable $n\mathbf{s}^2/\sigma^2$ depends only on σ while the distribution of $\bar{\mathbf{x}}$ depends not only on μ but also on σ. Gossett, working under the pseudonym "Student," introduced the random variable

$$\frac{(\bar{\mathbf{x}} - \mu)\sqrt{n-1}}{\mathbf{s}},$$

which depends on μ but not on σ, if the sample is from a normal population.

▶ ***Definition.*** *A random variable has* Student's t-distribution with n degrees of freedom *if it has the same distribution as the quotient* $\mathbf{u}\sqrt{n}/\mathbf{v}$, *where* $\mathbf{u}$ *and* $\mathbf{v}$ *are independent random variables,* $\mathbf{u}$ *having a normal distribution with mean* 0 *and standard deviation* 1, $\mathbf{v}^2$ *having a* χ^2 *distribution with* n *degrees of freedom.*

▶ ***Theorem L.*** *If* $\bar{\mathbf{x}}$ *and* $\mathbf{s}^2$ *are sample mean and sample variance of a sample of size* n *from a* normal *population with mean* μ *and standard deviation* σ, *then*

$$\frac{(\bar{\mathbf{x}} - \mu)\sqrt{n-1}}{\mathbf{s}}$$

has Student's t-distribution with $n - 1$ *degrees of freedom.*

Proof. Let $\mathbf{u} = (\bar{\mathbf{x}} - \mu)/(\sigma/\sqrt{n})$; by Corollary G, page 229, $\mathbf{u}$ is normal (0,1). Let $\mathbf{v}^2 = n\mathbf{s}^2/\sigma^2$; by Theorem K, $\mathbf{v}^2$ has a χ^2 distribution with $n - 1$ degrees of freedom. By Theorem J, page 232 (and the remark on page 82), $\mathbf{u}$ and $\mathbf{v}$ are independent. Let

$$\mathbf{t} = \frac{\mathbf{u}\sqrt{n-1}}{\mathbf{v}} = \frac{(\bar{\mathbf{x}} - \mu)\sqrt{n-1}}{\mathbf{s}};$$

by the definition of Student's t-distribution, $\mathbf{t}$ has Student's t-distribution with $n - 1$ degrees of freedom.

EXAMPLE 3. You are engaged in raising peafowl, and wish to determine the effect of a new diet on the weight of your peacocks, whose average weight is 15 lb. You select 5 peacocks at random from your flock and find that after 3 months of the new diet the mean weight of the 5 test birds is 20 lb., with a sample standard deviation of 5 lb. You are willing to assume that the weight of peacocks fed with the new diet is an approximately normally distributed random variable, and wish to test at the 5% significance level the hypothesis that the average weight of peacocks fed with the new diet is 15 lb. against the alternative that it is not. In your model, then, you have to deal with a sample of size 5 from a normal population, and wish to test the hypothesis $\mu = 15$, having obtained a sample for which $\bar{x} = 20$, $s = 5$, $n = 5$.

From tables of Student's t-distribution you determine two numbers a and b such that

$$Pr\{a < \mathbf{t} < b\} = 0.95.$$

This can be done in many ways. One way, which has some advantages at least in situations involving certain symmetries, is to choose a and b so that $a = -b$. Since $n - 1 = 4$, you have

$$Pr\{\mathbf{t} < -2.78\} = 0.025,$$

$$Pr\{\mathbf{t} > 2.78\} = 0.025.$$

Therefore

$$Pr\left\{-2.78 < \frac{(\bar{\mathbf{x}} - \mu)\sqrt{n-1}}{\mathbf{s}} < 2.78\right\} = 0.95.$$

On substituting $\bar{x} = 20$, $s = 5$, $\mu = 15$, $n = 5$, you have $(20 - 15)\sqrt{4}/5 = 2$, which does lie between -2.78 and 2.78, so that you cannot reject, at the 5% significance level, the hypothesis $\mu = 15$ in favor of the alternative $\mu \neq 15$; accordingly, you cannot conclude, at the 5% significance level, that the new diet affects the average weight.

★ 84. Proof of the Central Limit Theorem. Let $\mathbf{x}$ be the population random variable, μ its mean, and σ its standard deviation; we assume these exist. In order to avoid the use of the characteristic function, we shall assume also that the moment generating function, $M_x(t) = E(e^{\mathbf{x}t})$ exists, at least for values of t sufficiently near 0. (For a proof using the characteristic function, a proof under more general conditions, and for further references, see [3], Chapter 17; [6], Chapter 6). Let $\mathbf{x}_i$ denote the ith sample random variable, $i = 1, 2, \cdots, n$; these are independent random variables, each with the same distribution and hence the same moment generating function as $\mathbf{x}$. Let $\bar{\mathbf{x}}$ denote the sample mean: $\bar{\mathbf{x}} = \frac{1}{n}\sum_{i=1}^{n} \mathbf{x}_i$; then

$$n(\bar{\mathbf{x}} - \mu) = \sum_{i=1}^{n} (\mathbf{x}_i - \mu).$$

By Theorem E, the moment generating function of $n(\bar{\mathbf{x}} - \mu)$ is

$$M_{n(\bar{x}-\mu)}(t) = [M_{x-\mu}(t)]^n.$$

Now let $M^*(t)$ denote the moment generating function of

$$\frac{\bar{\mathbf{x}} - \mu}{\sigma/\sqrt{n}} = \frac{1}{\sigma\sqrt{n}}[n(\bar{\mathbf{x}} - \mu)]$$

By Theorem C,

$$M^*(t) = M_{n(\bar{x}-\mu)}\left(\frac{t}{\sigma\sqrt{n}}\right) = \left[M_{x-\mu}\left(\frac{t}{\sigma\sqrt{n}}\right)\right]^n.$$

The moment generating function, when it exists for t near 0, has derivatives of all orders at $t = 0$, so that we can apply Taylor's Theorem with remainder:

$$M_{x-\mu}(t) = M_{x-\mu}(0) + M'_{x-\mu}(0)t + M''_{x-\mu}(0)t^2/2 + M_{x-\mu}{}^{(3)}(\xi)t^3/3!,$$

where ξ is some number between 0 and t, and where $M_{x-\mu}{}^{(3)}(\xi)$ denotes the third derivative of $M_{x-\mu}(t)$ evaluated at ξ. We shall set

$$\epsilon(t) = tM_{x-\mu}{}^{(3)}(\xi)/3! \qquad \text{(note } \xi \text{ depends on } t\text{)}$$

We have $M_{x-\mu}(0) = 1$, $M'_{x-\mu}(0) = 0$, and $M''_{x-\mu}(0) = \sigma^2$ since $E(\mathbf{x} - \mu) = 0$, $E(\mathbf{x} - \mu)^2 = \sigma^2$ (page 225). Therefore

$$M_{x-\mu}(t) = 1 + \sigma^2t^2/2 + t^2\epsilon(t),$$

where $\epsilon(t) = tM_{x-\mu}{}^{(3)}(\xi)/3! \to 0$ as $t \to 0$. Hence

$$M_{x-\mu}\left(\frac{t}{\sigma\sqrt{n}}\right) = 1 + \frac{\sigma^2}{2}\left(\frac{t^2}{\sigma^2 n}\right) + \frac{t^2}{\sigma^2 n}\epsilon\left(\frac{t}{\sigma\sqrt{n}}\right)$$

and

$$M^*(t) = \left[1 + \frac{t^2}{2n} + \frac{t^2}{\sigma^2 n}\epsilon\left(\frac{t}{\sigma\sqrt{n}}\right)\right]^n.$$

As in the proof of Theorem B, page 119, we find that the limit of the right member as $n \to \infty$ is $e^{t^2/2}$. Thus by Corollary D, page 227, the limit as $n \to \infty$ of the moment generating function, $M^*(t)$, of $(\bar{\mathbf{x}} - \mu)/(\sigma/\sqrt{n})$ is precisely that of a normal (0,1) random variable. Using (without proof) the theorem that if the moment generating functions of a sequence of random variables approach the moment generating function of a certain distribution function, then their distribution functions converge also to that distribution function, we conclude that the limiting distribution of $(\bar{\mathbf{x}} - \mu)/(\sigma/\sqrt{n})$ is normal (0,1).

PROBLEMS

1. A sample of size 5 from a normal population with mean μ and standard deviation σ yielded $\bar{x} = 10$, $s = 2$.

(a) Test the hypothesis $\sigma = 5$ against the alternative $\sigma \neq 5$ at the 10% significance level; at the 4% significance level.

(b) Determine 90% confidence limits for σ; 96% confidence limits for σ.

2. A random sample of size 10 is drawn from a normal population of unknown mean and standard deviation. The sample mean is 10, the sample variance 2. Test at the 4% significance level the hypothesis that the population standard deviation is 5, against the alternative that it is not; repeat at the 2% significance level.

3. In Problem 1,

(a) Test the hypothesis $\mu = 14$ against the alternative $\mu \neq 14$, at the 5% significance level; at the 1% significance level.

(b) Determine 90% confidence limits for μ; 95% confidence limits for μ.

4. The result of a single observation using a certain physical apparatus for measuring wave length of monochromatic light is a normally distributed random variable whose mean is the "true" wave length. Twenty independent observations yield a sample mean of 5269.57 Å, and a sample standard deviation of 0.1 Å. (a) Find a 95% confidence interval for the wave length. (b) Find a 96% confidence interval for the standard deviation of a single observation.

5. The mean maximum length of antler of a random sample of 17 two-year-old bucks in a forest was determined to be 25 in., with a sample standard deviation of 4 in. Find a 90% confidence interval for the mean length of antler of two-year-old bucks in the forest. (Assume length of antler normally distributed.)

6. The lord of the castle has required his deputy in charge of hatcheries to institute a feeding program which will produce year-old trout to fit his plates: having a mean length between 10 and 12 in., a standard deviation not more than 1 in. After initiating a trial program, the deputy finds that in a random sample of size 11, the mean is 11.3 and the sample standard deviation 0.8 in. What confidence can he have that the population mean is between 10 and 12 in., and what confidence that the standard deviation is not more than 1 in.? (Assume length normal.)

7. (a) Suppose that $\mathbf{z} = \log_{10} \mathbf{y}$ and that $\mathbf{z}$ is normally distributed with mean μ and variance σ^2, i.e. $\mathbf{y}$ has a log-normal distribution (Problem 8, p. 162). Find the median of $\mathbf{y}$. (For definition of median, see p. 348.)

(b) A sample of size n is taken from the log-normal population defined in (a). Assuming μ and σ^2 unknown, obtain a $100(1 - \alpha)\%$ confidence interval for the median of $\mathbf{y}$ (exactly).

(c) Use the sample of size 20 in Problem 18 (c), page 159 and your answer to (b) to obtain a 95% confidence interval for the median number of words in a sentence in G. B. Shaw's book.

8. Obtain a 90% confidence interval for the standard deviation of the lifetime (in hours) of 40-watt light bulbs produced during the given week, using the sample of size 10 in Problem 20 (b), p. 160.

9. Suppose the heights of men aged 20 or more years have a normal distribution with mean 69 in. and standard deviation 3 in., and the distribution of heights of women aged 20 or more years is normal with mean 64 in. and standard deviation 2.8 in. What is the probability that if a man and a woman are chosen at random, the woman will prove to be taller than the man?

10. (a) Let $\mathbf{x}_1, \mathbf{x}_2, \cdots, \mathbf{x}_n$ be sample random variables from a normal population with mean μ and standard deviation σ. What is the distribution of $\sum_{i=1}^{n} (\mathbf{x}_i - \mu)^2/\sigma^2$?

(b) Find 90% confidence limits for σ^2 if for a sample $x_1, \cdots, x_{10}$ from a normal population with mean $\mu = 1$ and unknown standard deviation σ we have $\sum_{i=1}^{10} x_i = 9$ and $\sum_{i=1}^{10} x_i^2 = 12$.

11. (a) Find the moment generating function of a random variable $\mathbf{x}$ which assumes the value 1 with probability p and the value 0 with probability $q = 1 - p$.

(b) Use (a) and Theorem E, page 228, to find the moment generating function of a binomial random variable $\mathbf{s}$ with parameters n and p.

Hint. $\mathbf{s}$ is the sum of n independent random variables having the distribution in (a).

12. (a) Show directly from the definition of moment generating function that the moment generating function of a binomial random variable $\mathbf{s}$ with parameters n and p is

$$\sum_{x=0}^{n} \binom{n}{x} (pe^t)^x q^{n-x}.$$

(b) Verify that the moment generating function in (a) can be rewritten as $[pe^t + q]^n$.

13. Prove Theorem I, page 231.

14. Let $\mathbf{x}$ have a Poisson distribution with parameter m (Problem 3, page 156), so that $Pr\{\mathbf{x} = x\} = e^{-m}m^x/x!$, $x = 0, 1, 2, \cdots$. Show that the moment generating function of $\mathbf{x}$ is

$$e^{m(e^t-1)}.$$

Hint. $e^y = \sum_{k=0}^{\infty} y^k/k!$.

15. Let $\mathbf{x}$ have a Poisson distribution with parameter m so that $f(x) = Pr\{\mathbf{x} = x\} = e^{-m}m^x/x!$, $x = 0, 1, 2, \cdots$.

(a) Show that $\sum_x f(x) = 1$. (Cf. Hint, Problem 14.)

(b) Show that $E(\mathbf{x}) = V(\mathbf{x}) = m$.

16. Use the results of Problems 14 and 15 to show that the sum of independent random variables having Poisson distributions has a Poisson distribution whose mean is the sum of their means.

★ **85. Normal Regression.** A situation of the kind we shall discuss here was mentioned very briefly on pages 214, 215. We suppose that to each of certain values of an ordinary real variable or parameter x corresponds a random variable $\mathbf{y}$, the random variables $\mathbf{y}$ for different values of x being independent. For example, as sales manager of a chain of stores, you may wish to study the effect of price on sales volume of a certain article. In n comparable cities you offer the article for sale at prices $x_1, x_2, \cdots, x_n$, and you denote by $\mathbf{y}_1, \mathbf{y}_2, \cdots, \mathbf{y}_n$ suitably normalized measures of sales volume, such as percentage change from an established sales volume. Suppose you feel that in your situation you are justified in making the following assumptions:

► (1) The random variables $\mathbf{y}_1, \mathbf{y}_2, \cdots, \mathbf{y}_n$ are *independent*, all have the *same* standard deviation σ, and their joint distribution is (multivariate) *normal;* in particular, each has then a normal distribution.

(2) There are constants λ and β such that $E(\mathbf{y}_i) = \lambda x_i + \beta$, $i = 1, 2, \cdots, n$. In making these assumptions, you have adopted the *normal regression model.*

We emphasize that in the linear regression model x_i and $\mathbf{y}_i$ are not random variables with a bivariate normal joint distribution. Rather, $x_1, x_2, \cdots, x_n$ are not random variables at all, but known numbers.

Let us compute the maximum likelihood estimates $\hat{\sigma}^2$, $\hat{\lambda}$, $\hat{\beta}$ of the unknown parameters σ^2, λ, and β. By hypothesis, the joint distribution function of the random variables $\mathbf{y}_1, \mathbf{y}_2, \cdots, \mathbf{y}_n$ is

$$\prod_{i=1}^n \frac{1}{\sqrt{2\pi}\,\sigma} e^{-\frac{1}{2\sigma^2}(y_i - \lambda x_i - \beta)^2} = (2\pi)^{-n/2}(\sigma^2)^{-n/2} e^{-\frac{1}{2\sigma^2}\sum_{i=1}^n (y_i - \lambda x_i - \beta)^2}.$$

Here the numbers $x_1, x_2, \cdots, x_n$ are fixed, known numbers; the numbers $y_1, y_2, \cdots, y_n$ are observed values of the random variables $\mathbf{y}_1, \mathbf{y}_2, \cdots, \mathbf{y}_n$, and the numbers σ^2, λ, β are unknown constants, to be determined so as to maximize the above expression. This expression will attain its maximum value for those values of σ^2, λ, and β which minimize the negative of its logarithm. The problem may therefore be stated: find values $\hat{\sigma}^2$, $\hat{\lambda}$, and $\hat{\beta}$ of σ^2, λ, and β which minimize

$$\frac{n}{2}\log 2\pi + \frac{n}{2}\log \sigma^2 + \frac{1}{2\sigma^2}\sum_{i=1}^{n} (y_i - \lambda x_i - \beta)^2;$$

or equivalently,

$$\log \sigma^2 + \frac{1}{\sigma^2}\left[\frac{1}{n}\sum_{i=1}^{n} (y_i - \lambda x_i - \beta)^2\right].$$

The expression in brackets does not depend on σ^2; and since $\sigma^2 > 0$, values of λ and β which minimize the expression in brackets will also minimize the entire expression, regardless of what value σ^2 may have. But on pages 213-214 we found that these values are

$$\hat{\lambda} = \frac{\frac{1}{n}\sum_{i=1}^{n} (x_i - \bar{x})(y_i - \bar{y})}{\frac{1}{n}\sum_{i=1}^{n} (x_i - \bar{x})^2} = \frac{\sum_{i=1}^{n} x_i y_i - n\bar{x}\bar{y}}{\sum_{i=1}^{n} x_i^2 - n\bar{x}^2}$$

or

▶ $$\hat{\lambda} = \frac{1}{n s_x^2}\left[\sum_{i=1}^{n} x_i y_i - n\bar{x}\bar{y}\right]$$

and

$$\hat{\beta} = \bar{y} - \hat{\lambda}\bar{x},$$

where

$$\bar{x} = \frac{1}{n}\sum_{i=1}^{n} x_i,\quad \bar{y} = \frac{1}{n}\sum_{i=1}^{n} y_i,$$

$$s_x^2 = \frac{1}{n}\sum_{i=1}^{n} x_i^2 - \bar{x}^2.$$

The numbers λ and β having been chosen so as to minimize the expression in brackets, we now choose σ^2 so as to minimize the entire expression,

$$\log \sigma^2 + \frac{1}{\sigma^2}\left[\frac{1}{n}\sum_{i=1}^{n} (y_i - \hat{\lambda} x_i - \hat{\beta})^2\right].$$

Its derivative with respect to σ^2 is

$$\frac{1}{\sigma^2} - \frac{1}{\sigma^4}\left[\frac{1}{n}\sum_{i=1}^{n} (y_i - \hat{\lambda} x_i - \hat{\beta})^2\right],$$

and on setting this equal to zero we find that

$$\hat{\sigma}^2 = \frac{1}{n}\sum_{i=1}^{n} (y_i - \hat{\lambda} x_i - \hat{\beta})^2.$$

We found on pages 209, 213, 214 that when λ and β are chosen so as to minimize $\frac{1}{n}\sum_{i=1}^{n}(y_i - \lambda x_i - \beta)^2$, the minimum value is $\hat{\sigma}^2 = (1 - r^2)s_y^2$, where $r = \hat{\lambda}s_x/s_y$. Hence

$$\blacktriangleright \qquad \hat{\sigma}^2 = s_y^2 - \hat{\lambda}^2 s_x^2.$$

Since the numbers $x_1, x_2, \cdots, x_n$ are simply known constants, we see that the random variable

$$\hat{\boldsymbol{\lambda}} = \frac{\sum_{i=1}^{n} x_i\mathbf{y}_i - n\bar{x}\bar{\mathbf{y}}}{\sum_{i=1}^{n} x_i^2 - n\bar{x}^2}$$

is a linear combination of the random variables $\mathbf{y}_1, \mathbf{y}_2, \cdots, \mathbf{y}_n$. So also is $\hat{\boldsymbol{\beta}} = \bar{\mathbf{y}} - \hat{\boldsymbol{\lambda}}\bar{x}$. Consequently

▶ *$\hat{\boldsymbol{\beta}}$ and $\hat{\boldsymbol{\lambda}}$ have a bivariate normal distribution (page 229), and each is normally distributed.*

You have shown in Problem 14, page 220, that

$$\blacktriangleright \qquad E(\hat{\boldsymbol{\lambda}}) = \lambda \text{ and } E(\hat{\boldsymbol{\beta}}) = \beta,$$

so that each is an unbiased estimator of the corresponding parameter. We can readily compute $V(\hat{\boldsymbol{\lambda}})$, observing first that

$$\sum_{i=1}^{n} x_i\mathbf{y}_i - n\bar{x}\bar{\mathbf{y}} = \sum_{i=1}^{n} x_i\mathbf{y}_i - \bar{x}\sum_{i=1}^{n}\mathbf{y}_i = \sum_{i=1}^{n}(x_i - \bar{x})\mathbf{y}_i,$$

since $n\bar{\mathbf{y}} = \sum_{i=1}^{n}\mathbf{y}_i$. Since the random variables $\mathbf{y}_1, \mathbf{y}_2, \cdots, \mathbf{y}_n$ are independent, we have

$$V\left(\sum_{i=1}^{n}(x_i - \bar{x})\mathbf{y}_i\right) = \sum_{i=1}^{n}(x_i - \bar{x})^2 V(\mathbf{y}_i).$$

But by hypothesis $V(\mathbf{y}_i) = \sigma^2$ for $i = 1, 2, \cdots, n$, so that

$$V\left(\sum_{i=1}^{n}(x_i - \bar{x})\mathbf{y}_i\right) = \sigma^2\sum_{i=1}^{n}(x_i - \bar{x})^2 = n\sigma^2 s_x^2,$$

and finally

$$\blacktriangleright \qquad V(\hat{\boldsymbol{\lambda}}) = \sigma^2/ns_x^2.$$

Similarly,

$$\hat{\boldsymbol{\beta}} = \bar{\mathbf{y}} - \hat{\boldsymbol{\lambda}}\bar{x} = \bar{\mathbf{y}} - \frac{\bar{x}}{ns_x^2}\left[\sum_{i=1}^{n} x_i\mathbf{y}_i - n\bar{x}\bar{\mathbf{y}}\right]$$

$$= \bar{\mathbf{y}}\left[1 + \frac{\bar{x}^2}{s_x^2}\right] - \frac{\bar{x}}{ns_x^2}\sum_{i=1}^{n} x_i\mathbf{y}_i$$

$$= \frac{1}{ns_x^2}\left\{\sum_{i=1}^{n}(s_x^2 + \bar{x}^2 - \bar{x}x_i)\mathbf{y}_i\right\},$$

so that

$$V(\hat{\boldsymbol{\beta}}) = \frac{1}{n^2 s_x^4}\left\{\sum_{i=1}^{n}(s_x^2 + \bar{x}^2 - \bar{x}x_i)^2\sigma^2\right\}.$$

Using the definition, $\sum_{i=1}^{n} x_i = n\bar{x}$, we find that

▶ $$V(\hat{\boldsymbol{\beta}}) = \frac{\sigma^2(s_x^2 + \bar{x}^2)}{ns_x^2} = \frac{\sigma^2 \sum_{i=1}^{n} x_i^2}{\left[\sum_{i=1}^{n} x_i^2 - n\bar{x}^2\right]}.$$

Though the random variables $\hat{\boldsymbol{\lambda}}$ and $\hat{\boldsymbol{\beta}}$ are in general not independent, it can be shown that

▶ $n\hat{\boldsymbol{\sigma}}^2/\sigma^2$ has the χ^2 distribution with $n - 2$ degrees of freedom and is independent of $\hat{\boldsymbol{\lambda}}$ and $\hat{\boldsymbol{\beta}}$.

This statistic depends on the parameter σ alone, and can be used to determine confidence intervals for σ and to test hypotheses of the form $\sigma = \sigma_0$.

It follows from the definition of the t-distribution (page 235) that

$$[(\hat{\boldsymbol{\lambda}} - \lambda)/\sqrt{V(\hat{\boldsymbol{\lambda}})}]\sqrt{n-2}/[\sqrt{n}\hat{\boldsymbol{\sigma}}/\sigma]$$

and

$$[(\hat{\boldsymbol{\beta}} - \beta)/\sqrt{V(\hat{\boldsymbol{\beta}})}]\sqrt{n-2}/[\sqrt{n}\hat{\boldsymbol{\sigma}}/\sigma]$$

both have the t-distribution with $n - 2$ degrees of freedom. When we replace $V(\hat{\boldsymbol{\lambda}})$ and $V(\hat{\boldsymbol{\beta}})$ by the appropriate expressions above, we find that

▶ $$\frac{\sqrt{n-2}\,(\hat{\boldsymbol{\lambda}} - \lambda)\sqrt{\sum_{i=1}^{n} x_i^2 - n\bar{x}^2}}{\sqrt{\sum_{i=1}^{n}(y_i - \hat{\boldsymbol{\lambda}}x_i - \hat{\boldsymbol{\beta}})^2}} = \frac{\sqrt{n-2}\,(\hat{\boldsymbol{\lambda}} - \lambda)s_x}{\hat{\boldsymbol{\sigma}}}$$

and

$$\frac{\sqrt{n(n-2)}\,(\hat{\boldsymbol{\beta}} - \beta)\sqrt{\sum_{i=1}^{n} x_i^2 - n\bar{x}^2}}{\sqrt{\sum_{i=1}^{n} x_i^2}\sqrt{\sum_{i=1}^{n}(y_i - \hat{\boldsymbol{\lambda}}x_i - \hat{\boldsymbol{\beta}})^2}} = \frac{\sqrt{n-2}\,(\hat{\boldsymbol{\beta}} - \beta)s_x}{\sqrt{s_x^2 + \bar{x}^2}\,\hat{\boldsymbol{\sigma}}}$$

have t-distributions, each with $n - 2$ degrees of freedom.

Each of these statistics is, for fixed sample values, a function of a single parameter; they may be used to find confidence intervals for λ and β, and to test hypotheses of the form $\lambda = \lambda_0$ and $\beta = \beta_0$.

EXAMPLE 4. As manager of a meat-packing company, you are interested in the effect of cold storage on the tenderness of meat. You first devise a method for assigning a tenderness score y to a piece of meat. You then put 4 packages of the same kind in cold storage for 2 days, 4 for 4 days, etc., finally, 4 for 10 days; in all, 20 packages, 5 different storage periods. You find the *average* tenderness scores for the 5 storage periods are 22, 26, 28, 29, 30. To set up a model to analyze the data, you assume:

(1) The individual scores are determined independently; each is to be thought of before the experiment as a random variable, their joint distribution being normal, all with the same standard deviation, σ_1.

(2) The mean score is a linear function of length of storage.

Adopting the notation of the above discussion, we shall have $x_1 = 2$, $x_2 = 4$, $x_3 = 6$, $x_4 = 8$, $x_5 = 10$; $n = 5$, $\bar{x} = \frac{1}{5}\sum_{i=1}^{5} x_i = 6$, $s_x^2 = \frac{1}{5}\sum_{i=1}^{5} x_i^2 - \bar{x}^2 = 8$. The symbol $\mathbf{y}_1$ will represent the *average* of the scores of the 4 packages stored for 2 days. If the expected score of a package stored for 2 days is $2\lambda + \beta$, so also will be the expected *average* score of 4 packages. But if the standard deviation of the score of a package stored for 2 days is σ_1, then the standard deviation of the average score of 4 packages will be $\sigma = \sigma_1/2$. Similarly, $\mathbf{y}_i$ is the average score of the 4 packages stored $2i$ days, and we have

$$E(\mathbf{y}_i) = \lambda x_i + \beta = 2i\lambda + \beta,$$

$$V(\mathbf{y}_i) = \sigma^2 = \sigma_1^2/4, \; i = 1, 2, 3, 4, 5.$$

The observed values of the random variables are $y_1 = 22$, $y_2 = 26$, $y_3 = 28$, $y_4 = 29$, $y_5 = 30$. Then $\bar{y} = 27$,

$$\hat{\lambda} = \frac{\sum_{i=1}^{n} x_i y_i - n\bar{x}\bar{y}}{ns_x^2} = \frac{848 - 810}{40} = 0.95;$$

$$\hat{\beta} = \bar{y} - \hat{\lambda}\bar{x} = 27 - \frac{19}{20}(6) = 21.3,$$

$$n\hat{\sigma}^2 = \sum_{i=1}^{n} (y_i - \hat{\lambda}x_i - \hat{\beta})^2 = 3.9$$

The t-statistic involving λ has the value

$$\sqrt{n-2}(\hat{\lambda} - \lambda)\sqrt{ns_x^2}/\sqrt{n\hat{\sigma}^2} = \sqrt{3}(0.95 - \lambda)\sqrt{40}/\sqrt{3.9}$$

$= 5.55(0.95 - \lambda)$. In order to determine a 90% confidence interval for λ, we refer to the t-tables with $n - 2 = 3$ degrees of freedom, and find

$$Pr\{-2.353 < \mathbf{t} < 2.353\} = 0.90.$$

Solving the inequalities

$$-2.353 < 5.55(0.95 - \lambda) < 2.353$$

for λ, we find

$$0.53 < \lambda < 1.37$$

as a 90% confidence interval for λ. To achieve the precision you would probably prefer would evidently require more data.

The χ^2 statistic involving σ has the value

$$n\hat{\sigma}^2/\sigma^2 = 3.9/\sigma^2.$$

To determine a 90% confidence interval for σ, we refer to the χ^2 table for $n - 2 = 3$ degrees of freedom and find

$$Pr\{0.352 < \chi^2 < 7.815\} = 0.90.$$

On solving the inequality

$$0.352 < \frac{3.9}{\sigma^2} < 7.815$$

for σ, we find

$$0.71 < \sigma < 3.33$$

as a 90% confidence interval for σ. Correspondingly,

$$1.42 < \sigma_1 < 6.66$$

is a 90% confidence interval for $\sigma_1 = 2\sigma$, the standard deviation in tenderness score of an individual package.

Examination of the formulas for the statistics we have used reveals that a failure of the model to reflect accurately the physical situation may contribute to apparent poor precision and long confidence intervals. To obtain good precision, i.e., a short confidence interval for λ, the multiplier of $\hat{\lambda} - \lambda$ in the formula for the t-statistic must be large. When n (the number of storage periods) and the x values are fixed, this will be the case only if $\hat{\sigma}^2$ is small. But if the average score does not in fact vary linearly with x, increasing indefinitely the number of packages tested at each storage period will not render $\hat{\sigma}^2$ small.

There is a very close relationship between normal regression theory and the analysis of variance, to be discussed later; however, this relationship will not be exploited in this text. The reader is referred to excellent treatments in [10], [15], and [22].

★ PROBLEMS

1. You are interested in the relationship between shear strength and temperature of rods of a certain metal. You plan to select at random 5 rods, to subject them to a temperature of 100 degrees, to determine the

the shear strength of each, and finally to compute the average of their shear strengths. You plan to perform similar experiments using temperatures which are multiples of 10 degrees from 100 degrees to 200 degrees inclusive, thus using 11 temperatures and 55 rods. Let $\mathbf{y}_i$ denote the *average* of the shear strengths of the 5 rods to be tested at temperature $x_i = 100 + 10(i - 1)$ degrees, $i = 1, 2, \cdots, 11$.

(a) State the assumptions you require to fit a normal regression model to this situation.

(b) Find s_x and $\bar{x}$.

(c) Suppose on making the observations you find $\frac{1}{11} \sum_{i=1}^{11} x_i y_i = 15{,}300$, $\bar{y} = 100$, $s_y = 10$. Find 95% confidence limits for λ and β.

(d) Test at the 4% significance level the hypothesis $\sigma_1 = 6$ against the alternative $\sigma_1 \neq 6$, where σ_1 is the standard deviation in shear strength of an individual rod.

2. Suppose you have been experimenting with the effect on wheat yields of different concentrations of a fertilizer. You try 7 concentrations, with mean dose $\bar{x} = 40$ and standard deviation $s_x = 20$ in appropriate units. You use each concentration on 4 plots selected at random, and observe mean yields $y_1, y_2, \cdots, y_7$ such that $\bar{y} = 62$, $s_y^2 = 21$, $\sum_{i=1}^{7} x_i y_i = 17{,}900$. Make assumptions appropriate to a normal regression model.

(a) Find a 50% confidence interval for the mean yield without treatment.

(b) Find a 50% confidence interval for the rate of increase of mean yield with respect to concentration of the fertilizer.

3. Suppose $n = 2$, $x_1 = 0$, $x_2 = 1$.

(a) Give a formula for $\hat{\boldsymbol{\lambda}}$.

(b) What is the distribution of $\hat{\boldsymbol{\lambda}}$?

4. In the accompanying table, the y values are the weights in grams of four copper cents bearing dates 1951–1954.

x	1	2	3	4
y	2.985	3.000	3.150	3.106

(a) Find the regression line of y on x.

(b) Assuming the normal regression model, test at the 10% significance level the hypothesis that coins do not wear (i.e., that $\lambda = 0$). (*Source:* Youden, W. J. *Industrial and Engineering Chemistry*, Vol. 48 (April 1956), p. 107A.)

5. Each entry in the accompanying table refers to the *mean* of four determinations of relative volume change, y, in a sample of leather subjected to the stated pressure, x atmospheres. (a) Find the regression line of y on x. (b) Find 95% confidence limits for the slope of the "true" regression line. (c) Find 90% confidence limits for the variance of a *single* determination.

x	y	x	y
10,000	0.0692	5,000	0.0321
9,000	0.0633	4,000	0.0225
8,000	0.0565	3,000	0.0120
7,000	0.0492	2,000	0.0000
6,000	0.0407		

(*Source:* WEIR, C. E. "High-pressure Apparatus for Compressibility Studies and Its Application to Measurements on Leather and Collagen," *Journal of Research of National Bureau of Standards,* Vol. 45 (1950), pp. 468–476.)

6. The pressure p of a certain gas of fixed mass confined in a volume v is related to the volume by an equation: $pv^\gamma = c$, where γ and c are constants. Under the change of variable $x = \log v$ and $y = \log p$ the relation becomes $y + \gamma x = k$, where $k = \log c$. Suppose independent measurements of pressure are made on precisely measured volumes of specimens of the gas of the same mass, but that the measurements of pressure are subject to error. Suppose further that the *error* in the logarithm of the pressure is normally distributed about 0, with a standard deviation σ independent of the volume. If the measurements are as indicated in the table, find the maximum likelihood estimate of γ.

v	0.45	0.50	0.60	0.75	1.00	1.50
p	3.1	2.6	2.1	1.5	1.0	0.6

7. Show that $E(\hat{\boldsymbol{\sigma}}^2) = (n - 2)\sigma^2/n$.

8. Suppose that in one normal regression problem we have an ordinary real variable x with n values, $x_1, x_2, \cdots, x_n$, and for each x a random variable $\mathbf{y}$, with $E(\mathbf{y}) = \lambda_1 x + \beta_1$, $V(\mathbf{y}) = \sigma^2$; and in another normal regression problem, z is an ordinary real variable, having m values, $z_1, z_2, \cdots, z_m$, and corresponding to each z is a random variable $\mathbf{w}$ with $E(\mathbf{w}) = \lambda_2 z + \beta_2$, $V(\mathbf{w}) = \sigma^2 = V(\mathbf{y})$. The values of all parameters are assumed unknown. Find a statistic to use in testing the hypothesis $\lambda_1 = \lambda_2$, and describe the test.

9. Show that under the normal regression hypotheses $\bar{\mathbf{y}}$ is normally distributed with mean $\lambda\bar{x} + \beta$ and variance σ^2/n.

10. In two different normal regression problems, let σ_1 and σ_2 be the standard deviations, $\hat{\boldsymbol{\sigma}}_1$ and $\hat{\boldsymbol{\sigma}}_2$ respectively their maximum likelihood estimators, and n_1 and n_2 respectively the values of n. Then $\dfrac{n_1\hat{\boldsymbol{\sigma}}_1^2}{\sigma_1^2} + \dfrac{n_2\hat{\boldsymbol{\sigma}}_2^2}{\sigma_2^2}$ has the χ^2 distribution with $n_1 + n_2 - 4$ degrees of freedom.

11. In normal regression theory, the slope and the mean ordinate of the regression line are independent random variables.

Hint: $\text{cov}\,(\sigma_x{}^2\hat{\boldsymbol{\lambda}}, \bar{\mathbf{y}}) = E\{[\Sigma(x_i - \bar{x})\mathbf{y}_i][\bar{\mathbf{y}} - E(\bar{\mathbf{y}})]\}$.

12. In the accompanying table are given results of measurements of sorption of water vapor by two textile fibers for various relative water vapor pressures (P/P_0). Assume a normal regression model for each, with the same σ for both sets of measurements. Test at the 5% level the hypothesis that the expected mean sorption ($E(\bar{\mathbf{y}}) = \lambda\bar{x} + \beta$) is the same for wool and viscose rayon over the given range of relative water vapor pressure.

Hint: Develop a t-test, using the results of Problems 9 and 10; note also that since $\bar{\mathbf{y}} = \hat{\boldsymbol{\lambda}}\bar{x} + \hat{\boldsymbol{\beta}}$, $\bar{\mathbf{y}}$ and $\hat{\boldsymbol{\sigma}}^2$ are independent.

Millimoles of water vapor (per gram of solid)

P/P_0	Wool	Viscose rayon	P/P_0	Wool	Viscose rayon
0.034	1.3	1.2	0.471	5.7	4.8
.081	1.9	1.8	.620	7.1	6.2
.130	2.3	2.1	.778	9.5	8.4
.252	3.6	3.2	.866	11.6	10.8
.335	4.6	4.0	.968	14.4	14.5

(*Source:* Rowen, John W., and Blaine, R. L. "Sorption of Nitrogen and Water Vapor on Textile Fibers," *Journal of Research of National Bureau of Standards*, Vol. 39 (1947), pp. 479–486.)

CHAPTER
14

Testing Hypotheses

86. Introduction. In the examples we have discussed in which we wished to test a hypothesis of the form $\theta = \theta_0$, we have heretofore always chosen numbers a and b so that

$$Pr\{\mathbf{y} < a\} = \tfrac{1}{2}\alpha$$

and

$$Pr\{\mathbf{y} > b\} = \tfrac{1}{2}\alpha,$$

where $\mathbf{y}$ is a function of the sample random variables, and of the parameter θ, whose distribution is known. In this section we shall discuss some situations where another way of choosing the numbers a and b will appear more appropriate.

For some purposes it is convenient to classify hypotheses as simple or composite.

▶ *A* simple *hypothesis is one which specifies completely the distribution of the parent population.*

For example, the hypothesis $p = 1/2$ is simple if the parent population is that induced by a random variable $\mathbf{x}$ assuming only two values, 1 with probability p and 0 with probability $1 - p$. Another example of a simple hypothesis is the hypothesis $\mu = 0$ when the population is known to be normal with standard deviation 1 (or other known standard deviation). A hypothesis which is not simple is *composite*, as for example the hypothesis $\mu = 0$ when the population is known to be normally distributed with unknown mean μ and unknown standard deviation σ: if $\mu = 0$, the standard deviation σ remains unspecified so that infinitely many possibilities remain for the distribution of the population. In this text we consider only hypotheses of the form $\theta = \theta_0$, where θ_0 is a value of a parameter on which the distribution of the population depends. As shown by the examples immediately above, such a hypothesis may be either simple or composite.

87. Testing a Simple Hypothesis Against a Simple Alternative. This topic is introduced by the following example. (A more realistic example is suggested in the discussion of sampling inspection, especially page 340.)

EXAMPLE 1. A playful monarch hands one of his subjects a coin and states that either the coin is balanced or the probability of throwing heads is 0.6. The subject is required to toss the coin 50 times and then to state whether or not the coin is balanced. The reward for a correct statement is to be 100 gold pieces. The penalty for calling the coin unbalanced if in fact it is balanced is to be seven years of slavery. The penalty for calling the coin balanced if in fact it is unbalanced is to be a month on the road-building gang.

The statement of the problem is intended to suggest that while preferring to make no error, of the two possible errors the subject has a more pronounced aversion to making the first. The subject sets up a model involving a sample of size 50 from a parent population induced by a random variable which assumes the value 1 (heads) with probability p, the value 0 (tails) with probability $q = 1 - p$. His primary interest is in avoiding the decision $p = 0.6$ if in fact $p = 0.5$. He therefore sets up the hypothesis $p = 0.5$. If after his experiment he rejects the hypothesis $p = 0.5$ in favor of the alternative $p = 0.6$, and if p is in fact 0.5, he makes what is called a Type I error. If he fails to reject the hypothesis when in fact p is not 0.5, he makes a Type II error.

▶ *In testing a hypothesis, you make a* Type I error *if you reject the hypothesis when it is in fact true. You make a* Type II error *if you fail to reject the hypothesis when the alternative against which you are testing it is true.*

Emboldened by poverty, the subject decides to accept a probability 0.05 of a Type I error. That is, he decides to test the hypothesis $p = 1/2$ at the 5% significance level. Let $\mathbf{S}$ be the number of heads thrown in 50 tosses; $\mathbf{S} = \sum_{i=1}^{50} \mathbf{x}_i$, where $\mathbf{x}_i$ is the number of heads thrown in the ith toss $(i = 1, 2, \cdots, 50)$. If he were to test the simple hypothesis $p = 1/2$ against the composite alternative $p \neq 1/2$, in following the procedure we have used before he would determine numbers a and b such that

$$Pr\{\mathbf{S} \leq a\} = 0.025, \quad \text{if } p = 1/2,$$

and

$$Pr\{\mathbf{S} \geq b\} = 0.025, \quad \text{if } p = 1/2.$$

He would then reject the hypothesis $p = 1/2$ if the number S of heads actually thrown were outside the interval $a < S < b$. The *critical region* would be from 0 to a and from b to 50; that is, if $0 \leq S \leq a$ or if $b \leq S \leq 50$, he would reject the hypothesis. By DeMoivre's Theorem (Corollary B, page 165), $\mathbf{S}$ is approximately normally distributed with mean $np = 25$

and standard deviation $\sqrt{npq} = 5\sqrt{2}/2 = 3.54$, if $p = 1/2$. The probability that a normally distributed random variable will assume a value more than 1.96 standard deviations below its mean is about 0.025, so that if $p = 1/2$ then

$$Pr\{\mathbf{S} \leq 18.06\} \doteq 0.025,$$

and similarly

$$Pr\{\mathbf{S} \geq 31.94\} \doteq 0.025.$$

(Using binomial tables, or the improved normal approximation mentioned on page 169, we find actually $Pr\{\mathbf{S} \leq 18\} = Pr\{\mathbf{S} \geq 32\} \doteq 0.033$.) Therefore the subject would reject the hypothesis $p = 1/2$ in favor of the alternative $p \neq 1/2$, following the procedure we have used heretofore, only if 18 or fewer heads turned up, or if 32 or more heads turned up.

In Figure 26, the area under either of the curves over a certain interval represents approximately the probability that **S**, the number of heads, will lie in that interval; the top curve for $p = 1/2$, the bottom curve for $p = 0.6$. It is clear that the subject could reduce to 0 his probability

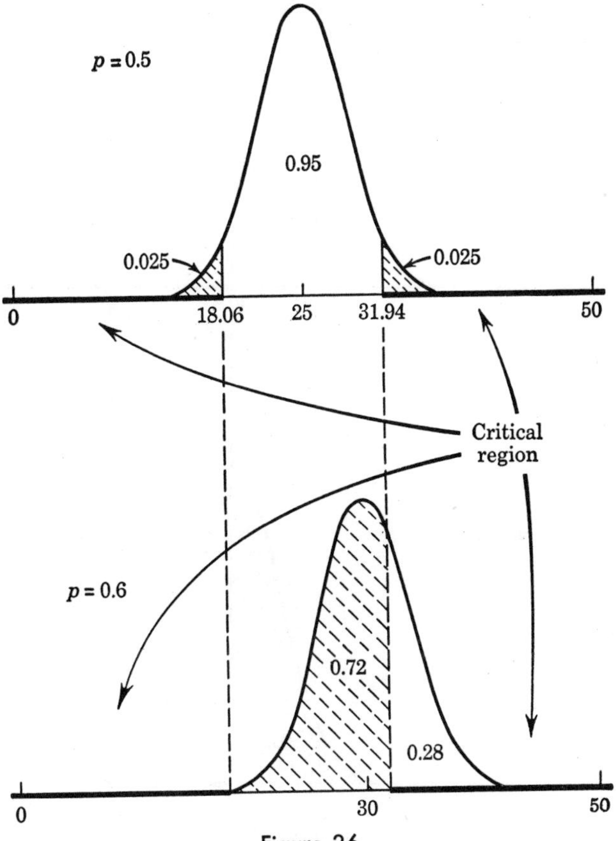

Figure 26

of rejecting the hypothesis if true, but only at the cost of raising to 1 the probability of failing to reject the hypothesis if false. He prefers to take a risk represented by a probability 0.05 of receiving 7 years slavery, rather than to accept the certainty of a month in the work camp and no gold, if in fact the coin is unbalanced.

Let us now compute the probability of a Type II error: the probability that he will fail to reject the hypothesis $p = 1/2$ if in fact $p = 0.6$. If $p = 0.6$, $\mathbf{S}$ is approximately normal with mean $np = 30$ and standard deviation $\sqrt{npq} = \sqrt{12} = 3.46$. We have

$$Pr\{18.06 < \mathbf{S} < 31.94\} = Pr\left\{\frac{18.06 - 30}{3.46} < \frac{\mathbf{S} - 30}{3.46} < \frac{31.94 - 30}{3.46}\right\}$$

$$\doteq \frac{1}{\sqrt{2\pi}} \int_{-3.5}^{0.58} e^{-z^2/2}\, dz \doteq 0.72, \text{ if } p = 0.6,$$

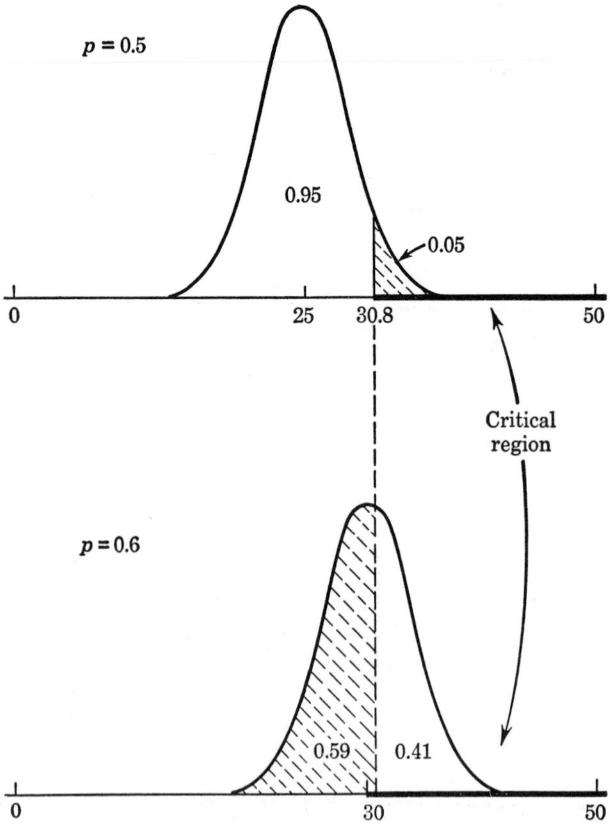

Figure 27

so that the probability is approximately 0.72 that the subject will incorrectly fail to reject the hypothesis $p = 1/2$ if in fact $p = 0.6$. Clearly the subject can do better than this, by moving the critical region to the extreme right. The probability is about 0.05 that a random variable which is normal (μ,σ) will assume a value greater than $\mu + 1.64\sigma$, so that if $p = 1/2$ we have

$$Pr\{\mathsf{S} \geq 25 + (3.54)(1.64)\} \doteq 0.05,$$

$$Pr\{\mathsf{S} \geq 30.8\} \doteq 0.05.$$

Thus the probability of rejecting the hypothesis $p = 1/2$ when true will still be 0.05 if the critical region is $S \geq 30.8$. However, if $p = 0.6$,

$$Pr\{\mathsf{S} < 30.8\} = Pr\left\{\frac{\mathsf{S} - 30}{3.46} < \frac{30.8 - 30}{3.46}\right\}$$

$$= Pr\left\{\frac{\mathsf{S} - 30}{3.46} < 0.23\right\} = 0.59.$$

Hence the probability of falsely accepting the hypothesis $p = 1/2$ when in fact $p = 0.6$ is only 0.59, if the critical region is $S \geq 30.8$.

The test just described may be referred to as the *one-tail test*, since the probability of a Type I error is represented by the area under one "tail" of the probability density curve of the statistic being used. For a given level of significance it would yield (approximately) the smallest probability of a Type II error in testing the hypothesis $p = 1/2$ against a single alternative $p = p_1$ if p_1 were any number greater than 1/2, and hence would also be appropriate in testing the hypothesis $p = 1/2$ against the composite alternative $p > 1/2$. On the other hand, if $0 \leq p_1 < p_0 \leq 1$, then for a given probability of a Type I error (if $p = p_0$), we should have (approximately) the smallest probability of a Type II error (if $p = p_1$) in testing the hypothesis $p = p_0$ against the alternative $p = p_1$, if the critical region were on the extreme left. A one-tail test with critical region on the extreme left would also be appropriate in testing the hypothesis $p = p_0$ against the composite alternative $p < p_0$.

By way of contrast, the test discussed earlier is referred to as the *two-tail test*. The probability of a Type II error is smaller for the one-tail test with critical region on the right than for the two-tail test, provided $p_1 > p_0$ (where the hypothesis $p = p_0$ is being tested against the alternative $p = p_1$); but if p_1 were smaller than p_0, the probability of a Type II error would be much greater with a critical region on the extreme right. If all $p \neq p_0$ are admitted as possible alternatives to the hypothesis $p = p_0$, then (approximately) the greatest possible probability of a Type II error obtainable for values of p different from p_0 is smaller for the two-tail test than for any other (assuming n is large enough for the validity of the normal approximation). Accordingly, the two-tail test is generally used in testing the hypothesis $p = p_0$ against the composite alternative $p \neq p_0$.

88. Choice of a Null Hypothesis. Frequently the hypothesis to be tested represents the contrary of a prediction from a theory or belief: the investigator sets up as hypothesis the conclusion he hopes to disprove. For example, the manufacturer of Feed A for baby pigs believes Feed A is superior to Feed B. He prepares to feed ten pigs with each feed, and to determine after two months the average increase in weight for each group. Let μ_1 be the (population) mean increase in weight of pigs fed for two months with Feed A and let μ_2 be that for Feed B. The manufacturer sets up the null hypothesis $\mu_1 - \mu_2 = 0$. His hope is that the difference in the sample means will prove sufficiently large that he can safely reject the hypothesis in favor of the alternative $\mu_1 - \mu_2 > 0$. In order that the results of his experiment may carry conviction to others, he insists on a fairly small level of significance, say 5%. That is, his test is designed so that the probability of a Type I error is only 0.05: if in fact $\mu_1 = \mu_2$, the probability is to be only 0.05 that he will reject the hypothesis in favor of the alternative.

The motivation of the investigator in this example is more or less representative of those occurring in many applications, but of course not in all. In general, the method is applicable in a situation in which the investigator foresees that on the basis of experimental results to be obtained, he may or may not be able to draw a certain conclusion. The conclusion is such that it can be put as the alternative to a statistical hypothesis; this latter is then the null hypothesis. In order to secure widespread acceptance of his findings, he insists on a small *a priori* probability that he will falsely reject the null hypothesis, that is, assert the alternative conclusion.

It is clear that the choice of a statistical test to use in testing a hypothesis must be made from the point of view of the experimenter before the experiment has been completed. Given the results of an experiment, tests can always be found which would result in the rejection of the hypothesis, and other tests which would not. It is in this sense that "you can prove anything with statistics." The investigator who allows the results of the experiment to influence his choice of a test places himself in a position somewhat similar to that of a bridge player who exclaims that he has an extremely improbable hand; of course he does, for the *a priori* probability of every specified hand is extremely small.

89. The Power Function. In testing a hypothesis $\theta = \theta_0$ against an alternative $\theta = \theta_1$, the probability of a Type II error is the probability that the test will fail to reject the hypothesis $\theta = \theta_0$ if in fact $\theta = \theta_1$. The *power* of the test at $\theta = \theta_1$ is 1 minus this probability. Alternatively, the power of the test at $\theta = \theta_1$ is the probability that the test will reject the hypothesis $\theta = \theta_0$ if in fact $\theta = \theta_1$. This probability will in general vary as θ_1 changes; it is a function of θ_1, called the *power function* of the test.

▶ *The* power function *of a test of a hypothesis* $\theta = \theta_0$ *is the function whose value at* $\theta = \theta_1$ *is the probability that the test will reject the hypothesis* $\theta = \theta_0$ *if in fact* $\theta = \theta_1$.

As we wish to minimize the probability of a Type II error, we wish to maximize the power function. A method of choosing the critical region which determines the test so as to maximize the power at a given alternative θ_1 is discussed in Section 93. When we wish to test the hypothesis $\theta = \theta_0$ against a composite alternative, for example $\theta \neq \theta_0$, at a given level of significance, it is often not possible to determine the critical region so as to maximize the power at *every* alternative $\theta_1 \neq \theta_0$. In such cases it may appear reasonable to choose the critical region so as to maximize the minimum of the power function: to choose the critical region so that the smallest power for $\theta_1 \neq \theta_0$ is as large as possible (cf. Example following). For the situation we have discussed, the two-tail test does this, at least approximately. Accordingly, in such situations we use the two-tail test when testing the hypothesis $\theta = \theta_0$ against the alternative $\theta \neq \theta_0$. On the other hand, we frequently find that a one-tail test will maximize the power function at each $\theta_1 < \theta_0$, so we use such a test in testing the hypothesis $\theta = \theta_0$ against the alternative $\theta_1 < \theta_0$; similarly, we use a one-tail test in testing the hypothesis $\theta = \theta_0$ against the alternative $\theta_1 > \theta_0$.

EXAMPLE 2. Let us return again to the example considered on pages 158 and 166 ff. The experimental scientist plans to make 36 measurements of a resistor by a method involving a variance of 10 ohms^2. He sets up the null hypothesis H_0: $\mu = 50$, where μ is the "true" resistance of the resistor. We found that a test of H_0 against the alternative $\mu \neq 50$ is obtained by rejecting the hypothesis if $|\bar{x} - 50| > 1.03$. This is the so-called two-tail test of H_0. Let us consider now the power function $p_1(\mu)$ of this test. The value at a number μ of the power function is the *a priori* probability that H_0 will be rejected if the true population mean is μ. Thus

$$p_1(\mu) = Pr\{|\bar{\mathbf{x}} - 50| > 1.03\} = Pr\{\bar{\mathbf{x}} > 51.03\} + Pr\{\bar{\mathbf{x}} < 48.97\},$$

this probability being computed on the assumption that the true population mean is μ. Now $\bar{\mathbf{x}}$ is approximately normally distributed with mean μ and standard deviation $\sqrt{10/36} = 0.527$. Thus $\mathbf{z} = (\bar{\mathbf{x}} - \mu)/0.527$ is approximately normal (0,1), and

$$p_1(\mu) = Pr\{\mathbf{z} > (51.03 - \mu)/0.527\} + Pr\{\mathbf{z} < (48.97 - \mu)/0.527\}.$$

Of course $p_1(50)$ is by definition the probability of the Type I error, and the test was devised so that this is 0.05.

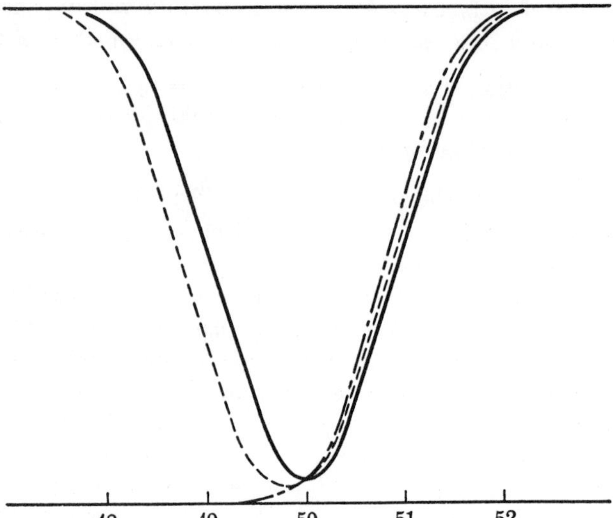

Figure 28. Power functions. Two-tail test, p_1(—); p_2(---); one-tail test, p_3(— — —).

Another test at the same significance level would be obtained by choosing a number $\beta < \alpha = 0.05$ and determining numbers b_1 and b_2 so that $Pr\{\mathbf{z} < b_1\} = \beta$, $Pr\{\mathbf{z} > b_2\} = \alpha - \beta$, where $\mathbf{z}$ is normal (0,1). The hypothesis H_0 would be rejected if a value of z (assuming $\mu = 50$) less than b_1 or greater than b_2 were observed. For example, if $\beta = 0.01$, we find $b_1 = -2.33$, $b_2 = 1.75$. The hypothesis H_0 would then be rejected if

$$\bar{x} < 50 - 2.33(0.527) = 48.77$$

or if

$$\bar{x} > 50 + 1.75(0.527) = 50.92.$$

The power function $p_2(\mu)$ of this test is given by

$$\begin{aligned} p_2(\mu) &= Pr\{\bar{\mathbf{x}} > 50.92\} + Pr\{\bar{\mathbf{x}} < 48.77\} \\ &= Pr\left\{\mathbf{z} > \frac{50.92 - \mu}{0.527}\right\} + Pr\left\{\mathbf{z} < \frac{48.77 - \mu}{0.527}\right\}, \end{aligned}$$

the probabilities again being computed on the assumption that the population mean is μ. Again of course $p_2(50) = 0.05$; this is the significance level of the test.

An extreme test, the one-tail test, would be obtained by choosing b so that $Pr\{\mathbf{z} > b\} = \alpha = 0.05$ if $\mu = 50$. This choice of b is 1.645. The hypothesis H_0 would then be rejected if a value $\bar{x}$ were observed greater than $50 + 1.645(0.527) = 50.87$. The power function $p_3(\mu)$ of this test is given by

$$p_3(\mu) = Pr\{\bar{\mathbf{x}} > 50.87\}$$
$$= Pr\left\{\mathbf{z} > \frac{50.87 - \mu}{0.527}\right\}.$$

Again $p_3(50) = 0.05$.

Let us compare the power functions of the first two tests, $p_1(\mu)$ and $p_2(\mu)$. The power of the second test is greater than that of the first when used against alternative values of μ greater than 50, but smaller when used against alternatives less than 50. Further, the smallest power of the second test is 0.04, at $\mu = 49.85$; while the smallest power of the first test is 0.05, at $\mu = 50$. Every test at the 5% significance level must have power 0.05 at $\mu = 50$, so that the first, or *two-tail test, has the greatest possible minimum power.* Its minimum power is 0.05 (for $\mu = 50$) while that of the second test is 0.04 (for $\mu = 49.85$) and that of the one-tail test is 0 (for $\mu \to -\infty$).

The two-tail test is generally considered appropriate in situations where there is a certain symmetry about $\mu = \mu_0$; where to underestimate μ by a certain amount is as serious an error as to overestimate it by the same amount. On the other hand, in some situations this symmetry is lacking. Suppose, for example, you have changed your bowling style. Suppose your average score with the old style was 160, and you set up the null hypothesis, H_0: $\mu = 160$, where μ is your mean score using the new style. You would like to have a high probability of rejecting H_0 if in fact $\mu > 160$, for then you would switch permanently to the new style. That is, you want a large power against alternatives greater than 160. But you are not concerned at all about whether or not there is a high probability of rejecting H_0 if in fact $\mu < 160$, for unless you have convincing evidence that $\mu > 160$, you will simply continue to use your former style, which has become comfortable to you. Thus you require a test with high power against alternatives greater than 160, the *one-tail test.*

▶ *The two-tail test is appropriate in testing a hypothesis* $\mu = \mu_0$ *against the alternative* $\mu \neq \mu_0$; *the one-tail test is appropriate in testing a hypothesis* $\mu = \mu_0$ *against the alternative* $\mu > \mu_0$.

Let us consider again the power function of the second test, $p_2(\mu)$. We noted above that $p_2(49.85) = 0.04$, while $p_2(50) = 0.05$. Thus the probability of rejecting the hypothesis H_0: $\mu = 50$ is *smaller* (using this test) if $\mu = 49.85$ than it is if $\mu = 50$. This undesirable property of the test is reflected in the description of it as a *biased* test. Similarly, the one-tail test is biased, when used against all alternatives $\mu \neq 50$. On the other hand, for the two-tail test, $p_1(\mu) > p_1(50) = 0.05$ if $\mu \neq 50$, so that there is a greater probability of rejecting H_0 if $\mu \neq 50$ than if $\mu = 50$.

▶ ***Definition.*** *A test of a hypothesis* $\theta = \theta_0$ *is* unbiased *if the probability of rejecting the hypothesis is smaller for no other value of the parameter than it is for* θ_0. *In other words, the test is unbiased if the power function has a minimum at* θ_0.

If the only acceptable alternative to $\mu = 50$ were $\mu > 50$, then all three tests would be unbiased, for then the minimum of each power function would come at $\mu = 50$.

90. Testing the Difference between Means from Normal Populations. This test is illustrated by the example which follows.

EXAMPLE 3. Suppose you are an industrial chemist, and have developed a new technique for treating synthetic fibers to increase their tensile strength. In a sample of size 10 treated by the standard technique, the average tensile strength was 10, with a sample standard deviation 3.2. In a sample of size 17, treated by the new technique, the average tensile strength was 20, with sample standard deviation 3.0. Are you justified in claiming the superiority of your new technique?

The problem is not yet completely stated: you must make some assumptions in constructing a mathematical model for the situation. Suppose you believe that the population of strengths of fibers treated by the standard process is normal with unknown mean μ_1 and unknown standard deviation σ_1, and that the population of strengths of fibers treated by the new process is normal with unknown mean μ_2 and unknown standard deviation σ_2. Suppose that you have reason to believe that σ_1 is approximately equal to σ_2. Let their common value be $\sigma = \sigma_1 = \sigma_2$. Suppose further that you are certain the new process yields a mean tensile strength not less than that for the old. You then wish to *test the hypothesis* $\mu_1 = \mu_2$, or $\mu_2 - \mu_1 = 0$, *against the alternative* $\mu_2 > \mu_1$, or $\mu_2 - \mu_1 > 0$.

You must first decide on a level of significance; suppose you choose 5%. You now require a random variable whose distribution is known and which is a function of the sample random variables and the unknown difference $\mu_2 - \mu_1$. In seeking such a random variable, you think immediately of the difference $\bar{\mathbf{x}}_2 - \bar{\mathbf{x}}_1$, where $\bar{\mathbf{x}}_2$ and $\bar{\mathbf{x}}_1$ are sample means of the samples from the two populations. By Corollary G, page 229, $\bar{\mathbf{x}}_2$ and $-\bar{\mathbf{x}}_1$ are normal; by Theorem F, page 228, their sum $\bar{\mathbf{x}}_2 - \bar{\mathbf{x}}_1$ is normal. Its mean is $E(\bar{\mathbf{x}}_2 - \bar{\mathbf{x}}_1) = \mu_2 - \mu_1$, and its standard deviation is

$$\sigma_{\bar{x}_2 - \bar{x}_1} = \sqrt{V(\bar{\mathbf{x}}_2) + V(\bar{\mathbf{x}}_1)} = \sqrt{\frac{\sigma^2}{n_2} + \frac{\sigma^2}{n_1}}$$

where $n_1 = 10$, $n_2 = 17$. Thus the distribution of $\bar{\mathbf{x}}_2 - \bar{\mathbf{x}}_1$, depends also on the unknown population standard deviation σ, and not on $\mu_2 - \mu_1$ alone. Still,

$$\mathbf{u} = [(\bar{\mathbf{x}}_2 - \bar{\mathbf{x}}_1) - (\mu_2 - \mu_1)]/\sigma\sqrt{\frac{1}{n_1} + \frac{1}{n_2}}$$

is normal (0,1), and can serve as the random variable $\mathbf{u}$ in the definition of Student's t-distribution (page 235). Also, if $\mathbf{s}_1^2$, $\mathbf{s}_2^2$ are the sample variances, then $n_1\mathbf{s}_1^2/\sigma^2$ and $n_2\mathbf{s}_2^2/\sigma^2$ have χ^2 distributions with $n_1 - 1$ and $n_2 - 1$ degrees of freedom respectively (Theorem K, page 232), so that by Theorem I, page 231, their sum

$$\frac{n_1\mathbf{s}_1^2 + n_2\mathbf{s}_2^2}{\sigma^2}$$

has a χ^2 distribution with $n_1 + n_2 - 2$ degrees of freedom. Noting further that $\bar{\mathbf{x}}_1$, $\bar{\mathbf{x}}_2$, $\mathbf{s}_1$, $\mathbf{s}_2$ are independent random variables by Theorem J, page 232, you find that the random variable

$$\mathbf{v}^2 = (n_1\mathbf{s}_1^2 + n_2\mathbf{s}_2^2)/\sigma^2$$

can play the role of the random variable $\mathbf{v}^2$ in the definition of Student's t-distribution. Therefore

$$\mathbf{t} = \frac{\mathbf{u}\sqrt{n_1 + n_2 - 2}}{\mathbf{v}}$$

has Student's t-distribution with $n_1 + n_2 - 2$ degrees of freedom. We have

$$\mathbf{t} = \frac{[(\bar{\mathbf{x}}_2 - \bar{\mathbf{x}}_1) - (\mu_2 - \mu_1)\sqrt{n_1 + n_2 - 2}}{\sigma\sqrt{\dfrac{1}{n_1} + \dfrac{1}{n_2}}} \Bigg/ \frac{\sqrt{n_1\mathbf{s}_1^2 + n_2\mathbf{s}_2^2}}{\sigma}$$

or

$$\mathbf{t} = \frac{[(\bar{\mathbf{x}}_2 - \bar{\mathbf{x}}_1) - (\mu_2 - \mu_1)]}{\sqrt{n_1\mathbf{s}_1^2 + n_2\mathbf{s}_2^2}}\sqrt{\frac{n_1n_2(n_1 + n_2 - 2)}{n_1 + n_2}}.$$

We may choose to use the one-tail test on the basis of the following somewhat intuitive considerations (cf. also pages 250–257). We shall compute the value of t from the sample values, assuming $\mu_2 - \mu_1 = 0$; i.e.,

$$t = \frac{(\bar{x}_2 - \bar{x}_1)\sqrt{n_1n_2(n_1 + n_2 - 2)}}{\sqrt{n_1s_1^2 + n_2s_2^2}\sqrt{n_1 + n_2}}.$$

If, in fact, $\mu_2 - \mu_1 > 0$, we expect this value of t to be high; so we want a test of the hypothesis $\mu_2 - \mu_1 = 0$ which will allow us to reject the hypothesis if the value of t we obtain is too high; the higher the value of t, the more reasonable it would appear to be to reject the hypothesis $\mu_2 - \mu_1 = 0$ in favor of the alternative $\mu_2 - \mu_1 > 0$. We choose then a number a from tables of the t-distribution with $n_1 + n_2 - 2 = 25$ degrees of freedom so that

$$Pr\{\mathbf{t} > a\} = 0.05,$$

and reject the hypothesis if a value of t greater than a is obtained on the assumption $\mu_2 - \mu_1 = 0$. Such a number a is 1.71. On substituting

$\bar{x}_2 = 20$, $\bar{x}_1 = 10$, $\mu_2 - \mu_1 = 0$, $n_1 = 10$, $n_2 = 17$, $s_2 = 3.0$, $s_1 = 3.2$ in the expression for t we find $t = 7.85$, which is greater than 1.71. Thus you may reject the hypothesis $\mu_2 = \mu_1$ in favor of the alternative $\mu_2 > \mu_1$ at the 5% significance level.

91. The F Distribution.

▶ ***Definition.*** *The random variable*

$$\mathbf{F} = \frac{\mathbf{v}_1^2/k_1}{\mathbf{v}_2^2/k_2}$$

has the F distribution *if* $\mathbf{v}_1^2$ *and* $\mathbf{v}_2^2$ *are independent random variables having* χ^2 *distributions with* k_1 *and* k_2 *degrees of freedom respectively.*

Let $\mathbf{s}_1^2$ denote the sample variance of a sample of size n_1 from a normal population with standard deviation σ_1, and $\mathbf{s}_2^2$ the sample variance of a sample of size n_2 from a normal population with standard deviation σ_2. Then by Theorem K, page 219, $\mathbf{v}_1^2 = n_1\mathbf{s}_1^2/\sigma_1^2$ and $\mathbf{v}_2^2 = n_2\mathbf{s}_2^2/\sigma_2^2$ have the properties required of $\mathbf{v}_1^2$ and $\mathbf{v}_2^2$ in the definition above, with $k_1 = n_1 - 1$ and $k_2 = n_2 - 1$. Accordingly, the ratio

$$\mathbf{F} = \frac{n_1\mathbf{s}_1^2}{(n_1 - 1)\sigma_1^2} \Big/ \frac{n_2\mathbf{s}_2^2}{(n_2 - 1)\sigma_2^2} = \frac{\left(\dfrac{n_1\mathbf{s}_1^2}{n_1 - 1}\right)}{\left(\dfrac{n_2\mathbf{s}_2^2}{n_2 - 1}\right)} \cdot \frac{\sigma_2^2}{\sigma_1^2}$$

has the F distribution with $n_1 - 1$ and $n_2 - 1$ degrees of freedom. You will observe that $n_1\mathbf{s}_1^2/(n_1 - 1)$ and $n_2\mathbf{s}_2^2/(n_2 - 1)$ are unbiased estimators of the population variances (page 139).

EXAMPLE 4. Suppose that as the industrial chemist in the preceding example you wish to test at the 10% significance level the hypothesis that the standard deviations of the two populations are equal, against the alternative that they are not. We have $n_1 - 1 = 9$ and $n_2 - 1 = 16$, so that $\mathbf{F}$ has the F distribution with 9 and 16 degrees of freedom. From the tables,

$$Pr\{\mathbf{F} \geq 2.54\} = 0.05.$$

In order to find a number a such that $Pr\{\mathbf{F} \leq a\} = 0.05$, we note that if we set $\mathbf{F}' = 1/\mathbf{F}$, then $\mathbf{F}'$ has the F distribution with 16 and 9 degrees of freedom, so that we find from the tables of the F distribution that

$$Pr\{\mathbf{F}' \geq 2.98\} = 0.05,$$

or

$$Pr\left\{\mathbf{F} \leq \frac{1}{2.98}\right\} = 0.05,$$

or

$$Pr\{\mathbf{F} \leq 0.335\} = 0.05.$$

On substituting $n_1 = 10$, $n_2 = 17$, $s_1^2 = 3.2^2$, $s_2^2 = 3.0^2$, $\sigma_2^2 = \sigma_1^2$, we find that

$$F = \frac{10(3.2)^2 16}{9(3.0)^2 17} = 1.19,$$

so that the observed value of F is well within the 90% confidence interval,

$$0.335 < F < 2.54.$$

There is consequently no basis for rejecting the hypothesis $\sigma_1 = \sigma_2$. Of course, this test does not offer convincing evidence in favor of the hypothesis either; it simply indicates that the observed result is not "unreasonable" on the basis of the hypothesis $\sigma_1 = \sigma_2$.

★ 92. The Likelihood Ratio Test. The method developed in the section starting on page 177 for deriving tests of hypotheses of the form $\theta = \theta_0$ requires that a random variable $\mathbf{z}$ be found whose distribution is known when the value of θ is fixed. One way of finding such a random variable $\mathbf{z}$ which often leads to useful tests is discussed in this section. As before, let $L(x_1, \cdots, x_n; \theta)$ denote the likelihood function, and let $L_{\max}$ denote its maximum value when θ ranges over all possible values. This number, $L_{\max}$, will depend on what the sample values $x_1, x_2, \cdots, x_n$ are, and is thus a function of $x_1, x_2, \cdots, x_n$. Now consider the ratio, called the *likelihood ratio*,

$$\Lambda(x_1, \cdots, x_n) = \frac{L(x_1, \cdots, x_n; \theta_0)}{L_{\max}},$$

obtained by dividing the likelihood function evaluated at θ_0 by $L_{\max}$. This likelihood ratio is a function of the sample values. If the sample values are replaced by the sample random variables, we obtain a statistic,

$$\boldsymbol{\lambda} = \Lambda(\mathbf{x}_1, \cdots, \mathbf{x}_n).$$

If the hypothesis $\theta = \theta_0$ is a simple hypothesis, the joint distribution of the sample random variables is completely known when $\theta = \theta_0$, and the distribution of $\boldsymbol{\lambda}$ is determined. The statistic $\boldsymbol{\lambda}$ is then such a random variable as is required by the method we discussed earlier.

Since the likelihood function is never negative, the likelihood ratio λ is never negative. Also, since θ_0 is a particular value of θ, the numerator cannot be greater than the denominator, and we always have $\lambda \leq 1$. The value of θ which maximizes $L(x_1, \cdots, x_n; \theta)$ is, by definition, the maximum likelihood estimate of θ. Thus if the maximum likelihood estimate turns out to be θ_0, the numerator and denominator of the likelihood ratio coincide, and the value of λ is 1. If the true parameter value is θ_0, we should expect the maximum likelihood estimate of θ to be near θ_0, and the value of λ correspondingly near 1. If the true parameter value is much different from θ_0, we should expect the maximum likelihood estimate of θ to differ greatly from θ_0, and the denominator to be considerably larger than the numerator. (Please do not be too critical of this argument, which is intended only to be suggestive, not rigorous. It is clearly conceivable that widely different values of θ might give the same or nearly the same values of the likelihood function, so that even if the maximum likelihood estimate differed greatly from θ_0 it would be possible to have a likelihood ratio near 1.) A test at the $100\alpha\%$ significance level of the hypothesis $\theta = \theta_0$ is accordingly constructed by finding a number a such that

$$Pr\{\lambda > a\} = Pr\{a < \lambda \leq 1\} = 1 - \alpha,$$

and rejecting the hypothesis if in fact the observed value of λ is less than a.

In any particular situation, it may be difficult to determine the distribution of λ, so as to be able to find the number a. However, it can be shown that, under suitable regularity conditions,

▶ *when the sample size is large, the random variable* $-2 \log \lambda$ *has approximately the* χ^2 *distribution with* 1 *degree of freedom, when the hypothesis* $\theta = \theta_0$ *is true.*

The likelihood ratio method extends to more general situations also; see [22]. (For an example of a possible defect of the general likelihood ratio test, see [8], Problem 18, p. 252.)

EXAMPLE 5. Let us consider from this point of view the same example we considered on page 180. In 100 tosses of a coin, heads came up 65 times. You wish to test the hypothesis that the probability θ of heads turning up in a single toss is 1/2. The probability function of the number of times heads will turn up is

$$f(x;\theta) = \theta^x(1 - \theta)^{1-x}, \quad x = 0, 1.$$

The likelihood function is

$$\begin{aligned} L(\theta) &= L(x_1, \cdots, x_n; \theta) = \textstyle\prod_{i=1}^n f(x_i;\theta) = \theta^{\sum_{i=1}^n x_i}(1 - \theta)^{n-\sum_{i=1}^n x_i} \\ &= \theta^{n\bar{x}}(1 - \theta)^{n-n\bar{x}}. \end{aligned}$$

We have

$$L_{\max} = \max_{\theta} L(\theta) = [\bar{x}^{\bar{x}}(1 - \bar{x})^{1-\bar{x}}]^n,$$

since the maximum value of L is achieved for $\theta = \bar{x}$. We have $\theta_0 = 1/2$ and $L(\theta_0) = L(1/2) = (1/2)^n$, so that

$$\lambda = \frac{(1/2)^n}{[\bar{x}^{\bar{x}}(1 - \bar{x})^{1-\bar{x}}]^n}.$$

We observe that $\lambda = 1$ if $\bar{x} = 1/2$. We note further that, as a function of $\bar{x}$, λ is symmetric about $\bar{x} = 1/2$; for when we replace $\bar{x}$ by its symmetric point, $1 - \bar{x}$, with respect to $\bar{x} = 1/2$, the value of λ is not altered. Thus if a is a positive number less than 1, the set of values of $\bar{x}$ for which

$a < \lambda < 1$ is an interval centered at 1/2. Using the ratio test, we would fail to reject the hypothesis if the value of λ obtained satisfied an inequality of the form $a < \lambda < 1$; but a value of λ satisfying such inequalities will be obtained if and only if a value of $\bar{x}$ is obtained satisfying inequalities $-c < \bar{x} - 1/2 < c$ for some constant c. Thus the ratio test, which rejects the hypothesis if a value of λ too small is observed, is equivalent in this case

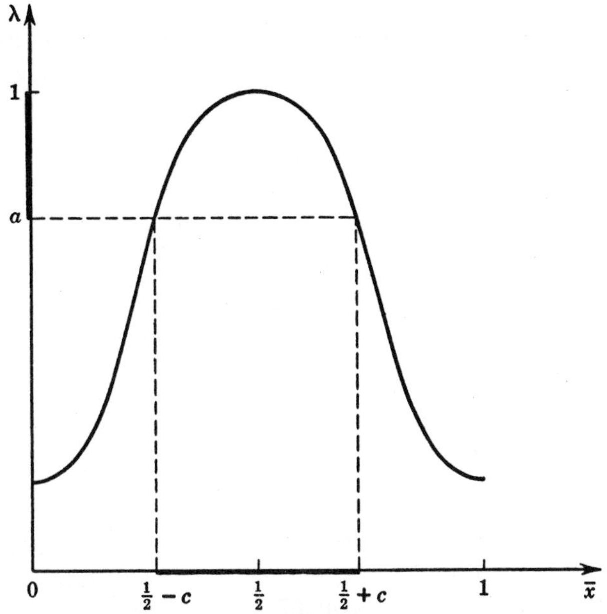

Figure 29

to the test which rejects the hypothesis $\theta = 1/2$ if a value of $\bar{x}$ too far from 1/2 is observed. If we find a number a such that

$$Pr\{a < \boldsymbol{\lambda}\} = 1 - \alpha$$

and a number c such that

$$Pr\{-c < \bar{\mathbf{x}} - 1/2 < c\} = 1 - \alpha,$$

then the events $\{a < \boldsymbol{\lambda}\}$ and $\{-c < \bar{\mathbf{x}} - 1/2 < c\}$ are the same event. In other words, in this example the likelihood ratio test and the symmetric, two-tail test discussed earlier (page 180) coincide.

Suppose the parent distribution depends not on a single parameter, but on several, say $\theta_1, \theta_2, \cdots, \theta_k$. Suppose you wish to test a hypothesis of the form $\theta_1 = \theta_1{}^0, \theta_2 = \theta_2{}^0, \cdots, \theta_h = \theta_h{}^0$, where $h \leq k$, where $\theta_1{}^0, \theta_2{}^0, \cdots, \theta_h{}^0$ are particular, specified values of the parameters $\theta_1, \theta_2, \cdots, \theta_h$, and where the remaining parameters (if any), $\theta_{h+1}, \theta_{h+2}, \cdots, \theta_k$ remain unspecified by the hypothesis. The likelihood function is now

$$L(\theta_1, \cdots, \theta_k) = L(x_1, \cdots, x_n; \theta_1, \cdots, \theta_k) = \prod_{i=1}^{n} f(x_i; \theta_1, \cdots, \theta_k).$$

Let N denote the largest possible value of L (for given, fixed sample values, $x_1, x_2, \cdots, x_n$) when $\theta_{h+1}, \theta_{h+2}, \cdots, \theta_k$ are allowed to assume any possible values, but $\theta_1 = \theta_1^0, \theta_2 = \theta_2^0, \cdots, \theta_h = \theta_h^0$:

$$N = \max_{\theta_{h+1}, \theta_{h+2}, \cdots, \theta_k} L(\theta_1^0, \theta_2^0, \cdots, \theta_h^0, \theta_{h+1}, \cdots, \theta_k).$$

In particular, if $h = k$, then $N = L(\theta_1^0, \theta_2^0, \cdots, \theta_k^0)$. Let D denote the largest possible value of L (for given, fixed sample values, $x_1, x_2, \cdots, x_n$) when all parameters range over all possible values:

$$D = L_{\max} = \max_{\theta_1, \theta_2, \cdots, \theta_k} L(\theta_1, \theta_2, \cdots, \theta_k).$$

The *likelihood ratio* is

$$\lambda = \lambda(x_1, x_2, \cdots, x_n) = N/D.$$

When symbols for the observed sample values are replaced by symbols for the sample random variables, λ becomes a random variable $\boldsymbol{\lambda}$; under suitable regularity conditions, and

► *if the sample size is large,* $-2 \log \boldsymbol{\lambda}$ *has approximately the* χ^2 *distribution with h degrees of freedom, when the hypothesis* $\theta_1 = \theta_1^0$, $\theta_2 = \theta_2^0, \cdots, \theta_h = \theta_h^0$ *is true.*

★ 93. Most Powerful Tests; the Neyman-Pearson Fundamental Lemma. In the first test considered on pages 255–256 the hypothesis H_0 was to be rejected if $\bar{x} > 51.03$ or if $\bar{x} < 48.97$. The value of $\bar{x}$ is determined by the sample point $(x_1, x_2, \cdots, x_n)$, so that one might say that H_0 was to be rejected if the sample point actually observed belonged to the set of all sample points for which $\bar{x} > 51.03$ or $\bar{x} < 48.97$. This set of sample points, a set of points in the sample space, is called the *critical region* of the test. A sample point $(x_1, x_2, \cdots, x_n)$ belongs to the critical region of this test if and only if, when its coordinates are used to compute $\bar{x}$, the resulting value of $\bar{x}$ is larger than 51.03 or smaller than 48.97. Similarly, each of the other tests has a critical region, and indeed not only does the test determine the critical region, but it is determined by the critical region.

In general, a test of a hypothesis is a rule for associating with each possible set of sample values, or sample point, one of two decisions: to reject the hypothesis, or to fail to reject it.

► The set of those sample points which, if observed, would lead to the decision to reject the hypothesis, is the *critical region* of the test.

Suppose the population has a distribution depending on a parameter θ; let $f(x;\theta)$ denote its density function or probability function according as the population is continuous or discrete. If S is a set of points in the sample space, a set of sample points, let

$$P(S;\theta) = Pr\{(\mathbf{x}_1, \mathbf{x}_2, \cdots, \mathbf{x}_n) \text{ in } S;\theta\}$$

denote the probability that the sample random variables will assume values which are coordinates of a point in S, if the true parameter value is θ. (We shall use the same symbol, S, for the set in the sample space, and for the event: "a sample point $(\mathbf{x}_1, \mathbf{x}_2, \cdots, \mathbf{x}_n)$ will lie in S.") Now suppose that the null hypothesis is H_0: $\theta = \theta_0$, and that there is only one possible alternative, H_1: $\theta = \theta_1$. Let us consider the likelihood ratio test of the hypothesis H_0 against the alternative H_1. We define

$$L_{\max}(x_1, \cdots, x_n) = \max_{\theta=\theta_0,\theta_1} L(x_1, x_2, \cdots, x_n; \theta),$$

where $L(x_1, \cdots, x_n;\theta) = \prod_{i=1}^{n} f(x_i;\theta)$ is the likelihood function. We define

$$\lambda = \lambda(x_1, \cdots, x_n) = \frac{L(x_1, \cdots, x_n; \theta_0)}{L_{\max}}.$$

On replacing $(x_1, \cdots, x_n)$ by the sample random variables $(\mathbf{x}_1, \cdots, \mathbf{x}_n)$, we obtain the statistic, $\boldsymbol{\lambda}$. If the significance level of the test is to be $100\alpha\%$, we choose a number a such that

$$Pr\{\boldsymbol{\lambda} \leq a\} = \alpha$$

and reject H_0 if a sample point $(x_1, \cdots, x_n)$ is observed such that $\lambda \leq a$. That is, the critical region is the set A of points $(x_1, \cdots, x_n)$ for which $\lambda \leq a$. We shall suppose $a < 1$; for if $a \geq 1$, the significance level is 100%, since λ is never greater than 1. Now if $(x_1, \cdots, x_n)$ is a point for which $\lambda < 1$, then $L_{\max} = L(x_1, \cdots, x_n; \theta_1)$; for if $L_{\max} = L(x_1, \cdots, x_n; \theta_0)$ then $\lambda = 1$. Thus at each point of A, $L_{\max} = L(x_1, \cdots, x_n; \theta_1)$, and the critical region might alternatively be described as the set of all points $(x_1, \cdots, x_n)$ for which

$$aL(x_1, \cdots, x_n; \theta_1) \geq L(x_1, \cdots, x_n; \theta_0).$$

The likelihood function, $L(x_1, \cdots, x_n; \theta)$, is just the joint density function (or probability function) of the sample random variables when the true parameter is θ. If the population is continuous, and if S is a set of sample points, a subset of the sample space, then

$$P(S;\theta) = Pr\{(\mathbf{x}_1, \cdots, \mathbf{x}_n) \text{ in } S;\theta\}$$

$$= \iint_S \cdots \int L(x_1, \cdots, x_n; \theta)\, dx_1 \cdots dx_n.$$

In the remainder of this discussion we shall suppose the population continuous; but if it is discrete one need only replace integrals by sums.

We now propose to show that the likelihood ratio test, discussed above, of the hypothesis H_0 against the alternative H_1 is the most powerful test possible. That is, the power at θ_1 of this test, whose critical region is A, is greater than that of any other test having the same level of significance. Let S be the critical region for another test having the same level of significance; that is,

$$P(S;\theta_0) = P(A;\theta_0) = \alpha;$$

we shall suppose $0 < \alpha < 1$. We wish to show

$$P(A;\theta_1) \geq P(S;\theta_1).$$

We note first that AS and $A - AS$ are mutually exclusive events whose union is A; and that AS and $S - AS$ are mutually exclusive events whose union is S. Therefore

$$\begin{aligned} P(S - AS;\theta_0) + P(AS;\theta_0) &= P(S;\theta_0) = P(A;\theta_0) \\ &= P(A - AS;\theta_0) + P(AS;\theta_0); \end{aligned}$$

hence

$$P(S - AS;\theta_0) = P(A - AS;\theta_0).$$

Further, by the definition of the critical region A, at every sample point in A we have $L(x_1, \cdots, x_n; \theta_0) \leq aL(x_1, \cdots, x_n; \theta_1)$; while at every sample point not in A, $L(x_1, \cdots, x_n; \theta_0) > aL(x_1, \cdots, x_n; \theta_1)$. Now every sample point in $A - AS$ is also in A, so that

$$\begin{aligned} P(A - SA;\theta_0) &= \iint_{A-SA} \cdots \int L(x_1, \cdots, x_n; \theta_0)\, dx_1 \cdots dx_n \\ &\leq a \iint_{A-SA} \cdots \int L(x_1, \cdots, x_n; \theta_1)\, dx_1 \cdots dx_n \\ &= aP(A - SA;\theta_1). \end{aligned}$$

Again, *no* sample point in $S - SA$ is in A, so that

$$\begin{aligned} P(S - SA;\theta_0) &= \iint_{S-SA} \cdots \int L(x_1, \cdots, x_n; \theta_0)\, dx_1 \cdots dx_n \\ &\geq a \iint_{S-SA} \cdots \int L(x_1, \cdots, x_n; \theta_1)\, dx_1 \cdots dx_n \\ &= aP(S - SA;\theta_1). \end{aligned}$$

(We shall have the strict inequality "$>$" unless $P(S - SA;\theta_0) = 0$.) On combining these last two inequalities with the equality $P(S - AS;\theta_0) =$

$P(A - AS;\theta_0)$, we have $aP(A - SA;\theta_1) \geq P(A - SA;\theta_0) = P(S - SA;\theta_0) \geq aP(S - SA;\theta_1)$; hence

$$P(A - SA;\theta_1) \geq P(S - SA;\theta_1).$$

(The strict inequality holds unless both members are 0.) On adding $P(SA;\theta_1)$ to both sides we find that

$$P(A;\theta_1) \geq P(S;\theta_1).$$

The left member is the power of the likelihood ratio test at θ_1; the right member is the power at θ_1 of the test whose critical region is S. Since this critical region was arbitrary, we have proved the

▶ ***Neyman-Pearson Fundamental Lemma:*** *the likelihood ratio test is the most powerful test of the hypothesis H_0: $\theta = \theta_0$ against the single alternative H_1: $\theta = \theta_1$.*

▶ ***Definition.*** A test of a hypothesis H_0: $\theta = \theta_0$ is *uniformly most powerful* if at every admissible $\theta_1 \neq \theta_0$ its power is at least as large as that of every other test at the same significance level.

In the example studied on pages 255–257, there exists *no* uniformly most powerful test of the hypothesis $\mu = 50$ against the alternative $\mu \neq 50$. However, the one-tail test is uniformly most powerful in testing the hypothesis $\mu = 50$ against the alternative $\mu > 50$.

★ 94. Consistent Tests. The idea of a consistent test is related to that of a consistent statistic: we have in mind a test having, for large sample sizes, a high probability of rejecting a false hypothesis, that is, a test having great power. To be more precise, let us suppose that to each positive integer n corresponds a test T_n of fixed significance level $100\alpha\%$, to be used when the sample size is n, of a hypothesis H_0. The hypothesis H_0 is assumed to refer, as always, to the probability distribution of the parent population.

▶ The sequence T_n $(n = 1, 2, \cdots,)$ of tests of fixed size α is *consistent*, if, when the population distribution fails to satisfy H_0, the probability that T_n will reject H_0 approaches 1 as $n \rightarrow \infty$.

▶ ***Theorem.*** *A consistent estimator of a parameter θ yields a consistent sequence of tests of a hypothesis H_0: $\theta = \theta_0$.*

Proof. Let $\hat{\theta}_n$ be a consistent estimator of the parameter θ. That is, if $\epsilon > 0$, $Pr\{|\hat{\theta}_n - \theta| > \epsilon; \theta\} \rightarrow 0$ as $n \rightarrow \infty$; the presence of the symbol θ after the semicolon is intended to serve as a reminder that the probability is to be computed on the assumption of θ as the true parameter value.

The conclusion of the theorem requires elaboration, for we have not stated precisely how the estimator $\hat{\boldsymbol{\theta}}_n$ is to be used to provide a test T_n when the sample size is n. Let $100\alpha\%$ be the desired significance level. We shall suppose the test T_n is formed in the following way. A positive number $\beta < \alpha$ is chosen, and for each positive integer n two positive numbers h_n and k_n are determined so that

$$Pr\{\hat{\boldsymbol{\theta}}_n > \theta_0 + k_n; \theta_0\} = \beta,$$

$$Pr\{\hat{\boldsymbol{\theta}}_n < \theta_0 - h_n; \theta_0\} = \alpha - \beta.$$

(If it should not be possible to attain these inequalities exactly, the following argument will remain valid with minor modifications if there are positive numbers $\gamma < \beta$ and $\delta < \alpha - \beta$ such that

$$\gamma \le Pr\{\hat{\boldsymbol{\theta}}_n > \theta_0 + k_n; \theta_0\} \le \beta,$$

$$\delta \le Pr\{\hat{\boldsymbol{\theta}}_n < \theta_0 - h_n; \theta_0\} \le \alpha - \beta.)$$

We shall then have

$$Pr\{\theta_0 - h_n \le \hat{\boldsymbol{\theta}}_n \le \theta_0 + k_n; \theta_0\} = 1 - \alpha.$$

The test T_n is to reject the hypothesis H_0: $\theta = \theta_0$ if a value $\hat{\theta}_n$ of $\hat{\boldsymbol{\theta}}_n$ is observed which fails to satisfy the inequalities

$$\theta_0 - h_n \le \hat{\theta}_n \le \theta_0 + k_n;$$

that is, T_n rejects H_0 if and only if

$$\hat{\theta}_n > \theta_0 + k_n \text{ or if } \hat{\theta}_n < \theta_0 - h_n.$$

Evidently T_n is a test of the hypothesis H_0 at the $100\alpha\%$ significance level. To establish the conclusion of the theorem, we have to show that if $\theta = \theta_1 \neq \theta_0$, then the probability that T_n will reject H_0 approaches 1 as $n \to \infty$. It is required then, to prove that

$$Pr\{\hat{\boldsymbol{\theta}}_n > \theta_0 + k_n \text{ or } \hat{\boldsymbol{\theta}}_n < \theta_0 - h_n; \theta_1\} \to 1$$

as $n \to \infty$.

We begin by observing that $h_n \to 0$ and $k_n \to 0$ as $n \to \infty$. We show that $k_n \to 0$ as $n \to \infty$ by proving that whatever positive number ϵ may represent, a positive integer N can be found such that $k_n \le \epsilon$ for $n > N$. We choose the positive integer N so large that

$$Pr\{|\hat{\boldsymbol{\theta}}_n - \theta_0| > \epsilon; \theta_0\} \le \beta \quad \text{for } n > N,$$

as we can do since $\hat{\boldsymbol{\theta}}_n$ is a consistent estimator of θ. We observe further that k_n was defined so that $Pr\{\hat{\boldsymbol{\theta}}_n - \theta_0 > k_n; \theta_0\} = \beta$; also that $\{\hat{\boldsymbol{\theta}}_n - \theta_0 > k_n\} \subset \{|\hat{\boldsymbol{\theta}}_n - \theta_0| > k_n\}$, so that

$$\beta = Pr\{\hat{\boldsymbol{\theta}}_n - \theta_0 > k_n; \theta_0\} \le Pr\{|\hat{\boldsymbol{\theta}}_n - \theta_0| > k_n; \theta_0\}.$$

We then have

$$Pr\{|\hat{\theta}_n - \theta_0| > \epsilon; \theta_0\} \leq \beta = Pr\{\hat{\theta}_n - \theta_0 > k_n; \theta_0\}$$
$$\leq Pr\{|\hat{\theta}_n - \theta_0| > k_n; \theta_0\}.$$

Since $\quad Pr\{|\hat{\theta}_n - \theta_0| > \epsilon; \theta_0\} \leq Pr\{|\hat{\theta}_n - \theta_0| > k_n; \theta_0\},$
and since $\quad \{|\hat{\theta}_n - \theta_0| > \epsilon\} \subset \{|\hat{\theta}_n - \theta_0| > k_n\}$

if and only if $k_n \leq \epsilon$, we must have $k_n \leq \epsilon$. This completes the proof that $k_n \to 0$ as $n \to \infty$; the proof that $h_n \to 0$ as $n \to \infty$ is similar.

It remains to prove that if $\theta_1 \neq \theta_0$ then

$$Pr\{\hat{\theta}_n > \theta_0 + k_n \text{ or } \hat{\theta}_n < \theta_0 - h_n; \theta_1\} \to 1 \text{ as } n \to \infty.$$

We shall prove that if $\theta_1 > \theta_0$ then

$$Pr\{\hat{\theta}_n > \theta_0 + k_n; \theta_1\} \to 1 \text{ as } n \to \infty;$$

since

$$\{\hat{\theta}_n > \theta_0 + k_n \text{ or } \hat{\theta}_n < \theta_0 - h_n\} \supset \{\hat{\theta}_n > \theta_0 + k_n\},$$

the statement above will follow. If $\theta_1 < \theta_0$ then one can show similarly that $Pr\{\hat{\theta}_n < \theta_0 - h_n; \theta_1\} \to 1$ as $n \to \infty$. Suppose, then, that $\theta_1 > \theta_0$. We choose a positive number ϵ so small that $\theta_1 - \epsilon > \theta_0$. Since $k_n \to 0$, we shall then have, for sufficiently large n, $\theta_0 + k_n < \theta_1 - \epsilon$. Hence

$$\{\hat{\theta}_n > \theta_0 + k_n\} \supset \{\hat{\theta}_n > \theta_1 - \epsilon\}.$$

But also

$$\{\hat{\theta}_n > \theta_1 - \epsilon\} = \{\hat{\theta}_n - \theta_1 > -\epsilon\} \supset \{|\hat{\theta}_n - \theta_1| < \epsilon\},$$

so that

$$Pr\{\hat{\theta}_n > \theta_0 + k_n; \theta_1\} \geq Pr\{|\hat{\theta}_n - \theta_1| < \epsilon; \theta_1\}$$

if n is sufficiently large. But the right member approaches 1 as $n \to \infty$, since $\hat{\theta}_n$ is a consistent estimator of θ; hence so also does the left. This completes the proof of the theorem.

PROBLEMS

1. In a random sample of 10 frogs in the natural state, the average life span was 10 years with standard deviation 3 years, while in a random sample of 20 well-cared-for frogs, the average life span was 15 years with standard deviation 4 years. Is one justified in concluding at the 5% significance level that the mean life span of well-cared-for frogs is greater than that of frogs in the natural state?

2. Your flock of hens lays an average of 200 eggs per hen per year. You choose twenty-six hens at random, feed a high-protein mash, and find they lay an average of 215 eggs per hen per year, with a sample variance of 2500. Assume that the number of eggs a hen will lay in a given year is approximately normally distributed.

200 if all were fed high-protein mash, against the alternative that it would be greater.

(b) Determine 90% confidence limits for the mean number of eggs per year per hen fed on high-protein mash.

(a) Test at the 5% significance level the hypothesis that the average number of eggs per hen per year from the whole population would be only

3. Given the following sample of size 3 from a normal population of mean μ, standard deviation σ: $x_1 = 6, x_2 = 4, x_3 = -1$.

(a) Test the hypothesis $\mu = 0$ against the alternative $\mu > 0$ at the 10% significance level. (b) Determine 90% confidence limits for μ.

4. In Problem 3, test the hypothesis $\sigma = 2$ at the 10% level, against the alternative $\sigma > 2$.

5. You have introduced into a process for manufacturing tuning forks an innovation which you hope will yield forks having a smaller variance about the true pitch (page 234). The standard deviation produced by the standard process is 1 cycle per second, and in a sample of 20 forks produced by the new process the sample standard deviation is 0.7 cycles per second. You believe the population of pitches of forks produced by the new process is normal, and wish to test at the 5% significance level the hypothesis that the standard deviation is 1 against the alternative that it is smaller.

6. In the example on pages 235–236, test at the 5% significance level the hypothesis $\mu = 15$ against the alternative $\mu > 15$.

7. In 49 tosses of two dice, 7 spots turned up 15 times (Problem 5, page 185). Test at the 1% significance level the hypothesis that the probability of 7 is 1/6 against the alternative that it is greater.

8. Suppose that the mean absolute visual threshold for college students is 2 in appropriate units, with standard deviation 0.3, and that, after spending a week at the beaches, 25 were found to have a mean threshold of 2.2. Would you consider the difference significant at the 1% level?

9. Ten bars of steel produced by Process A have mean breaking strength 50 with sample standard deviation 10, while eight produced by Process B have mean breaking strength 55 with sample standard deviation 12. Assume the populations of breaking strengths normal with the same standard deviation. Test at the 5% significance level the hypothesis that the two processes produce equally strong steel, against the alternative that they do not.

10. As psychologist in a mental hospital, you obtain scores on a visual-motor test for each of two groups of mental patients. The mean score for Group A (10 patients) is 80, with standard deviation 18, and that for Group B (15 patients) is 70, with standard deviation 22. You believe you have sufficient reason to consider the population standard deviations equal. Do the scores differ significantly at the 10% level?

11. At the beginning of a semester course, the members of Class A (20 students) and of Class B (100 students) are given a comprehensive examination over prior work in the field. Class A has mean score 80 with standard deviation 10, Class B has mean score 75 with standard deviation 12. Assume all populations of scores are normal.

(a) Test at the 10% significance level the hypothesis that Classes A and B represent samples from populations with equal standard deviations.

(b) Assuming the population standard deviations are equal, test at the 5% significance level the hypothesis that the population means are equal, against the alternative that they are not.

12. A fixed dose of a certain drug is known to cause in adults an average increase of 10 in pulse rate, with a standard deviation 4. You have found in 20 teen-age patients an average increase of 15, with a standard deviation 8. Test at the 0.5% significance level the hypothesis that the standard deviation of increase of pulse rate for teen-agers is 4, against the alternative that it is higher.

13. Under the assumption that a population has standard deviation 1, set up a test at the 1% significance level of the hypothesis that the mean μ is 0, against the alternative $\mu \neq 0$, using a sample of size 100.

(a) What is the critical region of your test?

(b) What is the power of the test at the alternative $\mu = 0.1$? at the alternative $\mu = -0.3$?

(c) What is the probability of a Type II error if in fact $\mu = 0.1$? if $\mu = -0.3$?

(d) Sketch the graph of the power function of this test.

(e) Would an assumption that the population is normal be critical in this problem?

14. (a) Set up a test at the 10% significance level of the hypothesis that a coin is balanced ($p = 1/2$), using 5 tosses of the coin.

(b) Determine the power of the test at $p = 0.8$; at $p = 0.4$.

15. Your friend claims psychokinetic powers, though you suspect he has been unduly influenced by reading imaginative stories. He proposes to affect, by mental concentration alone, the result of your toss of a coin, so that he will be able to announce the result, more often correctly than not, while the coin is still in the air.

(a) If you try it 100 times, how many successes must he have to claim a significant result at the 5% level? (What hypothesis are you testing, against what alternative?)

(b) What is the power of the one-tail test at the alternative $p = 0.75$? at the alternative $p = 0.65$? at the alternative $p = 0.55$?

16. Mr. S is running a large experiment in which he expects to test independently 50 hypotheses, each at the 5% significance level. Suppose that 25 of the hypotheses are actually true.

(a) What is his expected number of Type I errors?

★ (b) Find a number N such that the probability is at least 0.95 that he will falsely reject fewer than N hypotheses. (★Use the Poisson approximation to the binomial, pages 169, 170.)

17. (a) You are certain that the correlation ρ between yield of corn in your experimental plots and dose of fertilizer is not negative, and wish to test the hypothesis $\rho = 0$ against the alternative $\rho > 0$ at the 5% significance level. If $n = 19$, is $r = 0.55$ significant at the 5% level? at the 1% level? (Assume bivariate normal population.)

(b) Find 90% confidence limits for ρ in part (a).

18. Having been engaged in an intensive guinea pig training experiment, you hope to show your guinea pig is trained to respond to the more intense of two lights. You plan to test him 50 times.

(a) At least how many proper responses to the brighter light must be made in order to enable you to reject at the 5% level the hypothesis that he has not been trained; i.e., to reject the hypothesis that he is as likely to respond to one light as to the other, in favor of the alternative that he is more likely to respond to the brighter light?

(b) What is the power of your test against the alternative that he will respond correctly on the average 3 times out of 4?

19. You are to give a qualifying examination in German to a Ph.D. candidate. Of several books in his subject-matter field, you wish to select one which contains 20% or fewer technical words. If you will accept a probability 0.10 of rejecting the book if in fact it has 20% technical words, and a probability 0.10 of accepting the book if in fact it has 25% technical words, how many words must you select at random?

20. Let $\mathbf{x}$, $\mathbf{y}$ have a bivariate normal joint distribution, with equal standard deviations, $\sigma_x = \sigma_y = \sigma$, and correlation coefficient ρ. Consider a random sample of size n from the population they determine. Let (x_1,y_1), (x_2,y_2), $\cdots$, (x_n,y_n) be the sample pairs, let $u_i = x_i + y_i$, $v_i = x_i - y_i$, $i = 1, 2, \cdots, n$, and let $s_u^2 = \frac{1}{n}\sum_{i=1}^n (u_i - \bar{u})^2$, $s_v^2 = \frac{1}{n}\sum_{i=1}^n (v_i - \bar{v})^2$. Use the result of Problems 17 and 18, page 220 ($\mathbf{u}$ and $\mathbf{v}$ are independent as well as normal) to show that the ratio $(1 - \rho)\mathbf{s}_u^2/(1 + \rho)\mathbf{s}_v^2$ has the F distribution with $n - 1$ and $n - 1$ degrees of freedom.

21. Two different batches of cement are mixed, and from each batch a large number of cement-mortar briquettes is made. A sample of six briquettes is taken from each batch, and the tensile strength in lbs. per sq. inch is measured for each briquette in the two samples. Assuming that in batch i tensile strength is normally distributed with variance σ_i^2, $i = 1, 2$, test at the .05 level the hypothesis $\sigma_1^2 = \sigma_2^2$ against the alternative $\sigma_1^2 \neq \sigma_2^2$. Obtain a 95% confidence interval for the ratio of the standard deviations, σ_1/σ_2.

Batch 1: 536, 492, 528, 572, 582, 506
Batch 2: 555, 567, 550, 550, 535, 540

(*Source:* Davies, O. L., and Pearson, E. S. "Methods of Estimating from Samples the Population Standard Deviation," *Journal of the Royal Statistical Society Supplement*, Vol. 1 (1934), p. 92.)

22. There is a great deal of evidence showing that hatchability of the domestic hen's egg depends in part upon its weight. Very large eggs hatch less frequently than medium-sized eggs. The effect of small weight on hatchability is more obscure; it seems probable that small eggs hatch less frequently than medium-sized eggs, but more frequently than large ones. As eggs of extreme weight are less likely to hatch than eggs of medium weight, we may expect to find that the eggs which hatch are less variable in weight than those which fail to do so, and that natural selection is acting against variation in egg weight. It seems reasonable to suppose that this phenomenon applies to duck eggs as well as hen eggs, and to test this hypothesis a sample of 619 weights (in grams) of fertile duck eggs which hatched and a sample of 341 weights of fertile duck eggs which did not hatch were obtained:

Weight of eggs in grams	No. of hatched eggs with this weight	No. of unhatched eggs with this weight	Weight of eggs in grams	No. of hatched eggs with this weight	No. of unhatched eggs with this weight
105	1	0	76	38	13
100	1	0	75	37	14
99	0	1	74	39	12
97	0	1	73	28	19
96	0	3	72	32	15
94	0	5	71	35	18
93	2	0	70	43	13
92	1	2	69	27	20
91	2	2	68	34	17
90	3	6	67	23	18
89	2	2	66	21	15
88	6	1	65	27	8
87	6	4	64	14	6
86	4	6	63	6	7
85	8	4	62	3	8
84	8	7	61	1	2
83	15	7	60	1	2
82	10	12	59	3	2
81	19	5	58	5	2
80	21	15	57	1	1
79	27	17	55	0	2
78	36	10	52	0	1
77	29	16			

Assume the weights are normally distributed with variance σ_H^2 for hatched eggs and variance σ_U^2 for unhatched eggs.

(a) Test the null hypothesis $\sigma_H^2 = \sigma_U^2$ against the alternative hypothesis $\sigma_H^2 < \sigma_U^2$, using the 1% significance level.

(b) Obtain the 99% one-sided confidence interval for $\frac{\sigma_U}{\sigma_H}$ which corresponds to the test in (a). With what confidence coefficient would one say that σ_U is at least $\frac{11}{10}\sigma_H$?

(*Source:* Rendel, J. M., "Variations in the Weights of Hatched and Unhatched Ducks' Eggs," *Biometrika*, Vol. 33 (1943–1946), pp. 48–57.)

Note. Problems 23, 24, 25 depend on the likelihood ratio test, section 92.

23. Suppose the parent population is normal with unknown mean μ and standard deviation 1. Find the likelihood ratio test of the hypothesis $\mu = \mu_0$ at the $100\alpha\%$ significance level.

24. Suppose the parent population is normal with unknown mean μ and unknown standard deviation σ. Find the likelihood ratio test of the hypothesis $\mu = \mu_0$ at the $100\alpha\%$ significance level.

25. Suppose the parent population has the Poisson distribution, with probability function

$$f(x) = e^{-\mu}\mu^x/x!,\ x = 0, 1, 2, \cdots.$$

Derive the likelihood ratio test of the hypothesis $\mu = \mu_0$ against the alternative $\mu \neq \mu_0$ $(\mu > 0)$ at the $100\alpha\%$ significance level. Use numerical approximation methods or trial and error with tables to find for what values of $\bar{x}$ the hypothesis $\mu = 1$ will be rejected at the 5% significance level if $n = 100$.

★ 95. χ^2 Tests. Let us introduce the topic by this example.

Example 6. According to a theory designed to explain the occurence of a certain biological character, 1/3 of the individuals of a certain species should exhibit the character. In a random sample of size 70 you found that 20 exhibited the character, 50 did not. You wish to know whether or not this result is consistent with your theory. Let p denote the unknown probability that an individual will exhibit the character; you wish to test the hypothesis $p = p_0 = 1/3$. A statistic which leads to a test having particularly desirable properties is the sum of the relative squared discrepancies between observed frequencies and expected frequencies:

$$\mathbf{D}^2 = \frac{(\boldsymbol{\nu}_1 - np_0)^2}{np_0} + \frac{(\boldsymbol{\nu}_2 - nq_0)^2}{nq_0},$$

where $n = 70$ is the number of trials or the sample size, $p_0 = 1/3$, $q_0 = 1 - p_0 = 2/3$, $\boldsymbol{\nu}_1$ is the frequency of successes, or the total number of individuals exhibiting the character, and $\boldsymbol{\nu}_2 = n - \boldsymbol{\nu}_1 = 70 - \boldsymbol{\nu}_1$ is the number of failures, or number of individuals not exhibiting the character. The expression for $\mathbf{D}^2$ can be simplified by observing that $\boldsymbol{\nu}_2 - nq_0 = n - \boldsymbol{\nu}_1 - nq_0 = n(1 - q_0) - \boldsymbol{\nu}_1 = np_0 - \boldsymbol{\nu}_1$, so that

$$\mathbf{D}^2 = (\boldsymbol{\nu}_1 - np_0)^2 \left[\frac{1}{np_0} + \frac{1}{nq_0}\right],$$

or

$$\mathbf{D}^2 = \frac{(\boldsymbol{\nu}_1 - np_0)^2}{np_0q_0} = \frac{(\boldsymbol{\nu}_1 - 70/3)^2}{70(1/3)(2/3)}.$$

Since $\boldsymbol{\nu}_1$ represents the total number of successes in n independent trials of an event with constant probability p, we know that if $p = p_0$ is the true probability, then $(\boldsymbol{\nu}_1 - np_0)/\sqrt{np_0q_0}$ is, for large n, approximately normally distributed, with mean 0 and standard deviation 1, by De Moivre's Theorem (page 165). By the definition of the χ^2 distribution, page 230, the limiting distribution of $\mathbf{D}^2$ is then the χ^2 distribution with 1 degree of freedom.

As originally written, $\mathbf{D}^2$ was expressed as the sum of two squares. In developing an intuitive feeling for the concept "degrees of freedom," one may observe that those two squares were not independent, and indeed when one is given the other is determined.

The quantity $\mathbf{D}^2$ is traditionally called χ^2. We shall fail to adopt this notation simply because $\mathbf{D}^2$ does not in fact have a χ^2 distribution; only its limiting distribution as $n \to \infty$ is the χ^2 distribution.

Evidently we expect small discrepancies $\nu_1 - np_0$ and $\nu_2 - nq_0$ if in fact $p = p_0 = 1/3$; and we will reject the hypothesis $p = p_0$ if too large a value of $\mathbf{D}^2$ is observed.

From the χ^2 tables we find that

$$Pr\{\boldsymbol{\chi}^2 > 3.84\} = 0.05,$$

$$Pr\{\boldsymbol{\chi}^2 > 2.71\} = 0.10,$$

$$Pr\{\boldsymbol{\chi}^2 > 1.64\} = 0.20.$$

The value of $\mathbf{D}^2$ you obtained was

$$D^2 = \frac{(20 - 70/3)^2}{70(1/3)(2/3)} = 0.71,$$

so that the hypothesis $p = 1/3$ cannot be rejected, on the basis of your data, at the 5% significance level, at the 10% level, or even at the 20% level. It is consistent with the data at these levels of significance.

χ^2 Tests of Probabilities. Suppose in each of n independent trials, precisely *one* of r events, $A_1, A_2, \cdots, A_r$ must happen, and that their respective probabilities are $p_1, p_2, \cdots, p_r$, with $\sum_{j=1}^{r} p_j = 1$. Suppose that $p_{10}, p_{20}, \cdots, p_{r0}$ are numbers, with $\sum_{j=1}^{r} p_{j0} = 1$, and that you wish to test the hypothesis $p_1 = p_{10}, p_2 = p_{20}, \cdots, p_r = p_{r0}$. By analogy with the case $r = 2$ in the example above, you consider the statistic

$$\mathbf{D}^2 = \sum_{j=1}^{r} \frac{(\mathbf{v}_j - np_{j0})^2}{np_{j0}},$$

where $\mathbf{v}_j$ is the total number of occurrences of the event A_j ($j = 1, 2, \cdots, r$). It can be shown that $\mathbf{D}^2$ has asymptotically a χ^2 distribution with $r - 1$ degrees of freedom. Again a test of the null hypothesis

$$H_0\colon p_1 = p_{10}, p_2 = p_{20}, \cdots, p_r = p_{r0}$$

at the $100\alpha\%$ significance level is obtained by choosing a number b such that

$$Pr\{\chi^2 > b\} = \alpha,$$

where χ^2 has the χ^2 distribution with $r - 1$ degrees of freedom, and rejecting the hypothesis if a value of $\mathbf{D}^2$ greater than b is actually observed.

Evidently some error is made in assuming that the distribution of $\mathbf{D}^2$ is a χ^2 distribution; an error which approaches 0 as n becomes infinite. A rule of thumb which has been suggested is that the approximation be used if at least some of the classes have expected frequency 5 or more.

Testing Goodness of Fit to a Hypothetical Distribution. As an application of the general χ^2 test above, let us develop a test of the hypothesis that the distribution function of the parent population is a certain specified distribution function, $F_0(x)$. We divide the range of the population random variable $\mathbf{x}$ into a finite number r of intervals, using points of subdivision $-\infty = a_0 < a_1 < a_2 < \cdots < a_r = \infty$. Let $F(x)$ denote the unknown, "true" population distribution function, and set

$$p_j = F(a_j) - F(a_{j-1}), j = 1, 2, \cdots, r.$$

Then p_j represents the probability that $\mathbf{x}$ will lie in the interval (a_{j-1}, a_j). (For simplicity we assume that, in case $\mathbf{x}$ is discrete, no end point of an interval is a value $\mathbf{x}$ may assume with positive probability.) Similarly, we set

$$p_{j0} = F_0(a_j) - F_0(a_{j-1}), j = 1, 2, \cdots, r;$$

p_{j0} represents the probability that $\mathbf{x}$ will lie in the interval (a_{j-1}, a_j) if in fact $F_0(x)$ is the population distribution function. We shall let the events $A_j = \{a_{j-1} < \mathbf{x} < a_j\}, j = 1, 2, \cdots, r$, play the roles of the events A_j in the above discussion. The experiment of securing a random sample of size n from the population may then be regarded as a series of n independent trials, each of which must result in precisely one of the r events, $A_1, A_2, \cdots, A_r$. Thus if the first sample value x_1 falls between a_3 and a_4, the event A_4 will have occurred on the first trial. If the second sample value x_2 falls between a_0 and a_1, the event A_1 will have occurred on the second trial, etc. In this context, the frequency, $\boldsymbol{\nu}_j$, of occurrence of the event A_j, will be precisely the number of sample values which fall between a_{j-1} and a_j ($j = 1, 2, \cdots, r$). We consider again the statistic

$$\mathbf{D}^2 = \sum_{j=1}^{r} \frac{(\boldsymbol{\nu}_j - np_{j0})^2}{np_{j0}}.$$

We determine a number b such that $Pr\{\chi^2 > b\} = \alpha$. We shall then reject at the $100\alpha\%$ significance level the hypothesis that the population distribution function is $F_0(x)$ if a value of $\mathbf{D}^2$ greater than b is observed. As a rule of thumb, in order to use the approximation, the intervals should be chosen so that the expected frequency, $np_{j0} = n[F_0(a_j) - F_0(a_{j-1})]$, in some is at least 5.

Example 7. You are assistant professor of teleology in a private college which records scores, from 0 to 100, and also the grading symbols A (90–100), B (80–89), C (70–79), D (60–69), F (0–59). It is asserted by the registrar's office that the over-all distribution of scores tends to be normal, with mean 75 and standard deviation 10. You suspect that over the past several years the scores your students have earned in your course, Teleology 113.4, have deviated from this announced norm, and you propose to test at the 5% significance level the hypothesis that the distribution of scores in this course is normal with mean 75 and standard deviation 10.

It is clear from the discussion above that all that is tested by the χ^2 test is a hypothesis on the probabilities associated with certain class intervals. You propose, then, to test the hypothesis that the frequencies of A's, B's, etc., are what they would be if the population of scores were (approximately) normal with mean 75 and standard deviation 10: namely, 7% A's, 24% B's, 38% C's, 24% D's, and 7% F's. That is, you set up the hypothesis $p_{10} = 0.07$, $p_{20} = 0.24$, $p_{30} = 0.38$, $p_{40} = 0.24$, and $p_{50} = 0.07$. Here $p_{j0} = F_0(a_j) - F_0(a_{j-1}), j = 1, 2, \cdots, 5$, where F_0 is the normal distribution function with mean 75 and standard deviation 10, $a_0 = -\infty$, $a_1 = 60$, $a_2 = 70$, $a_3 = 80$, $a_4 = 90$, $a_5 = \infty$. You find that in the last five years you assigned, in Teleology 113.4, 20 A's, 60 B's, 75 C's, 35 D's, and 10 F's. The corresponding value of $\mathbf{D}^2$ is

$$D^2 = \sum_{j=1}^{5} \frac{(\nu_j - np_{j0})^2}{np_{j0}}$$

$$= \frac{(20-14)^2}{14} + \frac{(60-48)^2}{48} + \frac{(75-76)^2}{76} + \frac{(35-48)^2}{48} + \frac{(10-14)^2}{14}$$

$$= 10.25.$$

If χ^2 has the χ^2 distribution with 4 degrees of freedom, we find that $Pr\{\chi^2 > 9.49\} = 0.05$, $Pr\{\chi^2 > 13.3\} = 0.01$, so that the hypothesis can be rejected at the 5% significance level, but not at the 1% level. You conclude (at the 5% significance level) that your grading pattern for Teleology 113.4 is not in conformity with the announced norm.

χ^2 Test for Independence; Contingency Tables. Often, in problems of testing goodness of fit to hypothetical distributions, the distributions are not completely specified, but involve one or more unknown parameters. The probabilities p_{j0} then depend on these parameters. It can be shown that if the probabilities p_{j0} are replaced by suitably chosen estimates,

▶ *the distribution of $\mathbf{D}^2$ is still asymptotically χ^2, but with $r - k - 1$ degrees of freedom, where k is the number of unknown parameters.*

A detailed discussion of appropriate methods of estimation is given in [3]. (Further results, indicating that usual estimates based on ungrouped data may lead to underestimating the significance level of the test, are given in a paper by Herman Chernoff and E. L. Lehmann, *The use of maximum likelihood estimates in χ^2 tests for goodness of fit*, Ann. Math. Statist., Vol. 25 (1954), pp. 579–586.)

One of the most frequently useful applications of such tests is in testing for independence using contingency tables. A contingency table is a classification by two arguments or variables. For example, suppose you have conducted a sample survey of preferences for automobiles in a college community, and have obtained the following results:

	Make A	Make B	Make C	Totals
Men	40	80	30	150
Women	30	120	50	200
Totals	70	200	80	350

You wish to test the hypothesis that preference for automobiles (of the three makes) is independent of sex. That is, you wish to test the hypothesis: the event "a person chosen at random will prefer Make A," and the event "a person chosen at random will be male," are independent events; similarly for B and C. The table (a *contingency table*) may be regarded as giving results of 350 independent trials, it having been observed in each trial which of 6 possible events occurred.

Let p_{11} denote the probability that a person chosen at random will be a man preferring Make A; define p_{12}, p_{13} similarly with respect to Makes B and C, and p_{21}, p_{22}, p_{23} with respect to women and the three makes. The events described will be independent if and only if there are probabilities p_M (probability of choosing a man) and p_A, p_B, $p_C = 1 - p_A - p_B$ (probabilities of choosing persons preferring corresponding makes) such that $p_{11} = p_M p_A$, $p_{21} = (1 - p_M)p_A$, etc. There are thus 3 unknown parameters, p_M, p_A, p_B, to be estimated from the data. There are 6 classes, with associated probabilities $p_M p_A$, $p_M p_B$, etc. The "natural" estimates of the probabilities p_M, p_A, p_B are the frequency ratios determined by the marginal totals: $p_M = (40 + 80 + 30)/(70 + 200 + 80) = 3/7$ ($p_W = 1 - p_M = 4/7$); $p_A = (40 + 30)/350 = 1/5$; $p_B = (80 + 120)/350 = 4/7$ ($p_C = 80/350 = 8/35$). The value of $\mathbf{D}^2$ is

$$D^2 = \frac{[40 - 350(3/7)(1/5)]^2}{350(3/7)(1/5)} + \frac{[80 - 350(3/7)(4/7)]^2}{350(3/7)(4/7)}$$

$$+ \cdots + \frac{[50 - 350(4/7)(8/35)]^2}{350(4/7)(8/35)} = 7.88.$$

The number of classes is $r = 6$; the number of estimated parameters, $k = 3$; hence the number of degrees of freedom is $r - k - 1 = 2$. From the χ^2 tables, $Pr\{\chi^2 > 5.99\} = 0.05$, so that the hypothesis of independence can be rejected at the 5% significance level. You may therefore conclude (at this significance level) that in that community the preferences among these automobiles for women differ from those for men.

χ^2 Test for Homogeneity. In the example on page 278, the 150 men and 200 women were assumed to have been drawn at random from a mixed population; and from the *a priori* point of view, the numbers of men and women to be drawn were random variables. In some situations, however, the marginal totals must be regarded as given, fixed numbers. Thus if the interviewers had been instructed to interview 150 men and 200 women, these numbers would no longer properly be regarded as values of random variables.

In general, suppose we have made s independent sequences of independent trials, each corresponding to one row of a table. Let n_1 denote the number of trials in the first sequence, n_2 the number of trials in the second, etc. These numbers, $n_1, n_2, \cdots, n_s$ are now fixed numbers, determined before the performance of the experiment. In each trial it is to be observed which one of an exhaustive set of r mutually exclusive events $A_1, A_2, \cdots, A_r$ occurs. Let us suppose we wish to test the *homogeneity* of the s populations from which the s sequences of trials are made. That is, we wish to test the hypothesis H_0 *that the event A_k has the same probability in each trial of the first sequence as it does in each trial of the* jth *sequence*, $k = 1, 2, \cdots, r$, $j = 2, 3, \cdots, s$. The table of results will have the same appearance as the contingency table on page 266. The quantity $\mathbf{D}^2$ can be computed in the same way, and it can be shown (cf. [3], Section 30.6) to have, under hypothesis H_0, a limiting distribution which is χ^2 with $(r - 1)(s - 1)$ degrees of freedom as before.

★ 96. The Kolmogorov Test for Goodness of Fit. We mention in passing an interesting test of goodness of fit to a completely specified distribution. On page 137 we defined the empiric distribution function: the step function having a jump or saltus of size $1/n$ at each sample value, where n is the size of the sample. Using the notation of page 276, ν_j/n is the increase in the empiric distribution function over the jth interval, while p_{j0} is the increase in the hypothetical distribution function over the same interval. Therefore the statistic $\mathbf{D}^2$, used in the χ^2 test, may be regarded as a measure of the discrepancy between the empiric distribution function F_n and the hypothetical distribution function F_0. A more direct measure of the discrepancy is δ_n, the greatest absolute difference between the heights of the two distribution functions:

$$\boldsymbol{\delta}_n = \max_x |F_0(x) - \mathbf{F}_n(x)|,$$

where $F_0(x)$ is the hypothetical distribution function, assumed continuous, and $\mathbf{F}_n(x)$ is the empiric distribution function (a random variable, for each x, since it depends on the sample random variables). The limiting distribution of $\mathbf{z}_n = \boldsymbol{\delta}_n\sqrt{n}$ as $n \to \infty$ was found by Kolmogorov:

$$Pr\{\mathbf{z}_n < z\} \to 1 - 2\sum_{\nu=1}^{\infty} (-1)^{\nu-1}e^{-2\nu^2z^2}$$

$$= \frac{\sqrt{2\pi}}{z}\sum_{\nu=1}^{\infty} e^{-(2\nu-1)^2\pi^2/8z^2} \quad \text{if } z > 0.$$

A test of goodness of fit at the $100\alpha\%$ significance level is obtained by determining a number b such that $Pr\{\mathbf{z}_n > b\} = \alpha$, and rejecting the hypothesis that $F_0(x)$ is the population distribution function if a value of $\mathbf{z}_n$ greater than b is observed.

Descriptions of the test and related tests, as well as tables, can be found in [16].

★ PROBLEMS

1. Of 50 male students who were willing to express opinions, 30 expressed a preference for Atom Shoes and 20 for Nuclear Shoes. Use a χ^2 test to test at the 10% significance level the hypothesis that each brand is preferred by half of those male students who have preferences.

2. Commissioner Fisher claims that 50% of the population of Bass City is indifferent to the construction of an artificial lake, 30% favors it, and 20% opposes it. Of 500 polled, 200 were indifferent, 150 were in favor, and 150 opposed. Test at the 1% significance level the hypothesis that the commissioner's estimates are correct.

3. Ten percent of the students in Arbutus College were on the dean's honor list last year. Of 100 fraternity men chosen at random, 15 were on the dean's honor list. Is this difference from the expected number, 10 (on the assumption that 10% of fraternity men are on the honor list), significant at the 10% level? at the 5% level?

4. In a random sample of size 10,000 from a population, you have observed that 2300 bear a certain observable characteristic, while the remaining 7700 do not. Is this consistent at the 1% level with the hypothesis that the population ratio is 1:4?

5. Of 300 male students chosen at random, 15 fraternity men and 15 others were on the dean's honor list, while 85 fraternity men and 185 others were not. Test at the 1% significance level the hypothesis that being on the dean's honor list is independent of being a fraternity man.

6. Of 40 patients with illness A, 30 said they had observed symptom S, 10 said they had not. Of 50 patients with illness B, half said they had observed sympton S, half said they had not. Test at the 5% significance level the hypothesis that the symptom S has the same probability of being observed by a patient with illness A as by one with illness B.

7. A supermarket manager displayed canned corn of a single brand in two locations: one on the shelf in the usual location A, one in a special display, B, featuring a large photograph of an attractive girl eating corn. Each can at A was marked inconspicuously. Of 200 purchasers of that brand, the distribution was as follows:

	A	B
Male	20	35
Female	75	70

Test at the 5% significance level the hypothesis that the choice of corn location is independent of sex.

8. Sophomores, juniors, and seniors were asked to rate general instruction in the college as poor, fair, or good. The numbers in the three categories responding in specified ways are given in the table.

	Poor	Fair	Good
Sophomores	30	70	300
Juniors	30	50	230
Seniors	40	80	170

Test at the 1% level the hypothesis that the rating of instruction is independent of student classification.

9. You have obtained answers to the following questions from 200 persons selected at random.

(1) Do you believe a serious health hazard is involved in smoking?
(2) Do you smoke?

		Question (1) Yes	Question (1) No
Question (2)	Yes	80	80
	No	25	15

At what level of significance can you reject the hypothesis that a person's opinion on Question 1 is independent of whether or not he smokes?

10. In a test on the behavior of young children under simulated refrigerator entrapment, results listed in the accompanying contingency tables were observed. Test at the 5% level for homogeneity.

(a)

	Released selves	Did not release selves
Boys	49	52
Girls	48	52

(b)

Age (months)	Released selves	Did not release selves
31–41	16	25
42–54	28	26
55–65	34	14
66–78	14	9

(*Source:* Report prepared by Children's Bureau and National Bureau of Standards, March 26, 1957.)

11. You are working with a digital computer on a problem which requires the use of random numbers. In testing a process for generating them, you find that in a run of 10,000 the digits occur with the following frequencies:

Digit	0	1	2	3	4	5	6	7	8	9
Frequency	1010	990	990	960	1020	1000	1000	1030	1020	980

Apply the χ^2 test of fit to determine whether or not there is a significant deviation from randomness (10% in each category) at the 10% level. About what is the *a priori* probability of obtaining a value of D^2 as large as that observed or larger?

12. Fifty subsamples of estimated size about 2000 pebbles each were taken from a gravel deposit. In each subsample the largest pebble (cobble) was selected, and the length of the intermediate cobble axis was measured. The grouped data is given in the accompanying table. According to extreme-value theory, under suitable hypotheses the distribution function of the random variable "intermediate diameter of largest cobble" is given by $F(x) = e^{-e^{-y}}$, where $y = (x - u)/\beta$, where u is the mode (abscissa of the highest point on the graph of the density function) and β is proportional to the standard deviation. Assuming $u = 7.5$ and $\beta = 1$ *estimated from the tabulated data*, test at the 5% significance level the hypothesis that the selected largest cobbles represent extreme values of subsamples of a population (that is, test the hypothesis that the measured values of x are sample values from a population with distribution function $F(x)$).

Intermediate diameter, x	6.5	6.5–7.5	7.5–8.5	8.5–9.5	9.5–10.5	10.5
Frequency	4	11	22	7	5	1

(*Source:* KRUMBEIN, W. C. and LIEBLEIN, JULIUS. "Geological Application of Extreme-value Methods to Interpretation of Cobbles and Boulders in Gravel Deposits," *Transactions of American Geophysical Union*, Vol. 37 (1956), pp. 313–319.)

13. A sample of 22,361 Aberdeen (Scotland) school children was distributed by hair and eye colors as follows:

Eye Color	Hair Color				
	Fair	*Red*	*Medium*	*Dark*	*Black*
Blue	1368	170	1041	398	1
Light	2577	474	2703	932	11
Medium	1390	420	3826	1842	33
Dark	454	255	1848	2506	112

Test for independence of hair and eye color at the .001 significance level. (*Source:* MAUNG, F. "Measurement of Association in a Contingency Table with Special Reference to the Pigmentation of Hair and Eye Colours of Scottish School Children," *Annals of Eugenics*, Vol. 11 (1941), pp. 189–223.)

14. The following sample of size 20 was taken from a table of random N(0,1) numbers. Test at the 5% level the null hypothesis that the population from which the sample was drawn is N(0,1), using the Kolmogorov test.

.99	−.56	1.28	.75	1.20	−.41	−1.35	.81	.16	1.05
−.31	−.97	−1.26	−.61	.41	−.65	−1.02	−.13	.70	−.11

(*Source:* The Rand Corporation, *A Million Random Digits with* 100,000 *Normal Deviates*, 1955, The Free Press; the sample starts with column 3, row 5630, on p. 113 of "100,000 Random Digits" and reads as in English.)

15. In the same way that one may be left-handed, ambidextrous, or right-handed, one may be left-eyed, ambiocular, or right-eyed. In a test on the association between these two characteristics (as measured by a balance test and a visual acuity test) in British male college students, a sample of 413 students was distributed as in the following contingency table:

	Left-eyed	Ambiocular	Right-eyed
Left-handed	48	25	52
Ambidextrous	32	13	25
Right-handed	94	33	91

Test at the 5% level for independence.
(*Source:* Woo, T. L. "Dextrality and Sinistrality of Hand and Eye," *Biometrika*, Vol. 20A (1928), pp. 79–148.)

16. On July 18, 1951, 25 leaves were selected at random from each of six McIntosh apple trees in a single orchard receiving the same spray treatment, and the number of adult female European red mites counted on each leaf. The observed frequency distribution of mites on the 150 leaves was:

No. of mites per leaf, x	No. of leaves observed
0	70
1	38
2	17
3	10
4	9
5	3
6	2
7	1
over 7	0

It is thought that $\mathbf{x}$ has the *negative binomial* frequency function

$$f(x) = \frac{(k + x - 1)!}{x!(k - 1)!}\left(\frac{m}{k + m}\right)^x \left(\frac{k + m}{k}\right)^{-k}, \quad x = 0, 1, 2, \cdots.$$

Test the latter hypothesis using the χ^2 goodness-of-fit test and the 5% significance level. Use the estimates $\hat{m} = 1.14667$ and $\hat{k} = 1.02459$, which have been computed from the tabulated data. Combine the last four classes (i.e. 5, 6, 7, over 7) in order to obtain an expected number larger than 5 in the combined class.
(*Source:* Bliss, C. I. "Fitting the Negative Binomial Distribution to Biological Data," *Biometrics*, Vol. 9 (1953), pp. 176–196.)

17. A sample of 804 pieces of fabric knitted from a new type yarn and a sample of 485 pieces of fabric knitted from a standard type yarn are to be compared on the number of defects per piece of fabric:

No. of Defects per Piece	New Yarn	Standard Yarn
0	314	119
1	119	69
2	95	66
3	58	37
4	44	37
5	43	31
6	23	23
7	22	22
8	25	25
9	12	12
10	14	14
over 10	35	30

Test for homogeneity of yarns at the .01 level.
(*Source:* ROBBINS, H. E. "Some Applications of Standard Chi Square Significance Tests to Plant Problems," Middle Atlantic Conference Transactions, American Society of Quality Control, 1956, 43–51.)

★CHAPTER
15

Experimental Design and Analysis of Variance

It is a common complaint of statisticians that research workers seek their help too late: "Another fouled-up experiment. These people will never learn to ask for help in *designing* their experiments!" The (hypothetical) statistician just quoted realizes the difficulty of the problem, for no one feels embarrassed about coming to a professional for help with mathematics: "afraid I didn't do very well in the calculus." But to ask for help in the design of an experiment may appear to involve just a hint of a lack of complete competence in one's own subject-matter field. However this may be, it is often possible, by designing an experiment properly in advance, to secure one or more of the following advantages over an ill-planned experiment:

(1) More appropriate data may be secured, laying a foundation for more sound conclusions.

(2) More effective data may be secured, yielding more information per observation.

(3) Data may be secured in such form as to make possible simpler analysis.

While developing in the following sections a brief introduction to the analysis of variance, we shall indicate very briefly also a few of the many problems of design of which an experimenter should be aware, and some of the methods which have been proposed for meeting them.

97. The Analysis of Variance. The term *analysis of variance* refers to a general method of statistical inference. It is probably not susceptible of a very precise definition; but in general it consists of a body of tests of hypotheses, methods of estimation, etc., using statistics which are linear combinations of sums of squares of linear functions of the observed values. The sample variance is an example of such a statistic. We shall here study only a few examples of this method, of widespread applicability.

EXAMPLE 1. (*Testing the equality of means; one-factor experiments; or one-way classification*). As head of a department of a consumer's research organization, you have the responsibility for testing and comparing lengths of tread life for $k = 4$ brands of tires. Suppose you test the length of tread life of $n_1 = n_2 = n_3 = 3$ tires of each of the first three brands, and $n_4 = 5$ tires of the fourth brand. Your test data are as follows, each entry representing the tread life of a tire, measured in thousands of miles:

Brand

A	B	C	D
35	30	40	35
11	21	20	20
20	30	24	15
			25
			30

You assume:

(1) The tread life of a tire chosen at random from among those of the jth brand ($j = 1, 2, \cdots, k$; here $k = 4$) is a random variable $\mathbf{x}_j$ which is normally distributed.

▶ This kind of assumption is common to all problems to which the analysis of variance is customarily applied; the "observable" random variables entering are always assumed to be normally distributed.

Let $\mu_j = E(\mathbf{x}_j)$ denote the (unknown) mean tread life of the jth brand, and σ_j its (unknown) standard deviation.

(2) The standard deviations are the same; let σ denote their common value: $\sigma = \sigma_1 = \sigma_2 = \cdots = \sigma_k$.

▶ This also is a common assumption in analysis of variance problems, often called the assumption of *homoscedasticity*.

We suppose that in the present case it is supported by technical knowledge of the processes and/or by previous experience in similar situations.

(3) The tread lives of the n_j tires of the jth brand ($j = 1, 2, \cdots, k$) represent a random sample of size n_j from the population whose random variable is $\mathbf{x}_j$; and the sample random variables corresponding to each brand are independent of those corresponding to the other brands.

Let $\mathbf{x}_{ji}$ denote the ith sample random variable ($i = 1, 2, \cdots, n_j$) of the sample of size n_j from the population whose random variable is $\mathbf{x}_j$. Let $\bar{\mathbf{x}}_j$ denote the sample mean,

$$\bar{\mathbf{x}}_j = \frac{1}{n_j} \sum_i \mathbf{x}_{ji}, \quad (j = 1, 2, \cdots, k),$$

and $\bar{\mathbf{x}}$ the over-all sample mean,

$$\bar{\mathbf{x}} = \frac{1}{n} \sum_{i,j} \mathbf{x}_{ji} = \frac{1}{n} \sum_j n_j \bar{\mathbf{x}}_j,$$

where $n = \sum_j n_j$. (In the sums above and generally in the sections to follow the range of the "dummy" or running variable will not be indicated; when not specified, it is the full range. Further, sums over two or more variables will often be indicated using a single $\sum$ sign.) We shall consider the sum of squares, $\sum_{i,j} (\mathbf{x}_{ji} - \bar{\mathbf{x}})^2$, shall rewrite it as the sum of two separate sums of squares, and shall then interpret each sum. We have

$$\sum_{i,j} (\mathbf{x}_{ji} - \bar{\mathbf{x}})^2 = \sum_{i,j} [(\mathbf{x}_{ji} - \bar{\mathbf{x}}_j) + (\bar{\mathbf{x}}_j - \bar{\mathbf{x}})]^2$$

$$= \sum_{i,j} (\mathbf{x}_{ji} - \bar{\mathbf{x}}_j)^2 + \sum_{i,j} (\bar{\mathbf{x}}_j - \bar{\mathbf{x}})^2$$

$$+ 2 \sum_{i,j} (\mathbf{x}_{ji} - \bar{\mathbf{x}}_j)(\bar{\mathbf{x}}_j - \bar{\mathbf{x}}).$$

Now

$$\sum_{i,j} (\bar{\mathbf{x}}_j - \bar{\mathbf{x}})^2 = \sum_j n_j(\bar{\mathbf{x}}_j - \bar{\mathbf{x}})^2.$$

Also

$$\sum_{i,j} (\mathbf{x}_{ji} - \bar{\mathbf{x}}_j)(\bar{\mathbf{x}}_j - \bar{\mathbf{x}}) = \sum_j (\bar{\mathbf{x}}_j - \bar{\mathbf{x}}) \sum_i (\mathbf{x}_{ji} - \bar{\mathbf{x}}_j) = 0,$$

since $n_j\bar{\mathbf{x}}_j = \sum_i \mathbf{x}_{ji}$. Therefore

$$\mathbf{A} = \mathbf{B} + \mathbf{C},$$

where

$$\mathbf{A} = \sum_{i,j} (\mathbf{x}_{ji} - \bar{\mathbf{x}})^2 = \sum_{i,j} \mathbf{x}_{ji}^2 - n\bar{\mathbf{x}}^2,$$

$$\mathbf{B} = \sum_{i,j} (\mathbf{x}_{ji} - \bar{\mathbf{x}}_j)^2 = \sum_{i,j} \mathbf{x}_{ji}^2 - \sum_j n_j\bar{\mathbf{x}}_j^2,$$

and

$$\mathbf{C} = \sum_j n_j(\bar{\mathbf{x}}_j - \bar{\mathbf{x}})^2 = \sum_j n_j\bar{\mathbf{x}}_j^2 - n\bar{\mathbf{x}}^2.$$

First, let us look at $\mathbf{B}$. For $j = 1, 2, \cdots, k$, let

$$\mathbf{s}_j^2 = \frac{1}{n_j} \sum_i (\mathbf{x}_{ji} - \bar{\mathbf{x}}_j)^2;$$

then $\mathbf{s}_j^2$ is the sample variance of the jth sample, and also

$$\mathbf{B} = \sum_j n_j\mathbf{s}_j^2.$$

Thus $\mathbf{B}/n$ is a weighted average of the sample variances. For each j, $n_j\mathbf{s}_j^2/\sigma^2$ has a χ^2 distribution with $n_j - 1$ degrees of freedom, by Theorem K, page 232. Therefore by Theorem I, page 231,

▶ $\mathbf{B}/\sigma^2$ *has a* χ^2 *distribution with* $\sum_j (n_j - 1) = n - k$ *degrees of freedom.*

Notice particularly that the distribution of $\mathbf{B}$ does not depend on the means.

We note also, in passing, that

$$E(\mathbf{B}) = \sum_j n_j E(\mathbf{s}_j^2) = \sum_j n_j \left(\frac{n_j - 1}{n_j}\right) \sigma^2 = \sigma^2(n - k),$$

so that $\mathbf{B}/(n - k)$ *is an unbiased estimator of* σ^2. Each term $\sum_i (\mathbf{x}_{ji} - \bar{\mathbf{x}}_j)^2$ is a sum of squared deviations of sample random variables from sample mean in an individual group, so that $\mathbf{B}$ is called the *sum of squares within groups* or *within classes.* It is comparable to what is called the *residual* sum of squares in other analysis of variance situations (cf. pages 298, 304). The random variable $\mathbf{A}$ is called the *total sum of squares.*

By Theorem J, page 232, $\mathbf{s}_j^2$ and $\bar{\mathbf{x}}_j$ are independent random variables (cf. also page 295); and of course $\mathbf{s}_j^2$ and $\mathbf{x}_m$ are independent random variables if $j \neq m$, since they are functions of distinct independent random variables. Further, $\bar{\mathbf{x}}$ is a function of the random variables $\bar{\mathbf{x}}_j$; it follows that the random variables $\mathbf{B}$ and $\mathbf{C}$ are independent, for $\mathbf{B}$ is a function of the random variables $\mathbf{s}_j^2$ $(j = 1, 2, \cdots, k)$, and $\mathbf{C}$ is a function of the random variables $\bar{\mathbf{x}}_j$ $(j = 1, 2, \cdots, k)$.

We shall be interested in the distributions of A and C under the null hypothesis, that the means are all equal. Let their common value be μ;

$$H_0: \mu = \mu_1 = \mu_2 = \cdots = \mu_k.$$

The random variables $\mathbf{x}_{ji}$ are independent and normally distributed; *under the null hypothesis*, they also all have the same mean μ, as well as the same standard deviation σ. Thus by the definition of random sample, page 105, they are sample random variables of a random sample of size n from a normal population with mean μ and standard deviation σ; $\mathbf{A}/n$ is the sample variance of this sample. By Theorem K, page 232,

▶ *under the null hypothesis* H_0, $\mathbf{A}/\sigma^2$ *has a* χ^2 *distribution with* $n - 1$ *degrees of freedom, and* $\mathbf{A}/(n - 1)$ *is an unbiased estimator of* σ^2.

The sum $\mathbf{C}$ remains. It is a weighted average of squared deviations of sample means from the over-all sample mean, and is called the *sum of squares among groups*, or *among classes.* Using the method (pp. 233, 234) by which we determined the distribution of the sample variance (cf. also p. 295), it can be shown that

▶ *under the null hypothesis* H_0, $\mathbf{C}/\sigma^2$ *has a* χ^2 *distribution with* $k - 1$ *degrees of freedom, and* $\mathbf{C}/(k - 1)$ *is an unbiased estimator of* σ^2.

Also, we can easily compute $E(\mathbf{C})$ *without* assuming $\mu_1 = \mu_2 = \cdots = \mu_k = \mu$:

$$E(\mathbf{C}) = E\{\sum_j n_j(\bar{\mathbf{x}}_j - \bar{\mathbf{x}})^2\} = E\{\sum_j n_j\bar{\mathbf{x}}_j^2 - n\bar{\mathbf{x}}^2\}$$

$$= \sum_j n_j\{V(\bar{\mathbf{x}}_j) + [E(\bar{\mathbf{x}}_j)]^2\} - n\{V(\bar{\mathbf{x}}) + [E(\bar{\mathbf{x}})]^2\}. \quad \text{(p. 90)}$$

But $V(\bar{\mathbf{x}}_j) = \sigma^2/n_j$, and

$$V(\bar{\mathbf{x}}) = V\left(\frac{1}{n}\sum_j n_j\bar{\mathbf{x}}_j\right) = \frac{1}{n^2}\sum_j n_j^2 V(\bar{\mathbf{x}}_j) = \frac{1}{n^2}\sum_j n_j\sigma^2 = \sigma^2/n.$$

Hence

$$E(\mathbf{C}) = \sum_j n_j\left[\frac{\sigma^2}{n_j} + \mu_j^2\right] - n\left[\frac{\sigma^2}{n} + \bar{\mu}^2\right],$$

$$E(\mathbf{C}) = (k-1)\sigma^2 + \sum_j n_j\mu_j^2 - n\bar{\mu}^2,$$

where $\bar{\mu} = \dfrac{1}{n}\sum_j n_j\mu_j$; or

$$E(\mathbf{C}) = (k-1)\sigma^2 + \sum_j n_j(\mu_j - \bar{\mu})^2.$$

The second term on the right, $\sum_j n_j(\mu_j - \bar{\mu})^2$, will be zero if $\mu_1 = \mu_2 = \cdots = \mu_k = \mu$ (in which case also $\bar{\mu} = \mu$, and $\mathbf{C}/\sigma^2$ will have a χ^2 distribution with $k - 1$ degrees of freedom), but otherwise will be positive. Thus we anticipate a *larger* value of $\mathbf{C}$ if the null hypothesis H_0 is false than if it is true.

In order to test the hypothesis H_0 that the means are equal, we require a statistic whose distribution is known under the assumption that H_0 is valid. The distributions of both $\mathbf{B}$ and $\mathbf{C}$ involve the unknown population variance σ^2; but the distribution of their *ratio* does not. The statistic proposed for testing H_0 is

$$\mathbf{F} = \frac{\mathbf{C}/(k-1)\sigma^2}{\mathbf{B}/(n-k)\sigma^2} = \frac{\mathbf{C}(n-k)}{\mathbf{B}(k-1)} = \frac{(n-k)\sum_j n_j(\bar{\mathbf{x}}_j - \bar{\mathbf{x}})^2}{(k-1)\sum_{i,j}(\mathbf{x}_{ji} - \bar{\mathbf{x}}_j)^2}.$$

Thus $\mathbf{F}$ is $(n-k)/(k-1)$ *multiplied by the ratio of the sum of squares among classes to the sum of squares within classes.* If $\mu_1 = \mu_2 = \cdots = \mu_k$, then $E[\mathbf{C}/(k-1)] = \sigma^2$ and $E[\mathbf{B}/(n-k)] = \sigma^2$, so that $\mathbf{F}$ may be thought of as the ratio of an among-classes unbiased estimator of σ^2 to a within-classes unbiased estimator of σ^2. We have seen above that $\mathbf{B}$ and $\mathbf{C}$ are *independent* random variables; we have seen that $\mathbf{C}/(k-1)\sigma^2$ has a χ^2 distribution with $k - 1$ degrees of freedom and that $\mathbf{B}/(n-k)\sigma^2$ has a χ^2 distribution with $n - k$ degrees of freedom. From the definition of the F distribution (page 260), the random variable

▶ $\mathbf{F}$ *then has the F distribution with $k - 1$ and $n - k$ degrees of freedom.*

We have remarked that $E(\mathbf{C})$ is greater if H_0 fails than if it holds. A *one-tail* test of the hypothesis is therefore appropriate: we shall reject H_0 in favor of the alternative that the means are not equal if we observe too *large* a value of $\mathbf{F}$. Thus the hypothesis will be rejected at the $100\alpha\%$ level if the value F of $\mathbf{F}$ is greater than F_α, where F_α is chosen so that $Pr\{\mathbf{F} > F_\alpha\} = \alpha$.

Let us return now to our particular example. We have $k = 4$, $n_1 = n_2 = n_3 = 3$, $n_4 = 5$, $n = 14$. We observe that the addition of a constant to each observation x_{ji} results in the addition of the same constant to each mean $\bar{x}_j$ and to $\bar{x}$, so that B and C remain unchanged. Further, the multiplication of each observed value by a constant results in the multiplication of each mean $\bar{x}_j$ and of $\bar{x}$ by the same constant; so that each of the numbers B and C is multiplied by the square of that constant, and F remains unchanged. We shall therefore have the same F value if we perform any linear transformation on the observed values. For our problem, suppose we simply subtract 25 from each observed value, obtaining the table

$i \backslash j$	1	2	3	4
1	10	5	15	10
2	−14	−4	− 5	− 5
3	− 5	5	− 1	−10
4				0
5				5
sum	− 9	6	9	0

We find $\bar{x}_1 = -3$, $\bar{x}_2 = 2$, $\bar{x}_3 = 3$, $\bar{x}_4 = 0$, $\bar{x} = \frac{1}{n} \sum_j n_j\bar{x}_j = 6/14 = 3/7$. Also $B = \sum_{i,j} x_{ji}^2 - \sum_j n_j\bar{x}_j^2 = 822$, $C = \sum_j n_j\bar{x}_j^2 - n\bar{x}^2 = 63.4$, and $F = (n - k)C/(k - 1)B = 10C/3B = 0.26$. Suppose you wish to test H_0 at the 5% significance level. The random variable $\mathbf{F}$, whose sample value is 0.26, has the F distribution with $k - 1 = 3$ and $n - k = 10$ degrees of freedom. From the tables we find that $Pr\{\mathbf{F} > 3.71\} = 0.05$. Thus only if the observed value of F were greater than 3.71 would you reject at the 5% level the hypothesis that the population means are the same. Since it was only 0.26, you fail to reject the hypothesis. That is, your data and this test give you no justification for a statement that the different brands tested have significantly different mean tread lives.

It is interesting to observe that when $k = 2$ the analysis of variance test coincides with the two-tail t-test (cf. pages 258 ff.) for testing whether or not the means of two populations, both normal and having the same variance, are equal. The statistic used in the t-test is

$$\mathbf{t} = \frac{(\bar{\mathbf{x}}_2 - \bar{\mathbf{x}}_1)\sqrt{n_1 n_2(n_1 + n_2 - 2)}}{\sqrt{n_1\mathbf{s}_1^2 + n_2\mathbf{s}_2^2}\sqrt{n_1 + n_2}},$$

and the hypothesis $\mu_1 = \mu_2$ is rejected if one observes a value of $|t|$ which is too large; or equivalently, if the observed t^2 is too large. But

$$\mathbf{C} = n_1\left(\bar{\mathbf{x}}_1 - \frac{n_1\bar{\mathbf{x}}_1 + n_2\bar{\mathbf{x}}_2}{n_1 + n_2}\right)^2 + n_2\left(\bar{\mathbf{x}}_2 - \frac{n_1\bar{\mathbf{x}}_1 + n_2\bar{\mathbf{x}}_2}{n_1 + n_2}\right)^2$$

$$= \frac{n_1 n_2}{n_1 + n_2}(\bar{\mathbf{x}}_2 - \bar{\mathbf{x}}_1)^2,$$

while

$$\mathbf{B} = n_1\mathbf{s}_1{}^2 + n_2\mathbf{s}_2{}^2,$$

so that

$$\mathbf{F} = \frac{(n-k)\mathbf{C}}{(k-1)\mathbf{B}} = \frac{(n_1+n_2-2)\mathbf{C}}{\mathbf{B}} = \frac{(n_1+n_2-2)n_1n_2(\bar{\mathbf{x}}_2 - \bar{\mathbf{x}}_1)^2}{(n_1+n_2)(n_1\mathbf{s}_1{}^2 + n_2\mathbf{s}_2{}^2)} = \mathbf{t}^2.$$

98. Completely Randomized Design. Suppose you wish to study the effects of various additives to a basic etching solution. You have 4 preparations, A, B, C, and D, and 20 plates of steel on which to try them. Suppose you use A on the 5 plates on the top of the stack on the shelf, B on the next 5, etc. You discover the results of A were superior to those of D; but it occurs to you to wonder whether this is because of a superior preparation A, or because the first 5 plates, made by one manufacturer, were superior to the last 5, made by another. A *completely randomized design* would have tended to minimize effects of possible inhomogeneities among the plates. With such a design, the plates to receive a given preparation would be chosen at random. You might, for example, number the plates from 1 to 20, and number also 20 cards, shuffle them, and use preparation A on plates whose numbers correspond to the 5 top cards, etc.

99. Use of a Table of Random Numbers. As an alternative to preparing a deck of cards in the illustration above, you may prefer to use a table of random numbers. One way is to enter a table of random numbers, listing only those numbers whose first two digits give a number from 1 to 20. The first five numbers listed will be the numbers of the plates to receive preparation A, etc. Another way is to list the ranks of the first 20 random numbers:

Random number	Rank	Random number	Rank	Random number	Rank	Random number	Rank
171	3	295	7	341	10	676	17
282	6	235	4	533	13	449	12
093	1	578	16	829	19	331	9
312	8	553	15	548	14	846	20
361	11	100	2	254	5	718	18

If the above random numbers were listed, preparation A would be applied to plates 3, 6, 1, 8 and 11, etc.

To facilitate checking, it is recommended that a record be kept of the random numbers used. For your next problem using random numbers, you might enter the table at the next item beyond the last previously used.

A method of analyzing your data in the present example is described on pages 286–292.

100. Fisher's Lemma. Suppose we have at hand n^2 real numbers, $c_{11}, c_{12}, \cdots, c_{1n}; c_{21}, c_{22}, \cdots, c_{2n}; \cdots; c_{n1}, c_{n2}, \cdots, c_{nn}$, where n is a positive integer. Suppose they satisfy the *orthogonality* relations:

$$\sum_r c_{ir}c_{jr} = \begin{matrix} 1 & \text{if } i = j \\ 0 & \text{if } i \neq j, \quad i,j = 1, 2, \cdots, n \end{matrix}$$

For example, if $n = 2$ and if α is the radian measure of an angle, we might have $c_{11} = \cos\alpha$, $c_{12} = \sin\alpha$, $c_{21} = -\sin\alpha$, $c_{22} = \cos\alpha$; then $c_{11}c_{11} + c_{12}c_{12} = 1$, $c_{21}c_{21} + c_{22}c_{22} = 1$, $c_{11}c_{21} + c_{12}c_{22} = 0$, and $c_{21}c_{11} + c_{22}c_{12} = 0$. Now suppose $\mathbf{z}_1, \mathbf{z}_2, \cdots, \mathbf{z}_n$ are n *independent random variables, each normally distributed with mean* 0 *and standard deviation* σ. Consider n new random variables $\mathbf{y}_1, \mathbf{y}_2, \cdots, \mathbf{y}_n$ defined by

$$\mathbf{y}_i = \sum_r c_{ir}\mathbf{z}_r, \; i = 1, 2, \cdots, n.$$

(If $n = 2$ and if the c_{ij} are those mentioned immediately above, then the formulas $y_1 = c_{11}z_1 + c_{12}z_2$, $y_2 = c_{21}z_1 + c_{22}z_2$ are precisely the formulas for new plane rectangular coordinates y_1, y_2 in terms of the old, z_1, z_2, after a rotation of axes through the angle α.) Each random variable $c_{ir}\mathbf{z}_r$ is normally distributed with mean 0 and standard deviation $c_{ir}\sigma$, and it can be shown that the random variables $\mathbf{y}_i$ ($i = 1, 2, \cdots, n$) are jointly normally distributed. Further,

$$E(\mathbf{y}_i) = \sum_r c_{ir}E(\mathbf{z}_r) = 0,$$

and

$$\begin{aligned} \operatorname{cov}(\mathbf{y}_i,\mathbf{y}_j) &= E(\mathbf{y}_i\mathbf{y}_j) = E(\textstyle\sum_r c_{ir}\mathbf{z}_r)(\textstyle\sum_s c_{js}\mathbf{z}_s) \\ &= E[\textstyle\sum_{r,s} c_{ir}c_{js}\mathbf{z}_r\mathbf{z}_s] = \textstyle\sum_{r,s} c_{ir}c_{js}E(\mathbf{z}_r\mathbf{z}_s) \\ &= \textstyle\sum_{r,s} c_{ir}c_{js}\operatorname{cov}(\mathbf{z}_r,\mathbf{z}_s). \end{aligned}$$

But $\operatorname{cov}(\mathbf{z}_r,\mathbf{z}_s) = 0$ if $r \neq s$ and $\operatorname{cov}(\mathbf{z}_r,\mathbf{z}_r) = V(\mathbf{z}_r) = \sigma^2$, so that

$$\operatorname{cov}(\mathbf{y}_i,\mathbf{y}_j) = \sum_r c_{ir}c_{jr}\sigma^2 = \begin{matrix} \sigma^2 & \text{if } i = j \\ 0 & \text{if } i \neq j. \end{matrix}$$

Thus the random variables $\mathbf{y}_1, \mathbf{y}_2, \cdots, \mathbf{y}_n$ are *uncorrelated*. But *uncorrelated, jointly normally distributed* random variables are *independent* (see page 217); hence the random variables $\mathbf{y}_i$ are independent, and each is normally distributed with mean 0 and standard deviation σ.

Now suppose that for some positive integer $p < n$ we are given real numbers $c_{11}, c_{12}, \cdots, c_{1n}; c_{21}, c_{22}, \cdots, c_{2n}; \cdots; c_{p1}, c_{p2}, \cdots, c_{pn}$, satisfying the relations

$$\sum_r c_{ir}c_{jr} = \begin{matrix} 1 & \text{if } i = j \\ 0 & \text{if } i \neq j, \quad i,j = 1, 2, \cdots, p. \end{matrix}$$

It can be shown that other real numbers $c_{p+1,1}, c_{p+1,2}, \cdots, c_{p+1,n}; \cdots; c_{n1}, c_{n2}, \cdots, c_{nn}$ can be found so that all together the c_{ij} satisfy the orthogonality relations. Thus if we are given random variables $\mathbf{y}_1, \mathbf{y}_2, \cdots, \mathbf{y}_p$ with

$$\mathbf{y}_i = \sum_r c_{ir}\mathbf{z}_r, \quad i = 1, 2, \cdots, p,$$

then $n - p$ other random variables $\mathbf{y}_{p+1}, \mathbf{y}_{p+2}, \cdots \mathbf{y}_n$ can be found so that

$$\mathbf{y}_i = \sum_r c_{ir}\mathbf{z}_r, \quad i = p + 1, \cdots, n,$$

and so that the random variables $\mathbf{y}_1, \mathbf{y}_2, \cdots, \mathbf{y}_n$ are mutually independent, each normally distributed with mean 0 and standard deviation σ.

Consider the random variable

$$\mathbf{C} = \sum_{r=1}^{n} \mathbf{z}_r^2 - \sum_{r=1}^{p} \mathbf{y}_r^2.$$

It can be shown that $\sum_{r=1}^{n} \mathbf{z}_r^2 = \sum_{r=1}^{n} \mathbf{y}_r^2$, so that also

$$\mathbf{C} = \sum_{r=p+1}^{n} \mathbf{y}_r^2.$$

Therefore $\mathbf{C}/\sigma^2$ is the sum of the squares of $n - p$ independent random variables, each normally distributed with mean 0 and standard deviation 1. By definition (page 230), $\mathbf{C}/\sigma^2$ has a χ^2 distribution with $n - p$ degrees of freedom.

Further, $\mathbf{C}$ is independent of $\sum_{r=1}^{p} \mathbf{y}_r^2$. We have now sketched in outline the proof of Fisher's Lemma:

▶ *Let $\mathbf{z}_1, \mathbf{z}_2, \cdots, \mathbf{z}_n$ be independent, normally distributed with mean 0 and standard deviation σ. Let $\mathbf{y}_i = \sum_{r=1}^{n} c_{ir}\mathbf{z}_r$, $i = 1, 2, \cdots, p$, where $p < n$, and where*

$$\sum_{r=1}^{n} c_{ir}c_{jr} = \begin{matrix} 1 & \text{if } i = j \\ 0 & \text{if } i \neq j, \end{matrix}$$

$i,j = 1, 2, \cdots, p$. Let

$$\mathbf{C} = \sum_{r=1}^{n} \mathbf{z}_r^2 - \sum_{r=1}^{p} \mathbf{y}_r^2.$$

Then $\mathbf{C}$ is independent of the random variables $\mathbf{y}_1, \mathbf{y}_2, \cdots, \mathbf{y}_p$, and $\mathbf{C}/\sigma^2$ has a χ^2 distribution with $n - p$ degrees of freedom.

EXAMPLE 2. (*Independence of the sample mean and sample variance.*) Let $\mathbf{x}_1, \mathbf{x}_2, \cdots, \mathbf{x}_n$ be sample random variables of a sample of size n from a normal population with mean μ and standard deviation σ. Let $\bar{\mathbf{x}}$ be the sample mean, and $\mathbf{s}^2 = \frac{1}{n} \sum_{i=1}^{n} (\mathbf{x}_i - \bar{\mathbf{x}})^2$ the sample variance. In order to apply Fisher's Lemma as stated above, we set $\mathbf{z}_i = \mathbf{x}_i - \mu$, $\bar{\mathbf{z}} = \bar{\mathbf{x}} - \mu$, so that the $\mathbf{z}_i$ form a random sample of size n from a population which is normal with mean 0 and standard deviation σ. We now have

$$n\mathbf{s}^2 = \sum_i (\mathbf{x}_i - \bar{\mathbf{x}})^2 = \sum_i (\mathbf{z}_i - \bar{\mathbf{z}})^2 = \sum_i \mathbf{z}_i^2 - n\bar{\mathbf{z}}^2.$$

Thus

$$\sum_i \mathbf{z}_i^2 = n\bar{\mathbf{z}}^2 + n\mathbf{s}^2.$$

In applying Fisher's Lemma, put $p = 1$ and

$$\mathbf{y}_1 = \sqrt{n}\,\bar{\mathbf{z}} = \frac{1}{\sqrt{n}} \sum_i \mathbf{z}_i,$$

so that $c_{11} = c_{12} = \cdots = c_{1n} = 1/\sqrt{n}$. Since $p = 1$, there is only one orthogonality condition to be satisfied,

$$\sum_r c_{1r} c_{1r} = 1;$$

in the present situation this becomes $\sum_{r=1}^{n} \frac{1}{\sqrt{n}} \cdot \frac{1}{\sqrt{n}} = 1$, which indeed holds. The random variable $\mathbf{C}$ of Fisher's Lemma above is here $n\mathbf{s}^2$, so that a part of the conclusion of Fisher's Lemma is that $n\mathbf{s}^2$ and $\mathbf{y}_1$ are independent random variables. But $\mathbf{y}_1 = \sqrt{n}\,\bar{\mathbf{z}} = \sqrt{n}\,\bar{\mathbf{x}} - \sqrt{n}\,\mu$. Evidently $\bar{\mathbf{x}}$ is a (linear) function of $\mathbf{y}_1$, and $\mathbf{s}^2$ is a (linear) function of $n\mathbf{s}^2$, so that also $\bar{\mathbf{x}}$ and $\mathbf{s}^2$ are independent random variables (page 82). A further conclusion of Fisher's Lemma as it applies here is that $n\mathbf{s}^2/\sigma^2$ has a χ^2 distribution with $n - 1$ degrees of freedom, which is also the conclusion of Theorem K, page 232.

EXAMPLE 3. (*Distribution of the sum of squares among classes.*) On page 289 above it was stated without proof that the distribution of $\mathbf{C}/\sigma^2$ is χ^2 with $k - 1$ degrees of freedom, provided $\mu_1 = \mu_2 = \cdots = \mu_n = \mu$. We can base a proof of that assertion on Fisher's Lemma. In the notation used on pages 287 ff., we have

$$\mathbf{C} = \sum_j n_j(\bar{\mathbf{x}}_j - \bar{\mathbf{x}})^2 = \sum_j n_j[(\bar{\mathbf{x}}_j - \mu) - (\bar{\mathbf{x}} - \mu)]^2$$
$$= \sum_j \mathbf{z}_j^2 - n\bar{\mathbf{z}}^2,$$

or

$$\sum_j \mathbf{z}_j^2 = n\bar{\mathbf{z}}^2 + \mathbf{C},$$

where $\mathbf{z}_j = \sqrt{n_j}\,(\bar{\mathbf{x}}_j - \mu)$ and $\bar{\mathbf{z}} = \bar{\mathbf{x}} - \mu = \frac{1}{n} \sum_j \sqrt{n_j}\,\mathbf{z}_j$. Since $\bar{\mathbf{x}}_j$ is normally distributed with mean μ and variance σ^2/n_j, $\mathbf{z}_j$ is normally distributed with mean 0 and standard deviation σ. Let

$$\mathbf{y}_1 = \sqrt{n}\,\bar{\mathbf{z}} = \sum_j \sqrt{\frac{n_j}{n}}\,\mathbf{z}_j = \sum_j c_{1j}\mathbf{z}_j,$$

where $c_{1j} = \sqrt{n_j/n}$, $j = 1, 2, \cdots, k$. In applying Fisher's Lemma with $p = 1$, again there is only one orthogonality condition to verify:

$$\sum_r c_{1r}c_{1r} = \sum_r n_r/n = 1.$$

We conclude that $\mathbf{C}$ and $\bar{\mathbf{x}}$ are independent, and that $\mathbf{C}/\sigma^2$ has a χ^2 distribution with $k - 1$ degrees of freedom.

We note that Example 2 is a special case of Example 3.

101. Two-Way Classification; Two-Factor Experiments. As Supervisor in Charge of Soybean Research at an agricultural experiment station you have assembled data giving yield per acre (in bushels) for one planting each of three varieties, X, Y, Z, of soybean, for each of four dosages of nitrogen (in pounds per acre): 0, 50, 100, 150. Suppose you adopt the following notation. The subscript i will designate the variety: $i = 1, 2, \cdots I$; in your case $I = 3$. The subscript j will designate the dosage of nitrogen: $j = 1, 2, \cdots, J$; in your case $J = 4$. Let $\mathbf{x}_{ij}$ denote the random variable "yield per acre which will be obtained from the ith variety and jth dosage"; x_{ij} will denote the yield per acre actually observed in the planting with the ith variety and the jth dosage. We suppose you have sufficient reason to make the following assumption:

		Dosage			
Variety	$i \backslash j$	1	2	3	4
X	1	x_{11}	x_{12}	x_{13}	x_{14}
Y	2	x_{21}	x_{22}	x_{23}	x_{24}
Z	3	x_{31}	x_{32}	x_{33}	x_{34}

▶ ***Assumption** (1).* $\mathbf{x}_{ij}$ is normally distributed with mean μ_{ij} and standard deviation σ; this standard deviation is the same for all varieties and dosages ($i = 1, 2, \cdots, I; j = 1, 2, \cdots, J$).

Let

$$\bar{\mathbf{x}}_{\cdot j} = \frac{1}{I}\sum_i \mathbf{x}_{ij},$$

the mean of the sample values involving the ith variety;

the mean of the sample values involving the jth dosage, and

$$\bar{\mathbf{x}} = \frac{1}{I}\sum_i \bar{\mathbf{x}}_{i\cdot} = \frac{1}{J}\sum_j \bar{\mathbf{x}}_{\cdot j} = \frac{1}{IJ}\sum_{i,j} \mathbf{x}_{ij},$$

the over-all sample mean. Let

$$\mu_{ij} = E(\mathbf{x}_{ij}), \quad \bar{\mu}_{i\cdot} = \frac{1}{J}\sum_j \mu_{ij} = E(\bar{\mathbf{x}}_{i\cdot}),$$

$$\bar{\mu}_{\cdot j} = \frac{1}{I}\sum_i \mu_{ij} = E(\bar{\mathbf{x}}_{\cdot j}), \quad \text{and } \bar{\mu} = \frac{1}{I}\sum_i \bar{\mu}_{i\cdot} = \frac{1}{J}\sum_j \bar{\mu}_{\cdot j} = \frac{1}{IJ}\sum_{i,j} \mu_{ij}.$$

You might call $\bar{\mu}_{i\cdot} - \bar{\mu}$ the *effect of the i-th variety* on the over-all population mean, and $\bar{\mu}_{\cdot j} - \bar{\mu}$ the *effect of the j-th dosage.* If the (weighted) mean yield of variety A is greater than the over-all mean yield, then $\bar{\mu}_{1\cdot} - \bar{\mu} > 0$, etc. Further, you might call $\mu_{ij} - \bar{\mu} - [(\bar{\mu}_{i\cdot} - \bar{\mu}) + (\bar{\mu}_{\cdot j} - \bar{\mu})]$ the effect of *interaction* between the ith variety and the jth dosage. For example, it might be conceivable to you that in general the variety A is superior $(\bar{\mu}_{1\cdot} - \bar{\mu} > 0)$, and in general the dosage 100 lb. per acre is superior $(\bar{\mu}_{\cdot 3} - \bar{\mu} > 0)$, but that the combination, for some reason, is inferior $(\mu_{13} - \bar{\mu} < 0)$; in this case the effect of the *interaction* between variety A and dosage 100 lb. per acre would be negative. Even if the combination were superior, the joint effect, $\mu_{13} - \bar{\mu}$, might be less than the sum of the effects $\bar{\mu}_{1\cdot} - \bar{\mu}$ and $\bar{\mu}_{\cdot 3} - \bar{\mu}$, so that the effect of the interaction would be negative. It should be emphasized that the phrase "effect of interaction" is here *defined* as $\mu_{ij} - \bar{\mu} - [(\bar{\mu}_{i\cdot} - \bar{\mu}) + (\bar{\mu}_{\cdot j} - \bar{\mu})]$ and may not always correspond precisely to other usages of the term. We shall suppose you have sufficient reason to assume that the effect of the interaction between variety and dosage is 0, that is:

▶ ***Assumption* (2).** $\mu_{ij} = \bar{\mu}_{i\cdot} + \bar{\mu}_{\cdot j} - \bar{\mu}$, $i = 1, 2, \cdots, I$; $j = 1, 2, \cdots, J$.

Assumption (2) might also be stated as follows:

$$\mu_{ij} = \bar{\mu} + R_i + C_j, \quad i = 1, 2, \cdots, I; j = 1, 2, \cdots, J;$$

where R_i may be called the "*row effect,*" and C_j the "*column effect,*" and where $\sum_i R_i = 0$, $\sum_j C_j = 0$. We have here simply labelled $\bar{\mu}_{i\cdot} - \bar{\mu}$ as R_i, and $\bar{\mu}_{\cdot j} - \bar{\mu}$ as C_j. Assumption (2) gives us a model in which the observation to be made corresponding to the cell in the ith row and the jth column is the sum of an over-all mean $\bar{\mu}$, a row effect R_i, a column effect C_j, and a random effect ϵ_{ij}, where ϵ_{ij} is normal $(0,\sigma)$:

$$\mathbf{x}_{ij} = \bar{\mu} + R_i + C_j + \epsilon_{ij}, \quad i = 1, 2, \cdots, I; j = 1, 2, \cdots, J.$$

You might wish to test this assumption as a hypothesis; to do so, however, would require more than one planting for each pair, variety and dosage.

Suppose now you are interested in the answers to these questions:

(1) Does the variety affect the yield?
(2) Does the dosage affect the yield?

Accordingly you set up two hypotheses:

▶ $$H_1: \bar{\mu}_{i\cdot} = \bar{\mu}, \text{ or } R_i = 0 \ (i = 1, 2, \cdots, I);$$
$$H_2: \bar{\mu}_{\cdot j} = \bar{\mu}, \text{ or } C_j = 0 \ (j = 1, 2, \cdots, J).$$

The total sum of squares can again be partitioned, this time into three sums of squares: the sum of squares among rows, the sum of squares among columns, and a residual sum. We have

$$\begin{aligned}\sum_{i,j} (\mathbf{x}_{ij} - \bar{\mathbf{x}})^2 &= \sum_{i,j} [(\mathbf{x}_{ij} - \bar{\mathbf{x}}_{i\cdot} - \bar{\mathbf{x}}_{\cdot j} + \bar{\mathbf{x}}) + (\bar{\mathbf{x}}_{i\cdot} - \bar{\mathbf{x}}) + (\bar{\mathbf{x}}_{\cdot j} - \bar{\mathbf{x}})]^2 \\ &= J \sum_i (\bar{\mathbf{x}}_{i\cdot} - \bar{\mathbf{x}})^2 + I \sum_j (\bar{\mathbf{x}}_{\cdot j} - \bar{\mathbf{x}})^2 \\ &\quad + \sum_{i,j} (\mathbf{x}_{ij} - \bar{\mathbf{x}}_{i\cdot} - \bar{\mathbf{x}}_{\cdot j} + \bar{\mathbf{x}})^2,\end{aligned}$$

for you will find that the cross-product terms vanish. We write

$$\mathbf{A} = \mathbf{B} + \mathbf{C} + \mathbf{D},$$

where

$$\mathbf{A} = \sum_{i,j} (\mathbf{x}_{ij} - \bar{\mathbf{x}})^2 = \sum_{i,j} \mathbf{x}_{ij}^2 - IJ\bar{\mathbf{x}}^2,$$

the *total sum of squares*,

$$\mathbf{B} = J \sum_i (\bar{\mathbf{x}}_{i\cdot} - \bar{\mathbf{x}})^2 = J[\sum_i \bar{\mathbf{x}}_{i\cdot}^2 - I\bar{\mathbf{x}}^2],$$

the *sum of squares among rows*,

$$\mathbf{C} = I \sum_j (\bar{\mathbf{x}}_{\cdot j} - \bar{\mathbf{x}})^2 = I[\sum_j \bar{\mathbf{x}}_{\cdot j}^2 - J\bar{\mathbf{x}}^2],$$

the *sum of squares among columns*, and

$$\mathbf{D} = \sum_{i,j} (\mathbf{x}_{ij} - \bar{\mathbf{x}}_{i\cdot} - \bar{\mathbf{x}}_{\cdot j} + \bar{\mathbf{x}})^2,$$

the *residual sum of squares*.

We state without proof that:

▶ (a) *regardless of whether or not hypotheses H_1 and H_2 hold, $\mathbf{D}/\sigma^2$ has a χ^2 distribution with $(I - 1)(J - 1)$ degrees of freedom;*

(b) *if* H_1 *holds, then* $\mathbf{B}/\sigma^2$ *has the* χ^2 *distribution with* $I - 1$ *degrees of freedom, and* $\mathbf{B}$ *and* $\mathbf{D}$ *are independent;*

(c) *if* H_2 *holds, then* $\mathbf{C}/\sigma^2$ *has the* χ^2 *distribution with* $J - 1$ *degrees of freedom, and* $\mathbf{C}$ *and* $\mathbf{D}$ *are independent.*

In order to test the hypothesis H_1, you may then use the statistic

$$\mathbf{F}_1 = \frac{\mathbf{B}/(I-1)\sigma^2}{\mathbf{D}/(I-1)(J-1)\sigma^2} = \frac{(I-1)(J-1)\mathbf{B}}{(I-1)\mathbf{D}},$$

which has the F-distribution with $I - 1$ and $(I - 1)(J - 1)$ degrees of freedom.

As in the earlier example, we can compute $E(\mathbf{B})$ without assuming hypothesis H_1. We have

$$\begin{aligned}
E(\mathbf{B}) &= JE[\textstyle\sum_i (\bar{\mathbf{x}}_{i\cdot} - \bar{\mathbf{x}})^2] = JE[\textstyle\sum_i \bar{\mathbf{x}}_{i\cdot}{}^2 - I\bar{\mathbf{x}}^2] \\
&= J\{\textstyle\sum_i E(\bar{\mathbf{x}}_{i\cdot})^2 - IE(\bar{\mathbf{x}}^2)\} \\
&= J\{\textstyle\sum_i (V(\bar{\mathbf{x}}_{i\cdot}) + [E(\bar{\mathbf{x}}_{i\cdot})]^2) - I(V(\bar{\mathbf{x}}) + [E(\bar{\mathbf{x}})]^2)\} \\
&= J\left\{\textstyle\sum_i \left(\frac{\sigma^2}{J} + \bar{\mu}_{i\cdot}{}^2\right) - I\left(\frac{\sigma^2}{IJ} + \bar{\mu}^2\right)\right\} \\
&= (I-1)\sigma^2 + J(\textstyle\sum_i \bar{\mu}_{i\cdot}{}^2 - I\bar{\mu}^2) \\
&= (I-1)\sigma^2 + J\textstyle\sum_i (\bar{\mu}_{i\cdot} - \bar{\mu})^2.
\end{aligned}$$

Thus if H_1 holds, $E(\mathbf{B}) = (I-1)\sigma^2$, and $\mathbf{B}/(I - 1)$ *is an unbiased estimator of* σ^2. We observe that this checks with the statement above that under this hypothesis $\mathbf{B}/\sigma^2$ has a χ^2 distribution with $I - 1$ degrees of freedom. On the other hand, if H_1 does not hold, then $E(\mathbf{B}) > (I - 1)\sigma^2$. We therefore adopt again a one-tail test, rejecting the hypothesis H_1 if too large a value, F_1, of $\mathbf{F}_1$ is observed. Similarly, we reject the hypothesis H_2 if too large a value is observed of the statistic

$$\mathbf{F}_2 = \frac{(I-1)(J-1)\mathbf{C}}{(J-1)\mathbf{D}},$$

which has the F distribution with $J - 1$ and $(I - 1)(J - 1)$ degrees of freedom. A frequently adopted method of presenting the information is by means of an *analysis of variance table:*

	Sum of squared deviations	Degrees of freedom	Mean square deviation
Among rows	$B = J \sum_i (\bar{x}_{i\cdot} - \bar{x})^2$	$I - 1$	$B/(I-1)$
Among columns	$C = I \sum_j (\bar{x}_{\cdot j} - \bar{x})^2$	$J - 1$	$C/(J-1)$
Residual	$D = A - B - C$	$(I-1)(J-1)$	$D/(I-1)(J-1)$
Total	$A = \sum_{i,j} (x_{ij} - \bar{x})^2$	$IJ - 1$	

Now let us examine your particular problem. Suppose your data are as follows:

Variety of Soybean	Nitrogen Dosage				
	0	50	100	150	Totals
X	15	18	20	20	73
Y	10	8	12	15	45
Z	17	15	20	22	74
Total	42	41	52	57	192

We have $I = 3$, $J = 4$; $\bar{x}_{1\cdot} = 73/4 = 18.25$; $\bar{x}_{2\cdot} = 45/4 = 11.25$; $\bar{x}_{3\cdot} = 74/4 = 18.50$; $\bar{x}_{\cdot 1} = 42/3 = 14.00$; $\bar{x}_{\cdot 2} = 41/3 = 13.67$; $\bar{x}_{\cdot 3} = 52/3 = 17.33$; $\bar{x}_{\cdot 4} = 57/3 = 19.00$; and $\bar{x} = 192/12 = 16.00$. Then

$$B = J \sum_i (\bar{x}_{i\cdot} - \bar{x})^2 = J \left[\sum_i \bar{x}_{i\cdot}^2 - I\bar{x}^2 \right]$$

$$= 4 \left[\frac{73^2 + 45^2 + 74^2}{16} - 3(16)^2 \right] = 3208 - 3072 = 136;$$

$$C = I \sum_j (\bar{x}_{\cdot j} - \bar{x})^2 = I \left[\sum_j \bar{x}_{\cdot j}^2 - J\bar{x}^2 \right]$$

$$= 3 \left[\frac{42^2 + 41^2 + 52^2 + 57^2}{9} - 4(16)^2 \right] = 3133 - 3072 = 61;$$

$$A = \sum_{i,j} (x_{ij} - \bar{x})^2 = \sum_{i,j} x_{ij}^2 - IJ\bar{x}^2 = 3280 - 3072 = 208; \text{ and}$$

$$D = A - (B + C) = 208 - (136 + 61) = 11.$$

The analysis of variance table is

	Sum of squared deviations	Degrees of freedom	Mean square deviation
Among rows	136	2	68
Among columns	61	3	20.33
Residual	11	6	1.83
Total	208	11	

We have

$$F_1 = 68/1.83 = 37.1.$$

Since $\mathbf{F}_1$ has 2 and 6 degrees of freedom, from the tables of the F distribution we find $Pr\{\mathbf{F}_1 > 5.14\} = 0.05$. Therefore we reject, at the 5% significance level, the hypothesis H_1, and conclude (at this level of significance) that there is a significant row effect. In other words, there is a significant difference among the yields of the three varieties.

Also,

$$F_2 = 20.33/1.83 = 11.1.$$

Now $\mathbf{F}_2$ has 3 and 6 degrees of freedom, so that $Pr\{\mathbf{F}_2 > 4.76\} = 0.05$, and we reject the hypothesis H_2 at the 5% level, concluding that the nitrogen dosage has a significant effect. Further, $Pr\{\mathbf{F}_1 > 10.92\} = 0.01$, and $Pr\{\mathbf{F}_2 > 9.78\} = 0.01$, so that we should arrive at the same conclusions even at the 1% significance level.

102. Randomized Block Design. By means of randomized block design one is able in some situations to combine some of the advantages of stratified sampling (page 319) and of randomization (page 292). Suppose you are interested in the effects on milk production of 4 distinct diets, A, B, C, D. On farms cooperating in the study there are Guernsey, Holstein, and Jersey cows. In order to secure the advantage of increased precision in sampling from more nearly homogeneous groups, you divide your test animals into three groups, by breed. If you plan to test twelve animals, one for each combination of diet and breed, in your data will appear three *blocks* (Guernsey, Holstein, Jersey), of four items each (A, B, C, D). Using a *randomized block design*, you would select *at random* the individual animals of a given breed to which the four diets are to be given. You could analyze your data according to the plan discussed on pages 296–301, provided you feel you can safely make the appropriate assumptions:

(1) The milk to be produced by a test animal is a normally distributed random variable whose mean may depend on breed and on diet, but whose standard deviation is the same for all animals.

(2) There is no "interaction" between breed and diet; that is, the mean production for a given breed and diet is the sum of the over-all mean plus a "diet effect" plus a "breed effect" (page 297).

If possible, you would probably wish to test more than one animal of each breed with each diet. The modifications of the analysis required are discussed in [1], Ch. 23, and in [7].

103. Latin Squares. You are manager of the stenographic pool of a large government bureau. There are five competing makes of typewriters which you wish to test. You recognize that other factors play roles in determining the output of a typist, in particular, the ability of the typist and the difficulty of the work. You choose five typists of varying ability, and five samples of work of varying difficulty. There are 125 combinations of typist, work sample, and typewriter; however, the use of a 5×5 Latin Square will permit you to test the effects of using different makes of typewriters, without testing each of the 125 combinations. A 5×5 Latin Square is an array in which each of five symbols appears once in each row and once in each column.

		Machine				
		1	2	3	4	5
	1	1	2	3	4	5
	2	5	1	2	3	4
Typist	3	4	5	1	2	3
	4	3	4	5	1	2
	5	2	3	4	5	1

If the work samples are represented by the numerals 1, 2, 3, 4, 5 in the body of the table, the above Latin Square specifies one way in which each work sample can be done by each typist and on each machine. Evidently the roles of the three factors may be interchanged. For example, the following Latin Square, in which the numbers of the machines appear in the body of the table, prescribes precisely the same experiment.

		Work Sample				
		1	2	3	4	5
	1	1	2	3	4	5
	2	2	3	4	5	1
Typist	3	3	4	5	1	2
	4	4	5	1	2	3
	5	5	1	2	3	4

Let us analyze the data with this square in mind, in which the *first factor* is the typist, the *second factor* is the work sample, and the *treatment* is the typewriter. Let $\bar{\mu}$ denote the over-all (population) mean time required for a typist to type a work sample on a typewriter. Let $\mathbf{x}_{ijt}$ denote the time which will be required for the ith typist ($i = 1, 2, \cdots, r$) (in the present case $r = 5$) to type the jth work sample ($j = 1, 2, \cdots, r$) on the tth machine ($t = 1, 2, \cdots, r$), assigned by the Latin Square. Note that i, j, t may not vary independently. When two of the symbols are assigned values, the third is determined by the Latin Square. We assume that

▶ (1) The r^2 random variables $\mathbf{x}_{ijt}$ are independent and normally distributed with the same variance, σ^2; and
(2) The mean $\mu_{ijt} = E(\mathbf{x}_{ijt})$ is the sum of the over-all mean $\bar{\mu}$; a "row effect," R_i; a "column effect," C_j; and a "treatment effect," T_t:

$$\mu_{ijt} = \bar{\mu} + R_i + C_j + T_t;$$

that is, there is no "interaction."

We introduce the following notation:

$$\bar{\mathbf{x}}_{i\cdot\cdot} = \frac{1}{r}\sum_{j,t}\mathbf{x}_{ijt}, \quad \bar{\mathbf{x}}_{\cdot j\cdot} = \frac{1}{r}\sum_{i,t}\mathbf{x}_{ijt},$$

$$\bar{\mathbf{x}}_{\cdot\cdot t} = \frac{1}{r}\sum_{i,j}\mathbf{x}_{ijt}, \quad \bar{\mathbf{x}} = \frac{1}{r^2}\sum_{i,j,t}\mathbf{x}_{ijt}.$$

We note that, for example, there are only r terms in the sum $\sum_{j,t}\mathbf{x}_{ijt}$, for there are only r pairs (j,t) corresponding to a fixed i. We find as on page 298 that

$$\sum_{i,j,t}(\mathbf{x}_{ijt} - \bar{\mathbf{x}})^2 = r\sum_i(\bar{\mathbf{x}}_{i\cdot\cdot} - \bar{\mathbf{x}})^2 + r\sum_j(\bar{\mathbf{x}}_{\cdot j\cdot} - \bar{\mathbf{x}})^2$$
$$+ \sum_{i,j,t}(\mathbf{x}_{ijt} - \bar{\mathbf{x}}_{i\cdot\cdot} - \bar{\mathbf{x}}_{\cdot j\cdot} + \bar{\mathbf{x}})^2.$$

The last term we partition further. It can be written

$$\sum_{i,j,t}[(\mathbf{x}_{ijt} - \bar{\mathbf{x}}_{i\cdot\cdot} - \bar{\mathbf{x}}_{\cdot j\cdot} - \bar{\mathbf{x}}_{\cdot\cdot t} + 2\bar{\mathbf{x}}) + (\bar{\mathbf{x}}_{\cdot\cdot t} - \bar{\mathbf{x}})]^2$$
$$= \sum_{i,j,t}(\mathbf{x}_{ijt} - \bar{\mathbf{x}}_{i\cdot\cdot} - \bar{\mathbf{x}}_{\cdot j\cdot} - \bar{\mathbf{x}}_{\cdot\cdot t} + 2\bar{\mathbf{x}})^2 + \sum_{i,j,t}(\bar{\mathbf{x}}_{\cdot\cdot t} - \bar{\mathbf{x}})^2$$
$$+ 2\sum_{i,j,t}(\bar{\mathbf{x}}_{\cdot\cdot t} - \bar{\mathbf{x}})(\mathbf{x}_{ijt} - \bar{\mathbf{x}}_{i\cdot\cdot} - \bar{\mathbf{x}}_{\cdot j\cdot} - \bar{\mathbf{x}}_{\cdot\cdot t} + 2\bar{\mathbf{x}}).$$

Let us consider the last term on the right. The first factor is independent of i and j; summing first with respect to i and j for fixed t, the last term becomes

$$+ 2\sum_t(\bar{\mathbf{x}}_{\cdot\cdot t} - \bar{\mathbf{x}})\sum_{i,j}(\mathbf{x}_{ijt} - \bar{\mathbf{x}}_{i\cdot\cdot} - \bar{\mathbf{x}}_{\cdot j\cdot} - \bar{\mathbf{x}}_{\cdot\cdot t} + 2\bar{\mathbf{x}}).$$

Now by the definition of $\bar{\mathbf{x}}_{\cdot\cdot t}$ we have $\sum_{i,j}\mathbf{x}_{ijt} = r\bar{\mathbf{x}}_{\cdot\cdot t}$. Also, since each treatment occurs once in each row and once in each column, all r rows are represented in the sum $\sum_{i,j}$, so that $\sum_{i,j}\bar{\mathbf{x}}_{i\cdot\cdot} = r\bar{\mathbf{x}}$; and similarly, $\sum_{i,j}\bar{\mathbf{x}}_{\cdot j\cdot} = r\bar{\mathbf{x}}$. Hence

$$\begin{aligned}\sum_{i,j}(\mathbf{x}_{ijt} - \bar{\mathbf{x}}_{i\cdot\cdot} - \bar{\mathbf{x}}_{\cdot j\cdot} - \bar{\mathbf{x}}_{\cdot\cdot t} + 2\bar{\mathbf{x}}) &= r\bar{\mathbf{x}}_{\cdot\cdot t} - r\bar{\mathbf{x}} - r\bar{\mathbf{x}} - r\bar{\mathbf{x}}_{\cdot\cdot t} + 2r\bar{\mathbf{x}} \\ &= 0.\end{aligned}$$

Our final partition of the total sum of squares thus becomes

$$\sum_{i,j,t}(\mathbf{x}_{ijt} - \bar{\mathbf{x}})^2 = r\sum_i(\bar{\mathbf{x}}_{i\cdot\cdot} - \bar{\mathbf{x}})^2 + r\sum_j(\bar{\mathbf{x}}_{\cdot j\cdot} - \bar{\mathbf{x}})^2 + r\sum_t(\bar{\mathbf{x}}_{\cdot\cdot t} - \bar{\mathbf{x}})^2 + \sum_{i,j,t}(\mathbf{x}_{ijt} - \bar{\mathbf{x}}_{i\cdot\cdot} - \bar{\mathbf{x}}_{\cdot j\cdot} - \bar{\mathbf{x}}_{\cdot\cdot t} + 2\bar{\mathbf{x}})^2$$

or

$$\mathbf{A} = \mathbf{B} + \mathbf{C} + \mathbf{D} + \mathbf{E},$$

where

$$\mathbf{A} = \sum_{i,j,t}(\mathbf{x}_{ijt} - \bar{\mathbf{x}})^2 = \sum_{i,j,t}\mathbf{x}_{ijt}^2 - r^2\bar{\mathbf{x}}^2,$$

the *total* sum of squares;

$$\mathbf{B} = r\sum_i(\bar{\mathbf{x}}_{i\cdot\cdot} - \bar{\mathbf{x}})^2 = r\sum_i\bar{\mathbf{x}}_{i\cdot\cdot}^2 - r^2\bar{\mathbf{x}}^2,$$

the *row* sum of squares;

$$\mathbf{C} = r\sum_j(\bar{\mathbf{x}}_{\cdot j\cdot} - \bar{\mathbf{x}})^2 = r\sum_j\bar{\mathbf{x}}_{\cdot j\cdot}^2 - r^2\bar{\mathbf{x}}^2,$$

the *column* sum of squares;

$$\mathbf{D} = r\sum_t(\bar{\mathbf{x}}_{\cdot\cdot t} - \bar{\mathbf{x}})^2 = r\sum_t\bar{\mathbf{x}}_{\cdot\cdot t}^2 - r^2\bar{\mathbf{x}}^2,$$

the *treatment* sum of squares; and

$$\mathbf{E} = \sum_{i,j,t}(\mathbf{x}_{ijt} - \bar{\mathbf{x}}_{i\cdot\cdot} - \bar{\mathbf{x}}_{\cdot j\cdot} - \bar{\mathbf{x}}_{\cdot\cdot t} + 2\bar{\mathbf{x}})^2,$$

the *residual* sum of squares.

Let us consider now, for example, a test of the hypothesis

$$H\colon\ T_1 = T_2 = \cdots = T_r = 0.$$

As before, it can be shown that $\mathbf{E}/\sigma^2$ has the χ^2 distribution with $(r-1)(r-2)$ degrees of freedom, while under hypothesis H, $\mathbf{D}/\sigma^2$ has the χ^2 distribution with $(r-1)$ degrees of freedom. Under the hypothesis H, therefore, the ratio

$$\mathbf{F} = \frac{\mathbf{D}/(r-1)\sigma^2}{\mathbf{E}/(r-1)(r-2)\sigma^2} = \frac{(r-2)\mathbf{D}}{\mathbf{E}}$$

has the F distribution with $r-1$ and $(r-1)(r-2)$ degrees of freedom. The analysis of variance table would be:

	Sum of squared deviations	Degrees of freedom	Mean square deviation
Among rows	B	$r - 1$	$B/(r - 1)$
Among columns	C	$r - 1$	$C/(r - 1)$
Among treatments	D	$r - 1$	$D/(r - 1)$
Residual	E	$(r - 1)(r - 2)$	$E/(r - 1)(r - 2)$
Total	A	$r^2 - 1$	

104. Other Methods. Many techniques have been developed to deal with other situations similar to the few discussed above; examples are Graeco-Latin Squares, the components of variance model for analysis of variance, analysis of covariance, and rank correlation methods. You can find discussions of these and other methods in the texts and reference works in statistics listed on page 372. For proofs of some of the results stated here without proof, see [10], [15], [17], and [22].

PROBLEMS

1. You are planning the following experiment. You have 12 plots of land on which you will plant potatoes. On 4 you will apply dosage I of a disease-inhibiting chemical; on 4 you will apply dosage II; on 4 you will apply dosage III. The chemical will be applied in the spring to half of those given each dosage, and in the fall to the other half. Describe a method of using a table of random digits to achieve a completely randomized design, which assigns each of the 6 treatments (spring or fall; I, II, or III) to 2 plots. Use your method, and exhibit the result in a 4×3 rectangle, designating in each of the 12 squares the dosage to be applied to the corresponding plot and the time of year it is to be applied.

2. In Problem 1, suppose 6 of the plots are in river bottom land, 6 on a sloping hillside. Describe a method of randomized block design for assigning treatments to the 12 plots. Use a table of random digits actually to assign treatments.

3. In a study of corrosion of pipe to be used in a gas pipe line, samples of pipe were subjected for a period of time to three different soil conditions: A, B, and C. A means was developed of assigning a corrosion score to each. The average scores $\bar{x}_j$ of 10 samples of pipe, and the corresponding sample variances, $s_j^2 = \frac{1}{10} \sum_{i=1}^{10} (x_{ji} - \bar{x}_j)^2$ for the three soil conditions ($j = 1, 2, 3$) were as follows:

$$\bar{x}_1 = 20,\ s_1^2 = 16,\ \bar{x}_2 = 25,\ s_2^2 = 20;\ \bar{x}_3 = 15,\ s_3^2 = 24.$$

Test at the 1% significance level the hypothesis that soil type has no effect on corrosion.

4. Each of four instructors, A, B, C, and D, has written a set of instructions for the assembly of a simple mechanical toy. Twelve subjects are given the instructions, copies of each set being given to three subjects. After a period for study, each is given a set of parts to assemble. The assembly times in seconds are given in the table. Test at the 5% significance level the hypothesis that the 4 sets of instructions are equally effective.

A	B	C	D
80	100	70	140
150	120	80	120
100	150	100	120

5. The accompanying table gives results of carbon analysis, by chemists in five different laboratories, of benzoic acid, two samples each. Test at the 1% significance level for significant differences among analysts.

Analyst	First sample	Second sample
A	69.03	68.96
B	69.18	69.22
C	69.58	69.43
D	68.79	68.98
E	69.23	69.17

(For more complete data and discussion in this example, see YOUDEN, W. J. "Multiple Factor Experiments in Analytical Chemistry," *Analytical Chemistry*, Vol. 20 (1948), pp. 1136–1140. Data in the table is a partial listing of results reported by POWE, F. W. *Industrial Engineering Chemistry, Anal. Ed.*, Vol. 11 (1939), pp. 660–673.)

6. Each entry in the table represents the average percentage of scab on potatoes in plots of land receiving the specified treatment, I, II, or III, in the spring or fall.

	I	II	III
Spring	17	18	14
Fall	10	16	6

Test, at the 10% significance level, each of the hypotheses: (a) the treatments have the same effect on inhibition of scab formation; (b) it makes no difference whether the treatment is applied in the spring or in the fall. State the assumptions inherent in the model you use.

7. Each entry in the table represents the average reaction time of 20 men or 20 women to a light signal or to a sound signal (any resemblance to reaction times of living persons is purely coincidental).

(a) Show that no matter how low the significance level, you must reject both the hypothesis that people react equally quickly to light and sound signals and the hypothesis that men and women react at the same speed.

(b) What estimate of σ^2 is given by the residual sum of squares? Comment on whether or not you would expect this to occur if the data had been obtained by actual experiment.

	Light	Sound
Women	0.8	1.2
Men	0.4	0.8

8. In the table are given measured tensile strengths of samples of Ameripol SN and Hevea rubber subjected to different curing periods.

(a) Test at the 1% significance level the hypothesis that length of curing period has no effect on tensile strength.

(b) Assume the samples for a given column come from one mix of rubber; those for different columns necessarily come from different mixes. Which of the assumptions you used for the analysis of this two-factor experiment do you consider most suspect?

Cure, Minutes 280°F.	Tensile, lb./sq. in.			
	Ameripol	Hevea rubber		
	SN	Y	B	TB
15	2840	2540	2900	2490
30	3550	3150	3970	3410
45	3440	3850	3810	3210

(Data are a small part of data given in a paper in the April, 1956, issue of *Industrial and Engineering Chemistry;* cf. YOUDEN, W. J. "Statistical Design," *Industrial and Engineering Chemistry*, Vol. 48 (June, 1956), p. 104A, for discussion.)

9. The table gives tensile strengths of a corner area (CO), a central area (CE), and areas on two sides (S_1 and S_2) of each of 4 sheets of 0.025 gage titanium alloy. Test at the 5% significance level the hypothesis that the tensile strength is independent of position on the sheet (i.e., that the column means are the same).

	Area sampled			
Sheet	CO	CE	S_1	S_2
1	137.1	140.1	141.8	136.1
2	142.2	139.4	139.6	140.8
3	128.0	116.8	132.5	132.2
4	136.6	136.5	140.8	129.0

(*Source:* YOUDEN, W. J. "Testing Uniformity of Sheets and Plates," *Industrial and Engineering Chemistry*, Vol. 49 (August, 1957), p. 71A.)

10. Describe a method of complete randomization for assigning sets of instructions to the subjects in Problem 4.

11. Six of the subjects in Problem 4 were men, six women. Describe a method of randomizing in blocks for assigning sets of instructions to them.

12. An instructor wishes to study the effect of extraneous noise on effectiveness of work requiring extreme concentration. Half of his class of 50 are to be given a test in a quiet room, while the other half are to be given the test in the room directly under the typing class.

(a) Suggest a completely randomized design for this experiment.

(b) Suggest a randomized block design based on grade averages of the students.

13. The typing times in minutes in a particular experiment with 5 typists, 5 work samples, and 5 typewriters, using the Latin Square on page 302 are as follows:

	1	2	3	4	5
1	40	50	30	40	40
2	50	55	35	50	55
3	40	60	40	50	45
4	35	40	30	35	30
5	55	60	45	45	60

Test at the 5% level the hypothesis that the 5 machines are equally fast, that is, that the contributions $T_1, T_2, \cdots, T_5$ of the machines to the mean typing times are all 0.

14. In an experiment to test the equality of 6 means, 5 sample values were taken from each population. The total sum of squares was 160. Assuming the populations normal with equal means and equal standard deviations σ, find 95% confidence limits for σ^2.

15. Carry out the details leading to $\mathbf{A} = \mathbf{B} + \mathbf{C} + \mathbf{D}$ on page 298.

16. Forty-three post-operative hospital patients who required at least four injections in 24 hours for pain relief were the subjects in a comparison of three drugs used for the relief of pain. The comparison was made during peak pain intensities, right after surgery. The number of hours of relief provided by two ampules of one drug was observed for each patient:

Demerol (75 mg.)	Experimental Drug (1 mg.)	Experimental Drug (3 mg.)
2	2	6
6	0	4
4	3	4
13	3	0
5	0	1
8	0	8
4	8	2
6	1	8
7	4	12
6	2	1
8	2	5
12	1	2
4	3	1
4		4
		6
		5

Test the hypothesis that the drugs relieve pain for the same length of time (use the 1% level.)
(*Source:* MEIER, P., FREE, JR., S. M., and JACKSON, G. L. "Reconsideration of Methodology in Studies of Pain Relief," *Biometrics*, Vol. 14 (1958), pp. 330–342.)

17. An experiment at an agricultural experiment station was conducted to compare the ordinary seed drill with a new drill, which was designed to sow more uniformly than is possible with the ordinary drill. The plots were long strips of ground, two adjacent strips being allotted at random to the new drill (N) and the ordinary drill (O); these two adjacent strips form a block with two plots, two plots being allotted at random to N and O. There are 10 blocks. The observed yields of grain at harvest for the 20 plots were:

Block	N	O
1	8.0	5.6
2	8.4	7.4
3	8.0	7.3
4	6.4	6.4
5	8.6	7.5
6	7.7	6.1
7	7.7	6.6
8	5.6	6.0
9	5.6	5.5
10	6.2	5.5

(a) Test the null hypothesis of no difference in grain yield between the old and new drills, the alternative being that there is a difference; use the 1% level.

(b) The new drill is of interest only because it is anticipated that its use will give a larger yield than the old drill. Hence the appropriate alternative to the null hypothesis is that N gives a larger yield than O. How would you test the null hypothesis against the latter alternative? Would you reject the null hypothesis at the .01 level?
(*Source:* WISHART, J. "Statistics in Agricultural Research," *Journal of Royal Statistical Society Supplement*, Vol. 1 (1934), pp. 26–51.)

18. An experiment was designed to distinguish the differential effects on the yield of potatoes (if any) of potash manuring applied as sulphate (S), muriate (M), and low grade salt (L). There were thus three treatments, to which a fourth was added with no potash (O), to insure that an apparent equality in the efficacy of the three forms of potash was not due to non-effectiveness of potash and consequent lack of response. A 4 × 4 (randomized) Latin Square design was used, the 4 rows and 4 columns corresponding to the 4 rows and 4 columns of the rectangular field with 16 rectangular plots in which the potatoes were grown. The particular field layout used and the observed yield in pounds of potatoes per plot are:

The Field

M 444	L 422	O 173	S 398
O 279	S 439	M 423	L 409
L 436	M 428	S 445	O 212
S 453	O 237	L 410	M 393

Test at the 5% level the hypothesis that the effects of the three potash treatments are the same as the effect of no potash. Also, test to see if there was any row effect and if there was any column effect, using the 5% level.
(*Source:* EDEN, T. and FISHER, R. A. "Studies in Crop Variation, VI: Experiments on the Response of the Potato to Potash and Nitrogen"; *Journal of Agricultural Science*, Vol. 19 (1929), pp. 201–213.)

19. In looking for methods to increase the precision with which the atomic weight of iodine is determined, five different silvers were to be compared (silver is used as the standard). In the table are shown 16 determinations of the ratio of the reacting weights of iodine and silver; they involve the chemical combination of a preparation of iodine with the five different preparations of silver. Test at the 5% level the hypothesis that the ratio of iodine to silver does not depend upon which of the five silver preparations is used.

Silvers

A	B	C	D	E
1.76422	1.76441	1.76429	1.76449	1.76455
1.76425	1.76441	1.76420	1.76450	
1.76399	1.76423	1.76437	1.76461	
1.76440	1.76413			
1.76418				

(The data are taken from: YOUDEN, W. J., "Statistics in Analytical Chemistry," *Annals of the New York Academy of Sciences*, Vol. 52 (1950), pp. 815–819.)

20. From each of six retail gasoline pumps each of four inspectors drew five gallons of gas (according to the gauge on the pump). Each inspector measured each "five-gallon" draft that he had drawn, using his standard field gauge, and the difference between his measurement and five gallons (in cubic inches) was recorded:

		Gas Pumps					
		1	2	3	4	5	6
Inspectors:	A	−2	1	0	−1	1	−1
	C	−1	4	0	0	1	2
	E	0	3	−1	2	0	2
	G	−1	1	0	−1	1	1

Test at the 5% level each of the hypotheses:

(a) There is no difference between the four inspectors in the result of their inspection;

(b) There is no difference between the six gas pumps in the amount of gas delivered in a "five-gallon" draft.

(*Source:* YOUDEN, W. J., and JENSEN, M. W. "Performance of Inspectors and Gasoline Pumps." A paper presented before the 38th National Conference on Weights and Measures, Washington, D. C., May 22, 1953.)

21. It has been claimed that any stimulus (e.g. auditory, olfactory, tactile) produces changes in the sensitivity of the dark-adapted human eye. To test this claim an experiment was set up in which a human subject was given a 15-minute period for getting his eyes adapted to the dark and then stimulated with either a loud sound, weak sound, heavy pressure (a weight on the back of the subject's hand), light pressure, or nothing, while reading the *Luckiesh-Moss Low-Contrast Test Chart;* the number of correct responses on the latter test was taken as the measure of sensitivity (to contrasts) of the dark-adapted eye. A 5 × 5 (randomized) Latin Square design was used with 5 subjects, the 5 above-mentioned stimuli as "treatments," and 5 days (only one test per day); contrast sensitivity was the dependent variable.

The particular square used (days are in parentheses) and the observed test scores were:

	Stimulus				
Subject	*Loud Sound*	*Weak Sound*	*Heavy Pressure*	*Light Pressure*	*Nothing*
A	(2) 21	(3) 22	(4) 20	(5) 22	(1) 22
B	(4) 22	(1) 16	(5) 23	(2) 19	(3) 23
C	(1) 14	(5) 14	(2) 23	(3) 24	(4) 20
D	(5) 29	(4) 24	(3) 24	(1) 24	(2) 28
E	(3) 16	(2) 15	(1) 14	(4) 15	(5) 13

Test the hypothesis that these auditory and tactile stimuli have the same effect on contrast sensitivity as no stimulus; use the 5% level.
(*Source:* Chapanis, A., Rouse, R., and Schachter, S. "The Effect of Inter-Sensory Stimulation on Dark Adaptation and Night Vision." *Journal of Experimental Psychology*, Vol. 39 (1949), pp. 425–437.)

22. It is desired to determine if there is any difference in the yield of seed cotton between three planting dates (at a certain locality in Uganda). Four blocks, each divided into three plots of ground, are used. In every block the three planting dates are randomly allocated to three plots. The observed yields of seed cotton in kilograms per plot are:

	Planting Dates		
Blocks	*May 1*	*May 15*	*May 29*
1	3.35	3.86	1.99
2	1.49	2.71	2.89
3	2.44	2.18	1.68
4	2.44	1.95	2.13

Test at the 5% level the null hypothesis that the yield of seed cotton is the same no matter which of the three dates is used for planting.
(Data taken from Anderson, R. L., and Manning, H. L. "An Experimental Design Used to Estimate the Optimum Planting Date for Cotton," *Biometrics*, Vol. 4 (1948), pp. 171–196.)

23. In the biological assay of parathyroid extract, two doses (.125 and .205 cc/Kgm.) of a standard preparation (having known potencies) were to be compared with the same two doses of a new preparation (having unknown potencies) with respect to their effects on the final serum calcium level in dogs. (Call these 4 treatments S_1, S_2, N_1, N_2 respectively.) One treatment was administered once to each dog (4 dogs) over 4 treatment periods, using a 4 × 4 Latin Square design. The particular Latin Square used and the observed values of mg.-per cent serum calcium were:

Day When Dose Injected

Dogs	*3/15*	*3/25*	*4/5*	*4/15*
17	S_1 14.2	N_1 14.1	S_2 15.0	N_2 14.4
18	N_1 13.0	S_1 13.4	N_2 13.8	S_2 14.0
19	N_2 15.8	S_2 16.0	N_1 15.0	S_1 15.4
20	S_2 15.2	N_2 16.2	S_1 15.0	N_1 15.3

Test at the 5% level the null hypothesis of no difference between treatments.
(*Source:* Bliss, C. I., and Rose, C. L. "The Assay of Parathyroid Extract from the Serum Calcium of Dogs," *The American Journal of Hygiene*, Vol. 31 (1940), pp. 79–98.)

★CHAPTER
16

Other Sampling Methods

105. Sampling from a Finite Group. We continue in this section to use the term "experiment" in the broad sense in which we have interpreted it heretofore. For example, you may be planning a public opinion poll or a marketing survey; or you may be interested in the weights of the guinea pigs in your laboratory. Suppose there are N items, people or guinea pigs, available to you. In your experiment, you plan to choose one, measure it, choose another, measure it, etc., until in all n measurements have been made, i.e., until a sample of size n has been taken. Let $\mathbf{x}_i$ denote the result you will obtain as the ith measurement, $i = 1, 2, \cdots, n$.

Let $\mathbf{x}$ denote the random variable: "result of a measurement on an item to be chosen at random from the group of N items." If your random variables $\mathbf{x}_i$, $i = 1, 2, \cdots, n$, are to form a *random sample of size n* from the population induced by x (pp. 101ff.), they must be *independent*, and each must have the same probability distribution as $\mathbf{x}$. That is, each item must be selected at random from the whole group, independently of items selected previously. This is "sampling with replacement"; it involves the possibility of measuring the same item more than once.

The theory of *random sampling*, or "sampling with replacement," is simpler than that of "sampling without replacement," which we shall consider very briefly now. However, unless N is large compared with n, it is somewhat inefficient; you are not gaining the greatest possible information in your n measurements if two are made on the same item. If N is large relative to n, the results of the two theories nearly coincide, and it is customary to analyze the data as if it were obtained through random sampling, even if it was in fact obtained by sampling without replacement.

We may remark in passing that if $n = N$ then you have complete information about your group. You require no statistical analysis to set up confidence intervals for the mean, for you *know* the mean; no estimation of the proportion of items failing to satisfy certain criteria is necessary, for you know this proportion.

The finite set of N items from which we have in mind to draw n without replacement forms the basic set S of a probability space, in which every item is an elementary event, every combination of items an event, and in which the probability of an event containing k items is k/N. Our population random variable $\mathbf{x}$ is a random variable defined on this probability space. Suppose $\mathbf{x}$ has the value a_1 at each of b_1 items among the N, and, in general, the value a_j at each of b_j items, $j = 1, 2, \cdots, p$. Then the population from which we shall take a sample of size n without replacement has p elementary events of positive probability, the real numbers $a_1, a_2, \cdots, a_p$. The probability $b_j/N = Pr\{\mathbf{x} = a_j\}$ is associated with the elementary event $a_j, j = 1, 2, \cdots, p$; we have $\sum_{j=1}^{p} b_j = N$. Let

$$\mu = E(\mathbf{x}) = \frac{1}{N} \sum_{j=1}^{p} a_j b_j, \text{ and } \sigma^2 = V(\mathbf{x}) = \frac{1}{N} \sum_{j=1}^{p} a_j^2 b_j - \mu^2.$$

Elementary events in the sample space are again ordered n-tuples of real numbers $(x_1, x_2, \cdots, x_n)$, each x_i coming from a replica of the population, as they were (cf. pp.101ff.) for random sampling (with replacement). The sample random variables are defined as before on the sample space: $\mathbf{x}_1$ has the value x_1 at the elementary event $(x_1, x_2, \cdots, x_n)$, $\mathbf{x}_2$ the value x_2 at this event, etc. The difference lies in the assignment of probabilities to the elementary events. Before, we wanted to assign probabilities so that the sample random variables were independent and identically distributed. Here, they should clearly not be independent. For example, the conditional probability of obtaining a given value on the second draw, given the result of the first, must depend on what was drawn the first time, if there is no replacement. We need to assign probabilities to the elementary events so that if $(x_1, x_2, \cdots, x_n)$ is an elementary event, then its probability is

$$\begin{aligned} Pr\{\mathbf{x}_1 = x_1, \mathbf{x}_2 = x_2, \cdots, \mathbf{x}_n = x_n\} &= P\left[\bigcap_{i=1}^{n} \{\mathbf{x}_i = x_i\}\right] \\ &= Pr\{\mathbf{x}_1 = x_1\} Pr\{\mathbf{x}_2 = x_2 \mid \mathbf{x}_1 = x_1\} \cdots \\ &\qquad Pr\{\mathbf{x}_n = x_n \mid \mathbf{x}_1 = x_1, \cdots, \mathbf{x}_{n-1} = x_{n-1}\}. \end{aligned}$$

Given specific values for $x_1, x_2, \cdots, x_n$, one can readily calculate what each factor should be, though it is not convenient to set down a general formula. For example, $Pr\{\mathbf{x}_1 = a_j\} = b_j/N$; $Pr\{\mathbf{x}_2 = a_k \mid \mathbf{x}_1 = a_j\} = b_k/(N - 1)$ if $k \neq j$, $Pr\{\mathbf{x}_2 = a_j \mid \mathbf{x}_1 = a_j\} = (b_j - 1)/(N - 1)$, etc.

We shall not develop here the theory of sampling from a finite group without replacement beyond the calculation of the expectation and variance of the sample mean. (But see "sampling inspection," page 336. For further development and references to the literature, cf., e.g., [3], pp. 331, 515, 523; [22], Section 8.5.)

The distribution of $\mathbf{x}_1$, the first sample random variable, is clearly the same as that of $\mathbf{x}$; but so is the (marginal) distribution of each of the sample random variables. To understand clearly why this is so, let us compute, for example, $Pr\{\mathbf{x}_2 = a_j\}$ $(j = 1, 2, \cdots, p)$. Since the events $\{\mathbf{x}_1 = a_1\}$, $\cdots$, $\{\mathbf{x}_1 = a_p\}$ are mutually exclusive and exhaustive, we have

$$\begin{aligned} Pr\{\mathbf{x}_2 = a_j\} &= \textstyle\sum_{k=1}^{p} Pr\{\mathbf{x}_1 = a_k, x_2 = a_j\} \\ &= \textstyle\sum_{k=1}^{p} Pr\{\mathbf{x}_2 = a_j | \mathbf{x}_1 = a_k\} Pr\{\mathbf{x}_1 = a_k\} \\ &= \textstyle\sum_{k=1, k\neq j}^{p} \left(\dfrac{b_j}{N-1}\right)\left(\dfrac{b_k}{N}\right) + \left(\dfrac{b_j - 1}{N-1}\right)\left(\dfrac{b_j}{N}\right) \\ &= \dfrac{b_j}{N(N-1)} [\textstyle\sum_{k=1, k\neq j}^{p} b_k + b_j - 1] \\ &= \dfrac{b_j(N-1)}{N(N-1)} = \dfrac{b_j}{N}, \end{aligned}$$

since $\sum_{k=1}^{p} b_k = N$. Hence the probability function of $\mathbf{x}_2$ is that of $\mathbf{x}$; similarly, *each of the sample random variables has the same distribution as* $\mathbf{x}$. This becomes intuitively clear if we reflect that, for example, $Pr\{\mathbf{x}_2 = a_j\}$ is the unconditional probability that $\mathbf{x}_2$ will be equal to a_j. In computing this probability, we must assume the result of the first draw unknown, the result of the second draw then being any of the N items.

It follows that $E(\mathbf{x}_i) = E(\mathbf{x}) = \mu$, $i = 1, 2, \cdots, n$; and

$$E(\bar{\mathbf{x}}) = \frac{1}{n} \textstyle\sum_{i=1}^{n} E(\mathbf{x}_i) = \dfrac{1}{n} \textstyle\sum_{i=1}^{n} \mu = \mu;$$

so that

▶ *the expectation of the sample mean is equal to the population mean.*

You can verify that not only do the sample random variables have the same probability distribution, that of $\mathbf{x}$, but each pair (triple, quadruple, $\cdots$) has the same joint distribution as every other (ordered) pair (triple, quadruple, $\cdots$); that is, the joint probability function of the pair $(\mathbf{x}_1, \mathbf{x}_2)$ is the same as the joint probability function of any other pair $(\mathbf{x}_j, \mathbf{x}_k)$, with $j < k$. We shall compute cov $(\mathbf{x}_1, \mathbf{x}_2)$, which will be equal to cov $(\mathbf{x}_j, \mathbf{x}_k)$ for $j = 1, 2, \cdots, n - 1$; $k = j + 1, \cdots, n$. Consider first

$$E(\mathbf{x}_1\mathbf{x}_2) = \sum_{j=1}^{p} \sum_{k=1}^{p} a_j a_k \, Pr\{\mathbf{x}_1 = a_j, \mathbf{x}_2 = a_k\}$$

$$= \sum_{j=1}^{p} \sum_{k=1}^{p} a_j a_k \, Pr\{\mathbf{x}_2 = a_k | \mathbf{x}_1 = a_j\} Pr\{\mathbf{x}_1 = a_j\}$$

$$= \sum_{j=1}^{p} \sum_{k=1, k\neq j}^{p} a_j a_k \left(\frac{b_k}{N - 1}\right)\left(\frac{b_j}{N}\right) + \sum_{j=1}^{p} a_j^2 \left(\frac{b_j - 1}{N - 1}\right)\left(\frac{b_j}{N}\right)$$

$$= \frac{1}{N(N-1)} \sum_{j=1}^{p} \sum_{k=1}^{p} a_j a_k b_k b_j - \frac{1}{N(N-1)} \sum_{j=1}^{p} a_j^2 b_j^2$$

$$+ \frac{1}{N(N-1)} \sum_{j=1}^{p} a_j^2 (b_j^2 - b_j)$$

$$= \frac{N}{N-1} \left(\sum_{j=1}^{p} a_j b_j/N\right)\left(\sum_{k=1}^{p} a_k b_k/N\right) - \frac{1}{N-1} \sum_{j=1}^{p} a_j^2 b_j/N$$

$$= \frac{N}{N-1} [E(\mathbf{x})]^2 - \frac{1}{N-1} E(\mathbf{x}^2).$$

Now $E(\mathbf{x}) = \mu$, $E(\mathbf{x}^2) = \sigma^2 + \mu^2$, so that

$$E(\mathbf{x}_1\mathbf{x}_2) = \frac{N}{N-1} \mu^2 - \frac{1}{N-1} (\sigma^2 + \mu^2)$$

$$= \mu^2 - \frac{\sigma^2}{N-1}.$$

Now

$$\operatorname{cov}(\mathbf{x}_1,\mathbf{x}_2) = E[(\mathbf{x}_1 - \mu)(\mathbf{x}_2 - \mu)] = E(\mathbf{x}_1\mathbf{x}_2) - \mu^2$$

since $E(\mathbf{x}_1) = E(\mathbf{x}_2) = \mu$, so that

$$\operatorname{cov}(\mathbf{x}_1,\mathbf{x}_2) = -\sigma^2/(N-1).$$

The correlation coefficient of $\mathbf{x}_1,\mathbf{x}_2$ is

▶ $$\rho = \frac{1}{\sigma^2} \operatorname{cov}(\mathbf{x}_1,\mathbf{x}_2) = -1/(N-1),$$

so that $\mathbf{x}_1,\mathbf{x}_2$ (or any other two sample random variables) are negatively correlated, though only slightly so if N is large.

Now let us compute the variance of the sample mean, $\bar{\mathbf{x}}$. We have

$$E(\bar{\mathbf{x}}^2) = E\left(\frac{1}{n} \sum_{i=1}^{n} \mathbf{x}_i\right)^2 = E\left[\left(\frac{1}{n} \sum_{i=1}^{n} \mathbf{x}_i\right)\left(\frac{1}{n} \sum_{j=1}^{n} \mathbf{x}_j\right)\right],$$

$$E(\bar{\mathbf{x}}^2) = \frac{1}{n^2} \sum_{i=1}^{n} \sum_{j=1}^{n} E(\mathbf{x}_i\mathbf{x}_j).$$

Now $E(\mathbf{x}_i^2) = \sigma^2 + \mu^2$, while $E(\mathbf{x}_i\mathbf{x}_j) = \mu^2 - \sigma^2/(N-1)$ if $i \neq j$. Hence

$$E(\bar{\mathbf{x}}^2) = \frac{1}{n^2}\sum_{i=1}^{n}\left\{\sum_{j\neq i}\left(\mu^2 - \frac{\sigma^2}{N-1}\right) + \sigma^2 + \mu^2\right\}$$

$$= \frac{1}{n^2}\sum_{i=1}^{n}\left\{(n-1)\left(\mu^2 - \frac{\sigma^2}{N-1}\right) + \sigma^2 + \mu^2\right\}$$

$$= \mu^2 + \frac{\sigma^2}{n}\left(1 - \frac{n-1}{N-1}\right).$$

Therefore

$$E(\bar{\mathbf{x}}^2) - [E(\bar{\mathbf{x}})]^2 = \frac{\sigma^2}{n}\left(1 - \frac{n-1}{N-1}\right):$$

▶ $$V(\bar{\mathbf{x}}) = \frac{N-n}{N-1}\cdot\frac{\sigma^2}{n}.$$

If we let α denote the *sampling fraction*, $\alpha = n/N$, and if n and N are moderately large we have

$$V(\bar{\mathbf{x}}) \doteq \frac{\sigma^2}{n}(1-\alpha);$$

the factor $1 - \alpha$ is sometimes called the *finite sampling correction* for the variance of the mean, since in random sampling (with replacement) the formula for the variance of the sample mean is σ^2/n.

Let us compute also the expectation of the sample variance:

$$E(\mathbf{s}^2) = E\left[\frac{1}{n}\sum_{i=1}^{n}\mathbf{x}_i^2 - \bar{\mathbf{x}}^2\right] = \frac{1}{n}\sum_{i=1}^{n}E(\mathbf{x}_i^2) - E(\bar{\mathbf{x}}^2)$$

$$= \frac{1}{n}\sum_{i=1}^{n}(\mu^2 + \sigma^2) - \left[\mu^2 + \frac{\sigma^2}{n}\left(1 - \frac{n-1}{N-1}\right)\right]$$

$$= \sigma^2 - \frac{\sigma^2}{n}\left(1 - \frac{n-1}{N-1}\right) = \frac{n-1}{n}\frac{N}{N-1}\sigma^2.$$

Thus

▶ $\dfrac{n}{n-1}\dfrac{N-1}{N}\mathbf{s}^2$ is an unbiased estimator of the population variance, and $\dfrac{N-n}{N}\dfrac{\mathbf{s}^2}{n-1}$ is an unbiased estimator of the variance of the sample mean.

It can be shown that here also the distributions of

$$(\bar{\mathbf{x}} - \mu_{\bar{x}})/\sigma_{\bar{x}} = (\bar{\mathbf{x}} - \mu)\sqrt{n}/\sigma\sqrt{1-\alpha}$$

and

$$(\bar{\mathbf{x}} - \mu)\sqrt{N(n-1)}/\mathbf{s}\sqrt{N-n}$$

are approximately normal (0,1) when n and $N - n$ are both large.

EXAMPLE. You are editor of the "Hootin' Holler," monthly publication of the students of a small college, with 500 students. You wish to poll the student body on the question: "Should we petition for inclusion in the Big Fourteen football schedule?" but do not wish to contact more than 100 students. Using a table of random numbers (discarding those that appear a second time) with the student directory, you take a sample (without replacement) of size $n = 100$; here $N = 500$. Your basic probability space has 500 elementary events, each with probability 1/500. Let $\mathbf{x}$ denote the random variable which has, at each elementary event corresponding to a student favoring the proposal, the value 1, and at each other the value 0. (We disregard difficulties occasioned by failure to contact some students, obviously facetious responses, etc.) The population mean $\mu = E(\mathbf{x})$ is then the true proportion of students favoring the proposal. Suppose you find that 31 of the 100 polled favor the proposal. You then have

$$\bar{x} = 0.31,\ s^2 = \frac{1}{100}\sum_{i=1}^{100} x_i^2 - \bar{x}^2 = (0.31) - (0.31)^2.$$

The square root of the unbiased estimator of the variance of the sample mean developed above is $[(N - n)s^2/N(n - 1)]^{1/2} = 0.042$. Thus 95% confidence limits for the true proportion of students favoring the proposal are approximately $0.31 - 2(0.04) = 0.23$ and $0.31 + 2(0.04) = 0.39$.

106. Stratified Random Sampling. When it is possible to divide a population into subpopulations whose variances are smaller than that of the original population, one can use the technique of stratified random sampling to obtain a more precise estimate of the population mean than the sample mean of a random sample. For example, suppose you are engaged to plan a survey, one purpose of which is to determine the fraction of his income which the "average" married American under 40 years of age living in a city of over one million pays for housing. The problem of how to divide the population into subgroups relatively homogeneous with respect to the quantity under observation is by no means a trivial one. However, let us suppose you have decided on such a division, into M subgroups, perhaps after study of appropriate publications of the Bureau of the Census.

Let p_j denote the proportion of the whole group which fall into the jth subgroup ($j = 1, 2, \cdots, M$); let μ_j denote the average proportion of income spent for housing by members of the jth subgroup. Suppose you plan to take a random sample (with replacement) of size n_j from the jth subgroup, $j = 1, 2, \cdots, M$. For $i = 1, 2, \cdots, n_j$, let $\mathbf{x}_{ji}$ denote the proportion of his income which the ith individual chosen from the jth subgroup pays for housing. Thus $\mathbf{x}_{ji}$ is the ith sample random variable of a sample of size n_j from the population determined by the random variable $\mathbf{x}_j$: "proportion of his income spent for housing by an individual selected at random from the jth subgroup." Now consider, as over-all sample mean (see Problem 12, page 325),

$$\bar{\mathbf{x}} = \sum_{j=1}^{M} p_j \bar{\mathbf{x}}_j,$$

where

$$\bar{\mathbf{x}}_j = \frac{1}{n_j} \sum_{i=1}^{n_j} \mathbf{x}_{ji}.$$

We have

$$E(\bar{\mathbf{x}}) = \sum_{j=1}^{M} p_j E(\bar{\mathbf{x}}_j) = \sum_{j=1}^{M} p_j \mu_j.$$

Thus the expectation of the weighted average of the sample means is the weighted average of the population means; we shall call this μ:

$$\mu = \sum_{j=1}^{M} p_j \mu_j.$$

Further, since the random variables $\bar{\mathbf{x}}_j$ are independent, we have

$$V(\bar{\mathbf{x}}) = \sum_{j=1}^{M} V(p_j \bar{\mathbf{x}}_j) = \sum_{j=1}^{M} p_j^2 V(\bar{\mathbf{x}}_j);$$

but $\bar{\mathbf{x}}_j$ is the sample mean of a sample of size n_j from a population with standard deviation σ_j, so that $V(\bar{\mathbf{x}}_j) = \sigma_j^2/n_j$. Hence

$$V(\bar{\mathbf{x}}) = \sum_{j=1}^{M} p_j^2 \sigma_j^2 / n_j.$$

Let us now compare the precision of the estimate $\bar{\mathbf{x}}$ with that of the sample mean of a random sample of size

$$n = \sum_{j=1}^{M} n_j$$

from the original population. Let $\mathbf{x}$ denote the random variable: "fraction of his income spent for housing of an individual chosen at random from the original (undivided) group." Let $f(x) = Pr\{\mathbf{x} = x\}$ denote the probability function of $\mathbf{x}$, and $f_j(x) = Pr\{\mathbf{x}_j = x\}$ the probability function of $\mathbf{x}_j$, $j = 1, 2, \cdots, M$. Let A_j denote the event: "the individual to be selected at random from the complete original group will be selected from the jth subgroup," $j = 1, 2, \cdots, M$. Then $P(A_j) = p_j$ $(j = 1, 2, \cdots, M)$. The event $\{\mathbf{x} = x\}$ can be written:

$$\{\mathbf{x} = x\} = \bigcup_{j=1}^{M} [A_j \cap \{\mathbf{x} = x\}].$$

By the law of total probability,

$$f(x) = Pr\{\mathbf{x} = x\} = \sum_{j=1}^{M} P(A_j \cap \{\mathbf{x} = x\}).$$

By the law of compound probability,

$$P(A_j \cap \{\mathbf{x} = x\}) = P(\{\mathbf{x} = x\} \mid A_j)P(A_j).$$

But

$$P(\{\mathbf{x} = x\} \mid A_j) = f_j(x) = Pr\{\mathbf{x}_j = x\},$$

and $P(A_j) = p_j$, so that

$$f(x) = \sum_{j=1}^{M} p_j f_j(x).$$

Now we can compute $E(\mathbf{x})$ and $V(\mathbf{x})$:

$$E(\mathbf{x}) = \sum_x x\, f(x) = \sum_{j=1}^{M} p_j \sum_x x\, f_j(x) = \sum_{j=1}^{M} p_j E(\mathbf{x}_j)$$

$$= \sum_{j=1}^{M} p_j \mu_j = \mu;$$

$$E(\mathbf{x}^2) = \sum_x x^2 f(x) = \sum_{j=1}^{M} p_j \sum_x x^2 f_j(x) = \sum_{j=1}^{M} p_j E(\mathbf{x}_j^2)$$

$$= \sum_{j=1}^{M} p_j(\sigma_j^2 + \mu_j^2),$$

so that

$$V(\mathbf{x}) = E(\mathbf{x}^2) - [E(\mathbf{x})]^2 = \sum_{j=1}^{M} p_j\sigma_j^2 + \sum_{j=1}^{M} p_j\mu_j^2 - \left(\sum_{j=1}^{M} p_j\mu_j\right)^2,$$

or

$$\sigma^2 = \sum_{j=1}^{M} p_j\sigma_j^2 + \sum_{j=1}^{M} p_j(\mu_j - \mu)^2,$$

where σ^2 is the variance of the original population. Thus the variance of the population associated with the original undivided group is the weighted average of the variances of the subgroups *plus* the weighted average of the squared deviations from the over-all population mean μ of the means of the subpopulations. We see the over-all variance is certainly at least as large as the weighted average of the subpopulation variances, and is in fact larger, unless the subpopulations all have the same mean.

We now consider two distinct possibilities for the choice of the sample sizes n_j. The first is *proportional sampling:* we take the n_j proportional to the probabilities p_j,

$$n_j = np_j.$$

In this case

$$V(\bar{\mathbf{x}}) = \sum_{j=1}^{M} p_j^2\sigma_j^2/n_j = \frac{1}{n}\sum_{j=1}^{M} p_j\sigma_j^2.$$

Since

$$\sigma^2 = V(\mathbf{x}) = \sum_{j=1}^{M} p_j\sigma_i^2 + \sum_{j=1}^{M} p_j(\mu_j - \mu)^2$$

if we were to take a random sample of size n from the original population, its sample mean would have variance

$$\frac{\sigma^2}{n} = \frac{1}{n}\sum_{j=1}^{M} p_j\sigma_j^2 + \frac{1}{n}\sum_{j=1}^{M} p_j(\mu_j - \mu)^2.$$

Therefore *the use of stratified sampling with proportional sampling results in a reduction of the variance of the sample mean by the amount*

$$\frac{1}{n}\sum_{j=1}^{M} p_j(\mu_j - \mu)^2.$$

Evidently there would be no reduction if $\mu_j = \mu$ for $j = 1, 2, \cdots, M$; the *reduction depends on the variation of the subpopulation means.*

Now we consider the problem of *optimal allocation* of the sample: how should the sample sizes be chosen so as to obtain the greatest possible reduction in the variance of the sample mean? The problem is to choose the n_j, $j = 1, 2, \cdots, M$, so as to minimize

$$V(\bar{\mathbf{x}}) = \sum_{j=1}^{M} p_j^2\sigma_j^2/n_j,$$

given their sum $n = \sum_{j=1}^{M} n_j$. Of course the n_j are integers; but we shall obtain an approximate answer if we treat them as continuous variables. The values of the variables n_j which yield a minimum for $V(\bar{\mathbf{x}})$ will render its differential $dV \equiv 0$:

$$dV \equiv -\sum_{j=1}^{M} (p_j\sigma_j/n_j)^2 dn_j \equiv 0.$$

Further, in order for the sum $\sum_{j=1}^{M} n_j$ to be the given constant n, we must have

$$\sum_{j=1}^{M} dn_j \equiv 0.$$

These two equations will be satisfied identically in the variables $dn_1, dn_2, \cdots, dn_M$ if and only if both the second is satisfied and $p_j\sigma_j/n_j$ is a constant, say k. Then $n_j = p_j\sigma_j/k$, and in order that we may have $\sum_{j=1}^{M} n_j = n$, we must have $\sum_{j=1}^{M} p_j\sigma_j/k = n$, or $k = \frac{1}{n}\sum_{j=1}^{M} p_j\sigma_j$. Thus (approximately) the sample sizes which minimize the variance of the sample mean are

$$n_j = \frac{np_j\sigma_j}{\sum_{j=1}^{M} p_j\sigma_j}, \quad j = 1, 2, \cdots, M;$$

they are proportional, not to the probabilities p_j alone, but to the products $p_j\sigma_j$. In general, of course, the σ_j are not known; but if they can be estimated fairly accurately, this choice of sample sizes should result in a further improvement over the method of proportional sampling. Indeed, if it were possible to choose the sample sizes n_j precisely proportional to the products $p_j\sigma_j$, then we should have

$$V(\bar{\mathbf{x}}) = \sum_{j=1}^M p_j^2\sigma_j^2/n_j = \frac{1}{n}(\sum_{j=1}^M p_j\sigma_j)^2$$

$$= \frac{1}{n}\sum_{j=1}^M p_j\sigma_j^2 - \frac{1}{n}\sum_{j=1}^M p_j(\sigma_j - \bar{\sigma})^2,$$

where $\bar{\sigma} = \sum_{j=1}^M p_j\sigma_j$. The first term on the right of the last expression for $V(\bar{\mathbf{x}})$ is the variance of the sample mean for proportional sampling. Thus the reduction in the variance of $\bar{\mathbf{x}}$ in going from proportional sampling to optimal sampling would be

$$\frac{1}{n}\sum_{j=1}^M p_j(\sigma_j - \bar{\sigma})^2.$$

In the example above, the random variable $\mathbf{x}$ was defined on an elementary probability space, and was necessarily discrete, as were the random variables $\mathbf{x}_j$, $j = 1, 2, \cdots, M$. The results obtained, however, are still valid if the original group is infinite, and if the random variables are continuous. The proportions p_j must be interpreted as probabilities: $p_j = P(A_j)$, the probability that an individual chosen at random from the group will belong to the jth subgroup ($j = 1, 2, \cdots, M$). The only changes that need be made arise in connection with the use of the probability functions $f(x), f_1(x), \cdots, f_M(x)$, which must be replaced by probability density functions, as well as certain sums by integrals.

In the discussion above, we assumed the sampling from each subpopulation was random (with replacement). If each subpopulation is finite and if the sampling is done without replacement, some of the formulas must be changed in accordance with the preceding section.

PROBLEMS

1. A random sample of 50 men is taken without replacement from a group of 200. If their mean score on an aptitude test is 70, with a sample standard deviation 20, find an 80% confidence interval for the mean score of the whole group (if all were given the test).

2. The central parts depot of the company where you are employed has a stock of 200 of a certain part with mean life 40 days and standard deviation 10 days. If you withdraw 50 of these parts, what number of days will their mean life exceed with probability 0.99?

3. Suppose you choose, at random but without replacement, 150 students from a student body of 800, and find that 90 of them favor the establishment of an annual beauty contest. If in fact opinion were evenly divided on this question, approximately what would be the probability that in such a sample 90 or more would favor the proposal?

4. Newly installed equipment produces 60% of the total output of a small electrical gadget, with half the standard deviation of that produced by the older equipment. You are sampling to determine the over-all mean life.

(a) What increase in precision would you achieve by using proportional sampling instead of random sampling from the entire output, if the mean life is the same for both?

(b) What would be the ratio of standard deviation of estimator for random sampling to that for stratified sampling with optimal allocation, if the mean life is the same for both?

5. Does the *relative* reduction in variance from random sampling to proportional sampling depend on the sample size? From proportional sampling to optimal allocation?

6. Suppose each subpopulation has the same standard deviation, σ. How large must be the weighted average of the squared deviations of subpopulation means from the over-all mean, if proportional sampling will involve a standard deviation of the sample mean only one half of that for random sampling?

7. You are conducting, for the dean's office, an investigation of the study habits of students in your school. You decide on a sampling plan (with replacement) stratified by sex. You will ask each student his or her estimate of the average number of hours spent per week in study. You believe that with respect to this character, the women are more nearly homogeneous than the men, and estimate the standard deviation for the women as 2/3 of that for the men. There are 3 times as many men in your school as women.

(a) If you plan to ask 200 students, how many should be men and how many women, if you use proportional sampling?

(b) If your estimate of the relative variances is correct, how many of each sex would you ask under optimal allocation? How much more precise would your result be than with proportional sampling, if the standard deviation for women is 2 hours, and that for men is 3 hours?

(c) If the mean for women is 10 hours and the standard deviation 2 hours, and if the mean for men is 12 with standard deviation 3 hours, what would be the gain in precision obtained by using proportional sampling instead of random sampling from the whole group of students?

8. What relative error is involved in the use of the formula $\sigma/\sqrt{n}$ for the standard deviation of the mean, if in fact the sampling is without replacement from a finite population containing 50 members, and the sample size is 20?

***9.** Five fryers in your pen have weights in pounds: 4, 3, 5, 5, 4. You plan to eat them one at a time, catching each time the first one to come to hand. Assuming agility independent of weight, find the equation of the regression line of $\mathbf{y}$, the weight of the last one you will catch, on $\mathbf{x}$, the weight of the first one you will catch.

NOTE. Requires work on regression, pp. 208–223.

10. A group contains m subgroups with N_j members in the jth subgroup ($j = 1, 2, \cdots, m$). From the jth subgroup you take a sample of size n_j ($j = 1, 2, \cdots, m$) *without replacement.* Let $p_1, p_2, \cdots, p_m$ be m numbers whose sum is 1, and let $\bar{\mathbf{x}}_j$ denote the mean of the sample from the jth population. Define $\bar{\mathbf{x}} = \sum_{j=1}^{m} p_j \bar{\mathbf{x}}_j$.

(a) Find $E(\bar{\mathbf{x}})$, $V(\bar{\mathbf{x}})$.

(b) Determine the numbers $p_1, p_2, \cdots, p_m$ so that $\bar{\mathbf{x}}$ is an unbiased estimator of the over-all population mean μ, and so that $\bar{\mathbf{x}}$ will necessarily be equal to μ when $n_1 = N_1, n_2 = N_2, \cdots, n_m = N_m$.

11. Suppose you play the following game with your young nephew. You hold a sack containing b_j bills of denomination $a_j, j = 1, 2, \cdots, p$, with $a_1 < a_2 < \cdots < a_p$, and $\sum_{j=1}^{p} b_j = N$. You allow him 2 draws from the sack. After each draw he returns the bill to the sack if its denomination is a_r or smaller, but otherwise keeps it.

(a) Show that his expected gain is

$$\lambda \left[2 - \frac{1}{N-1} \sum_{i=1}^{r} \frac{b_i}{N} \right], \quad \text{where } \lambda = \frac{1}{N} \sum_{i=r+1}^{p} a_j b_j$$

is his expected gain on the first draw.

(b) What is his expected gain if there are in the sack 5 one-dollar bills, 5 five-dollar bills, and 1 ten-dollar bill, and if you require him to return one-dollar bills?

12. In the stratified sampling situation, show that $\bar{\mathbf{x}} = \sum_{j=1}^{M} p_j \bar{\mathbf{x}}_j$ is the maximum likelihood estimator of μ if $\bar{\mathbf{x}}_j$ is the maximum likelihood estimator of μ_j, $j = 1, 2, \cdots, M$.

107. Sequential Sampling. Satisfied users, as well as its promoters, claim that sequential testing of hypotheses can result in considerable savings, through reducing the number of sample values required to attain a given precision. The essential idea is that after each sample value is taken (or after a certain number of sample values are taken) the investigator decides whether to continue the experiment, or whether he is able, already at that stage, to reject either the hypothesis or its alternative.

A typical application of the idea of sequential sampling yields a test of a simple hypothesis $\theta = \theta_0$ against a simple alternative $\theta = \theta_1$ ([10], Chapter 15; [18], [9], Chapter 7; [21], Chapter 7; [8], Chapter 3; [22]). Suppose we consider again the playful monarch and his fearful, hopeful subject (page 250). If you have studied the section in which the subject's plight was discussed, you will recall that in this story the monarch hands his subject a coin and states (he is known not to lie) that either it is balanced or the probability of throwing heads is 0.6. The subject is required to test by tossing, and then to state which alternative is correct. The reward for a correct statement is to be 100 gold pieces. The penalty for calling the coin unbalanced if in fact it is balanced is to be very severe; the penalty for the other error is to be relatively mild. The subject sets up the hypothesis H_0: $\theta = \theta_0 = 0.5$, to be tested at, he decides, the 5% significance level. That is, he wishes to set up a test of the hypothesis H_0 against the alternative H_1: $\theta = \theta_1 = 0.6$ which will yield a probability, if the coin is balanced, 0.05 that he will falsely call the coin unbalanced.

In the earlier treatment, the subject was allowed 50 tosses of the coin, and we found that using the one-tail test his probability, if the coin is unbalanced, of falsely accepting the hypothesis $p = 0.5$ was 0.59. Let us now consider a sequential test. Let us denote as before the probability function of the population random variable by $f(x;\theta)$, so that

$$f(x;\theta) = \theta^x(1-\theta)^{1-x} \quad \text{for } x = 0, 1,$$

$$f(x;\theta) = 0 \quad \text{for all other } x$$

is the probability function of the random variable **x** which might be described as the number of heads which will turn up on a single toss of the coin. The joint probability function of the sample random variables in a sample of size n is

$$\prod_{i=1}^{n} f(x_i;\theta).$$

We consider the likelihood ratio (this ratio is related to, but different from, the likelihood ratio discussed on pages 261 ff.)

$$\lambda_n = \prod_{i=1}^{n} \frac{f(x_i;\theta_1)}{f(x_i;\theta_0)}.$$

The numerator of the likelihood ratio represents the probability that the sample values $x_1, x_2, \cdots, x_n$ will be observed if in fact the probability of a head is $\theta_1 = 0.6$, and the denominator the corresponding probability if $\theta = \theta_0 = 0.5$. Thus if θ is actually θ_1 one should, with high probability, obtain sample values for which the numerator is large relative to the denominator; thus we shall reject the hypothesis $\theta = \theta_0$ if λ_n is too large, accept if it is sufficiently small.

The sequential test the subject is to use is of the following kind: He determines two positive numbers A and B with $A > B$. After each toss he computes the likelihood ratio. If it is larger than A, he rejects the hypothesis H_0; if it is smaller than B, he accepts H_0; if neither, he tosses the coin again.

Now, how should he choose the numbers A and B? Our story becomes quite farfetched, but suppose he wishes to assure himself of a probability, if H_0 holds, not greater than $\alpha = 0.05$ of a Type I error; i.e., of rejecting the hypothesis $\theta = 0.5$ if in fact $\theta = 0.5$; and a probability not more than $\beta = 0.60$ of failing to reject the hypothesis $\theta = 0.5$ if in fact $\theta = 0.6$. He can achieve this, approximately, if he sets

$$A = \frac{1-\beta}{\alpha} = 8, \; B = \frac{\beta}{1-\alpha} = 0.63.$$

We shall discuss this choice of A and B below (actually, the approximation may be very poor with a value of β as large as 0.60); for the moment let us make sure we have clearly in mind the procedure the subject will follow. Suppose he first tosses a head. Then

$$\lambda_1 = \frac{f(x_1;\theta_1)}{f(x_1;\theta_0)} = \frac{f(1;0.6)}{f(1;0.5)} = \frac{(0.6)^1(0.4)^0}{(0.5)^1(0.5)^0} = 1.2.$$

Now

$$B = 0.63 < \lambda_1 = 1.2 < A = 8,$$

so he continues his experiment. Suppose he next tosses tails. Then

$$\lambda_2 = \prod_{i=1}^{2} \frac{f(x_i;\theta_1)}{f(x_i;\theta_0)} = \frac{f(1;0.6)f(0;0.6)}{f(1;0.5)f(0;0.5)} = \frac{(0.6)^1(0.4)^0(0.6)^0(0.4)^1}{(0.5)^1(0.5)^0(0.5)^0(0.5)^1} = 0.96.$$

Again,

$$B = 0.63 < \lambda_2 = 0.96 < A = 8,$$

so he continues his experiment. If again he tosses tails, he has

$$\lambda_3 = \frac{(0.6)^1(0.4)^2}{(0.5)^1(0.5)^2} = 0.77,$$

so that still he continues to toss. If the ratio λ_n eventually falls below $B = 0.63$, he will accept the hypothesis $\theta = 0.5$. If λ_n is eventually greater than 8, he will reject the hypothesis $\theta = 0.5$ in favor of the alternative $\theta = 0.6$. It can be shown that one or the other will eventually happen, with probability 1. This is reassuring, although of course it leaves open the logical possibility that the king may grow weary of watching before it happens.

Termination of the Sequential Procedure. It is evidently not logically certain that the sequential procedure will eventually terminate with the rejection or acceptance of H_0. The fact that it is stochastically certain to terminate is a consequence of the following theorem, as we shall see.

▶ ***Theorem A.*** *Let* $\mathbf{z}_1, \mathbf{z}_2, \cdots$ *be independent, identically distributed random variables, for which the mean and variance exist (not both* 0). *Let* a, b *be any two real numbers, with* $a > b$. *Then*

$$Pr\{b < \textstyle\sum_{i=1}^{n} \mathbf{z}_i < a\} \to 0 \text{ as } n \to \infty.$$

The conclusion of this theorem is true even if the independent random variables $\mathbf{z}_1, \mathbf{z}_2, \cdots$ are not identically distributed, provided their means and standard deviations do not approach zero too rapidly. We shall prove it here, however, as a consequence of the Central Limit Theorem.

Proof. Let $E(\mathbf{z}_i) = \mu$, $V(\mathbf{z}_i) = \sigma^2$, $i = 1, 2, \cdots$. Set $\bar{\mathbf{z}}_n = \frac{1}{n}\sum_{i=1}^{n} \mathbf{z}_i$. Then

$$\{b < \textstyle\sum_{i=1}^{n} \mathbf{z}_i < a\} = \{b/n < \bar{\mathbf{z}}_n < a/n\}$$

$$= \left\{\left(\frac{b}{n} - \mu\right)\frac{\sqrt{n}}{\sigma} < \frac{\bar{\mathbf{z}}_n - \mu}{\sigma/\sqrt{n}} < \left(\frac{a}{n} - \mu\right)\frac{\sqrt{n}}{\sigma}\right\}.$$

According to the Central Limit Theorem, the distribution of the random variable $(\bar{\mathbf{z}}_n - \mu)/(\sigma/\sqrt{n})$ approaches the normal (0,1) distribution as $n \to \infty$. If $\mu = 0$, both right and left members of the last inequalities tend to 0 as $n \to \infty$, so one would expect the limit of the probability of the event to be the probability that a normal (0,1) random variable will equal 0; this probability is 0. If $\mu > 0$, then both right and left members become negatively infinite, while if $\mu < 0$ both become positively infinite; the limit of the probability of the event in each case is 0. In order to follow this line of argument more carefully, we distinguish three cases.

CASE 1: $\mu = 0$.

Let ϵ be an arbitrary positive number. Choose a positive number h so that

$$\frac{1}{\sqrt{2\pi}}\int_{-h}^{h} e^{-u^2/2}\,du < \epsilon/2.$$

Now choose a positive integer N_1 so that

$$\left(\frac{b}{n} - \mu\right)\frac{\sqrt{n}}{\sigma} > -h \text{ and } \left(\frac{a}{n} - \mu\right)\frac{\sqrt{n}}{\sigma} < h$$

whenever $n > N_1$. Choose a positive integer N_2 so that

$$\left| Pr\left\{-h < \frac{\bar{\mathbf{z}}_n - \mu}{\sigma/\sqrt{n}} < h\right\} - \frac{1}{\sqrt{2\pi}}\int_{-h}^{h} e^{-u^2/2}\,du\right| < \epsilon/2$$

for $n > N_2$; the Central Limit Theorem assures us we can find such a positive integer N_2. Now let N be a positive integer greater than both N_1 and N_2, and suppose $n > N$. Since

$$\left(\frac{b}{n} - \mu\right)\frac{\sqrt{n}}{\sigma} > -h \text{ and } \left(\frac{a}{n} - \mu\right)\frac{\sqrt{n}}{\sigma} < h,$$

we have

$$\{b < \textstyle\sum_{i=1}^{n} \mathbf{z}_i < a\} = \left\{\left(\frac{b}{n} - \mu\right)\frac{\sqrt{n}}{\sigma} < \frac{\bar{\mathbf{z}}_n - \mu}{\sigma/\sqrt{n}} < \left(\frac{a}{n} - \mu\right)\frac{\sqrt{n}}{\sigma}\right\}$$

$$\subset \left\{-h < \frac{\bar{\mathbf{z}}_n - \mu}{\sigma/\sqrt{n}} < h\right\}.$$

Therefore

$$Pr\{b < \textstyle\sum_{i=1}^{n} \mathbf{z}_i < a\} \leq Pr\left\{-h < \frac{\bar{\mathbf{z}}_n - \mu}{\sigma/\sqrt{n}} < h\right\}$$

$$< \frac{1}{\sqrt{2\pi}}\int_{-h}^{h} e^{-u^2/2}\, du + \frac{\epsilon}{2} < \frac{\epsilon}{2} + \frac{\epsilon}{2} = \epsilon$$

if $n > N$. We have thus shown that

$$\lim_{n\to\infty} Pr\{b < \textstyle\sum_{i=1}^{n} \mathbf{z}_i < a\} = 0 \text{ if } \mu = 0.$$

Case 2: $\mu > 0$.

Let ϵ be an arbitrary positive number. Choose a negative number $-h$ such that

$$\frac{1}{\sqrt{2\pi}}\int_{-\infty}^{-h} e^{-u^2/2}\, du < \epsilon/2.$$

Choose a positive integer N_1 so that

$$\left(\frac{a}{n} - \mu\right)\frac{\sqrt{n}}{\sigma} < -h \quad \text{for } n > N_1,$$

as you can clearly do, since $\lim_{n\to\infty} (a/n - \mu)(\sqrt{n}/\sigma) = -\infty$. Then also

$$\left(\frac{b}{n} - \mu\right)\frac{\sqrt{n}}{\sigma} < -h \quad \text{for } n > N_1,$$

since $b < a$. Choose (using again the Central Limit Theorem) a positive integer N_2 such that

$$\left| Pr\left\{\frac{\bar{\mathbf{z}}_n - \mu}{\sigma/\sqrt{n}} < -h\right\} - \frac{1}{\sqrt{2\pi}}\int_{-\infty}^{-h} e^{-u^2/2}\, du\right| < \epsilon/2 \text{ for } n > N_2.$$

We have

$$\{b < \textstyle\sum_{i=1}^n \mathbf{z}_i < a\}$$

$$= \left\{\left(\frac{b}{n} - \mu\right)\frac{\sqrt{n}}{\sigma} < \frac{\bar{\mathbf{z}}_n - \mu}{\sigma/\sqrt{n}} < \left(\frac{a}{n} - \mu\right)\frac{\sqrt{n}}{\sigma}\right\} \subset \left\{\frac{\bar{\mathbf{z}}_n - \mu}{\sigma/\sqrt{n}} < -h\right\}.$$

Therefore

$$Pr\{b < \textstyle\sum_{i=1}^n \mathbf{z}_i < a\} \leq Pr\left\{\dfrac{\bar{\mathbf{z}}_n - \mu}{\sigma/\sqrt{n}} < -h\right\}$$

$$< \frac{1}{\sqrt{2\pi}}\int_{-\infty}^{-h} e^{-u^2/2}\,du + \frac{\epsilon}{2} < \frac{\epsilon}{2} + \frac{\epsilon}{2} = \epsilon.$$

The proof for Case 3, $\mu < 0$, is similar.

▶ ***Corollary B.*** *Under the conditions of Theorem A, the probability is* 0 *that for all k we shall have $b < \sum_{i=1}^k \mathbf{z}_i < a$.*

Proof. If n is any particular positive integer, and if $b < \sum_{i=1}^k \mathbf{z}_i < a$ for *every* k, then surely $b < \sum_{i=1}^n \mathbf{z}_i < a$. That is,

$$\{b < \textstyle\sum_{i=1}^k \mathbf{z}_i < a \text{ for all } k\} \subset \{b < \sum_{i=1}^n \mathbf{z}_i < a\};$$

hence

$$Pr\{b < \textstyle\sum_{i=1}^k \mathbf{z}_i < a \text{ for all } k\} \leq Pr\{b < \sum_{i=1}^n \mathbf{z}_i < a\}.$$

But this is true for each positive integer n, and the right member approaches 0 as $n \to \infty$, while the left member is independent of n. Thus the left member is a non-negative number smaller than every positive number, and must be 0.

▶ ***Corollary C.*** *The probability is* 1 *that the sequential procedure will terminate.*

Actually, some hypothesis is required; a suitable one will be stated in the proof.

Proof. The sequential procedure will terminate if and when a value of

$$\lambda_n = \frac{\prod_{i=1}^n f(\mathbf{x}_i; \theta_1)}{\prod_{i=1}^n f(\mathbf{x}_i; \theta_0)}$$

is reached which does not lie between B and A. This will occur when and only when

$$\log \boldsymbol{\lambda}_n = \sum_{i=1}^{n} [\log f(\mathbf{x}_i; \theta_1) - \log f(\mathbf{x}_i; \theta_0)]$$

fails to lie between $\log B$ and $\log A$. Set

$$\mathbf{z}_i = \log f(\mathbf{x}_i; \theta_1) - \log f(\mathbf{x}_i; \theta_0),\ i = 1, 2, \cdots.$$

Since the $\mathbf{x}_i$ are independent, identically distributed random variables, so are the $\mathbf{z}_i$. We now state explicitly the hypotheses referred to above; we suppose that $E(\mathbf{z}_i)$ and $V(\mathbf{z}_i)$ exist (finite). On applying Corollary B, with $a = \log A$ and $b = \log B$, we see that the probability is 0 that for all k the sum $\sum_{i=1}^{k} \mathbf{z}_i$ shall lie between $\log B$ and $\log A$. The probability of the complementary event is therefore 1: the probability is 1 that for some k either $\sum_{i=1}^{k} \mathbf{z}_i \leq \log B$ or $\sum_{i=1}^{k} \mathbf{z}_i \geq \log A$. This completes the proof of Corollary C.

Determination of A and B. Suppose you wish to use a sequential procedure which will give a probability α (if H_0 holds) of a Type I error (reject H_0 if H_0 is true) and a probability β (if H_1 holds) of a Type II error (accept H_0 if H_1 is true). In general, to set

$$A = \frac{1 - \beta}{\alpha},\ B = \frac{\beta}{1 - \alpha}$$

is not exact; that is, A, B are not exactly the numbers one should choose in order to have precisely the probability α of rejecting the hypothesis $\theta = \theta_0$ if in fact $\theta = \theta_0$, and the probability β of accepting the hypothesis $\theta = \theta_0$ if in fact $\theta = \theta_1$. Exact values for A and B are in general very hard to come by. However, the above approximations are, when α and β are small, very close to exact values. (On the other hand, you will readily see that if $\alpha + \beta \geq 1$, these choices of A and B give no test at all, for then A would be less than or equal to B.)

Let A and B now denote numbers for which the probabilities of errors of the two types are precisely α and β. Let us define two classes $\mathcal{A}$ and $\mathcal{B}$ of sample points. A sample point stopping at n $(x_1, x_2, \cdots, x_n)$ will belong to class $\mathcal{A}$ if for this sample point $B < \lambda_1 < A, B < \lambda_2 < A, \cdots, B < \lambda_{n-1} < A$, but $\lambda_n \geq A$. Similarly, a sample point $(x_1, x_2, \cdots, x_n)$ stopping at n will belong to class $\mathcal{B}$ if for this sample point $B < \lambda_1 < A, B < \lambda_2 < A, \cdots, B < \lambda_{n-1} < A$, but $\boldsymbol{\lambda}_n \leq B$. It is true that we can conceive of non-terminating sequences of sample values; but "almost all" terminate, for we have seen that the probability of obtaining a sample point for which the process does not terminate is zero. We recall that

$$\lambda_n = \frac{\prod_{i=1}^{n} f(x_i;\theta_1)}{\prod_{i=1}^{n} f(x_i;\theta_0)}, \qquad n = 1, 2, \cdots.$$

Let us suppose that the population is discrete, so that $f(x;\theta_0)$ is the population probability function if the true parameter value is θ_0, while $f(x;\theta_1)$ is the population probability function if the true parameter value is θ_1. (A similar discussion may be carried through if the population is continuous.) Thus the numerator of λ_n represents the probability, p_{1n}, that the first n sample values observed will be $x_1, x_2, \cdots, x_n$, provided $\theta = \theta_1$, while the denominator represents the probability, p_{0n}, of the same event if $\theta = \theta_0$. Suppose the sample point $(x_1, \cdots, x_n)$, stopping at n, belongs to class $\mathcal{A}$; then for this sample point, $\lambda_n = p_{1n}/p_{0n} \geq A$. That is, the probability of observing these sample values under hypothesis H_1 is at least A times as large as under hypothesis H_0. Since this is true for *every* sample point in class $\mathcal{A}$, the probability that the observed sample point will lie in $\mathcal{A}$ is at least A times as large under hypothesis H_1 as under hypothesis H_0. That is, the probability of rejecting H_0 is at least A times as large under hypothesis H_1 as under hypothesis H_0. But the probability of rejecting H_0 is α under hypothesis H_0 and is $1 - \beta$ under hypothesis H_1. Thus

$$1 - \beta \geq A\alpha.$$

A similar argument relative to the class $\mathcal{B}$ of sample points shows that

$$\beta \leq (1 - \alpha)B.$$

We thus have

$$A \leq \frac{1-\beta}{\alpha} \text{ and } B \geq \frac{\beta}{1-\alpha}.$$

We proposed above that $(1 - \beta)/\alpha$ and $\beta/(1 - \alpha)$ be used in place of A and B; let us denote these numbers by A' and B':

$$A' = \frac{1-\beta}{\alpha}, \quad B' = \frac{\beta}{1-\alpha}.$$

Now let us consider the probabilities α' and β' of errors of Type I and Type II using A' and B' instead of A and B. We have as before

$$1 - \beta' \geq A'\alpha' \text{ and } \beta' \leq (1 - \alpha')B',$$

so that

$$\frac{\alpha'}{1-\beta'} \leq \frac{1}{A'} = \frac{\alpha}{1-\beta},$$

and

$$\frac{\beta'}{1-\alpha'} \leq B' = \frac{\beta}{1-\alpha}.$$

Since each of the numbers α, β, α', β' lies between 0 and 1, we have

$$\alpha' \leq \frac{\alpha}{1-\beta}(1-\beta') < \frac{\alpha}{1-\beta},$$

and

$$\beta' \leq \frac{\beta}{1-\alpha}(1-\alpha') < \frac{\beta}{1-\alpha}.$$

Thus if β is near 0, α' cannot be much larger than α; and if α is near 0, β' cannot be much larger than β. Further, on multiplying the earlier equations by $(1-\beta')(1-\beta)$ and $(1-\alpha')(1-\alpha)$ respectively, we find that

$$\alpha'(1-\beta) \leq \alpha(1-\beta') \text{ and } \beta'(1-\alpha) \leq \beta(1-\alpha').$$

On adding, we see that

$$\alpha' + \beta' \leq \alpha + \beta,$$

whether or not α and β are small. Thus to replace A and B by A' and B' tends to be conservative, yielding probabilities of errors of Types I and II which cannot be much larger than α and β (if these are small) but may be smaller. Conceivably this might involve a larger expected number of trials than would the use of the exact A and B; but it can be argued that if α and β are small the increase in the expected number of trials should be small. For a more complete discussion of this point and of sequential analysis in general, cf. [8], [9], [10], [18], [21], [22].

Expected Number of Trials. Let $\mathbf{n}$ denote the random variable: "number of trials required before the likelihood ratio falls outside the interval (B,A)." Theoretically, we might compute its expectation directly from the definition:

$$E(\mathbf{n}) = 1 \cdot Pr\{\mathbf{n} = 1\} + 2 \cdot Pr\{\mathbf{n} = 2\} + \cdots ;$$

here $Pr\{\mathbf{n} = 1\} = Pr\{\boldsymbol{\lambda}_1 \leq B \text{ or } \boldsymbol{\lambda}_1 \geq A\}$, $Pr\{\mathbf{n} = 2\} = Pr\{B < \boldsymbol{\lambda}_1 < A, \boldsymbol{\lambda}_2 \leq B \text{ or } \boldsymbol{\lambda}_2 \geq A\}$, etc. In practice this is difficult to compute, and we resort to an indirect method.

Let $\mathbf{x}_i$ denote the result of the ith trial or observation, $i = 1, 2, \cdots$; these random variables are independent and identically distributed. While in fact the sequential procedure will terminate as soon as the likelihood ratio falls outside the interval (B,A), for our present purpose we imagine the process as continuing indefinitely; but we denote by $\mathbf{n}$ the index of the *first* likelihood ratio to fall outside the interval (B,A).

Again we set

$$\mathbf{z}_i = \log f(\mathbf{x}_i; \theta_1) - \log f(\mathbf{x}_i; \theta_0).$$

Let $\mathbf{S}_k = \sum_{i=1}^{k} \mathbf{z}_i$, $k = 1, 2, \cdots,$

so that

$$\mathbf{S}_k = \log \boldsymbol{\lambda}_k, \quad k = 1, 2, \cdots .$$

We set $b = \log B$, $a = \log A$, so that $\mathbf{n}$ denotes the index of the first of the sums $\mathbf{S}_k$ to fall outside the interval (b,a). For a fixed integer i, let $\mathbf{y}_i$ denote the random variable which is equal to 1 if $\mathbf{n} \geq i$ and is equal to 0 if $\mathbf{n} < i$. The value of $\mathbf{y}_i$ is completely determined by the values of $\mathbf{S}_1 = \mathbf{z}_1$, $\mathbf{S}_2 = \sum_{j=1}^{2} \mathbf{z}_j$, $\cdots$, $\mathbf{S}_{i-1} = \sum_{j=1}^{i-1} \mathbf{z}_j$, since $\mathbf{y}_i = 1$ if and only if $\mathbf{S}_1, \mathbf{S}_2, \cdots, \mathbf{S}_{i-1}$ all lie in the interval (b,a). Thus $\mathbf{y}_i$ is a function of $\mathbf{z}_1, \mathbf{z}_2, \cdots, \mathbf{z}_{i-1}$, and is therefore independent of $\mathbf{z}_i$. Since $\mathbf{y}_i = 0$ if $i > \mathbf{n}$, and $\mathbf{y}_i = 1$ if $i \leq \mathbf{n}$, we have

$$\mathbf{S_n} = \sum_{i=1}^{\mathbf{n}} \mathbf{z}_i = \sum_{i=1}^{\infty} \mathbf{y}_i \mathbf{z}_i,$$

so that

$$E(\mathbf{S_n}) = \sum_{i=1}^{\infty} E(\mathbf{y}_i \mathbf{z}_i).$$

(Here we use an extension of Corollary G, page 89, which can be justified using the existence of $E(\mathbf{z})$ and $E(\mathbf{n})$. For a proof of a theorem of Stein, that in fact all moments of $\mathbf{n}$ exist, see [22], page 484.) Thus

$$E(\mathbf{S_n}) = \sum_{i=1}^{\infty} E(\mathbf{y}_i) E(\mathbf{z}_i).$$

But $E(\mathbf{z}_i) = E(\mathbf{z})$ for each integer i, so that

$$E(\mathbf{S_n}) = E(\mathbf{z}) \sum_{i=1}^{\infty} E(\mathbf{y}_i) = E(z)\mathbf{E}\left[\sum_{i=1}^{\infty} \mathbf{y}_i\right] = E(\mathbf{z})E(\mathbf{n}).$$

Thus

$$E(\mathbf{S_n}) = E(\mathbf{z})E(\mathbf{n}).$$

(See Johnson, N. L., A proof of Wald's theorem on cumulative sums, Ann. Math. Stat., Vol. 30 (1959), pp. 1245–1247.)

We now resort to an approximation. We assume that a and b are large (numerically) compared with any value an individual random variable $\mathbf{z}$ is likely to assume, so that when a sum $\mathbf{S}$ does finally exceed a it will not exceed a by much (or similarly at b). Let $P(\theta)$ denote the probability of rejecting H_0 if θ is the true parameter value ($P(\theta_0) = \alpha$); then $1 - P(\theta)$ is the probability of accepting H_0 if θ is the true parameter value ($1 - P(\theta_1) = \beta$). In effect, we are assuming that $\mathbf{S_n}$ will be approximately equal to a with probability $P(\theta)$ and approximately equal to b with probability $1 - P(\theta)$. Hence

$$E(\mathbf{S_n}) \doteq aP(\theta) + b[1 - P(\theta)],$$

and

▶ $$E(\mathbf{n}) = \frac{E(\mathbf{S_n})}{E(\mathbf{z})} \doteq \frac{aP(\theta) + b[1 - P(\theta)]}{E(\mathbf{z})};$$

here $a = \log A$, $b = \log B$, $\mathbf{z} = \log f(\mathbf{x}; \theta_1) - \log f(\mathbf{x}; \theta_0)$.

108. Quality Control; Inspection Sampling; Acceptance Sampling. The terms used above originated in a producer-consumer context, though the methods referred to may be of wider applicability. The producer uses methods of *quality control* to maintain acceptable standards of quality in his product, and as an aid in keeping costs down. Producer and consumer may cooperate in maintaining an *inspection sampling* program which will protect the producer against rejection of acceptable goods and the consumer against delivery of an unacceptable product. In the absence of suitable inspection sampling, the consumer may rely on an *acceptance sampling* plan for protection against acceptance of an inferior product.

Control Chart. *Control charts* appear to be among the most widely used statistical devices for maintaining quality of product. Suppose you are employed by a manufacturing concern as manager of a department. Among the products of your department is a paper, produced by a process which has been producing paper with mean breaking strength 4 in appropriate units. The standard deviation of breaking strength has been 0.3, and the distribution of breaking strength has been approximately normal. You prepare a control chart, as below.

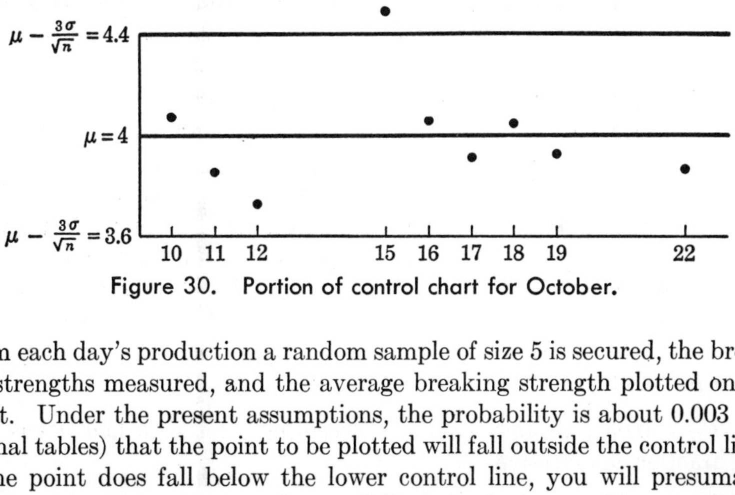

Figure 30. Portion of control chart for October.

From each day's production a random sample of size 5 is secured, the breaking strengths measured, and the average breaking strength plotted on the chart. Under the present assumptions, the probability is about 0.003 (see normal tables) that the point to be plotted will fall outside the control lines. If the point does fall below the lower control line, you will presumably initiate an investigation into the possibility of a faulty machine or a failure of some other component of the manufacturing process. If several plotted points should fall above the upper control line, you might conceivably try to discover a possible cause for the improvement of the product; perhaps the paper is too thick.

While control charts with control lines designed for different probabilities may be used also, the three standard deviation control lines appear to be most widely used. Even when the random variable under control is not normally distributed, they provide a useful means of keeping the quality under surveillance. It is worth remarking also that sample means tend to be more nearly normally distributed than the population random variable; further, Chebyshev's Theorem shows that the probability of getting outside the control band is less than 1/9 regardless of the population.

Besides the control chart for the sample mean, you might also wish to keep a check on the variability of your product. If the distribution of breaking strength is normal (μ,σ), you can readily construct a control chart for the variance or standard deviation, using the fact that if $\mathbf{s}^2$ is the sample variance then $n\mathbf{s}^2/\sigma^2$ has a χ^2 distribution with $(n - 1)$ degrees of freedom. More often control charts are kept on the *range*, the difference between the largest and smallest sample values.

Sampling Inspection. There are many methods of sampling inspection, each designed to meet specified objectives of producer and of consumer. We shall consider here only the *single sampling* plan.

You are chairman of a joint committee of the Solid Packers (producer) and the Come-And-Get-Em Food Distributors (consumer), charged with the responsibility for drawing up an inspection plan to be used on lots of packaged, dried fruit. The committee has agreed on a "go, no-go" criterion of quality; that is, it has agreed on a test which, when applied to an individual package will result in that package being labeled defective or nondefective. A subcommittee has proposed the following single sampling plan.

1. Given a lot of N packages, n of them will be tested.
2. If, among the n, d or fewer defectives are found, the lot will be accepted; otherwise it will be rejected.

The consumer insisted on being certain of a fraction defective of not more than $p_t = 0.01$ (*lot tolerance fraction defective*) in each accepted lot. After further discussion in which it was pointed out that this certainty could be achieved only with complete sampling, involving greater cost and consequent higher price (or could not be achieved at all if the test were destructive), the consumer has modified his position, and is willing to accept a probability

▶ $P_C = 0.05$ (*consumer's risk*) of accepting a lot if in fact it has fraction p_t defective.

Let us compute this probability, the probability of accepting a lot if in fact it has fraction p_t defective. As a mathematical model appropriate to the experiment of choosing n packages to be tested from among the N in the lot, we set up an elementary probability space in which there are $\binom{N}{n}$ elementary events, each representing one of the $\binom{N}{n}$ combinations of N things taken n at a time. Now let us consider how many of these elementary events represent combinations in which appear exactly x defective packages ($0 \leq x \leq N$). There are among the N packages $M = Np_t$ defective ones; and the number of combinations of M items taken x at a time is $\binom{M}{x}$. For each one of these $\binom{M}{x}$ combinations there are $\binom{N-M}{n-x}$ combinations of $N - M$ nondefective packages taken $n - x$ at a time, giving one of the combinations of n packages in which exactly x defective ones appear. Thus of the $\binom{N}{n}$ elementary events, exactly $\binom{M}{x}\binom{N-M}{n-x}$ are favorable to the event: "precisely x defective packages will be found among the n drawn." The lot is to be accepted if $\mathbf{x} \leq d$, where $\mathbf{x}$ is "the number of defectives which will be found." Thus the probability of accepting the lot if in fact the fraction defective is p_t is

$$P_C = \sum_{x=0}^{d} \frac{\binom{N_{pt}}{x}\binom{N - N_{pt}}{n-x}}{\binom{N}{n}}.$$

If N is large compared with n, then we obtain an approximately correct formula if we compute the probability as if we were concerned with n independent trials of an event with probability p_t:

$$P_C \doteq \sum_{x=0}^{d} \binom{n}{x} p_t^x (1 - p_t)^{n-x}.$$

The complete plan will include the specification of n and d for each N which may occur. Thus there are two "unknowns," n and d, and so far only one equation,

$$P_C = \sum_{x=0}^{d} \frac{\binom{N_{pt}}{x}\binom{N - N_{pt}}{n-x}}{\binom{N}{n}}$$

(in our situation, $P_C = 0.05$, $p_t = 0.01$). Suppose you now wish to compute some possible values of n and d. Apparently, you are free to choose one of the two, n or d, and to determine the other accordingly. But your choice is not quite so free as that, since if, for example, you choose $n = 1$, you have

$$\sum_{x=0}^{d} \binom{1}{x} (0.01)^x (0.99)^{1-x} = 0.99 \quad \text{if } d = 0,$$
$$= 1 \quad \text{if } d = 1,$$

so that $P_C \leq 0.05$ is achieved for neither $d = 0$ nor $d = 1$. It does appear to be an advantage to choose n as small as possible; and clearly you will have the smallest possible choice of n by setting $d = 0$. If N is large, you then have to solve

$$\binom{n}{0}(0.01)^0(0.99)^n = 0.05,$$

and find that

$$n = \frac{\log 0.05}{\log 0.99} \doteq 300.$$

When this figure is reported to the committee, some adjustments in position occur, due to the cost of testing such a large number. The consumer reports that he is willing to adjust his lot tolerance defective up to $p_t = 0.05$, and his consumer's risk up to 0.10, if the producer will make available quality control data indicating that the mean fraction defective $\bar{p}$ is not more than 0.02.

Meanwhile, the producer has given some thought to his own risk. He now insists on a probability

▶ P_R *(producer's risk)* of not more than 0.10 of rejecting the lot if in fact the mean fraction defective is $\bar{p} = 0.02$.

Now from the producer's point of view, in computing the producer's risk, the choice of a sample of n test items from the lot may be regarded as the choice of a random sample of size n from his (conceptually infinite) stock of all items of the kind produced or producible by a process yielding a mean fraction, $\bar{p}$ *(process average)*, defective. That is, the experiment under consideration assumes for him the aspect of n independent (Bernoullian) trials of an event with probability $\bar{p}$ in each trial. Then

$$P_R = \sum_{x=d+1}^{n} \binom{n}{x} \bar{p}^x(1 - \bar{p})^{n-x}$$

$$= 1 - \sum_{x=0}^{d} \binom{n}{x} \bar{p}^x(1 - \bar{p})^{n-x}.$$

The *producer's risk* P_R may alternatively (but not equivalently) be defined as the *probability that the lot will be rejected if in fact the fraction p defective of the lot is* $p = \bar{p}$. With this definition, we should have

$$P_R = \sum_{x=d+1}^{n} \binom{N\bar{p}}{x}\binom{N - N\bar{p}}{n - x}\bigg/\binom{N}{n}$$

$$= 1 - \sum_{x=0}^{d} \binom{N\bar{p}}{x}\binom{N - N\bar{p}}{n - x}\bigg/\binom{N}{n}.$$

Again we have approximately for large N,

$$P_R \doteq \sum_{x=d+1}^{n} \binom{n}{x} \bar{p}^x(1 - \bar{p})^{n-x}$$

$$= 1 - \sum_{x=0}^{d} \binom{n}{x} \bar{p}^x (1 - \bar{p})^{n-x},$$

which is exact with the other definition of producer's risk.

You now have two equations to satisfy:

$$\sum_{x=0}^{d} \binom{n}{x} p_t^x (1 - p_t)^{n-x} = P_C,$$

and

$$\sum_{x=0}^{d} \binom{n}{x} \bar{p}^x (1 - \bar{p})^{n-x} = 1 - P_R.$$

Evidently we must have $\bar{p} < p_t$ if these equations are to admit a solution, since presumably $1 - P_R > P_C$, while the left member of the second equation decreases as $\bar{p}$ increases. In your case the equations are

$$\sum_{x=0}^{d} \binom{n}{x} (0.05)^x (0.95)^{n-x} = 0.10,$$

$$\sum_{x=0}^{d} \binom{n}{x} (0.02)^x (0.98)^{n-x} = 0.90.$$

You may have at hand tables of the binomial adequate to determine n and d from these equations. If not, you will find the Central Limit Theorem does not give a sufficiently close approximation. It can be shown (page 120) that when x and np are small relative to n, and p is very small, the binomial probability $\binom{n}{x} p^x (1 - p)^{n-x}$ is closely approximated by the Poisson probability $e^{-np}(np)^x/x!$. Using the Poisson tables and trying successively several values of d, we find, for example, that when $m = np_t = 6.7$, we have $\sum_{x=4}^{\infty} e^{-m}m^x/x! = 0.90$; hence

$$\sum_{x=0}^{3} \binom{n}{p_t} p_t^x (1 - p_t)^{n-x} \doteq \sum_{x=0}^{3} e^{-m}m^x/x! = 0.10.$$

Here $p_t = 0.05$; hence $n = m/p_t = 134$. Also, for $m = n\bar{p} = 134(0.02) = 2.7$, we have

$$\sum_{x=4}^{134} \binom{134}{x} (0.02)^x (0.98)^{134-x} \doteq \sum_{x=4}^{\infty} e^{-m}m^x/x! = 0.29.$$

Thus if we take $n = 134$ and $d = 3$, we achieve $P_C = 0.10$ and $P_R = 0.29$. We require a smaller P_R, hence try larger n and d. We find eventually that when $m = np_t = 11.8$, we have $\sum_{x=8}^{\infty} e^{-m}m^x/x! = 0.90$, hence $\sum_{x=0}^{7} \binom{n}{x} p_t^x (1 - p_t)^{n-x} \doteq \sum_{x=0}^{7} e^{-m}m^x/x! = 0.10$. Here $p_t = 0.05$, hence $n = m/p_t = 236$. Also, for $m = np = 236(0.02) = 4.72$, we have

$$\sum_{x=8}^{236} \binom{236}{x} (0.02)^x (0.98)^{236-x} \doteq \sum_{x=8}^{\infty} e^{-m} m^x / x! = 0.10.$$

Thus if we take $n = 236$ and $d = 7$ we achieve $P_C = 0.10$ and $P_R = 0.10$. For smaller d (and n) we can achieve $P_C \leq 0.10$, but not $P_R \leq 0.10$; for larger d and smaller n, we can achieve $P_R \leq 0.10$, but not $P_C \leq 0.10$. For large N, then, the solution consistent with the demanded risks of consumer and producer requires that a sample of size 236 be taken, and accepted if 7 or fewer defectives are found.

The procedure is evidently closely analogous to that of testing a hypothesis. Indeed, it is possible to interpret it as a test of the hypothesis $p = \bar{p}$ against the alternative $p = p_t$. The producer's risk P_R is the probability of a *Type* I *error*, of falsely rejecting the hypothesis $p = \bar{p}$ when it is true; it is the significance level of the test. The consumer's risk P_C is the probability of a *Type* II *error*, of accepting the hypothesis $p = \bar{p}$ when in fact $p = p_t$. The *power* of the test at p_t is $1 - P_C$. Of course, the roles of the two hypotheses may be interchanged.

In this formulation it becomes clear that sequential methods, discussed on pages 325–334, are particularly adaptable to sampling inspection; for these methods are designed to test a simple hypothesis $\theta = \theta_0$ against a simple alternative $\theta = \theta_1$.

If we set

$$P(p) = \sum_{x=0}^{d} \binom{n}{x} p^x (1-p)^{n-x}$$

(assuming N large), then the graph of $P(p)$ as a function of p is called the operating characteristic curve.

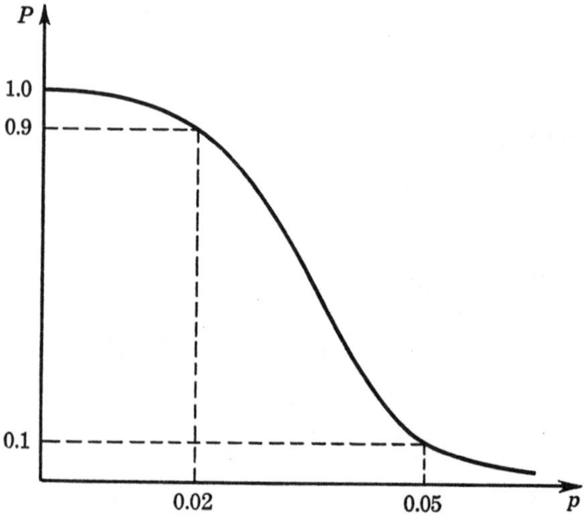

Figure 31

It is sketched here for $n = 236$, $d = 7$.

▶ The *operating characteristic curve* of a sampling inspection plan has for its ordinate at the point with abscissa p, the probability of accepting the lot if in fact it contains fraction p defective.

Now let us suppose the proposed procedure includes a specification as to the disposition of the rejected lots: namely,

3. Each lot rejected is to receive 100% inspection (this is possible, of course, only with nondestructive tests). Further, *all* defective items found are to be replaced by nondefective ones, whether or not they are found in lots which are rejected.

Now the consumer may assume an alternative attitude toward the problem of his protection: he may demand at least a certain outgoing quality. Suppose he insists that, no matter what fractions of defectives are in the lots originally, the procedure shall be such as to guarantee that the average (expected) fraction per lot finally accepted will not exceed $p_m = 0.05$. This number, p_m, is his *average outgoing quality limit.* Let p represent the fraction defective in a lot of size N, so that $M = Np$ is the actual number of defectives. Let $\tilde{\mathbf{p}}$ denote the fraction defective which will remain after steps 1, 2, and 3 are completed, and $\mathbf{M} = N\tilde{\mathbf{p}}$ the actual number of defectives which will remain. If no defectives are found, the value of $\mathbf{M}$ will be Np; the probability of this is

$$\binom{Np}{0}\binom{N-Np}{n}\Big/\binom{N}{n}. \qquad \text{(pages 336, 337)}$$

If x defectives are found, $0 \le x \le d$, the value of $\mathbf{M}$ will be $Np - x$, since the defective items will be replaced by nondefective ones; the probability of this, $Pr\{\mathbf{M} = Np - x\}$, is $\binom{Np}{x}\binom{N-Np}{n-x}\Big/\binom{N}{n}$. If more than d defectives are found, the value of $\mathbf{M}$ will be 0, since the lot will be subjected to complete inspection, and all defectives replaced. Thus the expected value of $\mathbf{M}$ is given by

$$E(\mathbf{M}) = \sum_{x=0}^{d} (Np - x)\binom{Np}{x}\binom{N-Np}{n-x}\Big/\binom{N}{n}.$$

The average (expected) outgoing fraction defective is then

$$E(\tilde{\mathbf{p}}) = E\left(\frac{\mathbf{M}}{N}\right) = \sum_{x=0}^{d}\left(p - \frac{x}{N}\right)\binom{Np}{x}\binom{N-Np}{n-x}\Big/\binom{N}{n}.$$

(For large N, the probability function $\binom{Np}{x}\binom{N-Np}{n-x}\Big/\binom{N}{n}$ may be approximated by $\binom{n}{x}p^x(1-p)^{n-x}$.) Obviously $E(\tilde{\mathbf{p}})$ depends on p; its largest possible value is the average outgoing quality limit, p_m:

$$\blacktriangleright \quad p_m = \max_{0 \le p \le 1} E(\tilde{\mathbf{p}}).$$

An alternative is open to the producer, also. Instead of specifying the maximum allowable probability of rejecting a lot if in fact the process is under control, he may prefer to minimize the average number of inspections, subject to the requirements of the consumer. Let $\mathbf{m}$ denote the number of packages which will be inspected before an acceptable lot is turned over to the consumer. If d or fewer defectives are found, the value of $\mathbf{m}$ will be n; the probability, $Pr\{\mathbf{m} = n\}$, is

$$P(p) = \sum_{x=0}^{d} \binom{Np}{x}\binom{N - Np}{n - x} \Big/ \binom{N}{n}.$$

If more than d are found, then N packages must be inspected (we neglect the possible inspection of replacement packages); the probability of this, $Pr\{\mathbf{m} = N\}$, is $1 - P(p)$. Thus the expected number of inspections is

$$E(\mathbf{m}) = nP(p) + N[1 - P(p)] = n + (N - n)[1 - P(p)].$$

In general, with the above single sampling plan, values of n and d must be adjusted to conform to the requirements of consumer and producer, whether as to risks, to average outgoing quality, or to number of inspections. In a particular situation, you are likely to find that other factors will enter, which will render the above discussion not wholly applicable. This remark is equally appropriate to almost all suggested applications in the text. We hope, however, that you will find these methods and ideas helpful in solving problems you meet in your particular applications.

These same methods and ideas are applicable in *acceptance sampling*, with the exception that, insofar as the inspection is carried out by the consumer, he may neglect the producer's point of view, and base his choice of n and d on consumer's risk and minimum inspection, or on average outgoing quality limit and minimum inspection.

Discussion of other plans, in particular double sampling and sequential sampling plans, will be found in [9], [10], [22].

PROBLEMS

1. The measure of quality of a product is a normally distributed random variable with mean 7 and standard deviation 0.5.

(a) Construct a 3 standard deviation control chart for the mean of a sample of size 10.

(b) Construct a control chart for the variance of a sample of size 10, designed to call attention to situations when the sample variance is too large (one-sided control chart). Choose the line so the probability is 0.01 that the sample variance will lie above it.

2. Prepare a control chart for checking the variability of the paper referred to on page 335. That is, compute ordinates of horizontal lines such that the probability is 0.01 that the sample variance will fall above the top line and 0.01 that it will fall below the bottom.

3. Two players plan to repeat indefinitely the play of a game of chance. The winner of each play will win a certain fixed amount, the other losing the same amount. What is the probability that one or the other will eventually lose all his money, and why?

4. Consider a sequential sampling procedure for testing the hypothesis $H_0: \mu = \mu_0$ against the alternative $H_1: \mu = \mu_1$, $\mu_1 > \mu_0$, when the population is normal (μ, σ) with known σ, unknown μ. Let x_i denote the ith sample value.

(a) Show that H_0 is accepted at the nth trial if

$$\sum_{i=1}^{n} x_i \leq \frac{\sigma^2 \log B}{\mu_1 - \mu_0} + \left(\frac{\mu_1 + \mu_0}{2}\right) n,$$

while H_1 is accepted at the nth trial if

$$\sum_{i=1}^{n} x_i \geq \frac{\sigma^2 \log A}{\mu_1 - \mu_0} + \left(\frac{\mu_1 + \mu_0}{2}\right) n.$$

(b) Describe a graphical procedure based on (a) in which $\sum_{i=1}^{n} x_i$ is plotted against n, a decision being reached when the plotted point wanders outside the region between two parallel lines. Does the common slope of the lines depend on σ?

5. Suppose, in Problem 4, that $\mu_0 = 0$, $\mu_1 = 0.5$, $\sigma = 1$, and that you will accept a probability 0.01 of rejecting H_0 if true, a probability 0.01 of accepting H_0 if false. What are equations of the lines referred to in Problem 4(b)?

6. (a) In Problem 4(a), what is the distribution of $\mathbf{z} = \log f(\mathbf{x}; \mu_1) - \log f(\mathbf{x}; \mu_0)$?

(b) Show that if the population mean is μ in Problem 4, then the average sample size is

$$\{aP(\mu) + b[1 - P(\mu)]\}\sigma^2/(\mu_1 - \mu_0)(\mu - \bar{\mu}),$$

where $\bar{\mu} = \frac{1}{2}(\mu_0 + \mu_1)$.

7. What are expected sample sizes in Problem 5 if H_0 is true? if H_1 is true?

8. Consider a sequential sampling procedure for testing the hypothesis $H_0: \lambda = \lambda_0$ against the alternative $H_1: \lambda = \lambda_1$, $\lambda_1 > \lambda_0$, when the population has the Poisson distribution, with probability function

$$e^{-\lambda}\lambda^x/x!, \quad x = 0, 1, 2, \cdots.$$

Let x_i denote the ith sample value. Find two lines in the (n,y) plane such that H_0 is to be rejected when the plotted point $(n, \sum_{i=1}^{k} x_i)$ falls above the top line, and is to be accepted when the point falls below the bottom line.

9. Find approximately the expected sample size in Problem 8 if H_1 is true, and if $\alpha = 0.01$, $\beta = 0.02$, $\lambda_0 = 1$, $\lambda_1 = 2$. (Note: $E(\mathbf{x}) = \lambda_1 = 2$.)

10. A retail chain contracts to purchase flashlight batteries under a single sampling inspection plan (steps 1 and 2, page 336). Choose sample size n and acceptance limit d for a consumer's risk 0.05, and a producer's risk 0.05, if the consumer's lot tolerance fraction defective is 0.10, and the producer's process average is 0.03. (Assume large lot size N.) Sketch its operating characteristic curve.

11. Devise a sequential plan for Problem 10. (Assume lot size large.)

12. You have to test a lot of reeds used in the manufacture of organs. The distribution of pitch is normal. You are satisfied that the mean pitch is correct, but are concerned about the possibility that the variance may be too large. (a) Design a sequential test with which you will have a probability 0.10 of rejecting the lot if $\sigma = 1$ and a probability 0.05 of accepting it if $\sigma = 3$ in appropriate units. (Assume you record, for each reed tested, its difference from true pitch.) (b) If the first 10 observations, after subtracting the mean pitch, were as follows, would the test terminate before $n = 10$ or not: -2.19, 0.50, 2.53, -1.85, -0.45, -1.15, -0.58, 5.65, 0.49, -1.16?

13. You are assigned to test a lot of flashlight bulbs.

(a) Design a sequential sampling test so that you have a probability 0.05 of rejecting the lot if there are 3% defective, and a probability 0.01 of accepting the lot if there are 7% defective. Assume the lot size large.

(b) What is the expected sample number with your test, if there are in fact 3% defective?

★CHAPTER
17

Distribution-Free Methods

109. Introduction. Many of the methods studied in earlier sections for analyzing data secured by random sampling have depended on one or the other of two basic assumptions:

1. The sample size is large enough so that certain functions of the sample random variables (for example, the sample mean) have distributions which are approximated by limiting distributions; or
2. The parent population is normal.

While in practice it very frequently occurs that one of these assumptions is appropriate, it is by no means always so. We shall discuss here some methods which depend solely on another assumption:

▶ 3. The random sample comes from a population whose probability distribution function is continuous.

In this book we have dealt only with continuous random variables and discrete random variables; discrete random variables are ruled out by assumption (3). Methods to be discussed here are not generally best for such problems as finding confidence intervals for the population mean (a parameter) or testing the hypothesis that the population variance (a parameter) is a specified number, when the form of the distribution is specified, and are often referred to as *nonparametric methods.* Further, they do not depend on assumptions such as (1) and (2) involving distributions (except that the distribution function be continuous); they are also called *distribution-free* methods. These methods often involve the use of *order statistics,* to be defined below.

Let $\mathbf{x}_1, \mathbf{x}_2, \cdots, \mathbf{x}_n$ be the sample random variables of a random sample of size n from the population determined by the continuous random variable $\mathbf{x}$, whose distribution function is $F(x) = Pr\{\mathbf{x} < x\}$.

▶ Let $\mathbf{y}_1$ denote the smallest of the sample random variables, $\mathbf{y}_2$ the next smallest, etc., so that $\mathbf{y}_n$ is the largest. The random variables $\mathbf{y}_1, \mathbf{y}_2, \cdots, \mathbf{y}_n$ are the *order statistics* of the sample.

Each is a function of the sample random variables and thus a statistic; the reason for the term *order* statistic is clear, since $\mathbf{y}_1 < \mathbf{y}_2 < \cdots < \mathbf{y}_n$. (We neglect the logical possibility that two or more may be equal, since this can happen only with zero probability.)

110. Distribution of $F(\mathbf{x})$. If we set $\mathbf{z}_1 = F(\mathbf{y}_1)$, $\mathbf{z}_2 = F(\mathbf{y}_2)$, $\cdots$, $\mathbf{z}_n = F(\mathbf{y}_n)$, where F is the distribution function of $\mathbf{x}$, then the joint distribution of $\mathbf{z}_1, \mathbf{z}_2, \cdots, \mathbf{z}_n$ is much more easily described than that of $\mathbf{y}_1, \cdots, \mathbf{y}_n$. Let us consider first the case $n = 1$. Then $\mathbf{y}_1 = \mathbf{x}_1$, and this random variable has the same distribution as does $\mathbf{x}$. The distribution of $\mathbf{z}_1 = F(\mathbf{x}_1)$ is that of $\mathbf{z} = F(\mathbf{x})$. Let us consider the distribution function of $\mathbf{z}$,

$$Pr\{\mathbf{z} < z\} = Pr\{F(\mathbf{x}) < z\}.$$

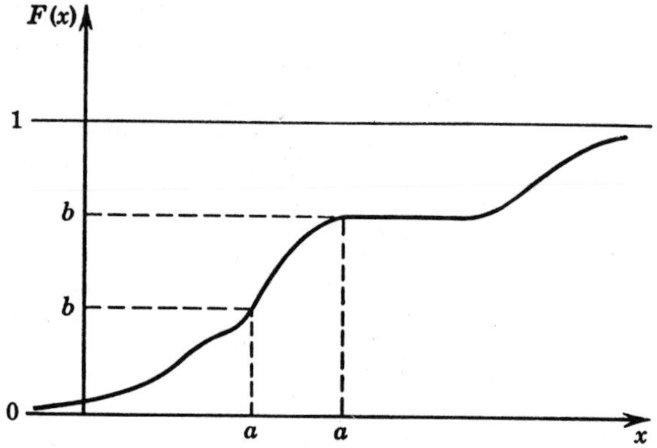

Figure 32

In order to emphasize that in the process of finding this probability we hold z fixed, let us find the distribution function of z at the fixed number b. We have $Pr\{\mathbf{z} < b\} = Pr\{F(\mathbf{x}) < b\}$. To find this probability, we ask first, Where do those values of x lie for which $F(x) < b$? Since F is nondecreasing and continuous, these values of x lie *to the left of the smallest value of x for which $F(x) = b$*. Let a be this smallest value. Then

$$Pr\{F(\mathbf{x}) < b\} = Pr\{\mathbf{x} < a\} = F(a) = b.$$

Thus $Pr\{\mathbf{z} < b\} = b$, if $0 < b < 1$. This is the distribution function of a random variable having a uniform distribution over the interval (0,1); that is,

▶ $\mathbf{z} = F(\mathbf{x})$ *is uniformly distributed over* (0,1).

This result, as well as that below giving the joint distribution of the order statistics, depends on the assumption that the distribution function F is continuous.

111. Joint Distribution of $F(y_1), F(y_2), \cdots, F(y_n)$. It is of course not quite so simple to determine the joint distribution of $F(\mathbf{y}_1)$ and $F(\mathbf{y}_2)$ as it was to determine the distribution of $F(\mathbf{y}_1)$ above. However, the same ideas we shall use in deriving this joint distribution can be used to derive the joint distribution of $F(\mathbf{y}_1), F(\mathbf{y}_2), \cdots, F(\mathbf{y}_n)$, and we shall discuss explicitly here only the case $n = 2$.

Let us set $\mathbf{z}_1 = F(\mathbf{y}_1)$ and $\mathbf{z}_2 = F(\mathbf{y}_2)$. Let z_1 and z_2 be two real numbers, Δz_1 and Δz_2 two positive numbers, and consider the probability

$$Pr\{z_1 < \mathbf{z}_1 < z_1 + \Delta z_1, z_2 < \mathbf{z}_2 < z_2 + \Delta z_2\}.$$

If $h(z_1,z_2)$ represents the joint density function of z_1 and z_2, then this probability is given by

$$\int_{z_1}^{z_1+\Delta z_1} \int_{z_2}^{z_2+\Delta z_2} h(z_1,z_2)\, dz_1\, dz_2,$$

so that

$$\lim_{\substack{\Delta z_1 \to 0 \\ \Delta z_2 \to 0}} \frac{1}{\Delta z_1 \Delta z_2} Pr\{z_1 < \mathbf{z}_1 < z_1 + \Delta z_1, z_2 < \mathbf{z}_2 < z_2 + \Delta z_2\} = h(z_1,z_2).$$

Now $\mathbf{y}_1$ represents the smaller of the two sample random variables $\mathbf{x}_1$ and $\mathbf{x}_2$, and $\mathbf{y}_2$ represents the larger. Therefore $\mathbf{y}_1 < \mathbf{y}_2$, and since F is non-decreasing, $\mathbf{z}_1 = F(\mathbf{y}_1) \leq \mathbf{z}_2 = F(\mathbf{y}_2)$. If $z_1 > z_2$, then in order for $\mathbf{z}_1$ and $\mathbf{z}_2$ to satisfy the inequalities in the braces when Δz_1 and Δz_2 are small, we should have $\mathbf{z}_1 > \mathbf{z}_2$; but this is impossible, hence has probability 0. Therefore

$$h(z_1,z_2) = 0 \text{ if } z_1 > z_2.$$

Suppose now that $0 < z_1 < z_2 < 1$. We have $\mathbf{z}_1 = F(\mathbf{x}_1)$, $\mathbf{z}_2 = F(\mathbf{x}_2)$ if $\mathbf{x}_1 < \mathbf{x}_2$, while $\mathbf{z}_1 = F(\mathbf{x}_2)$, $\mathbf{z}_2 = F(\mathbf{x}_1)$ if $\mathbf{x}_2 < \mathbf{x}_1$. In order to have $\mathbf{z}_1$ between z_1 and $z_1 + \Delta z_1$ and $\mathbf{z}_2$ between z_2 and $z_2 + \Delta z_2$, we must have either $z_1 < F(\mathbf{x}_1) < z_1 + \Delta z_1, z_2 < F(\mathbf{x}_2) < z_2 + \Delta z_2$, or $z_1 < F(\mathbf{x}_2) < z_1 + \Delta z_1, z_2 < F(\mathbf{x}_1) < z_2 + \Delta z_2$. That is,

$$\begin{aligned}\{z_1 < \mathbf{z}_1 < z_1 + \Delta z_1,\quad & z_2 < \mathbf{z}_2 < z_2 + \Delta z_2\} \\ &= [\{z_1 < F(\mathbf{x}_1) < z_1 + \Delta z_1\} \cap \{z_2 < F(\mathbf{x}_2) < z_2 + \Delta z_2\}] \\ &\quad \cup [\{z_1 < F(\mathbf{x}_2) < z_1 + \Delta z_1\} \cap \{z_2 < F(\mathbf{x}_1) < z_2 + \Delta z_2\}].\end{aligned}$$

But $\mathbf{x}_1, \mathbf{x}_2$ are independent, so that $F(\mathbf{x}_1)$ and $F(\mathbf{x}_2)$ are also independent. Therefore

$$\begin{aligned}Pr[\{z_1 < F(\mathbf{x}_1) < z_1 + \Delta z_1\} & \cap \{z_2 < F(\mathbf{x}_2) < z_2 + \Delta z_2\}] \\ &= Pr\{z_1 < F(\mathbf{x}_1) < z_1 + \Delta z_1\} \cdot Pr\{z_2 < F(\mathbf{x}_2) < z_2 + \Delta z_2\} \\ &= \Delta z_1 \cdot \Delta z_2,\end{aligned}$$

since, as we found above, $F(\mathbf{x}_1)$ (also $F(\mathbf{x}_2)$) has the uniform distribution over (0,1). Similarly

$$P(\{z_1 < F(\mathbf{x}_2) < z_1 + \Delta z_1\} \cap \{z_2 < F(\mathbf{x}_1) < z_2 + \Delta z_2\}) = \Delta z_1 \cdot \Delta z_2,$$

and we have

$$Pr\{z_1 < \mathbf{z}_1 < z_1 + \Delta z_1, z_2 < \mathbf{z}_2 < z_2 + \Delta z_2\} = 2\Delta z_1 \Delta z_2.$$

Dividing both sides by $\Delta z_1 \Delta z_2$ and taking the limit as $\Delta z_1 \to 0$, $\Delta z_2 \to 0$, we find that

$$h(z_1,z_2) = 2 \text{ if } 0 < z_1 < z_2 < 1.$$

▶ *The joint distribution of* $(\mathbf{z}_1,\mathbf{z}_2)$, *or of* $F(\mathbf{y}_1)$, $F(\mathbf{y}_2)$, *is the uniform distribution over the triangular region* $0 < z_1 < z_2 < 1$.

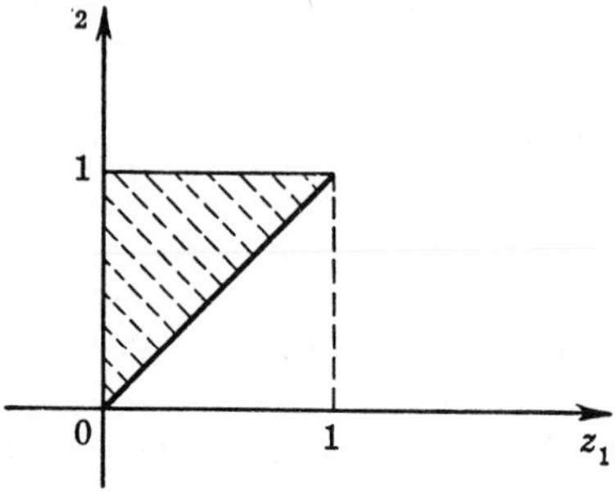

Figure 33

Using the same ideas, we should find that for an arbitrary positive integer n,

▶ *the joint distribution of* $\mathbf{z}_1 = F(\mathbf{y}_1)$, $\mathbf{z}_2 = F(\mathbf{y}_2)$, $\cdots$, $\mathbf{z}_n = F(\mathbf{y}_n)$ *is the uniform distribution (with the constant density function,* $n!$*) over the region* $0 < z_1 < z_2 < \cdots < z_n < 1$.

More generally, if $\mathbf{y}_1, \cdots, \mathbf{y}_n$ are the order statistics of a sample $\mathbf{x}_1, \cdots, \mathbf{x}_n$ of size n from a continuous population with density f, the joint density of $\mathbf{y}_1, \cdots, \mathbf{y}_n$ is given by

$$g(y_1, \cdots, y_n) = n! \prod_{i=1}^{n} f(y_i)$$

if $y_1 < y_2 < \cdots < y_n$, $g(y_1, \cdots, y_n) = 0$ else. (For a neat proof using permutation operators see [9], Chapter 8.)

112. Confidence Intervals for Median and Percentage Points. A *median* of a random variable $\mathbf{x}$ is a number ν such that $Pr\{\mathbf{x} < \nu\} \leq 1/2$, while also $Pr\{\mathbf{x} > \nu\} \leq 1/2$. If $\mathbf{x}$ is a continuous random variable, a median is a number ν such that $F(\nu) = 1/2$, where F is the distribution function of $\mathbf{x}$. If F is strictly increasing, there is just one such number ν.

A *p-quantile* is, similarly, a number ξ_p such that $Pr\{\mathbf{x} < \xi_p\} \leq p$, while also $Pr\{\mathbf{x} > \xi_p\} \leq 1 - p$; if $\mathbf{x}$ is continuous, then $F(\xi_p) = p$. Certain quantiles have special names: the *median*, defined above, which is the 0.5 quantile; the *quartiles*, the 0.25 and 0.75 quantiles; the *quintiles*, the 0.2, 0.4, 0.6, and 0.8 quantiles; the *deciles*, the $0.1, 0.2, \cdots, 0.9$ quantiles, and the *percentiles*, the $0.01, 0.02, \cdots, 0.99$ quantiles. A p-quantile is also called a $100p$ *percentage point.*

The median is a measure of central tendency, analogous to the mean or expectation; half of the distribution, so to speak, falls on either side of the median. The distance between two specified percentage points provides a measure of dispersion, a counterpart of the variance. Such is, for example, the 50 *percent range*, or *interquartile range*, $\xi_{0.75} - \xi_{0.25}$; half the distribution lies between $\xi_{0.25}$ and $\xi_{0.75}$.

We shall now develop a method for determining a confidence interval for a p-quantile, ξ_p.

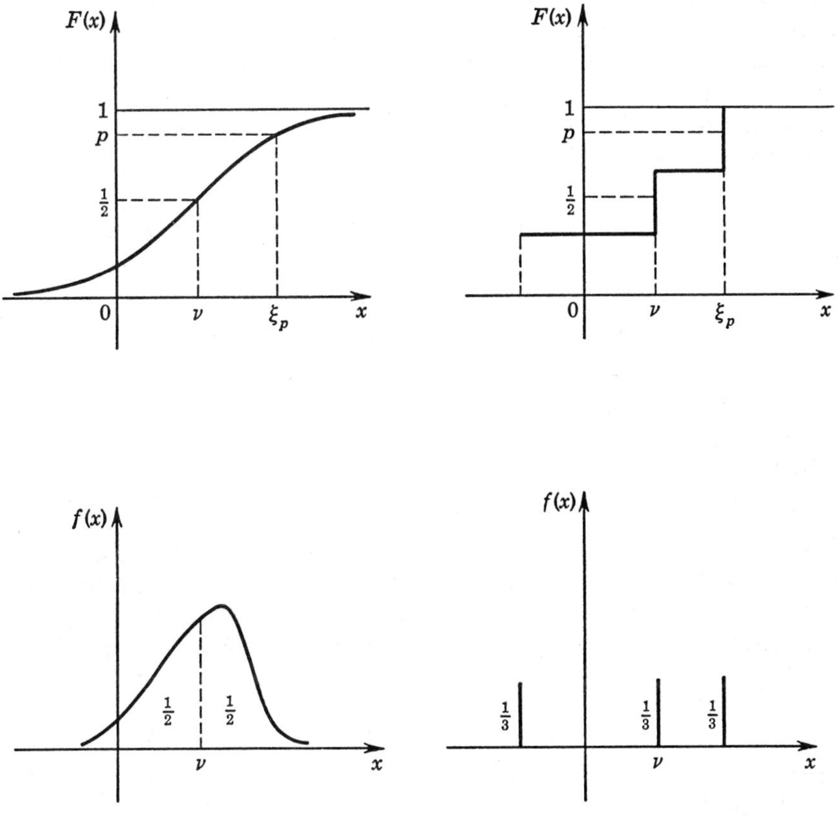

Continuous random variable **x** Discrete random variable **x**

Figure 34

Let $\mathbf{x}_1, \mathbf{x}_2, \cdots, \mathbf{x}_n$ be the sample random variables of a sample of size n from the population determined by a continuous random variable $\mathbf{x}$, whose $100p$ percentage point is ξ_p $(0 < p < 1)$. Again let $\mathbf{y}_1, \mathbf{y}_2, \cdots, \mathbf{y}_n$ denote the order statistics, and let $y_1, y_2, \cdots, y_n$ be their observed values. An interval $[y_i, y_j]$ $(j > i)$ will be a $100(1 - \alpha)\%$ confidence interval for ξ_p if $Pr\{\mathbf{y}_i < \xi_p \leq \mathbf{y}_j\} = 1 - \alpha$. Since this probability is also $Pr\{F(\mathbf{y}_i) < p \leq F(\mathbf{y}_j)\}$, it can be computed from the joint distribution, determined above, of the random variables $F(\mathbf{y}_1), F(\mathbf{y}_2), \cdots, F(\mathbf{y}_n)$. However, it is simpler to compute it as follows. We have

$$S = \{\mathbf{y}_i \geq \xi_p\} \cup \{\mathbf{y}_j < \xi_p\} \cup \{\mathbf{y}_i < \xi_p \leq \mathbf{y}_j\},$$

where S is the sure event. The three events on the right are mutually exclusive, because $\mathbf{y}_i$ cannot be greater than $\mathbf{y}_j$. Therefore

$$Pr\{\mathbf{y}_i < \xi_p \leq \mathbf{y}_j\} = 1 - Pr\{\mathbf{y}_i \geq \xi_p\} - Pr\{\mathbf{y}_j < \xi_p\}.$$

Let us compute $Pr\{\mathbf{y}_j < \xi_p\}$. The jth order statistic, $\mathbf{y}_j$, will be less than ξ_p if and only if at least j of the sample random variables $\mathbf{x}_1, \mathbf{x}_2, \cdots, \mathbf{x}_n$ are less than ξ_p. But these random variables are independent, and the probability that any one will be less than ξ_p is just p, by the definition of ξ_p. Thus this computation may be considered from the point of view of n independent trials of an event with probability p in each. We want the probability of at least j successes; this probability is given by

$$Pr\{\mathbf{y}_j < \xi_p\} = \sum_{k=j}^{n} \binom{n}{k} p^k(1 - p)^{n-k}.$$

Hence

$$Pr\{\mathbf{y}_i < \xi_p \leq \mathbf{y}_j\} = Pr\{\mathbf{y}_i < \xi_p\} - Pr\{\mathbf{y}_j < \xi_p\},$$

or

$$\blacktriangleright \quad Pr\{\mathbf{y}_i < \xi_p \leq \mathbf{y}_j\} = \sum_{k=i}^{j-1} \binom{n}{k} p^k(1 - p)^{n-k}.$$

In order to obtain a $100(1 - \alpha)\%$ confidence interval for ξ_p, it suffices to choose i and j so that $Pr\{\mathbf{y}_i < \xi_p \leq \mathbf{y}_j\}$ (which is the same as $Pr\{\mathbf{y}_i < \xi_p < \mathbf{y}_j\}$, since $\mathbf{x}$ is a continuous random variable) is at least $1 - \alpha$.

EXAMPLE 1. In making an economic survey of a certain state, you have chosen at random 20 farm families in a certain county and have ascertained the cash income of each for a certain year. After being arranged in order, these incomes, in thousands of dollars, were 1.0, 1.2, 1.6, 2.0, 2.1, 2.2, 2.5, 2.8, 3.0, 3.1, 3.2, 3.2, 3.4, 3.6, 4.2, 5.1, 6.0, 8.3, 25.0, 53.7. You wish to set up a 90% confidence interval for the median.

Suppose the number of farm families in the county is large enough so that you can analyze the data as if they were obtained by random sampling (with replacement). The random variable $\mathbf{x}$: "cash income of a farm family chosen at random, etc." is not, strictly speaking, a continuous random variable, but you will make little error if you work as if it were. The sample size is $n = 20$. The sample values of the 20 independent random variables $\mathbf{x}_1, \mathbf{x}_2, \cdots, \mathbf{x}_{20}$ are not given in the order in which they were found, but are arranged in increasing order; so that in effect you have listed the observed values, $y_1 = 1.0, y_2 = 1.2, \cdots, y_{20} = 53.7$, of the order statistics $\mathbf{y}_1, \mathbf{y}_2, \cdots, \mathbf{y}_{20}$.

To determine a 90% confidence interval for the median, you set $p = 1/2$ in the above discussion, and determine integers i and j such that

$$Pr\{\mathbf{y}_i < \nu \leq \mathbf{y}_j\} = \sum_{k=i}^{j-1} \binom{20}{k} \left(\frac{1}{2}\right)^{20} = 0.90.$$

From tables of the summed binomial distribution function we find

$$\sum_{k=7}^{20} \binom{20}{k} \left(\frac{1}{2}\right)^{20} = 0.9423,$$

while $\sum_{k=14}^{20} = 0.0577$, so that $i = 7, j = 14$ would give a probability $0.9423 - 0.0577 = 0.8846$. Also $\sum_{k=6}^{20} = 0.9793$, so that $i = 6$, $j = 14$ would give a probability 0.9216. Further, $\sum_{k=5}^{20} = 0.9941$ while $\sum_{k=13}^{20} = 0.1316$, so that $i = 5$, $j = 13$ gives a probability 0.8625. The confidence interval you would prefer to state might be (y_6, y_{14}) or $(2.2, 3.6)$, a 92% confidence interval for the median cash income, in thousands of dollars.

113. Tolerance Limits. Employed by a fabricating concern, you are assigned the problem of designing a simple inspection procedure to keep under surveillance incoming stocks of a certain kind of resistor, whose resistance is supposed to be about 50 ohms. You prefer to make no assumption other than continuity as to the distribution of the resistances, and to base your inspection program on order statistics, because of their simplicity. You choose appropriate numbers α and β, and propose to initiate a program which will involve taking a sample of size n, where n is so chosen that the probability is α that at least $100\beta\%$ of the population of resistances will lie between the smallest and the largest sample values. That is, the probability is to be α that sample values will be obtained such that $Pr\{y_1 < \mathbf{x} < y_n\} = \beta$; here $\mathbf{x}$ is the population random variable, and y_1, y_n are the smallest and largest sample values.

Let $\mathbf{x}$ be the random variable: "resistance of a resistor chosen at random from the resistors supplied," and let $F(x)$ be its distribution function. Let $\mathbf{x}_1, \mathbf{x}_2, \cdots, \mathbf{x}_n$ be the sample random variables of a random sample of size n, let $\mathbf{y}_1, \mathbf{y}_2, \cdots, \mathbf{y}_n$ be the order statistics, and let $\mathbf{z}_i = F(\mathbf{y}_i), i = 1, 2, \cdots, n$. For each number x, the proportion of the population less than x is represented by $F(x) = Pr\{\mathbf{x} < x\}$. Therefore the random variable: "proportion of the population smaller than the largest sample random variable" is $\mathbf{z}_n = F(\mathbf{y}_n)$; the random variable: "proportion of the population smaller than the smallest sample random variable" is $\mathbf{z}_1 = F(\mathbf{y}_1)$; and the random variable: "proportion of the population which lies between the smallest and largest sample random variables" is $\mathbf{z}_n - \mathbf{z}_1$. You seek, then, a sample size n such that

$$Pr\{\mathbf{z}_n - \mathbf{z}_1 \geq \beta\} = \alpha.$$

We have seen that the joint density function of the random variables $\mathbf{z}_1, \mathbf{z}_2, \cdots, \mathbf{z}_n$ is the constant $n!$ over the set $0 < z_1 < z_2 < \cdots < z_n < 1$ in the n-dimensional $z_1, z_2, \cdots, z_n$ space, and is 0 elsewhere. We can find the above probability by integrating this joint density function over the subset for which $z_n - z_1 \geq \beta$. In order for a point $(z_1, z_2, \cdots, z_n)$ to be in this subset, we must have $0 < z_1 < 1 - \beta$; with z_1 fixed, we must have $z_1 + \beta \leq z_n < 1$; with z_1 and z_n fixed, we must have $z_1 < z_{n-1} < z_n$; etc. Thus

$$\begin{aligned} Pr\{\mathbf{z}_n - \mathbf{z}_1 \geq \beta\} \\ &= n! \int_0^{1-\beta} dz_1 \int_{z_1+\beta}^{1} dz_n \int_{z_1}^{z_n} dz_{n-1} \int_{z_1}^{z_{n-1}} dz_{n-2} \cdots \int_{z_1}^{z_4} dz_3 \int_{z_1}^{z_3} dz_2 \\ &= 1 - \beta^n - n\beta^{n-1}(1 - \beta). \end{aligned}$$

If you decide on numbers β and α, then you have to solve the equation

$$1 - \beta^n - n\beta^{n-1}(1 - \beta) = \alpha,$$

and essentially this equation must be solved by trial and error. However, if, as is usual, β is near 1 so that $1 - \beta$ is small, you can find a trial value of n as follows: If we write

$$\beta^n + n\beta^{n-1}(1 - \beta) = 1 - \alpha,$$

the left number is an expression for the probability of fewer than 2 successes in n independent trials of an event with probability $(1 - \beta)$. Using the Poisson approximation (page 116) we have

$$\beta^n + n\beta^{n-1}(1 - \beta) \doteq e^{-\lambda}(1 + \lambda),$$

where $\lambda = n(1 - \beta)$. One can determine very quickly from a table of the negative exponential the value of λ for which

$$e^{-\lambda}(1 + \lambda) = 1 - \alpha;$$

then

$$n \doteq \frac{\lambda}{1 - \beta}.$$

For example, suppose you want a probability at least 0.95 that at least 95% of the population will lie between the smallest and greatest sample values. You have $\alpha = \beta = 0.95$, $1 - \alpha = 0.05$, and find $\lambda = 4.74$. A trial value of n is $\lambda/(1 - \beta) = 4.74/0.05 = 95$. You then find, by trial and error, or by an iterative method, such as Newton's, that $Pr\{\mathbf{z}_n - \mathbf{z}_1 \geq 0.95\} = 0.950$ if $n = 93$, so that 93 trials are required.

PROBLEMS

1. If $n = 10$, what degree of confidence will be associated with the interval $y_4 < \nu < y_7$, as a confidence interval for the median ν?

2. You have polled 20 farmers as to the percentage increase in feed bills during the past year. The responses, in percentages, were as follows: 19, 18, 11, 26, 12, 10, 19, 17, 23, 15, 18, 17, 20, 26, 29, 11, 11, 10, 24, 25. Use order statistics and binomial tables to determine an 80% confidence interval for the 0.25 quantile.

3. (a) Suppose that you wish to use order statistics to determine a $100\,(1 - \alpha)\%$ confidence interval for the p-quantile, from a random sample of size n. If n is sufficiently large for the use of the normal approximation to the binomial distribution with parameters n, p, explain how you would use normal tables to determine which order statistics will be the confidence limits.

(b) Apply (a) with $\alpha = 0.05$, $n = 30$, $p = 0.75$.

4. How large a sample size is required in order that the probability shall be 0.90 that at least 90% of the population will lie between the smallest and largest sample values?

5. Suppose the director of your division requires you to choose a sample size so that the probability is 0.99 that 99% of the population will lie between the smallest and largest sample values. How large a sample size is required?

6. Show that the distribution function $G(y_1)$ of the smallest sample value $\mathbf{y}_1$ in a sample of size n from the population determined by a random variable $\mathbf{x}$ having distribution function F is $G(y_1) = 1 - [1 - F(y_1)]^n$.

7. Show that the distribution function $H(y_n)$ of the largest sample value $\mathbf{y}_n$ in a sample of size n from the population determined by a random variable $\mathbf{x}$ having distribution function F is $H(y_n) = [F(y_n)]^n$.

8. A table of *random normal numbers* (*or random deviates*) is a table of numbers drawn from (or which might have been drawn from) a normal (0,1) distribution.

(a) Describe how you could use a table of random numbers and a table of the normal distribution function to secure a table of random deviates.

(b) Apply your technique in (a) to obtain from the table of random numbers a short table of 20 random normal numbers.

9. Show that if $\mathbf{x}$ is a continuous random variable whose distribution is symmetric about the origin (that is, $F(-x) = 1 - F(x)$, or $f(-x) = f(x)$) and if $E(\mathbf{x})$ exists (it must then be 0), then the average, $\frac{1}{2}[\mathbf{y}_1 + \mathbf{y}_n]$, of the largest and smallest sample random variables of a sample of size n has expectation 0.

10. What are the distribution function and density function of $\mathbf{z}_n - \mathbf{z}_1$ (see pages 345, 346 for notation)?

11. Suppose the population random variable $\mathbf{x}$ is uniformly distributed over $(-1,1)$. Find the distribution function and density function of $\mathbf{y}_n - \mathbf{y}_1$, the *range* (see pages 345, 346 for notation).

Hint. $\mathbf{y}_i = 2\mathbf{z}_i - 1$; why?

12. Let $\mathbf{y}_1, \mathbf{y}_2$ be the order statistics of a sample of size 2 from a normal population with mean 0 and standard deviation σ.

(a) Show that the density function of $\mathbf{y}_2$ is

$$\frac{1}{\pi\sigma^2} e^{-y_2^2/2\sigma^2} \int_{-\infty}^{y_2} e^{-t^2/2\sigma^2}\, dt.$$

(b) Show that $E(\mathbf{y}_2) = \sigma/\sqrt{\pi}$.

Hint. Change the order of integration in the integral defining $E(\mathbf{y}_2)$.

13. Let $\mathbf{y}_1, \cdots, \mathbf{y}_n$ be the order statistics of a random sample of size n from a population with continuous distribution function F, and set $\mathbf{z}_i = F(\mathbf{y}_i)$, $i = 1, 2, \cdots, n$. Show that $\mathbf{z}_{n-1}$ has the same distribution as $\mathbf{z}_n - \mathbf{z}_1$.

114. Runs Test for Randomness. In many sampling experiments, the nature of the experiment is such as to assure that the sample obtained is a random sample, or nearly so. In others, the investigator may wish to test whether or not the data secured are consistent with the assumption that the sample random variables are independent and identically distributed. For example, if the quality of an article produced by a machine is checked hourly, machine or operator fatigue may void the assumption that the article produced at 9 A.M. comes from the same population as that produced at 4 P.M.

As another example, suppose that you are engaged in the following problem in consumer research. You are employed by a candy manufacturer to test the preference of children for various kinds of candy. If you interview children on a playground from nine in the morning till noon, you may suspect that non-randomness may enter in either of two ways. First, the reaction of the child may change with the approach of lunch time, so that the quantity being measured at 11:30 may not have the same distribution as that being measured at 9:30. Second, conversations between children already interviewed and those to be interviewed may render the later results somewhat dependent on the earlier.

A frequently used test of randomness is the "runs" test. Suppose, for example, that in the period from nine till noon you have asked 20 children to express their preferences between sugar fluff (S) and chocolate bar (C). If the responses were

S C S C S C S C S C S C S C S C S C S C,

you would probably doubt that randomness was an appropriate assumption. You might suspect that some born leader had organized a campaign to confuse you. In general, an exceptionally large number of runs might lead you to suspect that the observations were not completely independent; in the above, there are 20 runs of length 1 each. Suppose you observed

S S S S S C C C C C C C C C C C C C C C.

Again you would be suspicious of the hypothesis of randomness. You might suspect that on the one hand conversations among the children were robbing the observations of independence, and on the other that there was an increasing preference for the more substantial chocolate bar as lunch time approached. Here there are only two runs. Had the results been

S C S S S C S C C S C S S C S C C C S S,

involving 13 runs, you might have considered your data consistent with the assumption of randomness.

Again, suppose that every 15 minutes the diameter of a bolt produced by a machine is measured, with the following results (in centimeters):

1.02, 0.97, 0.94, 1.05, 0.99, 1.03, 0.98, 1.07, 1.04, 1.00,
1.06, 1.04, 1.09, 1.05, 1.05, 1.10, 1.09, 1.04, 1.11, 1.07.

There seems a drift in the direction of larger diameters, suggesting that the later observations may be drawn from a different population, or different populations, than are the first. A "runs" test can be applied to the data, if each observation is first designated as *low* (L), if smaller than some conveniently chosen number such as the median, or *high* (H), if larger. Half are 1.04 or smaller, and designating these as L we obtain

L L L H L L L H L L H L H H H H H L H H,

which involves 10 runs.

In general, failures of randomness may result either in an unexpectedly large number of runs, or in an unexpectedly small number of runs. An appropriate test of randomness against both alternatives would reject the hypothesis if the number of runs observed were either too high or too low (two-tail test). It appears, however, that most frequently one is concerned with defects which tend to produce long runs and hence a small number of runs, whereas one is often able to discount the possibility of defects tending to produce short runs. In such a situation an appropriate test to employ would reject the hypothesis of randomness only if too few runs were observed (one-tail test).

115. The Distribution of the Number of Runs. To set up either test, we require the distribution of r, the number of runs, *under the hypothesis of random sampling.* We shall derive this distribution under the assumption that all arrangements of a given n_L symbols L and a given $n_H = n - n_L$ symbols H are equally probable. We propose now to describe more completely the procedure to be followed, with a view to justifying the assumption that the arrangements mentioned are equally probable.

Let $\mathbf{x}$ be the population random variable. *We abandon now the hypothesis that its distribution function is continuous; x may be continuous or discrete.* We let $\mathbf{x}_1, \mathbf{x}_2, \cdots, \mathbf{x}_n$ be the sample random variables of a sample of size n. *Before conducting the experiment,* the investigator chooses two integers, n_L and n_H, whose sum is n (at any rate, his choice should not be influenced by the results of the experiment). After obtaining sample values $x_1, x_2, \cdots, x_n$, arranged in the order in which they were obtained, he replaces each of the n_L smallest values by the symbol L, and each of the n_H largest by the symbol H. He then counts the number r of runs, and bases his decision on whether or not to reject the hypothesis of randomness on the observed value r.

If two or more sample values coincide, then it may not be possible to follow this procedure precisely as described, for there may not be exactly n_L observations smaller than the others. This will happen, theoretically, with probability 0 if the population is continuous; though of course, in practice, measurements are neither made nor recorded with absolute precision. In the discrete case, however, the probability is positive that two or more values will coincide; indeed, if the sample size is larger than the number of values attainable by the population random variable, then two or more sample values must coincide.

This was the situation, for example, of the instructor who had graded 100 examination papers, and wished to assign precisely 7 grades of F. However, 10 students had each scored 0 on the examination. He therefore stood at the head of a stair and tossed the ten papers down it. The seven papers falling nearest the bottom were assigned grade F, the others passing grades.

No doubt the instructor prided himself on his fair-minded attitude, and was surprised at the criticism his action evoked from his students and colleagues as well. However, to return to our sampling situation, if there are not precisely n_L lowest values, enough are to be chosen *at random* from the appropriate group of equal values to yield in all n_L values, each to be replaced by the symbol L. Each of the remaining is then replaced by the symbol H.

Let us consider the example above, where you are testing preference between sugar fluff (S) and chocolate bars (C). You can describe your experiment as a sampling experiment by letting the population random variable $\mathbf{x}$ assume only two values: 1, corresponding to S, and 0, corresponding to C.

The observed result

S C S S S C S C C S C S S C S C C C S S

could then be recorded as

1 0 1 1 1 0 1 0 0 1 0 1 1 0 1 0 0 0 1 1

($x_1 = 1, x_2 = 0, x_3 = 1$, etc.). As it stands, there are 13 runs. But *the a priori probability of obtaining* 13 *or more runs depends on the unknown probability p associated with the value* 1. On the other hand, suppose you had decided beforehand to record the 10 lowest scores as L, the 10 highest as H. You find that there are only nine 0's, and so choose at random (using a table of random numbers, for example), one of the eleven 1's to be recorded as L. Suppose you choose the third. Your recorded sequence is now

H L H L H L H L L H L H H L H L L L H H,

involving 10 L's and 10 H's, and 15 runs. The advantage of this procedure is that the probability, under the hypothesis of randomness, of a specified number of runs is now independent of the unknown probability p that a child will prefer sugar fluff.

We have yet to verify that in the general situation all arrangements of n_L symbols L and n_H symbols H are equally probable, *under the assumption that the* $\mathbf{x}_1, \mathbf{x}_2, \cdots, \mathbf{x}_n$ *form a random sample.* The reason this is true will be clearer if we describe the procedure in terms of the order statistics $\mathbf{y}_1, \mathbf{y}_2, \cdots, \mathbf{y}_n$. The sample values are to be written down in the order in which they were obtained:

$$x_1, x_2, \cdots, x_n.$$

Now replace each sample value by the order statistic to which it is equal. If two or more sample values are equal, they are to be ordered at random (for example, using a table of random numbers). For example, suppose that in the machine example above the use of a table of random numbers gives the ordering 3, 1, 2 to the three observations 1.04, the ordering 2, 1, 3 to the three observations 1.05, the ordering 1, 2 to the two observations 1.07, and the ordering 2, 1 to the two observations 1.09. On replacing each sample value x_i by the order statistic y_j to which it is equal, we obtain

$$y_6, y_2, y_1, y_{12}, y_4, y_7, y_3, y_{15}, y_{10}, y_5, y_{14}, y_8, y_{18}, y_{11}, y_{13}, y_{19}, y_{17}, y_9, y_{20}, y_{16}.$$

Suppose we had decided on $n_L = n_H = 10$. Then the order statistics $y_1, y_2, \cdots, y_{10}$ would each be replaced by L, and each of the others would be replaced by H, to obtain

L L L H L L L H L L H L H H H H H L H H.

Returning to the general situation, we observe first that there are $n!$ possible permutations of the order statistics; for in the first place may appear any one of the n order statistics, in the second place any of the remaining $n - 1$, etc. Further, these $n!$ permutations are equally probable; they have the same probability of occurring. This is guaranteed by considerations of symmetry: for the sample random variables are independent and identically distributed; hence for each i and j, and for each given index k, the probability that $\mathbf{x}_i$ will be the kth order statistic $\mathbf{y}_k$ is the same as the probability that $\mathbf{x}_j$ will be $\mathbf{y}_k$ $(k = 1, 2, \cdots, n;\ i = 1, 2, \cdots, n;\ j = 1, 2, \cdots n)$. Thus each $\mathbf{y}_k$ is as likely to appear in any place as in any other when the results are recorded in the order in which they were observed.

Each of the n_L smallest order statistics is to be replaced by the symbol L, and each of the others by the symbol H. If the positions of two of the n_L smallest order statistics were to be interchanged, the arrangement of L's and H's would not be affected. Thus for each fixed permutation of the n_H largest order statistics, there are $n_L!$ permutations of the n_L lowest order statistics which would leave the arrangement of L's and H's unchanged. But there are also $n_H!$ permutations of the n_H largest y's which would leave the arrangement of H's and L's unchanged; for each of these there are $n_L!$ permutations of the n_L smallest y's yielding the same arrangement of L's and H's. Thus each arrangement of L's and H's corresponds to $n_L!n_H!$ possible permutations of the y's. Since these permutations all have the same probability, $1/n!$, of occurrence, the probability of occurrence of any given arrangement is

$$\frac{n_L!n_H!}{n!} = \frac{1}{\binom{n}{n_L}} = \frac{1}{\binom{n}{n_H}}.$$

It follows that the arrangements are equally probable.

Before turning to the derivation of the distribution of the number of runs, we observe that it is a common practice to choose n_L and n_H to be equal, if n is even, and to differ by just 1 if n is odd.

The probability of any given arrangement was found to be $1\Big/\binom{n}{n_L}$ $= 1\Big/\binom{n}{n_H}$. It remains to determine, for each r, the number of arrangements which have r runs (cf. [5], Chapter 2). Let, first, k be a positive integer not greater than n_L. Imagine the n_L symbols L strung out in a row; consider how many ways points of division can be chosen so as to divide the string of n_L symbols L into k runs. Among $n_L - 1$ possible places, $k - 1$ must be chosen as points of subdivision, and this can be done in $\binom{n_L - 1}{k - 1}$ ways. Similarly, the n_H symbols H can be divided into k runs in $\binom{n_H - 1}{k - 1}$ ways. On inserting the first $k - 1$ runs of H

successively as division "points," for the $k-1$ runs of L, and adding the last run of H at the end, one obtains one of the possible arrangements of k runs of L and k runs of H, $2k$ runs in all. Thus there are $\binom{n_L-1}{k-1}\binom{n_H-1}{k-1}$ ways of obtaining $2k$ runs starting with a run of L and similarly $\binom{n_H-1}{k-1}\binom{n_L-1}{k-1}$ ways of obtaining $2k$ runs starting with a run of H. We find then that

$$\blacktriangleright \qquad Pr\{\mathbf{r}=2k\} = 2\binom{n_L-1}{k-1}\binom{n_H-1}{k-1}\bigg/\binom{n}{n_L}.$$

Also, the number of ways of choosing k points of subdivision to insert among n_L symbols L in order to obtain $k+1$ runs of L is $\binom{n_L-1}{k}$. If k runs of H are inserted, one obtains $2k+1$ runs in all. Thus the number of arrangements of $2k+1$ runs starting with a run of L is $\binom{n_L-1}{k}\binom{n_H-1}{k-1}$. Similarly, the number of arrangements of $2k+1$ runs starting with a run of H is $\binom{n_H-1}{k}\binom{n_L-1}{k-1}$, so that

$$\blacktriangleright \quad Pr\{\mathbf{r}=2k+1\} = \left[\binom{n_L-1}{k}\binom{n_H-1}{k-1} + \binom{n_H-1}{k}\binom{n_L-1}{k-1}\bigg/\binom{n}{n_L}\right]$$

The expectation and variance of $\mathbf{r}$ can be calculated directly from the definition, using the above expressions for the probability function. Another way utilizes the connection between sequences of n symbols L and H and sampling without replacement from a finite population. Under the hypothesis of random sampling, the arrangement of L's and H's may be regarded as obtained by sampling without replacement from a finite population of n_H symbols H and n_L symbols L. Let 1 be scored for H, -1 for L; i.e., let the population random variable $\mathbf{x}$ take the value 1 with probability $p = n_H/n$ and the value -1 with probability $q = n_L/n = 1-p$. The ith sample random variable $\mathbf{x}_i$ will be 1 if the symbol in the ith place is H, -1 if it is L. We note that the product $\mathbf{x}_i\mathbf{x}_{i-1}$ will be -1 if the symbols in the places $i-1$ and i are different, $+1$ if they are the same. Accordingly, if we set $\mathbf{z}_1 = 1$, $\mathbf{z}_i = (1-\mathbf{x}_i\mathbf{x}_{i-1})/2$, $i = 2, 3, \cdots, n$, then $\mathbf{z}_i$ will be 1 if a run starts in the ith place, 0 if it does not. Thus the number r of runs is given by the formula

$$\mathbf{r} = \sum_{i=1}^{n} \mathbf{z}_i = 1 + (n-1)/2 - \sum_{i=2}^{n} \mathbf{x}_i\mathbf{x}_{i-1}/2.$$

We have $E(\mathbf{x}) = (1)p + (-1)q = p - q$ and $E(\mathbf{x}^2) = 1$, since $\mathbf{x}^2$ is the constant 1. The formula obtained on page 317 for $E(\mathbf{x}_1\mathbf{x}_2)$ is:

$$E(\mathbf{x}_1\mathbf{x}_2) = \{n[E(\mathbf{x})]^2 - E(\mathbf{x}^2)\}/(n-1),$$

so that here

$$E(\mathbf{x}_i\mathbf{x}_{i-1}) = E(\mathbf{x}_1\mathbf{x}_2) = [n(p-q)^2 - 1]/(n-1)$$

which reduces to $1 - 4npq/(n-1)$, $i = 1, 2, \cdots, n$. Then

$$\begin{aligned} E(\mathbf{r}) &= 1 + (n-1)/2 - (n-1)[1 - 4npq/(n-1)]/2 \\ &= 1 + 2npq. \end{aligned}$$

A formula for $V(\mathbf{r})$ can be obtained similarly.

Let $\mu = E(\mathbf{r})$ and $\sigma^2 = V(\mathbf{r})$; then the results obtained are

▶
$$\mu = 2npq + 1,$$
$$\sigma^2 = (\mu - 1)(\mu - 2)/(n-1),$$

where $p = n_L/n$ *and* $q = 1 - p = n_H/n$.

It can be shown that the distribution of $(\mathbf{r} - \mu)/\sigma$ tends to the normal (0,1) distribution as $n \to \infty$ in such a way that p (and hence q) remains constant. It is claimed that the normal distribution with the above mean μ and standard deviation σ furnishes an adequate approximation to the distribution of $\mathbf{r}$ when n_L and n_H both exceed 10. For further discussion and references, see [5], [6], and [22].

EXAMPLE 2. Suppose $n_L = n_H = 10$, so that $p = q = 1/2$. We shall use the normal approximation, with $\mu = 2npq + 1 = 11$, $\sigma^2 = (\mu - 1) \cdot (\mu - 2)/(n-1) = 4.73$, $\sigma = 2.18$.

(a) Suppose we are in a situation such as that of the investigator of preferences for sugar fluff and chocolate bars, who does not feel able to discard *a priori* the possibility that non-randomness may give rise to too many runs. We therefore wish a two-tail test, one which will test against both alternatives: too many runs, and too few runs. If we decide to test at the 10% significance level, we choose numbers a and b such that $Pr\{\mathbf{r} < a\} = 0.05$ and $Pr\{\mathbf{r} > b\} = 0.05$. Assuming $\mathbf{r}$ approximately normal with mean 11 and standard deviation 2.18, we have $Pr\{(\mathbf{r} - 11)/2.18 < -1.64\} = 0.05$, $Pr\{(\mathbf{r} - 11)/2.18 > 1.64\} = 0.05$, and the critical region for the test consists of the two intervals $r < 11 - 1.64(2.18) = 7.42$ and $r > 11 + 1.64(2.18) = 14.58$. Suppose the observations were as reported on page 357. The procedure using $n_H = n_L = 10$ led to the sequence on page 357::

H L H L H L H L L H L H H L H L L L H H,

involving 15 runs. This number does fall in the critical region, and the hypothesis of randomness is to be rejected, at the 10% significance level.

(b) Let us consider now the machine situation discussed on page 355. Let us suppose here that the only possible causes of non-randomness about which we are concerned are such as would tend to produce long runs, few in number. We shall reject, at the $100\alpha\%$ significance level, the hypothesis of randomness in favor of non-randomness tending to produce too few runs, if too few runs are observed. The observed sequence was

L L L H L L L H L L H L H H H H H L H H,

involving 10 runs. Since $Pr\{\mathbf{r} < 7.42\} \doteq 0.05$, we would reject at the 5% significance level only if 7 or fewer runs were observed. Indeed, the observed number of runs is nearly equal to the expected number. If you suspect a drift in the machine, you will need a larger number of observations to detect it, using this test.

116. Runs Test for Identity of Two Distributions. Situations frequently arise in which the investigator requires a test enabling him to decide whether or not his data support the conclusion that two specified distributions fail to be identical. The *t*-test (page 258) for the difference between means is applicable to some situations of this kind, in which the populations are known to be normal with the same standard deviation. Sometimes, however, such an assumption will not be justified, and one will require a test which involves no assumption as to the form of the distribution.

Suppose, for example, you wish to test the hypothesis that two machines are producing bolts whose diameters have the same distribution. You take a random sample of size n_1 from the population of diameters of bolts produced by the first machine. Let $\mathbf{x}_1, \mathbf{x}_2, \cdots, \mathbf{x}_{n_1}$ denote the sample random variables of this sample. Similarly, let $\mathbf{y}_1, \mathbf{y}_2, \cdots, \mathbf{y}_{n_2}$ denote the sample random variables of a sample of size n_2 from the population of diameters of bolts produced by the second machine. Now order all $n = n_1 + n_2$ sample values in increasing order. You will have a row of groups of x values intermingled with groups of y values. Count the total number of runs: the number of runs of x values, plus the number of runs of y values. If the distributions of the two populations are not the same, there will tend to be longer runs, and hence fewer runs, than if the populations were the same. Thus a way of testing the hypothesis that the distributions are the same against the alternative that they are not is to reject the hypothesis if too few runs are obtained.

As another example, suppose you are a dentist, and wish to test the claims of rival manufacturers of dental cleansing preparations, A and B. You choose at random 12 of your patients and induce them to agree to use A for a year, while 15 others are persuaded to use B. At the end of a year, your records of the numbers of cavities developed in these patients are as follows:

A: 6 2 1 7 2 4 7 5 5 4 6 8

B: 11 1 3 7 6 7 10 3 8 6 7 2 12 6 11.

Let $x_1, x_2, \cdots, x_{12}$ denote the observed numbers of cavities of those using

A, and $y_1, y_2, \cdots, y_{15}$ the numbers of cavities of those using B. You order all 25 observed values according to increasing size, ordering by a random process those numbers occurring more than once, and obtain, say,

$$x_3\, y_2\, x_5\, x_2\, y_{12}\, y_3\, y_8\, x_{10}\, x_6\, x_8\, x_9\, x_1\, y_5\, y_{10}\, x_{11}\, y_{14}$$

$$y_6\, y_4\, x_7\, y_{11}\, x_4\, x_{12}\, y_9\, y_7\, y_{15}\, y_1\, y_{13};$$

there are 12 runs.

In order to be able to decide whether or not the number of runs is small enough to be significant at, say, the 5% level, you need to know the distribution of the number **r** of runs. We shall show that the distribution of **r** is just the same as that derived in the preceding section, with n_L and n_H replaced by n_1 and n_2. The earlier derivation of the distribution of the number of runs depended only on the fact that in that case all possible arrangements of L's and H's were equally probable. It will suffice here, then, to show that all possible arrangements of x's and y's are equally probable, *under the hypothesis to be tested:* namely, that the two samples, $x_1, x_2, \cdots, x_{n_1}$, and $y_1, y_2, \cdots, y_{n_2}$, come from populations with the same distribution. This again is clear from considerations of symmetry. For under the null hypothesis, the $n = n_1 + n_2$ random variables are independent and identically distributed. Therefore the probability that after they are arranged in increasing order the value of a particular random variable will occupy a specified place is the same as the probability that it will occupy any other. Or again, the probability of obtaining any particular ordering, or permutation, of the n sample random variables is the same as that of obtaining any other. We find as in the above section that there are precisely $n_1!n_2!$ different permutations which yield the same arrangement. The probability of any particular arrangement is therefore $n!/n_1!n_2! = \binom{n}{n_1} = \binom{n}{n_2}$, so that all arrangements have the same *a priori* probability, under the null hypothesis.

In the example we have been considering, we had $n_1 = 12$, $n_2 = 15$, $n = 27$, $r = 12$. Therefore $p = n_1/n = 4/9$, $q = n_2/n = 5/9$, $\mu = 2npq + 1 = 40/3$, and $\sigma^2 = (\mu - 1)(\mu - 2)/(n - 1) = (37/3)(34/3)/26 = 5.38$, $\sigma = 2.32$. To be significant at the 5% level, the observed value of **r** would have to satisfy

$$r < \mu - 1.64\sigma = 9.5,$$

whereas the observed value was 12. You are therefore not justified in rejecting the hypothesis that the populations have the same distribution. Neither, of course, can you conclude that the preparations are in fact equivalent; your result suggests only that the difference, if any, is not great enough to be substantiated by a sample of this size.

117. Kolmogorov-Smirnov Test of Identity of Populations. The Kolmogorov-Smirnov test is applicable when the distributions of the parent populations are continuous. Let $\mathbf{S} = \mathbf{S}(u)$ denote the empiric distribution function determined by the sample random variables $\mathbf{x}_1, \mathbf{x}_2, \cdots, \mathbf{x}_{n_1}$ (page 137); plotted against the real variable u, it has a saltus, or jump, of magnitude $1/n_1$ at each observed value $u = x_1, u = x_2$, etc. of one of the sample random variables. Similarly, let $\mathbf{T} = \mathbf{T}(u)$ denote the empiric distribution function determined by sample random variables $\mathbf{y}_1, \mathbf{y}_2, \cdots, \mathbf{y}_{n_2}$. The Kolmogorov-Smirnov test of the hypothesis that the two populations have the same distribution uses the statistic

$$\mathbf{A} = \max_u |\mathbf{S}(u) - \mathbf{T}(u)|;$$

the observed value A of $\mathbf{A}$ will be the greatest absolute difference in height between the two empiric distribution functions, S and T. If an appropriately large value of $\mathbf{A}$ is observed, one rejects the hypothesis that the populations have the same distribution in favor of the alternative that they do not. The asymptotic distribution of $\mathbf{A}$ is given by

$$Pr\{\mathbf{A} \le zN^{-1/2}\} \to L(z) \text{ as } n_1, n_2 \to \infty;$$

here

$$N = n_1 n_2/(n_1 + n_2),$$

and

$$L(z) = 1 - 2\sum_{j=1}^{\infty} (-1)^{j-1} e^{-2j^2 z^2} = \frac{\sqrt{2\pi}}{z} \sum_{j=1}^{\infty} e^{-(2j-1)^2\pi^2/8z^2} \text{ for } z > 0,$$

$$L(z) = 0 \text{ for } z \le 0.$$

118. Median Test. The runs test, roughly speaking, tests against differences in location and shape of the distribution function indiscriminately. The median test, on the other hand, is sensitive to differences in location, very insensitive to differences in shape. That is, the median test may be regarded as a test of the hypothesis that two distributions have the same median against the alternative that their medians are different (two-tail test), or against the alternative that a specified one of the two distributions has a greater median than the other (one-tail test).

Strictly speaking, however, the distribution of the statistic we shall use is not determined solely by the hypothesis that the two distributions have the same median, and the test is put again as a test of the null hypothesis,

H_0: *the distributions of the* $\mathbf{x}$ *population and the* $\mathbf{y}$ *population are identical.*

Let $\mathbf{x}_1, \mathbf{x}_2, \cdots, \mathbf{x}_{n_1}$ be the random variables of a random sample of size n_1 from the $\mathbf{x}$ population, and $\mathbf{y}_1, \mathbf{y}_2, \cdots, \mathbf{y}_{n_2}$ the random variables of a random sample of size n_2 from the $\mathbf{y}$ population. Order the $n = n_1 + n_2$ observed values in order of increasing size. Let m_1 denote the number of x values appearing to the right of the sample median, and m_2 the number of y values appearing to the right of the sample median. If the sample medians are the same, one should expect, with large samples, that m_1 would be about half of n_1, and m_2 about half of n_2.

We shall now proceed to derive the probability distribution of $\mathbf{m}_1$, under the assumption that the two populations have the same distribution; so that $\mathbf{x}_1, \mathbf{x}_2, \cdots, \mathbf{x}_{n_1}; \mathbf{y}_1, \mathbf{y}_2, \cdots, \mathbf{y}_{n_2}$ are independent and identically distributed random variables. For a fixed positive integer $r < n$, let $\mathbf{z}_r$ denote the rth order statistic of the sample of size n. When the n sample values, x's and y's, are arranged in increasing order, there will then be exactly $n - r$ of them greater than z_r. For the moment we shall not insist on taking z_r to be the median. Let $\mathbf{m}_1$ denote the number of x values which will be greater than $\mathbf{z}_r$, and $\mathbf{m}_2 = n - r - \mathbf{m}_1$ the number of y values which will be greater than $\mathbf{z}_r$. There are $n(n-1)\cdots(n-[n-r]+1) = n!/r!$ possible *permutations* of the x's and y's which may fall in the last $n - r$ spaces in the ordering. As in the previous discussions, these permutations are equally likely, since the n sample random variables are independent and identically distributed, under the null hypothesis H_0. Let us count now the number of these permutations in which will appear m_1 symbols x and $m_2 = n - r - m_1$ symbols y. First, there are $\binom{n-r}{m_1}$ ways in which m_1 of the $n - r$ last spaces can be chosen, to be filled with x's. For each choice of m_1 spaces, there are $n_1(n_1 - 1) \cdots (n_1 - m_1 + 1) = n_1!/(n_1 - m_1)!$ permutations of the m_1 x's in those spaces, chosen from among the n_1 x's available. For each of these, there are $n_2(n_2 - 1) \cdots (n_2 - m_2 + 1) = n_2!/(n_2 - m_2)!$ permutations of the n_2 y's available to fill the remaining m_2 spaces. Thus the total number of permutations involving precisely m_1 symbols x and $m_2 = n - r - m_1$ symbols y is

$$\binom{n-r}{m_1}\frac{n_1!}{(n_1 - m_1)!}\frac{n_2!}{(n_2 - m_2)!} = (n-r)!\binom{n_1}{m_1}\binom{n_2}{m_2}.$$

The *a priori* probability of the realization of any particular permutation is $1/(n!/r!) = r!/n!$. Therefore the probability that there will be m_1 symbols x and m_2 symbols y in the last $n - r$ spaces is

$$\frac{r!}{n!}(n-r)!\binom{n_1}{m_1}\binom{n_2}{m_2} = \frac{\binom{n_1}{m_1}\binom{n_2}{m_2}}{\binom{n}{r}}.$$

Let $\mathbf{m}_1$ denote the number of x's which will appear among the last $n - r$ observations when they are written in increasing order. We have found that

▶ *the probability function of* $\mathbf{m}_1$ *(or* $\mathbf{m}_2$*) is given, under the hypothesis* H_0*, by* $Pr\{\mathbf{m}_1 = m_1\} = Pr\{\mathbf{m}_2 = m_2\} = \binom{n_1}{m_1}\binom{n_2}{m_2}\Big/\binom{n}{r}$; *here* $m_1 + m_2 = n - r$, $n = n_1 + n_2$.

In order for z_r to be the sample median, we take $r = (n + 1)/2$ if n is odd; and it is customary to set $r = n/2$ if n is even.

When n_1 and n_2 are fairly large, it is tedious to perform the calculation of the probabilities above. We can use a related statistic, having approximately a χ^2 distribution with 1 degree of freedom, obtained as follows. We arrange our results in a two-way table, formally similar to the contingency table discussed on pages 278 ff.

	x	y	Total
Above median	m_1	m_2	$n - r$
Below median	$n_1 - m_1$	$n_2 - m_2$	r
Total	n_1	n_2	n

It is true that the situation here is quite different from that discussed there. In particular, the marginal totals $n_1, n_2, n - r, r$ are all fixed beforehand, whereas in the discussion of the χ^2 test for independence they also were random variables (cf., however, page 279). Let us consider what the χ^2 statistic would be if the table above did occur in a test for independence. The marginal probabilities would be respectively $n_1/n, n_2/n$; $(n - r)/n$, r/n. The χ^2 statistic would be

$$D^2 = \frac{\left[m_1 - n\left(\frac{n_1}{n}\right)\left(\frac{n-r}{n}\right)\right]^2}{n\left(\frac{n_1}{n}\right)\left(\frac{n-r}{n}\right)} + \frac{\left[m_2 - n\left(\frac{n_2}{n}\right)\left(\frac{n-r}{n}\right)\right]^2}{n\left(\frac{n_2}{n}\right)\left(\frac{n-r}{n}\right)}$$

$$+ \frac{\left[n_1 - m_1 - n\left(\frac{n_1}{n}\right)\left(\frac{r}{n}\right)\right]^2}{n\left(\frac{n_1}{n}\right)\left(\frac{r}{n}\right)} + \frac{\left[n_2 - m_2 - n\left(\frac{n_2}{n}\right)\left(\frac{r}{n}\right)\right]^2}{n\left(\frac{n_2}{n}\right)\left(\frac{r}{n}\right)}.$$

On simplifying this expression for D^2, using $m_2 = n - r - m_1$ and $n_2 = n - n_1$, we obtain

$$D^2 = \frac{n}{n_1 n_2 r(n - r)} (m_1 n - n_1 n + n_1 r)^2,$$

or

$$D^2 = \frac{n^3}{n_1 n_2 r(n-r)} \left[m_1 - (n-r)\frac{n_1}{n} \right]^2.$$

It can be shown (see the following paragraph) that

▶ *D^2 has asymptotically the χ^2 distribution with* 1 *degree of freedom.*

Of course, the statistic $\mathbf{D}^2$ is appropriate only for testing against the alternative that the medians are different and not against the alternative that a specified one is larger; for one will obtain a large value of $\mathbf{D}^2$ if either population has a median much larger than the other.

The statement above giving the asymptotic distribution of $\mathbf{D}^2$ can be justified on the basis of the theory of sampling from a finite population (see pages 314–318). We put our present situation in that context by thinking of the n_1 symbols x and the n_2 symbols y available for the $n - r$ last spaces as forming an elementary probability space containing $N = n = n_1 + n_2$ elementary events; from this group we are to choose, without replacement, $n - r$. We introduce a population random variable $\mathbf{z}$ which is 1 at each of the n_1 x's and is 0 at each of the n_2 y's. Its distribution is the elementary binomial: $\mathbf{z}$ takes the value 1 with probability n_1/n and the value 0 with probability n_2/n. Its expectation is $\mu = E(\mathbf{z}) = n_1/n$, and its variance is $\sigma^2 = V(\mathbf{z}) = n_1 n_2/n^2$. We now consider a random sample, without replacement, of size $n - r$, from the population determined by $\mathbf{z}$. The number, $\mathbf{m}_1$, of x's occurring becomes in this context the number of 1's drawn, which is

$$\mathbf{m}_1 = (n - r)\bar{\mathbf{z}};$$

for $\bar{\mathbf{z}}$ is the sum of the sample values divided by $(n - r)$, or, equivalently, the total number of 1's drawn, divided by $(n - r)$. The formula on page 316 gives

$$E(\bar{\mathbf{z}}) = \mu = n_1/n; \text{ hence}$$

▶ $$E(\mathbf{m}_1) = (n - r)n_1/n.$$

Also $V(\bar{\mathbf{z}}) = [n - (n - r)]\sigma^2/(n - 1)(n - r) = rn_1n_2/(n - 1)n^2(n - r)$, so that

▶ $$V(\mathbf{m}_1) = \frac{r(n - r)n_1 n_2}{(n - 1)n^2}.$$

Referring to the last formula above for D^2, we see that

$$\mathbf{D}^2 = \frac{n}{n - 1} \frac{[\mathbf{m}_1 - E(\mathbf{m}_1)]^2}{V(\mathbf{m}_1)}.$$

Since

▶ $\mathbf{m}_1$ *is asymptotically normal*

(page 319), $\mathbf{D}^2$ has asymptotically the χ^2 distribution with 1 degree of freedom (cf. the definition of the χ^2 distribution, page 230). We see that the use of $\mathbf{D}^2$ is (except for the factor $n/(n-1)$, which is near 1 for large n) equivalent to the use of $\mathbf{m}_1$ as an asymptotically normally distributed statistic, with a two-tail test. A one-tail test using $\mathbf{m}_1$ can be used against an alternative specifying that the median of one population is larger than that of the other.

EXAMPLE 3. Two classes, A and B, were given identical tests. The 15 scores of the members of A were:

61 94 42 23 100 35 59 46 32 69 45 94 98 33 80.

The 20 scores in B were:

83 82 63 69 70 88 64 83 62 75 88 91 59 71 67 99 71 66 53 88.

Is the performance of class B significantly better, at the 5% level, than that of A?

As posed, the question suggests the use of a one-tail test. If in fact the students in B are "better" than those in A, more than half of the B-scores would be expected above the median for all scores. Let $\mathbf{x}$ denote the population random variable associated with class A, and $\mathbf{y}$ that associated with B. We shall reject H_0 if the observed value of $\mathbf{m}_2$, the number of y scores above the median, is too large. When arranged in increasing order the array of scores is represented by:

$$x_4 \ x_9 \ x_{14} \ x_6 \ x_3 \ x_{11} \ x_8 \ y_{19} \ x_7 \ y_{13} \ x_1 \ y_9 \ y_3 \ y_7 \ y_{18}$$
$$y_{15} \ y_4 \ x_{10} \ y_5 \ y_{14} \ y_{17} \ y_{10} \ x_{15} \ y_2 \ y_8 \ y_1 \ y_6 \ y_{20} \ y_{11} \ y_{12}$$
$$x_{12} \ x_2 \ x_{13} \ y_{16} \ x_5.$$

(When two or more scores were the same, the choice of order was made using a table of random numbers.) The median score is $x_{10} = 69$. We have $n_1 = 15$, $n_2 = 20$, $n = n_1 + n_2 = 35$; $r = 18$, $z_r = x_{10} = 69$. The observed numbers m_1 and m_2 are $m_1 = 5$, $m_2 = 12$. We need now to know the probability of observing $\mathbf{m}_2 \geq 12$:

$$Pr\{\mathbf{m}_2 \geq 12\} = \sum_{m_2=12}^{17} \binom{15}{15 - m_2}\binom{20}{m_2} \Big/ \binom{35}{18}.$$

We have

$$E(\mathbf{m}_2) = (n - r)n_2/n = (17)(20)/(35) = 9.71,$$
$$V(\mathbf{m}_2) = r(n - r)n_1n_2/(n - 1)n^2 = (18)(17)(15)(20)/(34)(35)^2 = 2.21.$$

Since $\mathbf{m}_2$ is an integer-valued random variable, we may expect the normal approximation to be improved if we use $m_2 - 1/2$ instead of m_2 in using the normal tables (cf. page 169). We have

$$Pr\{m_2 \geq 11.5\} = Pr\{(m_2 - 9.71)/\sqrt{2.21} \geq 1.20\} \doteq 0.115.$$

Thus the observed value is significantly large only at about the 10% level.

PROBLEMS

1. The Central City Weather Bureau has records extending back 70 years. The annual precipitation is listed for each year, the figures being arranged chronologically. Suppose you replace each of the 35 lowest figures by the symbol L, and each of the 35 highest by H, and then count a total of 28 runs of L's and H's. Can you conclude, at the 5% significance level, that the distribution of precipitation has changed?

2. Zoologist Z_1 asserts that young bats gain weight (proportionately) much faster than do young rats, while Z_2 is dubious. They measure the relative increases in weight for 30 young bats (x) and 41 young rats (y) for a period of a month. They find that there are 20 x values (bats) above the median for all relative increases in weight. Can they conclude, at the 1% level, that young bats grow faster (relatively) than young rats?

3. Each entry in the accompanying table represents the percentage of defective watch springs produced by a certain machine in the indicated month. Test at the 5% significance level the hypothesis that the machine has not deteriorated, that is, that the entries may be regarded as obtained by random sampling from a fixed population.

	J	F	M	A	M	J	J	A	S	O	N	D
1953	15	27	39	19	29	16	15	30	16	11	30	24
1954	12	39	28	11	33	25	34	14	17	11	14	21
1955	28	37	33	29	25	34	40	35	37	34	36	37
1956	25	43	32	36	43	29	36	45	41	40	32	49
1957	31	36	34	33	39	19	50	43	41	35	32	48

4. The members of a class of 50 beginning a course in analytic geometry and calculus, and of a class of 30 beginning a second semester of analytic geometry and calculus, were given a comprehensive examination in algebra. It was hoped the tests would provide information as to whether or not the study of analytic geometry and calculus reinforces significantly one's ability to use algebra. The scores made by the two classes are given in the accompanying table (all data fictitious).

x	17	73	85	43	36	21	0	35	50	32	75	21	78	41	92	70	
y	79	45	95	62	46	45	79	74	64	93	76	20	27	87	22	47	
x	80	84	55	42	72	86	50	69	55	94	80	32	94	73	2	17	19
y	68	30	66	54	74	53	99	66	74	61	44	34	45	59			
x	49	42	32	6	8	39	4	28	48	86	26	60	92	15	85	26	14

(a) Use the runs test to test the hypothesis that the two groups come from the same population of scores. At what level is the difference barely significant?

(b) Use the median test to test the hypothesis that the two groups come from the same population of scores against the alternative that the y scores are higher. At what level is the difference barely significant?

5. You have tomatoes planted around your garden fence; some plants are healthy (H), while some have been attacked by a disease (D):

H H H H D H D D D H H D D D D H H H H H.

Can you reject at the 10% significance level the hypothesis that the disease struck at random, that is, that each plant had the same (unknown) probability of being attacked, independently of its position? Use a runs test, with 10 H, 10 L.

6. Tests of sieves were to be made using small glass spheres. The spheres were divided into a number of large groups in a way intended to assure identically distributed groups. In the accompanying table are given diameters measured to the nearest 0.05 (1 unit = 419μ) of a sample of size 25 from each of two groups. Apply at the 10% significance level the runs test of the identity of the two populations.

I: 2.00, 2.05, 1.80, 1.80, 1.80, 1.90, 1.95, 1.75, 1.90, 1.85, 2.05, 1.90, 2.05, 1.80, 1.75, 2.00, 2.00, 1.80, 1.85, 2.00, 1.90, 1.80, 1.85, 1.85, 1.80

II: 1.80, 1.95, 1.85, 1.85, 1.85, 1.80, 1.80, 1.80, 1.90, 1.80, 1.80, 1.85, 1.90, 1.85, 1.80, 2.00, 1.80, 1.90, 1.85, 1.85, 1.90, 1.80, 1.90, 1.85, 1.90

(*Source:* Carpenter, F. G. and Deitz, V. R. "Glass Spheres for the Measurement of the Effective Opening of Testing Sieves," *Journal of Research of the National Bureau of Standards*, Vol. 47 (1951), pp. 139–147.)

7. Two independent samples of ten 40-watt incandescent light bulbs are obtained, each sample being from one week's total production of light bulbs in a factory. The lifetime (in hours) for each bulb is obtained by a "forced life" test and is listed below. Use the Kolmogorov-Smirnov statistic to test at the (nominal) .05 level the null hypothesis of no difference between distributions of lifetime for bulbs produced in the two different weeks. If the null hypothesis is true, what is $Pr(\mathbf{A} \geqq A)$? (Cf. formulas pp. 280, 363; use Table XIII.)

Week										
10–23–47:	1024,	1240,	1157,	1415,	1385,	824,	1690,	1302,	1233,	1331
10–30–47:	1109,	827,	1209,	1202,	1229,	1079,	1176,	1173,	769,	905

(*Source:* Davis, D. J. "An Analysis of Some Failure Data," *Journal of the American Statistical Association*, Vol. 47 (1952), p. 142.)

Note: The following table is useful. Massey, Jr., F. J. "Distribution

Table for the Deviation between Two Sample Cumulatives." *Annals of Mathematical Statistics*, 23 (1952), pp. 435–441.

8. (a) The number of trout caught each year in Lake Opeongo, Ontario, has been counted by means of a creel census:

1936	'37	'38	'39	'40	'41	'42	'43	'44	'45	'46	'47
2600	2700	1650	1550	1400	1100	630	900	1050	1420	1220	885

Use the runs test to test the hypothesis that (i) the distribution of the annual catch has not changed with time and (ii) the annual catches are independent. The one-tailed alternative hypothesis is that there are too few runs. Classify observations above or below the sample median and use the (nominal) 10% significance level. What is the smallest level at which the null hypothesis would be rejected? For what reason might this one-tailed alternative hypothesis be appropriate?
(*Source:* FRY, F. E. J. "Statistics of a Lake Trout Fishery," *Biometrics*, Vol. 5 (1949), p. 29.)

9. Two bookkeepers use recording machines to enter bank statement and ledger accounts. For each bookkeeper a sample of 25 observations on the number of correct entries before an error is obtained; these samples are independent. Use the two-sample runs test to test at the 1% level the null hypothesis that the distribution of the number of correct entries before an error is the same for both bookkeepers.

Bookkeeper A	Bookkeeper B	Bookkeeper A	Bookkeeper B
725	148	247	19
882	73	194	607
141	169	547	18
195	1	233	63
13	128	1095	112
1904	2	529	412
455	64	337	74
2564	43	355	21
609	203	216	402
1262	332	194	298
346	59	76	395
880	10	391	5
1213	59		

(Use the normal approximation to the null distribution of **r**.)
(*Source:* DAVIS, D. J. "An Analysis of Some Failure Data," *Journal of the American Statistical Association*, Vol. 47 (1952), pp. 113–150).

10. The yield of barley in Ireland (in quarters per acre) is given for 14 successive four-year periods. Test at the 5% level the hypothesis that (i) the distribution of barley yield has not changed with time and (ii) the barley yields are independent. Use the two-tailed runs test with sample median.

1866–1870	4.0	1901–1905	4.5
1871–1875	4.1	1906–1910	4.7
1876–1880	3.9	1911–1915	4.8
1881–1885	3.9	1916–1920	4.1
1886–1890	3.9	1921–1925	4.1
1891–1895	4.3	1926–1930	5.3
1896–1900	4.3	1931–1935	5.1

(*Source:* GOSSET, W. S. "Co-Operation in Large-Scale Experiments", *Journal of the Royal Statistical Society Supplement*, 3(1936), p. 115.)

11. You and a friend fire five shots each at a target. If you are equally good shots, what is the probability that of the 6 closest shots, 4 will be yours? (Assume the two distributions of shots identical.)

12. How many possible distinct distributions of family sizes among 5 families are there, if there are 10 children in all and if each family has at least one child (two distributions are the same if each family has the same number of children in each of the two distributions)?

13. (a) If $n_L = 1$, $n_H = 2$, find the distribution of $\mathbf{r}$ by inspection, and compare with the formulas derived in the text.

(b) Calculate directly from (a) the expectation and variance of $\mathbf{r}$ and compare with the results given by the formulas in the text.

REFERENCES

1. Anderson, R. L., and Bancroft, T. A., *Statistical Theory in Research*, McGraw-Hill Book Company, Inc., New York, 1952
2. Blackwell, D., and Girshick, M. A., *Theory of Games and Statistical Decisions*, John Wiley and Sons, Inc., New York, 1954.
3. Cramér, H., *Mathematical Methods of Statistics*, Princeton University Press, Princeton, N. J., 1946
4. Chernoff, Herman, and Moses, Lincoln E., *Elementary Decision Theory*, John Wiley and Sons, Inc., New York, 1959
5. Feller, W., *An Introduction to Probability Theory and Its Applications*, Vol. I, Second Edition, John Wiley and Sons, Inc., New York, 1957
6. Fisz, Marek, *Probability Theory and Mathematical Statistics*, John Wiley and Sons, Inc., New York, 1963
7. Kendall, Maurice G., and Stuart, Alan, *The Advanced Theory of Statistics*, Vol. I, Hafner Publishing Company, New York, 1958; Vol. II, Hafner Publishing Company, New York, 1961; and Vol. III, Hafner Publishing Company, New York (to be published).
8. Lehmann, E. L., *Testing Statistical Hypotheses*, John Wiley and Sons, Inc., New York, 1959
9. Lindgren, B. W., *Statistical Theory*, The Macmillan Company, New York, 1962
10. Mood, Alexander M., and Graybill, Franklin A., *Introduction to the Theory of Statistics*, Second Edition, McGraw-Hill Book Company, Inc., 1963
11. Munroe, M. E., *Theory of Probability*, McGraw-Hill Book Company, Inc., New York, 1951
12. Neyman, J., *First Course in Probability and Statistics*, Henry Holt and Company, Inc., New York, 1950
13. Savage, Leonard J., *The Foundations of Statistics*, John Wiley and Sons, Inc., New York, 1954
14. Savage, Leonard J., et al., *The Foundations of Statistical Inference*, John Wiley and Sons, Inc., New York, 1962
15. Scheffé, Henry, *The Analysis of Variance*, John Wiley and Sons, Inc., New York, 1959
16. Siegel, S., *Nonparametric Statistics for the Behavioral Sciences*, McGraw-Hill Book Company, Inc., New York, 1956
17. Tucker, Howard G., *An Introduction to Probability and Mathematical Statistics*, Academic Press, Inc., New York, 1962
18. Wald, A., *Sequential Analysis*, John Wiley and Sons, Inc., New York, 1947
19. Wald, A., *Statistical Decision Functions*, John Wiley and Sons, Inc., New York, 1950
20. Wallis, W. Allen, and Roberts, Harry V., *Statistics: A New Approach*, The Free Press, Glencoe, Illinois, 1956
21. Weiss, Lionel, *Statistical Decision Theory*, McGraw-Hill Book Company, Inc., New York, 1961
22. Wilks, Samuel S., *Mathematical Statistics*, John Wiley and Sons, Inc., New York, 1962

Table I

Binomial Probability Function $\binom{n}{x}p^x(1-p)^{n-x}$

Entries in the table are values of $\binom{n}{x}p^x(1-p)^{n-x}$ for the indicated values of n, x and p. When $p > 0.5$, the value of $\binom{n}{x}p^x(1-p)^{n-x}$ for a given n, x and p is obtained by finding the tabular entry for the given n, with $n - x$ in place of the given x, and $1 - p$ in place of the given p.

n	x	p = .05	.10	.15	.20	.25	.30	.35	.40	.45	.50
1	0	.9500	.9000	.8500	.8000	.7500	.7000	.6500	.6000	.5500	.5000
	1	.0500	.1000	.1500	.2000	.2500	.3000	.3500	.4000	.4500	.5000
2	0	.9025	.8100	.7225	.6400	.5625	.4900	.4225	.3600	.3025	.2500
	1	.0950	.1800	.2550	.3200	.3750	.4200	.4550	.4800	.4950	.5000
	2	.0025	.0100	.0225	.0400	.0625	.0900	.1225	.1600	.2025	.2500
3	0	.8574	.7290	.6141	.5120	.4219	.3430	.2746	.2160	.1664	.1250
	1	.1354	.2430	.3251	.3840	.4219	.4410	.4436	.4320	.4084	.3750
	2	.0071	.0270	.0574	.0960	.1406	.1890	.2389	.2880	.3341	.3750
	3	.0001	.0010	.0034	.0080	.0156	.0270	.0429	.0640	.0911	.1250
4	0	.8145	.6561	.5220	.4096	.3164	.2401	.1785	.1296	.0915	.0625
	1	.1715	.2916	.3685	.4096	.4219	.4116	.3845	.3456	.2995	.2500
	2	.0135	.0486	.0975	.1536	.2109	.2646	.3105	.3456	.3675	.3750
	3	.0005	.0036	.0115	.0256	.0469	.0756	.1115	.1536	.2005	.2500
	4	.0000	.0001	.0005	.0016	.0039	.0081	.0150	.0256	.0410	.0625
5	0	.7738	.5905	.4437	.3277	.2373	.1681	.1160	.0778	.0503	.0312
	1	.2036	.3280	.3915	.4096	.3955	.3602	.3124	.2592	.2059	.1562
	2	.0214	.0729	.1382	.2048	.2637	.3087	.3364	.3456	.3369	.3125
	3	.0011	.0081	.0244	.0512	.0879	.1323	.1811	.2304	.2757	.3125
	4	.0000	.0004	.0022	.0064	.0146	.0284	.0488	.0768	.1128	.1562
	5	.0000	.0000	.0001	.0003	.0010	.0024	.0053	.0102	.0185	.0312
6	0	.7351	.5314	.3771	.2621	.1780	.1176	.0754	.0467	.0277	.0156
	1	.2321	.3543	.3993	.3932	.3560	.3025	.2437	.1866	.1359	.0938
	2	.0305	.0984	.1762	.2458	.2966	.3241	.3280	.3110	.2780	.2344
	3	.0021	.0146	.0415	.0819	.1318	.1852	.2355	.2765	.3032	.3125
	4	.0001	.0012	.0055	.0154	.0330	.0595	.0951	.1382	.1861	.2344
	5	.0000	.0001	.0004	.0015	.0044	.0102	.0205	.0369	.0609	.0938
	6	.0000	.0000	.0000	.0001	.0002	.0007	.0018	.0041	.0083	.0156
7	0	.6983	.4783	.3206	.2097	.1335	.0824	.0490	.0280	.0152	.0078
	1	.2573	.3720	.3960	.3670	.3115	.2471	.1848	.1306	.0872	.0547
	2	.0406	.1240	.2097	.2753	.3115	.3177	.2985	.2613	.2140	.1641
	3	.0036	.0230	.0617	.1147	.1730	.2269	.2679	.2903	.2918	.2734
	4	.0002	.0026	.0109	.0287	.0577	.0972	.1442	.1935	.2388	.2734
	5	.0000	.0002	.0012	.0043	.0115	.0250	.0466	.0774	.1172	.1641
	6	.0000	.0000	.0001	.0004	.0013	.0036	.0084	.0172	.0320	.0547
	7	.0000	.0000	.0000	.0000	.0001	.0002	.0006	.0016	.0037	.0078
8	0	.6634	.4305	.2725	.1678	.1001	.0576	.0319	.0168	.0084	.0039
	1	.2793	.3826	.3847	.3355	.2670	.1977	.1373	.0896	.0548	.0312
	2	.0515	.1488	.2376	.2936	.3115	.2965	.2587	.2090	.1569	.1094
	3	.0054	.0331	.0839	.1468	.2076	.2541	.2786	.2787	.2568	.2188
	4	.0004	.0046	.0185	.0459	.0865	.1361	.1875	.2322	.2627	.2734
	5	.0000	.0004	.0026	.0092	.0231	.0467	.0808	.1239	.1719	.2188
	6	.0000	.0000	.0002	.0011	.0038	.0100	.0217	.0413	.0703	.1094
	7	.0000	.0000	.0000	.0001	.0004	.0012	.0033	.0079	.0164	.0312
	8	.0000	.0000	.0000	.0000	.0000	.0001	.0002	.0007	.0017	.0039

Linear interpolation with respect to p will generally not be accurate to more than two decimal places, and sometimes less.

For extensive tables of $\binom{n}{x}p^x(1-p)^{n-x}$ see *Tables of the Binomial Probability Distribution*, National Bureau of Standards, Applied Mathematics Series 6, Washington, D. C., 1950.

Table I is used by permission from *Handbook of Probability and Statistics with Tables*, by Burington and May. Copyright, 1953. McGraw-Hill Book Co.

BINOMIAL PROBABILITY FUNCTION $\binom{n}{x}p^x(1-p)^{n-x}$

n	x	p = .05	.10	.15	.20	.25	.30	.35	.40	.45	.50
9	0	.6302	.3874	.2316	.1342	.0751	.0404	.0207	.0101	.0046	.0020
	1	.2985	.3874	.3679	.3020	.2253	.1556	.1004	.0605	.0339	.0176
	2	.0629	.1722	.2597	.3020	.3003	.2668	.2162	.1612	.1110	.0703
	3	.0077	.0446	.1069	.1762	.2336	.2668	.2716	.2508	.2119	.1641
	4	.0006	.0074	.0283	.0661	.1168	.1715	.2194	.2508	.2600	.2461
	5	.0000	.0008	.0050	.0165	.0389	.0735	.1181	.1672	.2128	.2461
	6	.0000	.0001	.0006	.0028	.0087	.0210	.0424	.0743	.1160	.1641
	7	.0000	.0000	.0000	.0003	.0012	.0039	.0098	.0212	.0407	.0703
	8	.0000	.0000	.0000	.0000	.0001	.0004	.0013	.0035	.0083	.0176
	9	.0000	.0000	.0000	.0000	.0000	.0000	.0001	.0003	.0008	.0020
10	0	.5987	.3487	.1969	.1074	.0563	.0282	.0135	.0060	.0025	.0010
	1	.3151	.3874	.3474	.2684	.1877	.1211	.0725	.0403	.0207	.0098
	2	.0746	.1937	.2759	.3020	.2816	.2335	.1757	.1209	.0763	.0439
	3	.0105	.0574	.1298	.2013	.2503	.2668	.2522	.2150	.1665	.1172
	4	.0010	.0112	.0401	.0881	.1460	.2001	.2377	.2508	.2384	.2051
	5	.0001	.0015	.0085	.0264	.0584	.1029	.1536	.2007	.2340	.2461
	6	.0000	.0001	.0012	.0055	.0162	.0368	.0689	.1115	.1596	.2051
	7	.0000	.0000	.0001	.0008	.0031	.0090	.0212	.0425	.0746	.1172
	8	.0000	.0000	.0000	.0001	.0004	.0014	.0043	.0106	.0229	.0439
	9	.0000	.0000	.0000	.0000	.0000	.0001	.0005	.0016	.0042	.0098
	10	.0000	.0000	.0000	.0000	.0000	.0000	.0000	.0001	.0003	.0010
11	0	.5688	.3138	.1673	.0859	.0422	.0198	.0088	.0036	.0014	.0005
	1	.3293	.3835	.3248	.2362	.1549	.0932	.0518	.0266	.0125	.0054
	2	.0867	.2131	.2866	.2953	.2581	.1998	.1395	.0887	.0513	.0269
	3	.0137	.0710	.1517	.2215	.2581	.2568	.2254	.1774	.1259	.0806
	4	.0014	.0158	.0536	.1107	.1721	.2201	.2428	.2365	.2060	.1611
	5	.0001	.0025	.0132	.0388	.0803	.1321	.1830	.2207	.2360	.2256
	6	.0000	.0003	.0023	.0097	.0268	.0566	.0985	.1471	.1931	.2256
	7	.0000	.0000	.0003	.0017	.0064	.0173	.0379	.0701	.1128	.1611
	8	.0000	.0000	.0000	.0002	.0011	.0037	.0102	.0234	.0462	.0806
	9	.0000	.0000	.0000	.0000	.0001	.0005	.0018	.0052	.0126	.0269
	10	.0000	.0000	.0000	.0000	.0000	.0000	.0002	.0007	.0021	.0054
	11	.0000	.0000	.0000	.0000	.0000	.0000	.0000	.0000	.0002	.0005
12	0	.5404	.2824	.1422	.0687	.0317	.0138	.0057	.0022	.0008	.0002
	1	.3413	.3766	.3012	.2062	.1267	.0712	.0368	.0174	.0075	.0029
	2	.0988	.2301	.2924	.2835	.2323	.1678	.1088	.0639	.0339	.0161
	3	.0173	.0852	.1720	.2362	.2581	.2397	.1954	.1419	.0923	.0537
	4	.0021	.0213	.0683	.1329	.1936	.2311	.2367	.2128	.1700	.1208
	5	.0002	.0038	.0193	.0532	.1032	.1585	.2039	.2270	.2225	.1934
	6	.0000	.0005	.0040	.0155	.0401	.0792	.1281	.1766	.2124	.2256
	7	.0000	.0000	.0006	.0033	.0115	.0291	.0591	.1009	.1489	.1934
	8	.0000	.0000	.0001	.0005	.0024	.0078	.0199	.0420	.0762	.1208
	9	.0000	.0000	.0000	.0001	.0004	.0015	.0048	.0125	.0277	.0537
	10	.0000	.0000	.0000	.0000	.0000	.0002	.0008	.0025	.0068	.0161
	11	.0000	.0000	.0000	.0000	.0000	.0000	.0001	.0003	.0010	.0029
	12	.0000	.0000	.0000	.0000	.0000	.0000	.0000	.0000	.0001	.0002
13	0	.5133	.2542	.1209	.0550	.0238	.0097	.0037	.0013	.0004	.0001
	1	.3512	.3672	.2774	.1787	.1029	.0540	.0259	.0113	.0045	.0016
	2	.1109	.2448	.2937	.2680	.2059	.1388	.0836	.0453	.0220	.0095
	3	.0214	.0997	.1900	.2457	.2517	.2181	.1651	.1107	.0660	.0349
	4	.0028	.0277	.0838	.1535	.2097	.2337	.2222	.1845	.1350	.0873
	5	.0003	.0055	.0266	.0691	.1258	.1803	.2154	.2214	.1989	.1571
	6	.0000	.0008	.0063	.0230	.0559	.1030	.1546	.1968	.2169	.2095
	7	.0000	.0001	.0011	.0058	.0186	.0442	.0833	.1312	.1775	.2095
	8	.0000	.0000	.0001	.0011	.0047	.0142	.0336	.0656	.1089	.1571
	9	.0000	.0000	.0000	.0001	.0009	.0034	.0101	.0243	.0495	.0873
	10	.0000	.0000	.0000	.0000	.0001	.0006	.0022	.0065	.0162	.0349
	11	.0000	.0000	.0000	.0000	.0000	.0001	.0003	.0012	.0036	.0095
	12	.0000	.0000	.0000	.0000	.0000	.0000	.0000	.0001	.0005	.0016
	13	.0000	.0000	.0000	.0000	.0000	.0000	.0000	.0000	.0000	.0001

BINOMIAL PROBABILITY FUNCTION $\binom{n}{x}p^x(1-p)^{n-x}$

n	x	p = .05	.10	.15	.20	.25	.30	.35	.40	.45	.50
14	0	.4877	.2288	.1028	.0440	.0178	.0068	.0024	.0008	.0002	.0001
	1	.3593	.3559	.2539	.1539	.0832	.0407	.0181	.0073	.0027	.0009
	2	.1229	.2570	.2912	.2501	.1802	.1134	.0634	.0317	.0141	.0056
	3	.0259	.1142	.2056	.2501	.2402	.1943	.1366	.0845	.0462	.0222
	4	.0037	.0349	.0998	.1720	.2202	.2290	.2022	.1549	.1040	.0611
	5	.0004	.0078	.0352	.0860	.1468	.1963	.2178	.2066	.1701	.1222
	6	.0000	.0013	.0093	.0322	.0734	.1262	.1759	.2066	.2088	.1833
	7	.0000	.0002	.0019	.0092	.0280	.0618	.1082	.1574	.1952	.2095
	8	.0000	.0000	.0003	.0020	.0082	.0232	.0510	.0918	.1398	.1833
	9	.0000	.0000	.0000	.0003	.0018	.0066	.0183	.0408	.0762	.1222
	10	.0000	.0000	.0000	.0000	.0003	.0014	.0049	.0136	.0312	.0611
	11	.0000	.0000	.0000	.0000	.0000	.0002	.0010	.0033	.0093	.0222
	12	.0000	.0000	.0000	.0000	.0000	.0000	.0001	.0005	.0019	.0056
	13	.0000	.0000	.0000	.0000	.0000	.0000	.0000	.0001	.0002	.0009
	14	.0000	.0000	.0000	.0000	.0000	.0000	.0000	.0000	.0000	.0001
15	0	.4633	.2059	.0874	.0352	.0134	.0047	.0016	.0005	.0001	.0000
	1	.3658	.3432	.2312	.1319	.0668	.0305	.0126	.0047	.0016	.0005
	2	.1348	.2669	.2856	.2309	.1559	.0916	.0476	.0219	.0090	.0032
	3	.0307	.1285	.2184	.2501	.2252	.1700	.1110	.0634	.0318	.0139
	4	.0049	.0428	.1156	.1876	.2252	.2186	.1792	.1268	.0780	.0417
	5	.0006	.0105	.0449	.1032	.1651	.2061	.2123	.1859	.1404	.0916
	6	.0000	.0019	.0132	.0430	.0917	.1472	.1906	.2066	.1914	.1527
	7	.0000	.0003	.0030	.0138	.0393	.0811	.1319	.1771	.2013	.1964
	8	.0000	.0000	.0005	.0035	.0131	.0348	.0710	.1181	.1647	.1964
	9	.0000	.0000	.0001	.0007	.0034	.0116	.0298	.0612	.1048	.1527
	10	.0000	.0000	.0000	.0001	.0007	.0030	.0096	.0245	.0515	.0916
	11	.0000	.0000	.0000	.0000	.0001	.0006	.0024	.0074	.0191	.0417
	12	.0000	.0000	.0000	.0000	.0000	.0001	.0004	.0016	.0052	.0139
	13	.0000	.0000	.0000	.0000	.0000	.0000	.0001	.0003	.0010	.0032
	14	.0000	.0000	.0000	.0000	.0000	.0000	.0000	.0000	.0001	.0005
	15	.0000	.0000	.0000	.0000	.0000	.0000	.0000	.0000	.0000	0000
16	0	.4401	.1853	.0743	.0281	.0100	.0033	.0010	.0003	.0001	.0000
	1	.3706	.3294	.2097	.1126	.0535	.0228	.0087	.0030	.0009	.0002
	2	.1463	.2745	.2775	.2111	.1336	.0732	.0353	.0150	.0056	.0018
	3	.0359	.1423	.2285	.2463	.2079	.1465	.0888	.0468	.0215	.0085
	4	.0061	.0514	.1311	.2001	.2252	.2040	.1553	.1014	.0572	.0278
	5	.0008	.0137	.0555	.1201	.1802	.2099	.2008	.1623	.1123	.0667
	6	.0001	.0028	.0180	.0550	.1101	.1649	.1982	.1983	.1684	.1222
	7	.0000	.0004	.0045	.0197	.0524	.1010	.1524	.1889	.1969	.1746
	8	.0000	.0001	.0009	.0055	.0197	.0487	.0923	.1417	.1812	.1964
	9	.0000	.0000	.0001	.0012	.0058	.0185	.0442	.0840	.1318	.1746
	10	.0000	.0000	.0000	.0002	.0014	.0056	.0167	.0392	.0755	.1222
	11	.0000	.0000	.0000	.0000	.0002	.0013	.0049	.0142	.0337	.0667
	12	.0000	.0000	.0000	.0000	.0000	.0002	.0011	.0040	.0115	.0278
	13	.0000	.0000	.0000	.0000	.0000	.0000	.0002	.0008	.0029	.0085
	14	.0000	.0000	.0000	.0000	.0000	.0000	.0000	.0001	.0005	.0018
	15	.0000	.0000	.0000	.0000	.0000	.0000	.0000	.0000	.0001	.0002
	16	.0000	.0000	.0000	.0000	.0000	.0000	.0000	.0000	.0000	.0000
17	0	.4181	.1668	.0631	.0225	.0075	.0023	.0007	.0002	.0000	.0000
	1	.3741	.3150	.1893	.0957	.0426	.0169	.0060	.0019	.0005	.0001
	2	.1575	.2800	.2673	.1914	.1136	.0581	.0260	.0102	.0035	.0010
	3	.0415	.1556	.2359	.2393	.1893	.1245	.0701	.0341	.0144	.0052
	4	.0076	.0605	.1457	.2093	.2209	.1868	.1320	.0796	.0411	.0182
	5	.0010	.0175	.0668	.1361	.1914	.2081	.1849	.1379	.0875	.0472
	6	.0001	.0039	.0236	.0680	.1276	.1784	.1991	.1839	.1432	.0944
	7	.0000	.0007	.0065	.0267	.0668	.1201	.1685	.1927	.1841	.1484
	8	.0000	.0001	.0014	.0084	.0279	.0644	.1134	.1606	.1883	.1855
	9	.0000	.0000	.0003	.0021	.0093	.0276	.0611	.1070	.1540	.1855
	10	.0000	.0000	.0000	.0004	.0025	.0095	.0263	.0571	.1008	.1484
	11	.0000	.0000	.0000	.0001	.0005	.0026	.0090	.0242	.0525	.0944
	12	.0000	.0000	.0000	.0000	.0001	.0006	.0024	.0081	.0215	.0472
	13	.0000	.0000	.0000	.0000	.0000	.0001	.0005	.0021	.0068	.0182
	14	.0000	.0000	.0000	.0000	.0000	.0000	.0001	.0004	.0016	.0052

Binomial Probability Function $\binom{n}{x}p^x(1-p)^{n-x}$

n	x	p = .05	.10	.15	.20	.25	.30	.35	.40	.45	.50
17	15	.0000	.0000	.0000	.0000	.0000	.0000	.0000	.0001	.0003	.0010
	16	.0000	.0000	.0000	.0000	.0000	.0000	.0000	.0000	.0000	.0001
	17	.0000	.0000	.0000	.0000	.0000	.0000	.0000	.0000	.0000	.0000
18	0	.3972	.1501	.0536	.0180	.0056	.0016	.0004	.0001	.0000	.0000
	1	.3763	.3002	.1704	.0811	.0338	.0126	.0042	.0012	.0003	.0001
	2	.1683	.2835	.2556	.1723	.0958	.0458	.0190	.0069	.0022	.0006
	3	.0473	.1680	.2406	.2297	.1704	.1046	.0547	.0246	.0095	.0031
	4	.0093	.0700	.1592	.2153	.2130	.1681	.1104	.0614	.0291	.0117
	5	.0014	.0218	.0787	.1507	.1988	.2017	.1664	.1146	.0666	.0327
	6	.0002	.0052	.0301	.0816	.1436	.1873	.1941	.1655	.1181	.0708
	7	.0000	.0010	.0091	.0350	.0820	.1376	.1792	.1892	.1657	.1214
	8	.0000	.0002	.0022	.0120	.0376	.0811	.1327	.1734	.1864	.1669
	9	.0000	.0000	.0004	.0033	.0139	.0386	.0794	.1284	.1694	.1855
	10	.0000	.0000	.0001	.0008	.0042	.0149	.0385	.0771	.1248	.1669
	11	.0000	.0000	.0000	.0001	.0010	.0046	.0151	.0374	.0742	.1214
	12	.0000	.0000	.0000	.0000	.0002	.0012	.0047	.0145	.0354	.0708
	13	.0000	.0000	.0000	.0000	.0000	.0002	.0012	.0045	.0134	.0327
	14	.0000	.0000	.0000	.0000	.0000	.0000	.0002	.0011	.0039	.0117
	15	.0000	.0000	.0000	.0000	.0000	.0000	.0000	.0002	.0009	.0031
	16	.0000	.0000	.0000	.0000	.0000	.0000	.0000	.0000	.0001	.0006
	17	.0000	.0000	.0000	.0000	.0000	.0000	.0000	.0000	.0000	.0001
	18	.0000	.0000	.0000	.0000	.0000	.0000	.0000	.0000	.0000	.0000
19	0	.3774	.1351	.0456	.0144	.0042	.0011	.0003	.0001	.0000	.0000
	1	.3774	.2852	.1529	.0685	.0268	.0093	.0029	.0008	.0002	.0000
	2	.1787	.2852	.2428	.1540	.0803	.0358	.0138	.0046	.0013	.0003
	3	.0533	.1796	.2428	.2182	.1517	.0869	.0422	.0175	.0062	.0018
	4	.0112	.0798	.1714	.2182	.2023	.1491	.0909	.0467	.0203	.0074
	5	.0018	.0266	.0907	.1636	.2023	.1916	.1468	.0933	.0497	.0222
	6	.0002	.0069	.0374	.0955	.1574	.1916	.1844	.1451	.0949	.0518
	7	.0000	.0014	.0122	.0443	.0974	.1525	.1844	.1797	.1443	.0961
	8	.0000	.0002	.0032	.0166	.0487	.0981	.1489	.1797	.1771	.1442
	9	.0000	.0000	.0007	.0051	.0198	.0514	.0980	.1464	.1771	.1762
	10	.0000	.0000	.0001	.0013	.0066	.0220	.0528	.0976	.1449	.1762
	11	.0000	.0000	.0000	.0003	.0018	.0077	.0233	.0532	.0970	.1442
	12	.0000	.0000	.0000	.0000	.0004	.0022	.0083	.0237	.0529	.0961
	13	.0000	.0000	.0000	.0000	.0001	.0005	.0024	.0085	.0233	.0518
	14	.0000	.0000	.0000	.0000	.0000	.0001	.0006	.0024	.0082	.0222
	15	.0000	.0000	.0000	.0000	.0000	.0000	.0001	.0005	.0022	.0074
	16	.0000	.0000	.0000	.0000	.0000	.0000	.0000	.0001	.0005	.0018
	17	.0000	.0000	.0000	.0000	.0000	.0000	.0000	.0000	.0001	.0003
	18	.0000	.0000	.0000	.0000	.0000	.0000	.0000	.0000	.0000	.0000
	19	.0000	.0000	.0000	.0000	.0000	.0000	.0000	.0000	.0000	.0000
20	0	.3585	.1216	.0388	.0115	.0032	.0008	.0002	.0000	.0000	.0000
	1	.3774	.2702	.1368	.0576	.0211	.0068	.0020	.0005	.0001	.0000
	2	.1887	.2852	.2293	.1369	.0669	.0278	.0100	.0031	.0008	.0002
	3	.0596	.1901	.2428	.2054	.1339	.0716	.0323	.0123	.0040	.0011
	4	.0133	.0898	.1821	.2182	.1897	.1304	.0738	.0350	.0139	.0046
	5	.0022	.0319	.1028	.1746	.2023	.1789	.1272	.0746	.0365	.0148
	6	.0003	.0089	.0454	.1091	.1686	.1916	.1712	.1244	.0746	.0370
	7	.0000	.0020	.0160	.0545	.1124	.1643	.1844	.1659	.1221	.0739
	8	.0000	.0004	.0046	.0222	.0609	.1144	.1614	.1797	.1623	.1201
	9	.0000	.0001	.0011	.0074	.0271	.0654	.1158	.1597	.1771	.1602
	10	.0000	.0000	.0002	.0020	.0099	.0308	.0686	.1171	.1593	.1762
	11	.0000	.0000	.0000	.0005	.0030	.0120	.0336	.0710	.1185	.1602
	12	.0000	.0000	.0000	.0001	.0008	.0039	.0136	.0355	.0727	.1201
	13	.0000	.0000	.0000	.0000	.0002	.0010	.0045	.0146	.0366	.0739
	14	.0000	.0000	.0000	.0000	.0000	.0002	.0012	.0049	.0150	.0370
	15	.0000	.0000	.0000	.0000	.0000	.0000	.0003	.0013	.0049	.0148
	16	.0000	.0000	.0000	.0000	.0000	.0000	.0000	.0003	.0013	.0046
	17	.0000	.0000	.0000	.0000	.0000	.0000	.0000	.0000	.0002	.0011
	18	.0000	.0000	.0000	.0000	.0000	.0000	.0000	.0000	.0000	.0002
	19	.0000	.0000	.0000	.0000	.0000	.0000	.0000	.0000	.0000	.0000
	20	.0000	.0000	.0000	.0000	.0000	.0000	.0000	.0000	.0000	.0000

Table II

Summed Binomial Probability Function

$$\sum_{x=x'}^{x=n} \binom{n}{x} p^x (1-p)^{n-x}$$

Entries in the table are values of $\sum_{x=x'}^{x=n} \binom{n}{x} p^x (1-p)^{n-x}$ for the indicated values of n, x' and p. When $p > 0.5$, the value of $\sum_{x=x'}^{x=n} \binom{n}{x} p^x (1-p)^{n-x}$ for a given n, x' and p is equal to one minus the tabular entry for the given n, with $n - x' + 1$ in place of the given value of x', and $1 - p$ in place of the given value of p.

n	x'	p = .05	.10	.15	.20	.25	.30	.35	.40	.45	.50
2	1	.0975	.1900	.2775	.3600	.4375	.5100	.5775	.6400	.6975	.7500
	2	.0025	.0100	.0225	.0400	.0625	.0900	.1225	.1600	.2025	.2500
3	1	.1426	.2710	.3859	.4880	.5781	.6570	.7254	.7840	.8336	.8750
	2	.0072	.0280	.0608	.1040	.1562	.2160	.2818	.3520	.4252	.5000
	3	.0001	.0010	.0034	.0080	.0156	.0270	.0429	.0640	.0911	.1250
4	1	.1855	.3439	.4780	.5904	.6836	.7599	.8215	.8704	.9085	.9375
	2	.0140	.0523	.1095	.1808	.2617	.3483	.4370	.5248	.6090	.6875
	3	.0005	.0037	.0120	.0272	.0508	.0837	.1265	.1792	.2415	.3125
	4	.0000	.0001	.0005	.0016	.0039	.0081	.0150	.0256	.0410	.0625
5	1	.2262	.4095	.5563	.6723	.7627	.8319	.8840	.9222	.9497	.9688
	2	.0226	.0815	.1648	.2627	.3672	.4718	.5716	.6630	.7438	.8125
	3	.0012	.0086	.0266	.0579	.1035	.1631	.2352	.3174	.4069	.5000
	4	.0000	.0005	.0022	.0067	.0156	.0308	.0540	.0870	.1312	.1875
	5	.0000	.0000	.0001	.0003	.0010	.0024	.0053	.0102	.0185	.0312
6	1	.2649	.4686	.6229	.7379	.8220	.8824	.9246	.9533	.9723	.9844
	2	.0328	.1143	.2235	.3446	.4661	.5798	.6809	.7667	.8364	.8906
	3	.0022	.0158	.0473	.0989	.1694	.2557	.3529	.4557	.5585	.6562
	4	.0001	.0013	.0059	.0170	.0376	.0705	.1174	.1792	.2553	.3438
	5	.0000	.0001	.0004	.0016	.0046	.0109	.0223	.0410	.0692	.1094
	6	.0000	.0000	.0000	.0001	.0002	.0007	.0018	.0041	.0083	.0156
7	1	.3017	.5217	.6794	.7903	.8665	.9176	.9510	.9720	.9848	.9922
	2	.0444	.1497	.2834	.4233	.5551	.6706	.7662	.8414	.8976	.9375
	3	.0038	.0257	.0738	.1480	.2436	.3529	.4677	.5801	.6836	.7734
	4	.0002	.0027	.0121	.0333	.0706	.1260	.1998	.2898	.3917	.5000
	5	.0000	.0002	.0012	.0047	.0129	.0288	.0556	.0963	.1529	.2266
	6	.0000	.0000	.0001	.0004	.0013	.0038	.0090	.0188	.0357	.0625
	7	.0000	.0000	.0000	.0000	.0001	.0002	.0006	.0016	.0037	.0078
8	1	.3366	.5695	.7275	.8322	.8999	.9424	.9681	.9832	.9916	.9961
	2	.0572	.1869	.3428	.4967	.6329	.7447	.8309	.8936	.9368	.9648
	3	.0058	.0381	.1052	.2031	.3215	.4482	.5722	.6846	.7799	.8555
	4	.0004	.0050	.0214	.0563	.1138	.1941	.2936	.4059	.5230	.6367
	5	.0000	.0004	.0029	.0104	.0273	.0580	.1061	.1737	.2604	.3633
	6	.0000	.0000	.0002	.0012	.0042	.0113	.0253	.0498	.0885	.1445
	7	.0000	.0000	.0000	.0001	.0004	.0013	.0036	.0085	.0181	.0352
	8	.0000	.0000	.0000	.0000	.0000	.0001	.0002	.0007	.0017	.0039

Linear interpolation with respect to p will generally not be accurate to more than two decimal places, and sometimes less.

For extensive tables of $\sum_{x=x'}^{x=n} \binom{n}{x} p^x (1-p)^{n-x}$ see *Tables of the Binomial Probability Distribution*, National Bureau of Standards, Applied Mathematics Series 6, Washington, D. C., 1950.

Table II is used by permission from *Handbook of Probability and Statistics with Tables*, by Burington and May. Copyright, 1953. McGraw-Hill Book Co.

Summed Binomial Probability Function

$$\sum_{x=x'}^{x=n} \binom{n}{x} p^x (1-p)^{n-x}$$

n	x'	p = .05	.10	.15	.20	.25	.30	.35	.40	.45	.50
9	1	.3698	.6126	.7684	.8658	.9249	.9596	.9793	.9899	.9954	.9980
	2	.0712	.2252	.4005	.5638	.6997	.8040	.8789	.9295	.9615	.9805
	3	.0084	.0530	.1409	.2618	.3993	.5372	.6627	.7682	.8505	.9102
	4	.0006	.0083	.0339	.0856	.1657	.2703	.3911	.5174	.6386	.7461
	5	.0000	.0009	.0056	.0196	.0489	.0988	.1717	.2666	.3786	.5000
	6	.0000	.0001	.0006	.0031	.0100	.0253	.0536	.0994	.1658	.2539
	7	.0000	.0000	.0000	.0003	.0013	.0043	.0112	.0250	.0498	.0898
	8	.0000	.0000	.0000	.0000	.0001	.0004	.0014	.0038	.0091	.0195
	9	.0000	.0000	.0000	.0000	.0000	.0000	.0001	.0003	.0008	.0020
10	1	.4013	.6513	.8031	.8926	.9437	.9718	.9865	.9940	.9975	.9990
	2	.0861	.2639	.4557	.6242	.7560	.8507	.9140	.9536	.9767	.9893
	3	.0115	.0702	.1798	.3222	.4744	.6172	.7384	.8327	.9004	.9453
	4	.0010	.0128	.0500	.1209	.2241	.3504	.4862	.6177	.7340	.8281
	5	.0001	.0016	.0099	.0328	.0781	.1503	.2485	.3669	.4956	.6230
	6	.0000	.0001	.0014	.0064	.0197	.0473	.0949	.1662	.2616	.3770
	7	.0000	.0000	.0001	.0009	.0035	.0106	.0260	.0548	.1020	.1719
	8	.0000	.0000	.0000	.0001	.0004	.0016	.0048	.0123	.0274	.0547
	9	.0000	.0000	.0000	.0000	.0000	.0001	.0005	.0017	.0045	.0107
	10	.0000	.0000	.0000	.0000	.0000	.0000	.0000	.0001	.0003	.0010
11	1	.4312	.6862	.8327	.9141	.9578	.9802	.9912	.9964	.9986	.9995
	2	.1019	.3026	.5078	.6779	.8029	.8870	.9394	.9698	.9861	.9941
	3	.0152	.0896	.2212	.3826	.5448	.6873	.7999	.8811	.9348	.9673
	4	.0016	.0185	.0694	.1611	.2867	.4304	.5744	.7037	.8089	.8867
	5	.0001	.0028	.0159	.0504	.1146	.2103	.3317	.4672	.6029	.7256
	6	.0000	.0003	.0027	.0117	.0343	.0782	.1487	.2465	.3669	.5000
	7	.0000	.0000	.0003	.0020	.0076	.0216	.0501	.0994	.1738	.2744
	8	.0000	.0000	.0000	.0002	.0012	.0043	.0122	.0293	.0610	.1133
	9	.0000	.0000	.0000	.0000	.0001	.0006	.0020	.0059	.0148	.0327
	10	.0000	.0000	.0000	.0000	.0000	.0000	.0002	.0007	.0022	.0059
	11	.0000	.0000	.0000	.0000	.0000	.0000	.0000	.0000	.0002	.0005
12	1	.4596	.7176	.8578	.9313	.9683	.9862	.9943	.9978	.9992	.9998
	2	.1184	.3410	.5565	.7251	.8416	.9150	.9576	.9804	.9917	.9968
	3	.0196	.1109	.2642	.4417	.6093	.7472	.8487	.9166	.9579	.9807
	4	.0022	.0256	.0922	.2054	.3512	.5075	.6533	.7747	.8655	.9270
	5	.0002	.0043	.0239	.0726	.1576	.2763	.4167	.5618	.6956	.8062
	6	.0000	.0005	.0046	.0194	.0544	.1178	.2127	.3348	.4731	.6128
	7	.0000	.0001	.0007	.0039	.0143	.0386	.0846	.1582	.2607	.3872
	8	.0000	.0000	.0001	.0006	.0028	.0095	.0255	.0573	.1117	.1938
	9	.0000	.0000	.0000	.0001	.0004	.0017	.0056	.0153	.0356	.0730
	10	.0000	.0000	.0000	.0000	.0000	.0002	.0008	.0028	.0079	.0193
	11	.0000	.0000	.0000	.0000	.0000	.0000	.0001	.0003	.0011	.0032
	12	.0000	.0000	.0000	.0000	.0000	.0000	.0000	.0000	.0001	.0002
13	1	.4867	.7458	.8791	.9450	.9762	.9903	.9963	.9987	.9996	.9999
	2	.1354	.3787	.6017	.7664	.8733	.9363	.9704	.9874	.9951	.9983
	3	.0245	.1339	.2704	.4983	.6674	.7975	.8868	.9421	.9731	.9888
	4	.0031	.0342	.0967	.2527	.4157	.5794	.7217	.8314	.9071	.9539
	5	.0003	.0065	.0260	.0991	.2060	.3457	.4995	.6470	.7721	.8666
	6	.0000	.0009	.0053	.0300	.0802	.1654	.2841	.4256	.5732	.7095
	7	.0000	.0001	.0013	.0070	.0243	.0624	.1295	.2288	.3563	.5000
	8	.0000	.0000	.0002	.0012	.0056	.0182	.0462	.0977	.1788	.2905
	9	.0000	.0000	.0000	.0002	.0010	.0040	.0126	.0321	.0698	.1334
	10	.0000	.0000	.0000	.0000	.0001	.0007	.0025	.0078	.0203	.0461
	11	.0000	.0000	.0000	.0000	.0000	.0001	.0003	.0013	.0041	.0112
	12	.0000	.0000	.0000	.0000	.0000	.0000	.0000	.0001	.0005	.0017
	13	.0000	.0000	.0000	.0000	.0000	.0000	.0000	.0000	.0000	.0001

Summed Binomial Probability Function

$$\sum_{x=x'}^{x=n} \binom{n}{x} p^x (1-p)^{n-x}$$

n	x′	p = .05	.10	.15	.20	.25	.30	.35	.40	.45	.50
14	1	.5123	.7712	.8972	.9560	.9822	.9932	.9976	.9992	.9998	.9999
	2	.1530	.4154	.6433	.8021	.8990	.9525	.9795	.9919	.9971	.9991
	3	.0301	.1584	.3521	.5519	.7189	.8392	.9161	.9602	.9830	.9935
	4	.0042	.0441	.1465	.3018	.4787	.6448	.7795	.8757	.9368	.9713
	5	.0004	.0092	.0467	.1298	.2585	.4158	.5773	.7207	.8328	.9102
	6	.0000	.0015	.0115	.0439	.1117	.2195	.3595	.5141	.6627	.7880
	7	.0000	.0002	.0022	.0116	.0383	.0933	.1836	.3075	.4539	.6047
	8	.0000	.0000	.0003	.0024	.0103	.0315	.0753	.1501	.2586	.3953
	9	.0000	.0000	.0000	.0004	.0022	.0083	.0243	.0583	.1189	.2120
	10	.0000	.0000	.0000	.0000	.0003	.0017	.0060	.0175	.0426	.0898
	11	.0000	.0000	.0000	.0000	.0000	.0002	.0011	.0039	.0114	.0287
	12	.0000	.0000	.0000	.0000	.0000	.0000	.0001	.0006	.0022	.0065
	13	.0000	.0000	.0000	.0000	.0000	.0000	.0000	.0001	.0003	.0009
	14	.0000	.0000	.0000	.0000	.0000	.0000	.0000	.0000	.0000	.0001
15	1	.5367	.7941	.9126	.9648	.9866	.9953	.9984	.9995	.9999	1.0000
	2	.1710	.4510	.6814	.8329	.9198	.9647	.9858	.9948	.9983	.9995
	3	.0362	.1841	.3958	.6020	.7639	.8732	.9383	.9729	.9893	.9963
	4	.0055	.0556	.1773	.3518	.5387	.7031	.8273	.9095	.9576	.9824
	5	.0006	.0127	.0617	.1642	.3135	.4845	.6481	.7827	.8796	.9408
	6	.0001	.0022	.0168	.0611	.1484	.2784	.4357	.5968	.7392	.8491
	7	.0000	.0003	.0036	.0181	.0566	.1311	.2452	.3902	.5478	.6964
	8	.0000	.0000	.0006	.0042	.0173	.0500	.1132	.2131	.3465	.5000
	9	.0000	.0000	.0001	.0008	.0042	.0152	.0422	.0950	.1818	.3036
	10	.0000	.0000	.0000	.0001	.0008	.0037	.0124	.0338	.0769	.1509
	11	.0000	.0000	.0000	.0000	.0001	.0007	.0028	.0093	.0255	.0592
	12	.0000	.0000	.0000	.0000	.0000	.0001	.0005	.0019	.0063	.0176
	13	.0000	.0000	.0000	.0000	.0000	.0000	.0001	.0003	.0011	.0037
	14	.0000	.0000	.0000	.0000	.0000	.0000	.0000	.0000	.0001	.0005
	15	.0000	.0000	.0000	.0000	.0000	.0000	.0000	.0000	.0000	.0000
16	1	.5599	.8147	.9257	.9719	.9900	.9967	.9990	.9997	.9999	1.0000
	2	.1892	.4853	.7161	.8593	.9365	.9739	.9902	.9967	.9990	.9997
	3	.0429	.2108	.4386	.6482	.8029	.9006	.9549	.9817	.9934	.9979
	4	.0070	.0684	.2101	.4019	.5950	.7541	.8661	.9349	.9719	.9894
	5	.0009	.0170	.0791	.2018	.3698	.5501	.7108	.8334	.9147	.9616
	6	.0001	.0033	.0235	.0817	.1897	.3402	.5100	.6712	.8024	.8949
	7	.0000	.0005	.0056	.0267	.0796	.1753	.3119	.4728	.6340	.7228
	8	.0000	.0001	.0011	.0070	.0271	.0744	.1594	.2839	.4371	.5982
	9	.0000	.0000	.0002	.0015	.0075	.0257	.0671	.1423	.2559	.4018
	10	.0000	.0000	.0000	.0002	.0016	.0071	.0229	.0583	.1241	.2272
	11	.0000	.0000	.0000	.0000	.0003	.0016	.0062	.0191	.0486	.1051
	12	.0000	.0000	.0000	.0000	.0000	.0003	.0013	.0049	.0149	.0384
	13	.0000	.0000	.0000	.0000	.0000	.0000	.0002	.0009	.0035	.0106
	14	.0000	.0000	.0000	.0000	.0000	.0000	.0000	.0001	.0006	.0021
	15	.0000	.0000	.0000	.0000	.0000	.0000	.0000	.0000	.0001	.0003
	16	.0000	.0000	.0000	.0000	.0000	.0000	.0000	.0000	.0000	.0000
17	1	.5819	.8332	.9369	.9775	.9925	.9977	.9993	.9998	1.0000	1.0000
	2	.2078	.5182	.7475	.8818	.9499	.9807	.9933	.9979	.9994	.9999
	3	.0503	.2382	.4802	.6904	.8363	.9226	.9673	.9877	.9959	.9988
	4	.0088	.0826	.2444	.4511	.6470	.7981	.8972	.9536	.9816	.9936
	5	.0012	.0221	.0987	.2418	.4261	.6113	.7652	.8740	.9404	.9755
	6	.0001	.0047	.0319	.1057	.2347	.4032	.5803	.7361	.8529	.9283
	7	.0000	.0008	.0083	.0377	.1071	.2248	.3812	.5522	.7098	.8338
	8	.0000	.0001	.0017	.0109	.0402	.1046	.2128	.3595	.5257	.6855
	9	.0000	.0000	.0003	.0026	.0124	.0403	.0994	.1989	.3374	.5000
	10	.0000	.0000	.0000	.0005	.0031	.0127	.0383	.0919	.1834	.3145
	11	.0000	.0000	.0000	.0001	.0006	.0032	.0120	.0348	.0826	.1662
	12	.0000	.0000	.0000	.0000	.0001	.0007	.0030	.0106	.0301	.0717
	13	.0000	.0000	.0000	.0000	.0000	.0001	.0006	.0025	.0086	.0245
	14	.0000	.0000	.0000	.0000	.0000	.0000	.0001	.0005	.0019	.0064
	15	.0000	.0000	.0000	.0000	.0000	.0000	.0000	.0001	.0003	.0012
	16	.0000	.0000	.0000	.0000	.0000	.0000	.0000	.0000	.0000	.0001
	17	.0000	.0000	.0000	.0000	.0000	.0000	.0000	.0000	.0000	.0000

Summed Binomial Probability Function

$$\sum_{x=x'}^{x=n} \binom{n}{x} p^x (1-p)^{n-x}$$

n	x′	p = .05	.10	.15	.20	.25	.30	.35	.40	.45	.50
18	1	.6028	.8499	.9464	.9820	.9944	.9984	.9996	.9999	1.0000	1.0000
	2	.2265	.5497	.7759	.9009	.9605	.9858	.9954	.9987	.9997	.9999
	3	.0581	.2662	.5203	.7287	.8647	.9400	.9764	.9918	.9975	.9993
	4	.0109	.0982	.2798	.4990	.6943	.8354	.9217	.9672	.9880	.9962
	5	.0015	.0282	.1206	.2836	.4813	.6673	.8114	.9058	.9589	.9846
	6	.0002	.0064	.0419	.1329	.2825	.4656	.6450	.7912	.8923	.9519
	7	.0000	.0012	.0118	.0513	.1390	.2783	.4509	.6257	.7742	.8811
	8	.0000	.0002	.0027	.0163	.0569	.1407	.2717	.4366	.6085	.7597
	9	.0000	.0000	.0005	.0043	.0193	.0596	.1391	.2632	.4222	.5927
	10	.0000	.0000	.0001	.0009	.0054	.0210	.0597	.1347	.2527	.4073
	11	.0000	.0000	.0000	.0002	.0012	.0061	.0212	.0576	.1280	.2403
	12	.0000	.0000	.0000	.0000	.0002	.0014	.0062	.0203	.0537	.1189
	13	.0000	.0000	.0000	.0000	.0000	.0003	.0014	.0058	.0183	.0481
	14	.0000	.0000	.0000	.0000	.0000	.0000	.0003	.0013	.0049	.0154
	15	.0000	.0000	.0000	.0000	.0000	.0000	.0000	.0002	.0010	.0038
	16	.0000	.0000	.0000	.0000	.0000	.0000	.0000	.0000	.0001	.0007
	17	.0000	.0000	.0000	.0000	.0000	.0000	.0000	.0000	.0000	.0001
	18	.0000	.0000	.0000	.0000	.0000	.0000	.0000	.0000	.0000	.0000
19	1	.6226	.8649	.9544	.9856	.9958	.9989	.9997	.9999	1.0000	1.0000
	2	.2453	.5797	.8015	.9171	.9690	.9896	.9969	.9992	.9998	1.0000
	3	.0665	.2946	.5587	.7631	.8887	.9538	.9830	.9945	.9985	.9996
	4	.0132	.1150	.3159	.5449	.7369	.8668	.9409	.9770	.9923	.9978
	5	.0020	.0352	.1444	.3267	.5346	.7178	.8500	.9304	.9720	.9904
	6	.0002	.0086	.0537	.1631	.3322	.5261	.7032	.8371	.9223	.9682
	7	.0000	.0017	.0163	.0676	.1749	.3345	.5188	.6919	.8273	.9165
	8	.0000	.0003	.0041	.0233	.0775	.1820	.3344	.5122	.6831	.8204
	9	.0000	.0000	.0008	.0067	.0287	.0839	.1855	.3325	.5060	.6762
	10	.0000	.0000	.0001	.0016	.0089	.0326	.0875	.1861	.3290	.5000
	11	.0000	.0000	.0000	.0003	.0023	.0105	.0347	.0885	.1841	.3238
	12	.0000	.0000	.0000	.0000	.0005	.0028	.0114	.0352	.0871	.1796
	13	.0000	.0000	.0000	.0000	.0001	.0006	.0031	.0116	.0342	.0835
	14	.0000	.0000	.0000	.0000	.0000	.0001	.0007	.0031	.0109	.0318
	15	.0000	.0000	.0000	.0000	.0000	.0000	.0001	.0006	.0028	.0096
	16	.0000	.0000	.0000	.0000	.0000	.0000	.0000	.0001	.0005	.0022
	17	.0000	.0000	.0000	.0000	.0000	.0000	.0000	.0000	.0001	.0004
	18	.0000	.0000	.0000	.0000	.0000	.0000	.0000	.0000	.0000	.0000
	19	.0000	.0000	.0000	.0000	.0000	.0000	.0000	.0000	.0000	.0000
20	1	.6415	.8784	.9612	.9885	.9968	.9992	.9998	1.0000	1.0000	1.0000
	2	.2642	.6083	.8244	.9308	.9757	.9924	.9979	.9995	.9999	1.0000
	3	.0755	.3231	.5951	.7939	.9087	.9645	.9879	.9964	.9991	.9998
	4	.0159	.1330	.3523	.5886	.7748	.8929	.9556	.9840	.9951	.9987
	5	.0026	.0432	.1702	.3704	.5852	.7625	.8818	.9490	.9811	.9941
	6	.0003	.0113	.0673	.1958	.3828	.5836	.7546	.8744	.9447	.9793
	7	.0000	.0024	.0219	.0867	.2142	.3920	.5834	.7500	.8701	.9423
	8	.0000	.0004	.0059	.0321	.1018	.2277	.3990	.5841	.7480	.8684
	9	.0000	.0001	.0013	.0100	.0409	.1133	.2376	.4044	.5857	.7483
	10	.0000	.0000	.0002	.0026	.0139	.0480	.1218	.2447	.4086	.5881
	11	.0000	.0000	.0000	.0006	.0039	.0171	.0532	.1275	.2493	.4119
	12	.0000	.0000	.0000	.0001	.0009	.0051	.0196	.0565	.1308	.2517
	13	.0000	.0000	.0000	.0000	.0002	.0013	.0060	.0210	.0580	.1316
	14	.0000	.0000	.0000	.0000	.0000	.0003	.0015	.0065	.0214	.0577
	15	.0000	.0000	.0000	.0000	.0000	.0000	.0003	.0016	.0064	.0207
	16	.0000	.0000	.0000	.0000	.0000	.0000	.0000	.0003	.0015	.0059
	17	.0000	.0000	.0000	.0000	.0000	.0000	.0000	.0000	.0003	.0013
	18	.0000	.0000	.0000	.0000	.0000	.0000	.0000	.0000	.0000	.0002
	19	.0000	.0000	.0000	.0000	.0000	.0000	.0000	.0000	.0000	.0000
	20	.0000	.0000	.0000	.0000	.0000	.0000	.0000	.0000	.0000	.0000

Table III

Poisson Probability Function $e^{-m}m^x/x!$

Entries in the table are values of $e^{-m}m^x/x!$ for the indicated values of x and m.

x	0.1	0.2	0.3	0.4	0.5	0.6	0.7	0.8	0.9	1.0
0	.9048	.8187	.7408	.6703	.6065	.5488	.4966	.4493	.4066	.3679
1	.0905	.1637	.2222	.2681	.3033	.3293	.3476	.3595	.3659	.3679
2	.0045	.0164	.0333	.0536	.0758	.0988	.1217	.1438	.1647	.1839
3	.0002	.0011	.0033	.0072	.0126	.0198	.0284	.0383	.0494	.0613
4	.0000	.0001	.0002	.0007	.0016	.0030	.0050	.0077	.0111	.0153
5	.0000	.0000	.0000	.0001	.0002	.0004	.0007	.0012	.0020	.0031
6	.0000	.0000	.0000	.0000	.0000	.0000	.0001	.0002	.0003	.0005
7	.0000	.0000	.0000	.0000	.0000	.0000	.0000	.0000	.0000	.0001

x	1.1	1.2	1.3	1.4	1.5	1.6	1.7	1.8	1.9	2.0
0	.3329	.3012	.2725	.2466	.2231	.2019	.1827	.1653	.1496	.1353
1	.3662	.3614	.3543	.3452	.3347	.3230	.3106	.2975	.2842	.2707
2	.2014	.2169	.2303	.2417	.2510	.2584	.2640	.2678	.2700	.2707
3	.0738	.0867	.0998	.1128	.1255	.1378	.1496	.1607	.1710	.1804
4	.0203	.0260	.0324	.0395	.0471	.0551	.0636	.0723	.0812	.0902
5	.0045	.0062	.0084	.0111	.0141	.0176	.0216	.0260	.0309	.0361
6	.0008	.0012	.0018	.0026	.0035	.0047	.0061	.0078	.0098	.0120
7	.0001	.0002	.0003	.0005	.0008	.0011	.0015	.0020	.0027	.0034
8	.0000	.0000	.0001	.0001	.0001	.0002	.0003	.0005	.0006	.0009
9	.0000	.0000	.0000	.0000	.0000	.0000	.0001	.0001	.0001	.0002

x	2.1	2.2	2.3	2.4	2.5	2.6	2.7	2.8	2.9	3.0
0	.1225	.1108	.1003	.0907	.0821	.0743	.0672	.0608	.0550	.0498
1	.2572	.2438	.2306	.2177	.2052	.1931	.1815	.1703	.1596	.1494
2	.2700	.2681	.2652	.2613	.2565	.2510	.2450	.2384	.2314	.2240
3	.1890	.1966	.2033	.2090	.2138	.2176	.2205	.2225	.2237	.2240
4	.0992	.1082	.1169	.1254	.1336	.1414	.1488	.1557	.1622	.1680
5	.0417	.0476	.0538	.0602	.0668	.0735	.0804	.0872	.0940	.1008
6	.0146	.0174	.0206	.0241	.0278	.0319	.0362	.0407	.0455	.0504
7	.0044	.0055	.0068	.0083	.0099	.0118	.0139	.0163	.0188	.0216
8	.0011	.0015	.0019	.0025	.0031	.0038	.0047	.0057	.0068	.0081
9	.0003	.0004	.0005	.0007	.0009	.0011	.0014	.0018	.0022	.0027
10	.0001	.0001	.0001	.0002	.0002	.0003	.0004	.0005	.0006	.0008
11	.0000	.0000	.0000	.0000	.0000	.0001	.0001	.0001	.0002	.0002
12	.0000	.0000	.0000	.0000	.0000	.0000	.0000	.0000	.0000	.0001

x	3.1	3.2	3.3	3.4	3.5	3.6	3.7	3.8	3.9	4.0
0	.0450	.0408	.0369	.0334	.0302	.0273	.0247	.0224	.0202	.0183
1	.1397	.1304	.1217	.1135	.1057	.0984	.0915	.0850	.0789	.0733
2	.2165	.2087	.2008	.1929	.1850	.1771	.1692	.1615	.1539	.1465
3	.2237	.2226	.2209	.2186	.2158	.2125	.2087	.2046	.2001	.1954
4	.1734	.1781	.1823	.1858	.1888	.1912	.1931	.1944	.1951	.1954
5	.1075	.1140	.1203	.1264	.1322	.1377	.1429	.1477	.1522	.1563
6	.0555	.0608	.0662	.0716	.0771	.0826	.0881	.0936	.0989	.1042
7	.0246	.0278	.0312	.0348	.0385	.0425	.0466	.0508	.0551	.0595
8	.0095	.0111	.0129	.0148	.0169	.0191	.0215	.0241	.0269	.0298
9	.0033	.0040	.0047	.0056	.0066	.0076	.0089	.0102	.0116	.0132
10	.0010	.0013	.0016	.0019	.0023	.0028	.0033	.0039	.0045	.0053
11	.0003	.0004	.0005	.0006	.0007	.0009	.0011	.0013	.0016	.0019
12	.0001	.0001	.0001	.0002	.0002	.0003	.0003	.0004	.0005	.0006
13	.0000	.0000	.0000	.0000	.0001	.0001	.0001	.0001	.0002	.0002
14	.0000	.0000	.0000	.0000	.0000	.0000	.0000	.0000	.0000	.0001

Table III is used by permission from *Handbook of Probability and Statistics with Tables*, by Burington and May. Copyright, 1953. McGraw-Hill Book Co.

Poisson Probability Function $e^{-m}m^x/x!$

x	m = 4.1	4.2	4.3	4.4	4.5	4.6	4.7	4.8	4.9	5.0
0	.0166	.0150	.0136	.0123	.0111	.0101	.0091	.0082	.0074	.0067
1	.0679	.0630	.0583	.0540	.0500	.0462	.0427	.0395	.0365	.0337
2	.1393	.1323	.1254	.1188	.1125	.1063	.1005	.0948	.0894	.0842
3	.1904	.1852	.1798	.1743	.1687	.1631	.1574	.1517	.1460	.1404
4	.1951	.1944	.1933	.1917	.1898	.1875	.1849	.1820	.1789	.1755
5	.1600	.1633	.1662	.1687	.1708	.1725	.1738	.1747	.1753	.1755
6	.1093	.1143	.1191	.1237	.1281	.1323	.1362	.1398	.1432	.1462
7	.0640	.0686	.0732	.0778	.0824	.0869	.0914	.0959	.1002	.1044
8	.0328	.0360	.0393	.0428	.0463	.0500	.0537	.0575	.0614	.0653
9	.0150	.0168	.0188	.0209	.0232	.0255	.0280	.0307	.0334	.0363
10	.0061	.0071	.0081	.0092	.0104	.0118	.0132	.0147	.0164	.0181
11	.0023	.0027	.0032	.0037	.0043	.0049	.0056	.0064	.0073	.0082
12	.0008	.0009	.0011	.0014	.0016	.0019	.0022	.0026	.0030	.0034
13	.0002	.0003	.0004	.0005	.0006	.0007	.0008	.0009	.0011	.0013
14	.0001	.0001	.0001	.0001	.0002	.0002	.0003	.0003	.0004	.0005
15	.0000	.0000	.0000	.0000	.0001	.0001	.0001	.0001	.0001	.0002

x	m = 5.1	5.2	5.3	5.4	5.5	5.6	5.7	5.8	5.9	6.0
0	.0061	.0055	.0050	.0045	.0041	.0037	.0033	.0030	.0027	.0025
1	.0311	.0287	.0265	.0244	.0225	.0207	.0191	.0176	.0162	.0149
2	.0793	.0746	.0701	.0659	.0618	.0580	.0544	.0509	.0477	.0446
3	.1348	.1293	.1239	.1185	.1133	.1082	.1033	.0985	.0938	.0892
4	.1719	.1681	.1641	.1600	.1558	.1515	.1472	.1428	.1383	.1339
5	.1753	.1748	.1740	.1728	.1714	.1697	.1678	.1656	.1632	.1606
6	.1490	.1515	.1537	.1555	.1571	.1584	.1594	.1601	.1605	.1606
7	.1086	.1125	.1163	.1200	.1234	.1267	.1298	.1326	.1353	.1377
8	.0692	.0731	.0771	.0810	.0849	.0887	.0925	.0962	.0998	.1033
9	.0392	.0423	.0454	.0486	.0519	.0552	.0586	.0620	.0654	.0688
10	.0200	.0220	.0241	.0262	.0285	.0309	.0334	.0359	.0386	.0413
11	.0093	.0104	.0116	.0129	.0143	.0157	.0173	.0190	.0207	.0225
12	.0039	.0045	.0051	.0058	.0065	.0073	.0082	.0092	.0102	.0113
13	.0015	.0018	.0021	.0024	.0028	.0032	.0036	.0041	.0046	.0052
14	.0006	.0007	.0008	.0009	.0011	.0013	.0015	.0017	.0019	.0022
15	.0002	.0002	.0003	.0003	.0004	.0005	.0006	.0007	.0008	.0009
16	.0001	.0001	.0001	.0001	.0001	.0002	.0002	.0002	.0003	.0003
17	.0000	.0000	.0000	.0000	.0000	.0001	.0001	.0001	.0001	.0001

x	m = 6.1	6.2	6.3	6.4	6.5	6.6	6.7	6.8	6.9	7.0
0	.0022	.0020	.0018	.0017	.0015	.0014	.0012	.0011	.0010	.0009
1	.0137	.0126	.0116	.0106	.0098	.0090	.0082	.0076	.0070	.0064
2	.0417	.0390	.0364	.0340	.0318	.0296	.0276	.0258	.0240	.0223
3	.0848	.0806	.0765	.0726	.0688	.0652	.0617	.0584	.0552	.0521
4	.1294	.1249	.1205	.1162	.1118	.1076	.1034	.0992	.0952	.0912
5	.1579	.1549	.1519	.1487	.1454	.1420	.1385	.1349	.1314	.1277
6	.1605	.1601	.1595	.1586	.1575	.1562	.1546	.1529	.1511	.1490
7	.1399	.1418	.1435	.1450	.1462	.1472	.1480	.1486	.1489	.1490
8	.1066	.1099	.1130	.1160	.1188	.1215	.1240	.1263	.1284	.1304
9	.0723	.0757	.0791	.0825	.0858	.0891	.0923	.0954	.0985	.1014
10	.0441	.0469	.0498	.0528	.0558	.0588	.0618	.0649	.0679	.0710
11	.0245	.0265	.0285	.0307	.0330	.0353	.0377	.0401	.0426	.0452
12	.0124	.0137	.0150	.0164	.0179	.0194	.0210	.0227	.0245	.0264
13	.0058	.0065	.0073	.0081	.0089	.0098	.0108	.0119	.0130	.0142
14	.0025	.0029	.0033	.0037	.0041	.0046	.0052	.0058	.0064	.0071
15	.0010	.0012	.0014	.0016	.0018	.0020	.0023	.0026	.0029	.0033
16	.0004	.0005	.0005	.0006	.0007	.0008	.0010	.0011	.0013	.0014
17	.0001	.0002	.0002	.0002	.0003	.0003	.0004	.0004	.0005	.0006
18	.0000	.0001	.0001	.0001	.0001	.0001	.0001	.0002	.0002	.0002
19	.0000	.0000	.0000	.0000	.0000	.0000	.0000	.0001	.0001	.0001

Poisson Probability Function $e^{-m}m^x/x!$

x	m = 7.1	7.2	7.3	7.4	7.5	7.6	7.7	7.8	7.9	8.0
0	.0008	.0007	.0007	.0006	.0006	.0005	.0005	.0004	.0004	.0003
1	.0059	.0054	.0049	.0045	.0041	.0038	.0035	.0032	.0029	.0027
2	.0208	.0194	.0180	.0167	.0156	.0145	.0134	.0125	.0116	.0107
3	.0492	.0464	.0438	.0413	.0389	.0366	.0345	.0324	.0305	.0286
4	.0874	.0836	.0799	.0764	.0729	.0696	0663	.0632	.0602	.0573
5	.1241	.1204	.1167	.1130	.1094	.1057	.1021	.0986	.0951	.0916
6	.1468	.1445	.1420	.1394	.1367	.1339	.1311	.1282	.1252	.1221
7	.1489	.1486	.1481	.1474	.1465	.1454	.1442	.1428	.1413	.1396
8	.1321	.1337	.1351	.1363	.1373	.1382	.1388	.1392	.1395	.1396
9	.1042	.1070	.1096	.1121	.1144	.1167	.1187	.1207	.1224	.1241
10	.0740	.0770	.0800	.0829	.0858	.0887	.0914	.0941	.0967	.0993
11	.0478	.0504	.0531	.0558	.0585	.0613	.0640	.0667	.0695	.0722
12	.0283	.0303	.0323	.0344	.0366	.0388	.0411	.0434	.0457	.0481
13	.0154	.0168	.0181	.0196	.0211	.0227	.0243	.0260	.0278	.0296
14	.0078	.0086	.0095	.0104	.0113	.0123	.0134	.0145	.0157	.0169
15	.0037	.0041	.0046	.0051	.0057	.0062	.0069	.0075	.0083	.0090
16	.0016	.0019	.0021	.0024	.0026	.0030	.0033	.0037	.0041	.0045
17	.0007	.0008	.0009	.0010	.0012	.0013	.0015	.0017	.0019	.0021
18	.0003	.0003	.0004	.0004	.0005	.0006	.0006	.0007	.0008	.0009
19	.0001	.0001	.0001	.0002	.0002	.0002	.0003	.0003	.0003	.0004
20	.0000	.0000	.0001	.0001	.0001	.0001	.0001	.0001	.0001	.0002
21	.0000	.0000	.0000	.0000	.0000	.0000	.0000	.0000	.0001	.0001

x	m = 8.1	8.2	8.3	8.4	8.5	8.6	8.7	8.8	8.9	9.0
0	.0003	.0003	.0002	.0002	.0002	.0002	.0002	.0002	.0001	.0001
1	.0025	.0023	.0021	.0019	.0017	.0016	.0014	.0013	.0012	.0011
2	.0100	.0092	.0086	.0079	.0074	.0068	.0063	.0058	.0054	.0050
3	.0269	.0252	.0237	.0222	.0208	.0195	.0183	.0171	.0160	.0150
4	.0544	.0517	.0491	.0466	.0443	.0420	.0398	.0377	.0357	.0337
5	.0882	.0849	.0816	.0784	.0752	.0722	.0692	.0663	.0635	.0607
6	.1191	.1160	.1128	.1097	.1066	.1034	.1003	.0972	.0941	.0911
7	.1378	.1358	.1338	.1317	.1294	.1271	.1247	.1222	.1197	.1171
8	.1395	.1392	.1388	.1382	.1375	.1366	.1356	.1344	.1332	.1318
9	.1256	.1269	.1280	.1290	.1299	.1306	.1311	.1315	.1317	.1318
10	.1017	.1040	.1063	.1084	.1104	.1123	.1140	.1157	.1172	.1186
11	.0749	.0776	.0802	.0828	.0853	.0878	.0902	.0925	.0948	.0970
12	.0505	.0530	.0555	.0579	.0604	.0629	.0654	.0679	.0703	.0728
13	.0315	.0334	.0354	.0374	.0395	.0416	.0438	.0459	.0481	.0504
14	.0182	.0196	.0210	.0225	.0240	.0256	.0272	.0289	.0306	.0324
15	.0098	.0107	.0116	.0126	.0136	.0147	.0158	.0169	.0182	.0194
16	.0050	.0055	.0060	.0066	.0072	.0079	.0086	.0093	.0101	.0109
17	.0024	.0026	.0029	.0033	.0036	.0040	.0044	.0048	.0053	.0058
18	.0011	.0012	.0014	.0015	.0017	.0019	.0021	.0024	.0026	.0029
19	.0005	.0005	.0006	.0007	.0008	.0009	.0010	.0011	.0012	.0014
20	.0002	.0002	.0002	.0003	.0003	.0004	.0004	.0005	.0005	.0006
21	.0001	.0001	.0001	.0001	.0001	.0002	.0002	.0002	.0002	.0003
22	.0000	.0000	.0000	.0000	.0001	.0001	.0001	.0001	.0001	.0001

x	m = 9.1	9.2	9.3	9.4	9.5	9.6	9.7	9.8	9.9	10
0	.0001	.0001	.0001	.0001	.0001	.0001	.0001	.0001	.0001	.0000
1	.0010	.0009	.0009	.0008	.0007	.0007	.0006	.0005	.0005	.0005
2	.0046	.0043	.0040	.0037	.0034	.0031	.0029	.0027	.0025	.0023
3	.0140	.0131	.0123	.0115	.0107	.0100	.0093	.0087	.0081	.0076
4	.0319	.0302	.0285	.0269	.0254	.0240	.0226	.0213	.0201	.0189
5	.0581	.0555	.0530	.0506	.0483	.0460	.0439	.0418	.0398	.0378
6	.0881	.0851	.0822	.0793	.0764	.0736	.0709	.0682	.0656	.0631
7	.1145	.1118	.1091	.1064	.1037	.1010	.0982	.0955	.0928	.0901
8	.1302	.1286	.1269	.1251	.1232	.1212	.1191	.1170	.1148	.1126
9	.1317	.1315	.1311	.1306	.1300	.1293	.1284	.1274	.1263	.1251

POISSON PROBABILITY FUNCTION $e^{-m}m^x/x!$

x	m = 9.1	9.2	9.3	9.4	9.5	9.6	9.7	9.8	9.9	10
10	.1198	.1210	.1219	.1228	.1235	.1241	.1245	.1249	.1250	.1251
11	.0991	.1012	.1031	.1049	.1067	.1083	.1098	.1112	.1125	.1137
12	.0752	.0776	.0799	.0822	.0844	.0866	.0888	.0908	.0928	.0948
13	.0526	.0549	.0572	.0594	.0617	.0640	.0662	.0685	.0707	.0729
14	.0342	.0361	.0380	.0399	.0419	.0439	.0459	.0479	.0500	.0521
15	.0208	.0221	.0235	.0250	.0265	.0281	.0297	.0313	.0330	.0347
16	.0118	.0127	.0137	.0147	.0157	.0168	.0180	.0192	.0204	.0217
17	.0063	.0069	.0075	.0081	.0088	.0095	.0103	.0111	.0119	.0128
18	.0032	.0035	.0039	.0042	.0046	.0051	.0055	.0060	.0065	.0071
19	.0015	.0017	.0019	.0021	.0023	.0026	.0028	.0031	.0034	.0037
20	.0007	.0008	.0009	.0010	.0011	.0012	.0014	.0015	.0017	.0019
21	.0003	.0003	.0004	.0004	.0005	.0006	.0006	.0007	.0008	.0009
22	.0001	.0001	.0002	.0002	.0002	.0002	.0003	.0003	.0004	.0004
23	.0000	.0001	.0001	.0001	.0001	.0001	.0001	.0001	.0002	.0002
24	.0000	.0000	.0000	.0000	.0000	.0000	.0000	.0001	.0001	.0001

x	m = 11	12	13	14	15	16	17	18	19	20
0	.0000	.0000	.0000	.0000	.0000	.0000	.0000	.0000	.0000	.0000
1	.0002	.0001	.0000	.0000	.0000	.0000	.0000	.0000	.0000	.0000
2	.0010	.0004	.0002	.0001	.0000	.0000	.0000	.0000	.0000	.0000
3	.0037	.0018	.0008	.0004	.0002	.0001	.0000	.0000	.0000	.0000
4	.0102	.0053	.0027	.0013	.0006	.0003	.0001	.0001	.0000	.0000
5	.0224	.0127	.0070	.0037	.0019	.0010	.0005	.0002	.0001	.0001
6	.0411	.0255	.0152	.0087	.0048	.0026	.0014	.0007	.0004	.0002
7	.0646	.0437	.0281	.0174	.0104	.0060	.0034	.0018	.0010	.0005
8	.0888	.0655	.0457	.0304	.0194	.0120	.0072	.0042	.0024	.0013
9	.1085	.0874	.0661	.0473	.0324	.0213	.0135	.0083	.0050	.0029
10	.1194	.1048	.0859	.0663	.0486	.0341	.0230	.0150	.0095	.0058
11	.1194	.1144	.1015	.0844	.0663	.0496	.0355	.0245	.0164	.0106
12	.1094	.1144	.1099	.0984	.0829	.0661	.0504	.0368	.0259	.0176
13	.0926	.1056	.1099	.1060	.0956	.0814	.0658	.0509	.0378	.0271
14	.0728	.0905	.1021	.1060	.1024	.0930	.0800	.0655	.0514	.0387
15	.0534	.0724	.0885	.0989	.1024	.0992	.0906	.0786	.0650	.0516
16	.0367	.0543	.0719	.0866	.0960	.0992	.0963	.0884	.0772	.0646
17	.0237	.0383	.0550	.0713	.0847	.0934	.0963	.0936	.0863	.0760
18	.0145	.0256	.0397	.0554	.0706	.0830	.0909	.0936	.0911	.0844
19	.0084	.0161	.0272	.0409	.0557	.0699	.0814	.0887	.0911	.0888
20	.0046	.0097	.0177	.0286	.0418	.0559	.0692	.0798	.0866	.0888
21	.0024	.0055	.0109	.0191	.0299	.0426	.0560	.0684	.0783	.0846
22	.0012	.0030	.0065	.0121	.0204	.0310	.0433	.0560	.0676	.0769
23	.0006	.0016	.0037	.0074	.0133	.0216	.0320	.0438	.0559	.0669
24	.0003	.0008	.0020	.0043	.0083	.0144	.0226	.0328	.0442	.0557
25	.0001	.0004	.0010	.0024	.0050	.0092	.0154	.0237	.0336	.0446
26	.0000	.0002	.0005	.0013	.0029	.0057	.0101	.0164	.0246	.0343
27	.0000	.0001	.0002	.0007	.0016	.0034	.0063	.0109	.0173	.0254
28	.0000	.0000	.0001	.0003	.0009	.0019	.0038	.0070	.0117	.0181
29	.0000	.0000	.0001	.0002	.0004	.0011	.0023	.0044	.0077	.0125
30	.0000	.0000	.0000	.0001	.0002	.0006	.0013	.0026	.0049	.0083
31	.0000	.0000	.0000	.0000	.0001	.0003	.0007	.0015	.0030	.0054
32	.0000	.0000	.0000	.0000	.0001	.0001	.0004	.0009	.0018	.0034
33	.0000	.0000	.0000	.0000	.0000	.0001	.0002	.0005	.0010	.0020
34	.0000	.0000	.0000	.0000	.0000	.0000	.0001	.0002	.0006	.0012
35	.0000	.0000	.0000	.0000	.0000	.0000	.0000	.0001	.0003	.0007
36	.0000	.0000	.0000	.0000	.0000	.0000	.0000	.0001	.0002	.0004
37	.0000	.0000	.0000	.0000	.0000	.0000	.0000	.0000	.0001	.0002
38	.0000	.0000	.0000	.0000	.0000	.0000	.0000	.0000	.0000	.0001
39	.0000	.0000	.0000	.0000	.0000	.0000	.0000	.0000	.0000	.0001

Table IV

Summed Poisson Probability Function

$$\sum_{x=x'}^{x=\infty} e^{-m}m^x/x!$$

Entries in the table are values of $\sum_{x=x'}^{x=\infty} e^{-m}m^x/x!$ for the indicated values of x' and m.

x' \ m	0.1	0.2	0.3	0.4	0.5	0.6	0.7	0.8	0.9	1.0
0	1.0000	1.0000	1.0000	1.0000	1.0000	1.0000	1.0000	1.0000	1.0000	1.0000
1	.0952	.1813	.2592	.3297	.3935	.4512	.5034	.5507	.5934	.6321
2	.0047	.0175	.0369	.0616	.0902	.1219	.1558	.1912	.2275	.2642
3	.0002	.0011	.0036	.0079	.0144	.0231	.0341	.0474	.0629	.0803
4	.0000	.0001	.0003	.0008	.0018	.0034	.0058	.0091	.0135	.0190
5	.0000	.0000	.0000	.0001	.0002	.0004	.0008	.0014	.0023	.0037
6	.0000	.0000	.0000	.0000	.0000	.0000	.0001	.0002	.0003	.0006
7	.0000	.0000	.0000	.0000	.0000	.0000	.0000	.0000	.0000	.0001

x' \ m	1.1	1.2	1.3	1.4	1.5	1.6	1.7	1.8	1.9	2.0
0	1.0000	1.0000	1.0000	1.0000	1.0000	1.0000	1.0000	1.0000	1.0000	1.0000
1	.6671	.6988	.7275	.7534	.7769	.7981	.8173	.8347	.8504	.8647
2	.3010	.3374	.3732	.4082	.4422	.4751	.5068	.5372	.5663	.5940
3	.0996	.1205	.1429	.1665	.1912	.2166	.2428	.2694	.2963	.3233
4	.0257	.0338	.0431	.0537	.0656	.0788	.0932	.1087	.1253	.1429
5	.0054	.0077	.0107	.0143	.0186	.0237	.0296	.0364	.0441	.0527
6	.0010	.0015	.0022	.0032	.0045	.0060	.0080	.0104	.0132	.0166
7	.0001	.0003	.0004	.0006	.0009	.0013	.0019	.0026	.0034	.0045
8	.0000	.0000	.0001	.0001	.0002	.0003	.0004	.0006	.0008	.0011
9	.0000	.0000	.0000	.0000	.0000	.0000	.0001	.0001	.0002	.0002

x' \ m	2.1	2.2	2.3	2.4	2.5	2.6	2.7	2.8	2.9	3.0
0	1.0000	1.0000	1.0000	1.0000	1.0000	1.0000	1.0000	1.0000	1.0000	1.0000
1	.8775	.8892	.8997	.9093	.9179	.9257	.9328	.9392	.9450	.9502
2	.6204	.6454	.6691	.6916	.7127	.7326	.7513	.7689	.7854	.8009
3	.3504	.3773	.4040	.4303	.4562	.4816	.5064	.5305	.5540	.5768
4	.1614	.1806	.2007	.2213	.2424	.2640	.2859	.3081	.3304	.3528
5	.0621	.0725	.0838	.0959	.1088	.1226	.1371	.1523	.1682	.1847
6	.0204	.0249	.0300	.0357	.0420	.0490	.0567	.0651	.0742	.0839
7	.0059	.0075	.0094	.0116	.0142	.0172	.0206	.0244	.0287	.0335
8	.0015	.0020	.0026	.0033	.0042	.0053	.0066	.0081	.0099	.0119
9	.0003	.0005	.0006	.0009	.0011	.0015	.0019	.0024	.0031	.0038
10	.0001	.0001	.0001	.0002	.0003	.0004	.0005	.0007	.0009	.0011
11	.0000	.0000	.0000	.0000	.0001	.0001	.0001	.0002	.0002	.0003
12	.0000	.0000	.0000	.0000	.0000	.0000	.0000	.0000	.0001	.0001

x' \ m	3.1	3.2	3.3	3.4	3.5	3.6	3.7	3.8	3.9	4.0
0	1.0000	1.0000	1.0000	1.0000	1.0000	1.0000	1.0000	1.0000	1.0000	1.0000
1	.9550	.9592	.9631	.9666	.9698	.9727	.9753	.9776	.9798	.9817
2	.8153	.8288	.8414	.8532	.8641	.8743	.8838	.8926	.9008	.9084
3	.5988	.6201	.6406	.6603	.6792	.6973	.7146	.7311	.7469	.7619
4	.3752	.3975	.4197	.4416	.4634	.4848	.5058	.5265	.5468	.5665
5	.2018	.2194	.2374	.2558	.2746	.2936	.3128	.3322	.3516	.3712
6	.0943	.1054	.1171	.1295	.1424	.1559	.1699	.1844	.1994	.2149
7	.0388	.0446	.0510	.0579	.0653	.0733	.0818	.0909	.1005	.1107
8	.0142	.0168	.0198	.0231	.0267	.0308	.0352	.0401	.0454	.0511
9	.0047	.0057	.0069	.0083	.0099	.0117	.0137	.0160	.0185	.0214
10	.0014	.0018	.0022	.0027	.0033	.0040	.0048	.0058	.0069	.0081
11	.0004	.0005	.0006	.0008	.0010	.0013	.0016	.0019	.0023	.0028
12	.0001	.0001	.0002	.0002	.0003	.0004	.0005	.0006	.0007	.0009
13	.0000	.0000	.0000	.0001	.0001	.0001	.0001	.0002	.0002	.0003
14	.0000	.0000	.0000	.0000	.0000	.0000	.0000	.0000	.0001	.0001

Summed Poisson Probability Function

$$\sum_{x=x'}^{x=\infty} e^{-m}m^x/x!$$

x'	m 4.1	4.2	4.3	4.4	4.5	4.6	4.7	4.8	4.9	5.0
0	1.0000	1.0000	1.0000	1.0000	1.0000	1.0000	1.0000	1.0000	1.0000	1.0000
1	.9834	.9850	.9864	.9877	.9889	.9899	.9909	.9918	.9926	.9933
2	.9155	.9220	.9281	.9337	.9389	.9437	.9482	.9523	.9561	.9596
3	.7762	.7898	.8026	.8149	.8264	.8374	.8477	.8575	.8667	.8753
4	.5858	.6046	.6228	.6406	.6577	.6743	.6903	.7058	.7207	.7350
5	.3907	.4102	.4296	.4488	.4679	.4868	.5054	.5237	.5418	.5595
6	.2307	.2469	.2633	.2801	.2971	.3142	.3316	.3490	.3665	.3840
7	.1214	.1325	.1442	.1564	.1689	.1820	.1954	.2092	.2233	.2378
8	.0573	.0639	.0710	.0786	.0866	.0951	.1040	.1133	.1231	.1334
9	.0245	.0279	.0317	.0358	.0403	.0451	.0503	.0558	.0618	.0681
10	.0095	.0111	.0129	.0149	.0171	.0195	.0222	.0251	.0283	.0318
11	.0034	.0041	.0048	.0057	.0067	.0078	.0090	.0104	.0120	.0137
12	.0011	.0014	.0017	.0020	.0024	.0029	.0034	.0040	.0047	.0055
13	.0003	.0004	.0005	.0007	.0008	.0010	.0012	.0014	.0017	.0020
14	.0001	.0001	.0002	.0002	.0003	.0003	.0004	.0005	.0006	.0007
15	.0000	.0000	.0000	.0001	.0001	.0001	.0001	.0001	.0002	.0002
16	.0000	.0000	.0000	.0000	.0000	.0000	.0000	.0000	.0001	.0001

x'	m 5.1	5.2	5.3	5.4	5.5	5.6	5.7	5.8	5.9	6.0
0	1.0000	1.0000	1.0000	1.0000	1.0000	1.0000	1.0000	1.0000	1.0000	1.0000
1	.9939	.9945	.9950	.9955	.9959	.9963	.9967	.9970	.9973	.9975
2	.9628	.9658	.9686	.9711	.9734	.9756	.9776	.9794	.9811	.9826
3	.8835	.8912	.8984	.9052	.9116	.9176	.9232	.9285	.9334	.9380
4	.7487	.7619	.7746	.7867	.7983	.8094	.8200	.8300	.8396	.8488
5	.5769	.5939	.6105	.6267	.6425	.6579	.6728	.6873	.7013	.7149
6	.4016	.4191	.4365	.4539	.4711	.4881	.5050	.5217	.5381	.5543
7	.2526	.2676	.2829	.2983	.3140	.3297	.3456	.3616	.3776	.3937
8	.1440	.1551	.1665	.1783	.1905	.2030	.2159	.2290	.2424	.2560
9	.0748	.0819	.0894	.0974	.1056	.1143	.1234	.1328	.1426	.1528
10	.0356	.0397	.0441	.0488	.0538	.0591	.0648	.0708	.0772	.0839
11	.0156	.0177	.0200	.0225	.0253	.0282	.0314	.0349	.0386	.0426
12	.0063	.0073	.0084	.0096	.0110	.0125	.0141	.0160	.0179	.0201
13	.0024	.0028	.0033	.0038	.0045	.0051	.0059	.0068	.0078	.0088
14	.0008	.0010	.0012	.0014	.0017	.0020	.0023	.0027	.0031	.0036
15	.0003	.0003	.0004	.0005	.0006	.0007	.0009	.0010	.0012	.0014
16	.0001	.0001	.0001	.0002	.0002	.0002	.0003	.0004	.0004	.0005
17	.0000	.0000	.0000	.0001	.0001	.0001	.0001	.0001	.0001	.0002
18	.0000	.0000	.0000	.0000	.0000	.0000	.0000	.0000	.0000	.0001

x'	m 6.1	6.2	6.3	6.4	6.5	6.6	6.7	6.8	6.9	7.0
0	1.0000	1.0000	1.0000	1.0000	1.0000	1.0000	1.0000	1.0000	1.0000	1.0000
1	.9978	.9980	.9982	.9983	.9985	.9986	.9988	.9989	.9990	.9991
2	.9841	.9854	.9866	.9877	.9887	.9897	.9905	.9913	.9920	.9927
3	.9423	.9464	.9502	.9537	.9570	.9600	.9629	.9656	.9680	.9704
4	.8575	.8658	.8736	.8811	.8882	.8948	.9012	.9072	.9129	.9182
5	.7281	.7408	.7531	.7649	.7763	.7873	.7978	.8080	.8177	.8270
6	.5702	.5859	.6012	.6163	.6310	.6453	.6594	.6730	.6863	.6993
7	.4098	.4258	.4418	.4577	.4735	.4892	.5047	.5201	.5353	.5503
8	.2699	.2840	.2983	.3127	.3272	.3419	.3567	.3715	.3864	.4013
9	.1633	.1741	.1852	.1967	.2084	.2204	.2327	.2452	.2580	.2709
10	.0910	.0984	.1061	.1142	.1226	.1314	.1404	.1498	.1505	.1695
11	.0469	.0514	.0563	.0614	.0668	.0726	.0786	.0849	.0916	.0985
12	.0224	.0250	.0277	.0307	.0339	.0373	.0409	.0448	.0490	.0534
13	.0100	.0113	.0127	.0143	.0160	.0179	.0199	.0221	.0245	.0270
14	.0042	.0048	.0055	.0063	.0071	.0080	.0091	.0102	.0115	.0128
15	.0016	.0019	.0022	.0026	.0030	.0034	.0039	.0044	.0050	.0057
16	.0006	.0007	.0008	.0010	.0012	.0014	.0016	.0018	.0021	.0024
17	.0002	.0003	.0003	.0004	.0004	.0005	.0006	.0007	.0008	.0010
18	.0001	.0001	.0001	.0001	.0002	.0002	.0002	.0003	.0003	.0004
19	.0000	.0000	.0000	.0000	.0001	.0001	.0001	.0001	.0001	.0001

Summed Poisson Probability Function

$$\sum_{x=x'}^{x=\infty} e^{-m}m^x/x!$$

x'	m 7.1	7.2	7.3	7.4	7.5	7.6	7.7	7.8	7.9	8.0
0	1.0000	1.0000	1.0000	1.0000	1.0000	1.0000	1.0000	1.0000	1.0000	1.0000
1	.9992	.9993	.9993	.9994	.9994	.9995	.9995	.9996	.9996	.9997
2	.9933	.9939	.9944	.9949	.9953	.9957	.9961	.9964	.9967	.9970
3	.9725	.9745	.9764	.9781	.9797	.9812	.9826	.9839	.9851	.9862
4	.9233	.9281	.9326	.9368	.9409	.9446	.9482	.9515	.9547	.9576
5	.8359	.8445	.8527	.8605	.8679	.8751	.8819	.8883	.8945	.9004
6	.7119	.7241	.7360	.7474	.7586	.7693	.7797	.7897	.7994	.8088
7	.5651	.5796	.5940	.6080	.6218	.6354	.6486	.6616	.6743	.6866
8	.4162	.4311	.4459	.4607	.4754	.4900	.5044	.5188	.5330	.5470
9	.2840	.2973	.3108	.3243	.3380	.3518	.3657	.3796	.3935	.4075
10	.1798	.1904	.2012	.2123	.2236	.2351	.2469	.2589	.2710	.2834
11	.1058	.1133	.1212	.1293	.1378	.1465	.1555	.1648	.1743	.1841
12	.0580	.0629	.0681	.0735	.0792	.0852	.0915	.0980	.1048	.1119
13	.0297	.0327	.0358	.0391	.0427	.0464	.0504	.0546	.0591	.0638
14	.0143	.0159	.0176	.0195	.0216	.0238	.0261	.0286	.0313	.0342
15	.0065	.0073	.0082	.0092	.0103	.0114	.0127	.0141	.0156	.0173
16	.0028	.0031	.0036	.0041	.0046	.0052	.0059	.0066	.0074	.0082
17	.0011	.0013	.0015	.0017	.0020	.0022	.0026	.0029	.0033	.0037
18	.0004	.0005	.0006	.0007	.0008	.0009	.0011	.0012	.0014	.0016
19	.0002	.0002	.0002	.0003	.0003	.0004	.0004	.0005	.0006	.0006
20	.0001	.0001	.0001	.0001	.0001	.0001	.0002	.0002	.0002	.0003
21	.0000	.0000	.0000	.0000	.0000	.0000	.0001	.0001	.0001	.0001

x'	m 8.1	8.2	8.3	8.4	8.5	8.6	8.7	8.8	8.9	9.0
0	1.0000	1.0000	1.0000	1.0000	1.0000	1.0000	1.0000	1.0000	1.0000	1.0000
1	.9997	.9997	.9998	.9998	.9998	.9998	.9998	.9998	.9999	.9999
2	.9972	.9975	.9977	.9979	.9981	.9982	.9984	.9985	.9987	.9988
3	.9873	.9882	.9891	.9900	.9907	.9914	.9921	.9927	.9932	.9938
4	.9604	.9630	.9654	.9677	.9699	.9719	.9738	.9756	.9772	.9788
5	.9060	.9113	.9163	.9211	.9256	.9299	.9340	.9379	.9416	.9450
6	.8178	.8264	.8347	.8427	.8504	.8578	.8648	.8716	.8781	.8843
7	.6987	.7104	.7219	.7330	.7438	.7543	.7645	.7744	.7840	.7932
8	.5609	.5746	.5881	.6013	.6144	.6272	.6398	.6522	.6643	.6761
9	.4214	.4353	.4493	.4631	.4769	.4906	.5042	.5177	.5311	.5443
10	.2959	.3085	.3212	.3341	.3470	.3600	.3731	.3863	.3994	.4126
11	.1942	.2045	.2150	.2257	.2366	.2478	.2591	.2706	.2822	.2940
12	.1193	.1269	.1348	.1429	.1513	.1600	.1689	.1780	.1874	.1970
13	.0687	.0739	.0793	.0850	.0909	.0971	.1035	.1102	.1171	.1242
14	.0372	.0405	.0439	.0476	.0514	.0555	.0597	.0642	.0689	.0739
15	.0190	.0209	.0229	.0251	.0274	.0299	.0325	.0353	.0383	.0415
16	.0092	.0102	.0113	.0125	.0138	.0152	.0168	.0184	.0202	.0220
17	.0042	.0047	.0053	.0059	.0066	.0074	.0082	.0091	.0101	.0111
18	.0018	.0021	.0023	.0027	.0030	.0034	.0038	.0043	.0048	.0053
19	.0008	.0009	.0010	.0011	.0013	.0015	.0017	.0019	.0022	.0024
20	.0003	.0003	.0004	.0005	.0005	.0006	.0007	.0008	.0009	.0011
21	.0001	.0001	.0002	.0002	.0002	.0002	.0003	.0003	.0004	.0004
22	.0000	.0000	.0001	.0001	.0001	.0001	.0001	.0001	.0002	.0002
23	.0000	.0000	.0000	.0000	.0000	.0000	.0000	.0000	.0001	.0001

x'	m 9.1	9.2	9.3	9.4	9.5	9.6	9.7	9.8	9.9	10
0	1.0000	1.0000	1.0000	1.0000	1.0000	1.0000	1.0000	1.0000	1.0000	1.0000
1	.9999	.9999	.9999	.9999	.9999	.9999	.9999	.9999	1.0000	1.0000
2	.9989	.9990	.9991	.9991	.9992	.9993	.9993	.9994	.9995	.9995
3	.9942	.9947	.9951	.9955	.9958	.9962	.9965	.9967	.9970	.9972
4	.9802	.9816	.9828	.9840	.9851	.9862	.9871	.9880	.9889	.9897
5	.9483	.9514	.9544	.9571	.9597	.9622	.9645	.9667	.9688	.9707
6	.8902	.8959	.9014	.9065	.9115	.9162	.9207	.9250	.9290	.9329
7	.8022	.8108	.8192	.8273	.8351	.8426	.8498	.8567	.8634	.8699
8	.6877	.6990	.7101	.7208	.7313	.7416	.7515	.7612	.7706	.7798
9	.5574	.5704	.5832	.5958	.6082	.6204	.6324	.6442	.6558	.6672

Summed Poisson Probability Function

$$\sum_{x=x'}^{x=\infty} e^{-m} m^x / x!$$

x'	m 9.1	9.2	9.3	9.4	9.5	9.6	9.7	9.8	9.9	10
10	.4258	.4389	.4521	.4651	.4782	.4911	.5040	.5168	.5295	.5421
11	.3059	.3180	.3301	.3424	.3547	.3671	.3795	.3920	.4045	.4170
12	.2068	.2168	.2270	.2374	.2480	.2588	.2697	.2807	.2919	.3032
13	.1316	.1393	.1471	.1552	.1636	.1721	.1809	.1899	.1991	.2084
14	.0790	.0844	.0900	.0958	.1019	.1081	.1147	.1214	.1284	.1355
15	.0448	.0483	.0520	.0559	.0600	.0643	.0688	.0735	.0784	.0835
16	.0240	.0262	.0285	.0309	.0335	.0362	.0391	.0421	.0454	.0487
17	.0122	.0135	.0148	.0162	.0177	.0194	.0211	.0230	.0249	.0270
18	.0059	.0066	.0073	.0081	.0089	.0098	.0108	.0119	.0130	.0143
19	.0027	.0031	.0034	.0038	.0043	.0048	.0053	.0059	.0065	.0072
20	.0012	.0014	.0015	.0017	.0020	.0022	.0025	.0028	.0031	.0035
21	.0005	.0006	.0007	.0008	.0009	.0010	.0011	.0013	.0014	.0016
22	.0002	.0002	.0003	.0003	.0004	.0004	.0005	.0005	.0006	.0007
23	.0001	.0001	.0001	.0001	.0001	.0002	.0002	.0002	.0003	.0003
24	.0000	.0000	.0000	.0000	.0001	.0001	.0001	.0001	.0001	.0001

x'	m 11	12	13	14	15	16	17	18	19	20
0	1.0000	1.0000	1.0000	1.0000	1.0000	1.0000	1.0000	1.0000	1.0000	1.0000
1	1.0000	1.0000	1.0000	1.0000	1.0000	1.0000	1.0000	1.0000	1.0000	1.0000
2	.9998	.9999	1.0000	1.0000	1.0000	1.0000	1.0000	1.0000	1.0000	1.0000
3	.9988	.9995	.9998	.9999	1.0000	1.0000	1.0000	1.0000	1.0000	1.0000
4	.9951	.9977	.9990	.9995	.9998	.9999	1.0000	1.0000	1.0000	1.0000
5	.9849	.9924	.9963	.9982	.9991	.9996	.9998	.9999	1.0000	1.0000
6	.9625	.9797	.9893	.9945	.9972	.9986	.9993	.9997	.9998	.9999
7	.9214	.9542	.9741	.9858	.9924	.9960	.9979	.9990	.9995	.9997
8	.8568	.9105	.9460	.9684	.9820	.9900	.9946	.9971	.9985	.9992
9	.7680	.8450	.9002	.9379	.9626	.9780	.9874	.9929	.9961	.9979
10	.6595	.7576	.8342	.8906	.9301	.9567	.9739	.9846	.9911	.9950
11	.5401	.6528	.7483	.8243	.8815	.9226	.9509	.9696	.9817	.9892
12	.4207	.5384	.6468	.7400	.8152	.8730	.9153	.9451	.9653	.9786
13	.3113	.4240	.5369	.6415	.7324	.8069	.8650	.9083	.9394	.9610
14	.2187	.3185	.4270	.5356	.6368	.7255	.7991	.8574	.9016	.9339
15	.1460	.2280	.3249	.4296	.5343	.6325	.7192	.7919	.8503	.8951
16	.0926	.1556	.2364	.3306	.4319	.5333	.6285	.7133	.7852	.8435
17	.0559	.1013	.1645	.2441	.3359	.4340	.5323	.6250	.7080	.7789
18	.0322	.0630	.1095	.1728	.2511	.3407	.4360	.5314	.6216	.7030
19	.0177	.0374	.0698	.1174	.1805	.2577	.3450	.4378	.5305	.6186
20	.0093	.0213	.0427	.0765	.1248	.1878	.2637	.3491	.4394	.5297
21	.0047	.0116	.0250	.0479	.0830	.1318	.1945	.2693	.3528	.4409
22	.0023	.0061	.0141	.0288	.0531	.0892	.1385	.2009	.2745	.3563
23	.0010	.0030	.0076	.0167	.0327	.0582	.0953	.1449	.2069	.2794
24	.0005	.0015	.0040	.0093	.0195	.0367	.0633	.1011	.1510	.2125
25	.0002	.0007	.0020	.0050	.0112	.0223	.0406	.0683	.1067	.1568
26	.0001	.0003	.0010	.0026	.0062	.0131	.0252	.0446	.0731	.1122
27	.0000	.0001	.0005	.0013	.0033	.0075	.0152	.0282	.0486	.0779
28	.0000	.0001	.0002	.0006	.0017	.0041	.0088	.0173	.0313	.0525
29	.0000	.0000	.0001	.0003	.0009	.0022	.0050	.0103	.0195	.0343
30	.0000	.0000	.0000	.0001	.0004	.0011	.0027	.0059	.0118	.0218
31	.0000	.0000	.0000	.0001	.0002	.0006	.0014	.0033	.0070	.0135
32	.0000	.0000	.0000	.0000	.0001	.0003	.0007	.0018	.0040	.0081
33	.0000	.0000	.0000	.0000	.0000	.0001	.0004	.0010	.0022	.0047
34	.0000	.0000	.0000	.0000	.0000	.0001	.0002	.0005	.0012	.0027
35	.0000	.0000	.0000	.0000	.0000	.0000	.0001	.0002	.0006	.0015
36	.0000	.0000	.0000	.0000	.0000	.0000	.0000	.0001	.0003	.0008
37	.0000	.0000	.0000	.0000	.0000	.0000	.0000	.0001	.0002	.0004
38	.0000	.0000	.0000	.0000	.0000	.0000	.0000	.0000	.0001	.0002
39	.0000	.0000	.0000	.0000	.0000	.0000	.0000	.0000	.0000	.0001
40	.0000	.0000	.0000	.0000	.0000	.0000	.0000	.0000	.0000	.0001

Table V

Normal Distribution

$$F(x) = \int_{-\infty}^{x} \frac{1}{\sqrt{2\pi}} e^{-t^2/2}\, dt$$

x	.00	.01	.02	.03	.04	.05	.06	.07	.08	.09
.0	.5000	.5040	.5080	.5120	.5160	.5199	.5239	.5279	.5319	.5359
.1	.5398	.5438	.5478	.5517	.5557	.5596	.5636	.5675	.5714	.5753
.2	.5793	.5832	.5871	.5910	.5948	.5987	.6026	.6064	.6103	.6141
.3	.6179	.6217	.6255	.6293	.6331	.6368	.6406	.6443	.6480	.6517
.4	.6554	.6591	.6628	.6664	.6700	.6736	.6772	.6808	.6844	.6879
.5	.6915	.6950	.6985	.7019	.7054	.7088	.7123	.7157	.7190	.7224
.6	.7257	.7291	.7324	.7357	.7389	.7422	.7454	.7486	.7517	.7549
.7	.7580	.7611	.7642	.7673	.7704	.7734	.7764	.7794	.7823	.7852
.8	.7881	.7910	.7939	.7967	.7995	.8023	.8051	.8078	.8106	.8133
.9	.8159	.8186	.8212	.8238	.8264	.8289	.8315	.8340	.8365	.8389
1.0	.8413	.8438	.8461	.8485	.8508	.8531	.8554	.8577	.8599	.8621
1.1	.8643	.8665	.8686	.8708	.8729	.8749	.8770	.8790	.8810	.8830
1.2	.8849	.8869	.8888	.8907	.8925	.8944	.8962	.8980	.8997	.9015
1.3	.9032	.9049	.9066	.9082	.9099	.9115	.9131	.9147	.9162	.9177
1.4	.9192	.9207	.9222	.9236	.9251	.9265	.9279	.9292	.9306	.9319
1.5	.9332	.9345	.9357	.9370	.9382	.9394	.9406	.9418	.9429	.9441
1.6	.9452	.9463	.9474	.9484	.9495	.9505	.9515	.9525	.9535	.9545
1.7	.9554	.9564	.9573	.9582	.9591	.9599	.9608	.9616	.9625	.9633
1.8	.9641	.9649	.9656	.9664	.9671	.9678	.9686	.9693	.9699	.9706
1.9	.9713	.9719	.9726	.9732	.9738	.9744	.9750	.9756	.9761	.9767
2.0	.9772	.9778	.9783	.9788	.9793	.9798	.9803	.9808	.9812	.9817
2.1	.9821	.9826	.9830	.9834	.9838	.9842	.9846	.9850	.9854	.9857
2.2	.9861	.9864	.9868	.9871	.9875	.9878	.9881	.9884	.9887	.9890
2.3	.9893	.9896	.9898	.9901	.9904	.9906	.9909	.9911	.9913	.9916
2.4	.9918	.9920	.9922	.9925	.9927	.9929	.9931	.9932	.9934	.9936
2.5	.9938	.9940	.9941	.9943	.9945	.9946	.9948	.9949	.9951	.9952
2.6	.9953	.9955	.9956	.9957	.9959	.9960	.9961	.9962	.9963	.9964
2.7	.9965	.9966	.9967	.9968	.9969	.9970	.9971	.9972	.9973	.9974
2.8	.9974	.9975	.9976	.9977	.9977	.9978	.9979	.9979	.9980	.9981
2.9	.9981	.9982	.9982	.9983	.9984	.9984	.9985	.9985	.9986	.9986
3.0	.9987	.9987	.9987	.9988	.9988	.9989	.9989	.9989	.9990	.9990
3.1	.9990	.9991	.9991	.9991	.9992	.9992	.9992	.9992	.9993	.9993
3.2	.9993	.9993	.9994	.9994	.9994	.9994	.9994	.9995	.9995	.9995
3.3	.9995	.9995	.9995	.9996	.9996	.9996	.9996	.9996	.9996	.9997
3.4	.9997	.9997	.9997	.9997	.9997	.9997	.9997	.9997	.9997	.9998

x	1.282	1.645	1.960	2.326	2.576	3.090	3.291	3.891	4.417
$F(x)$	.90	.95	.975	.99	.995	.999	.9995	.99995	.999995
$2[1 - F(x)]$	.20	.10	.05	.02	.01	.002	.001	.0001	.00001

Table VI

Chi-square Distribution

$$F(u) = \int_0^u \frac{x^{(n-2)/2}e^{-x/2}}{2^{n/2}\Gamma(n/2)}\,dx$$

n \ F	.005	.010	.025	.050	.100	.250	.500	.750	.900	.950	.975	.990	.995
1	$.0^4393$	$.0^3157$	$.0^3982$	$.0^2393$	.0158	.102	.455	1.32	2.71	3.84	5.02	6.63	7.88
2	.0100	.0201	.0506	.103	.211	.575	1.39	2.77	4.61	5.99	7.38	9.21	10.6
3	.0717	.115	.216	.352	.584	1.21	2.37	4.11	6.25	7.81	9.35	11.3	12.8
4	.207	.297	.484	.711	1.06	1.92	3.36	5.39	7.78	9.49	11.1	13.3	14.9
5	.412	.554	.831	1.15	1.61	2.67	4.35	6.63	9.24	11.1	12.8	15.1	16.7
6	.676	.872	1.24	1.64	2.20	3.45	5.35	7.84	10.6	12.6	14.4	16.8	18.5
7	.989	1.24	1.69	2.17	2.83	4.25	6.35	9.04	12.0	14.1	16.0	18.5	20.3
8	1.34	1.65	2.18	2.73	3.49	5.07	7.34	10.2	13.4	15.5	17.5	20.1	22.0
9	1.73	2.09	2.70	3.33	4.17	5.90	8.34	11.4	14.7	16.9	19.0	21.7	23.6
10	2.16	2.56	3.25	3.94	4.87	6.74	9.34	12.5	16.0	18.3	20.5	23.2	25.2
11	2.60	3.05	3.82	4.57	5.58	7.58	10.3	13.7	17.3	19.7	21.9	24.7	26.8
12	3.07	3.57	4.40	5.23	6.30	8.44	11.3	14.8	18.5	21.0	23.3	26.2	28.3
13	3.57	4.11	5.01	5.89	7.04	9.30	12.3	16.0	19.8	22.4	24.7	27.7	29.8
14	4.07	4.66	5.63	6.57	7.79	10.2	13.3	17.1	21.1	23.7	26.1	29.1	31.3
15	4.60	5.23	6.26	7.26	8.55	11.0	14.3	18.2	22.3	25.0	27.5	30.6	32.8
16	5.14	5.81	6.91	7.96	9.31	11.9	15.3	19.4	23.5	26.3	28.8	32.0	34.3
17	5.70	6.41	7.56	8.67	10.1	12.8	16.3	20.5	24.8	27.6	30.2	33.4	35.7
18	6.26	7.01	8.23	9.39	10.9	13.7	17.3	21.6	26.0	28.9	31.5	34.8	37.2
19	6.84	7.63	8.91	10.1	11.7	14.6	18.3	22.7	27.2	30.1	32.9	36.2	38.6
20	7.43	8.26	9.59	10.9	12.4	15.5	19.3	23.8	28.4	31.4	34.2	37.6	40.0
21	8.03	8.90	10.3	11.6	13.2	16.3	20.3	24.9	29.6	32.7	35.5	38.9	41.4
22	8.64	9.54	11.0	12.3	14.0	17.2	21.3	26.0	30.8	33.9	36.8	40.3	42.8
23	9.26	10.2	11.7	13.1	14.8	18.1	22.3	27.1	32.0	35.2	38.1	41.6	44.2
24	9.89	10.9	12.4	13.8	15.7	19.0	23.3	28.2	33.2	36.4	39.4	43.0	45.6
25	10.5	11.5	13.1	14.6	16.5	19.9	24.3	29.3	34.4	37.7	40.6	44.3	46.9
26	11.2	12.2	13.8	15.4	17.3	20.8	25.3	30.4	35.6	38.9	41.9	45.6	48.3
27	11.8	12.9	14.6	16.2	18.1	21.7	26.3	31.5	36.7	40.1	43.2	47.0	49.6
28	12.5	13.6	15.3	16.9	18.9	22.7	27.3	32.6	37.9	41.3	44.5	48.3	51.0
29	13.1	14.3	16.0	17.7	19.8	23.6	28.3	33.7	39.1	42.6	45.7	49.6	52.3
30	13.8	15.0	16.8	18.5	20.6	24.5	29.3	34.8	40.3	43.8	47.0	50.9	53.7

Reproduced by permission of the *Biometrika* Trustees from *Biometrica*, Vol. 32 (1941) and abridged by A. M. Mood in *Introduction to the Theory of Statistics*, McGraw-Hill Book Co.

Table VII

"STUDENT'S" DISTRIBUTION

$$F(t) = \int_{-\infty}^{t} \frac{\Gamma\left(\frac{n+1}{2}\right)}{\sqrt{\pi n}\,\Gamma(n/2)\left(1 + \frac{x^2}{n}\right)^{(n+1)/2}}\,dx$$

n \ F	.75	.90	.95	.975	.99	.995	.9995
1	1.000	3.078	6.314	12.706	31.821	63.657	636.619
2	.816	1.886	2.920	4.303	6.965	9.925	31.598
3	.765	1.638	2.353	3.182	4.541	5.841	12.941
4	.741	1.533	2.132	2.776	3.747	4.604	8.610
5	.727	1.476	2 015	2.571	3.365	4.032	6.859
6	.718	1.440	1.943	2.447	3.143	3.707	5.959
7	.711	1.415	1.895	2.365	2.998	3.499	5.405
8	.706	1.397	1.860	2.306	2.896	3.355	5.041
9	.703	1.383	1.833	2.262	2.821	3.250	4.781
10	.700	1.372	1.812	2.228	2.764	3.169	4.587
11	.697	1.363	1.796	2.201	2.718	3.106	4.437
12	.695	1.356	1.782	2.179	2.681	3.055	4.318
13	.694	1.350	1.771	2.160	2.650	3.012	4.221
14	.692	1.345	1.761	2.145	2.624	2.977	4.140
15	.691	1.341	1.753	2.131	2.602	2.947	4.073
16	.690	1.337	1.746	2.120	2.583	2.921	4.015
17	.689	1.333	1.740	2.110	2.567	2.898	3.965
18	.688	1.330	1.734	2.101	2.552	2.878	3.922
19	.688	1.328	1.729	2.093	2.539	2.861	3.883
20	.687	1.325	1.725	2.086	2.528	2.845	3.850
21	.686	1.323	1.721	2.080	2.518	2.831	3.819
22	.686	1.321	1.717	2.074	2.508	2.819	3.792
23	.685	1.319	1.714	2.069	2.500	2.807	3.767
24	.685	1.318	1.711	2.064	2.492	2.797	3.745
25	.684	1.316	1.708	2.060	2.485	2.787	3.725
26	.684	1.315	1.706	2.056	2.479	2.779	3.707
27	.684	1.314	1.703	2.052	2.473	2.771	3.690
28	.683	1.313	1.701	2.048	2.467	2.763	3.674
29	.683	1.311	1.699	2.045	2.462	2.756	3.659
30	.683	1.310	1.697	2.042	2.457	2.750	3.646
40	.681	1.303	1.684	2.021	2.423	2.704	3.551
60	.679	1.296	1.671	2.000	2.390	2.660	3.460
120	.677	1.289	1.658	1.980	2.358	2.617	3.373
∞	.674	1.282	1.645	1.960	2.326	2.576	3.291

This table is abridged by A. M. Mood in *Introduction to the Theory of Statistics*, **McGraw-Hill Book Co.**, from Table III of Fisher and Yates: Statistical Tables for Biological, Agricultural, and Medical Research, published by Oliver and Boyd Ltd., Edinburgh, and used here by permission of the authors and publishers.

Table VIII

F Distribution

m degrees of freedom in numerator; *n* in denominator

$$G(F) = \int_0^F \frac{\Gamma[(m+n)/2]m^{m/2}n^{n/2}x^{(m-2)/2}(n+mx)^{-(m+n)/2}}{\Gamma(m/2)\Gamma(n/2)}\,dx$$

G	n \ m	1	2	3	4	5	6	7	8	9	10	12	15	20	30	60	120	∞
.90		39.9	49.5	53.6	55.8	57.2	58.2	58.9	59.4	59.9	60.2	60.7	61.2	61.7	62.3	62.8	63.1	63.3
.95		161	200	216	225	230	234	237	239	241	242	244	246	248	250	252	253	254
.975	1	648	800	864	900	922	937	948	957	963	969	977	985	993	1000	1010	1010	1020
.99		4,050	5,000	5,400	5,620	5,760	5,860	5,930	5,980	6,020	6,060	6,110	6,160	6,210	6,260	6,310	6,340	6,370
.995		16,200	20,000	21,600	22,500	23,100	23,400	23,700	23,900	24,100	24,200	24,400	24,600	24,800	25,000	25,200	25,400	25,500
.90		8.53	9.00	9.16	9.24	9.29	9.33	9.35	9.37	9.38	9.39	9.41	9.42	9.44	9.46	9.47	9.48	9.49
.95		18.5	19.0	19.2	19.2	19.3	19.3	19.4	19.4	19.4	19.4	19.4	19.4	19.5	19.5	19.5	19.5	19.5
.975	2	38.5	39.0	39.2	39.2	39.3	39.3	39.4	39.4	39.4	39.4	39.4	39.4	39.4	39.5	39.5	39.5	39.5
.99		98.5	99.0	99.2	99.2	99.3	99.3	99.4	99.4	99.4	99.4	99.4	99.4	99.4	99.5	99.5	99.5	99.5
.995		199	199	199	199	199	199	199	199	199	199	199	199	199	199	199	199	199
.90		5.54	5.46	5.39	5.34	5.31	5.28	5.27	5.25	5.24	5.23	5.22	5.20	5.18	5.17	5.15	5.14	5.13
.95		10.1	9.55	9.28	9.12	9.01	8.94	8.89	8.85	8.81	8.79	8.74	8.70	8.66	8.62	8.57	8.55	8.53
.975	3	17.4	16.0	15.4	15.1	14.9	14.7	14.6	14.5	14.5	14.4	14.3	14.3	14.2	14.1	14.0	13.9	13.9
.99		34.1	30.8	29.5	28.7	28.2	27.9	27.7	27.5	27.3	27.2	27.1	26.9	26.7	26.5	26.3	26.2	26.1
.995		55.6	49.8	47.5	46.2	45.4	44.8	44.4	44.1	43.9	43.7	43.4	43.1	42.8	42.5	42.1	42.0	41.8
.90		4.54	4.32	4.19	4.11	4.05	4.01	3.98	3.95	3.93	3.92	3.90	3.87	3.84	3.82	3.79	3.78	3.76
.95		7.71	6.94	6.59	6.39	6.26	6.16	6.09	6.04	6.00	5.96	5.91	5.86	5.80	5.75	5.69	5.66	5.63
.975	4	12.2	10.6	9.98	9.60	9.36	9.20	9.07	8.98	8.90	8.84	8.75	8.66	8.56	8.46	8.36	8.31	8.26
.99		21.2	18.0	16.7	16.0	15.5	15.2	15.0	14.8	14.7	14.5	14.4	14.2	14.0	13.8	13.7	13.6	13.5
.995		31.3	26.3	24.3	23.2	22.5	22.0	21.6	21.4	21.1	21.0	20.7	20.4	20.2	19.9	19.6	19.5	19.3
.90		4.06	3.78	3.62	3.52	3.45	3.40	3.37	3.34	3.32	3.30	3.27	3.24	3.21	3.17	3.14	3.12	3.11
.95		6.61	5.79	5.41	5.19	5.05	4.95	4.88	4.82	4.77	4.74	4.68	4.62	4.56	4.50	4.43	4.40	4.37
.975	5	10.0	8.43	7.76	7.39	7.15	6.98	6.85	6.76	6.68	6.62	6.52	6.43	6.33	6.23	6.12	6.07	6.02
.99		16.3	13.3	12.1	11.4	11.0	10.7	10.5	10.3	10.2	10.1	9.89	9.72	9.55	9.38	9.20	9.11	9.02
.995		22.8	18.3	16.5	15.6	14.9	14.5	14.2	14.0	13.8	13.6	13.4	13.1	12.9	12.7	12.4	12.3	12.1
.90		3.78	3.46	3.29	3.18	3.11	3.05	3.01	2.98	2.96	2.94	2.90	2.87	2.84	2.80	2.76	2.74	2.72
.95		5.99	5.14	4.76	4.53	4.39	4.28	4.21	4.15	4.10	4.06	4.00	3.94	3.87	3.81	3.74	3.70	3.67
.975	6	8.81	7.26	6.60	6.23	5.99	5.82	5.70	5.60	5.52	5.46	5.37	5.27	5.17	5.07	4.96	4.90	4.85
.99		13.7	10.9	9.78	9.15	8.75	8.47	8.26	8.10	7.98	7.87	7.72	7.56	7.40	7.23	7.06	6.97	6.88
.995		18.6	14.5	12.9	12.0	11.5	11.1	10.8	10.6	10.4	10.2	10.0	9.81	9.59	9.36	9.12	9.00	8.88
.90		3.59	3.26	3.07	2.96	2.88	2.83	2.78	2.75	2.72	2.70	2.67	2.63	2.59	2.56	2.51	2.49	2.47
.95		5.59	4.74	4.35	4.12	3.97	3.87	3.79	3.73	3.68	3.64	3.57	3.51	3.44	3.38	3.30	3.27	3.23
.975	7	8.07	6.54	5.89	5.52	5.29	5.12	4.99	4.90	4.82	4.76	4.67	4.57	4.47	4.36	4.25	4.20	4.14
.99		12.2	9.55	8.45	7.85	7.46	7.19	6.99	6.84	6.72	6.62	6.47	6.31	6.16	5.99	5.82	5.74	5.65
.995		16.2	12.4	10.9	10.1	9.52	9.16	8.89	8.68	8.51	8.38	8.18	7.97	7.75	7.53	7.31	7.19	7.08
.90		3.46	3.11	2.92	2.81	2.73	2.67	2.62	2.59	2.56	2.54	2.50	2.46	2.42	2.38	2.34	2.31	2.29
.95		5.32	4.46	4.07	3.84	3.69	3.58	3.50	3.44	3.39	3.35	3.28	3.22	3.15	3.08	3.01	2.97	2.93
.975	8	7.57	6.06	5.42	5.05	4.82	4.65	4.53	4.43	4.36	4.30	4.20	4.10	4.00	3.89	3.78	3.73	3.67
.99		11.3	8.65	7.59	7.01	6.63	6.37	6.18	6.03	5.91	5.81	5.67	5.52	5.36	5.20	5.03	4.95	4.86
.995		14.7	11.0	9.60	8.81	8.30	7.95	7.69	7.50	7.34	7.21	7.01	6.81	6.61	6.40	6.18	6.06	5.95

.90		3.36	3.01	2.81	2.69	2.61	2.55	2.51	2.47	2.44	2.42	2.38	2.34	2.30	2.25	2.21	2.18	2.16
.95		5.12	4.26	3.86	3.63	3.48	3.37	3.29	3.23	3.18	3.14	3.07	3.01	2.94	2.86	2.79	2.75	2.71
.975	9	7.21	5.71	5.08	4.72	4.48	4.32	4.20	4.10	4.03	3.96	3.87	3.77	3.67	3.56	3.45	3.39	3.33
.99		10.6	8.02	6.99	6.42	6.06	5.80	5.61	5.47	5.35	5.26	5.11	4.96	4.81	4.65	4.48	4.40	4.31
.995		13.6	10.1	8.72	7.96	7.47	7.13	6.88	6.69	6.54	6.42	6.23	6.03	5.83	5.62	5.41	5.30	5.19
.90		3.29	2.92	2.73	2.61	2.52	2.46	2.41	2.38	2.35	2.32	2.28	2.24	2.20	2.15	2.11	2.08	2.06
.95		4.96	4.10	3.71	3.48	3.33	3.22	3.14	3.07	3.02	2.98	2.91	2.84	2.77	2.70	2.62	2.58	2.54
.975	10	6.94	5.46	4.83	4.47	4.24	4.07	3.95	3.85	3.78	3.72	3.62	3.52	3.42	3.31	3.20	3.14	3.08
.99		10.0	7.56	6.55	5.99	5.64	5.39	5.20	5.06	4.94	4.85	4.71	4.56	4.41	4.25	4.08	4.00	3.91
.995		12.8	9.43	8.08	7.34	6.87	6.54	6.30	6.12	5.97	5.85	5.66	5.47	5.27	5.07	4.86	4.75	4.64
.90		3.18	2.81	2.61	2.48	2.39	2.33	2.28	2.24	2.21	2.19	2.15	2.10	2.06	2.01	1.96	1.93	1.90
.95		4.75	3.89	3.49	3.26	3.11	3.00	2.91	2.85	2.80	2.75	2.69	2.62	2.54	2.47	2.38	2.34	2.30
.975	12	6.55	5.10	4.47	4.12	3.89	3.73	3.61	3.51	3.44	3.37	3.28	3.18	3.07	2.96	2.85	2.79	2.72
.99		9.33	6.93	5.95	5.41	5.06	4.82	4.64	4.50	4.39	4.30	4.16	4.01	3.86	3.70	3.54	3.45	3.36
.995		11.8	8.51	7.23	6.52	6.07	5.76	5.52	5.35	5.20	5.09	4.91	4.72	4.53	4.33	4.12	4.01	3.90
.90		3.07	2.70	2.49	2.36	2.27	2.21	2.16	2.12	2.09	2.06	2.02	1.97	1.92	1.87	1.82	1.79	1.76
.95		4.54	3.68	3.29	3.06	2.90	2.79	2.71	2.64	2.59	2.54	2.48	2.40	2.33	2.25	2.16	2.11	2.07
.975	15	6.20	4.77	4.15	3.80	3.58	3.41	3.29	3.20	3.12	3.06	2.96	2.86	2.76	2.64	2.52	2.46	2.40
.99		8.68	6.36	5.42	4.89	4.56	4.32	4.14	4.00	3.89	3.80	3.67	3.52	3.37	3.21	3.05	2.96	2.87
.995		10.8	7.70	6.48	5.80	5.37	5.07	4.85	4.67	4.54	4.42	4.25	4.07	3.88	3.69	3.48	3.37	3.26
.90		2.97	2.59	2.38	2.25	2.16	2.09	2.04	2.00	1.96	1.94	1.89	1.84	1.79	1.74	1.68	1.64	1.61
.95		4.35	3.49	3.10	2.87	2.71	2.60	2.51	2.45	2.39	2.35	2.28	2.20	2.12	2.04	1.95	1.90	1.84
.975	20	5.87	4.46	3.86	3.51	3.29	3.13	3.01	2.91	2.84	2.77	2.68	2.57	2.46	2.35	2.22	2.16	2.09
.99		8.10	5.85	4.94	4.43	4.10	3.87	3.70	3.56	3.46	3.37	3.23	3.09	2.94	2.78	2.61	2.52	2.42
.995		9.94	6.99	5.82	5.17	4.76	4.47	4.26	4.09	3.96	3.85	3.68	3.50	3.32	3.12	2.92	2.81	2.69
.90		2.88	2.49	2.28	2.14	2.05	1.98	1.93	1.88	1.85	1.82	1.77	1.72	1.67	1.61	1.54	1.50	1.46
.95		4.17	3.32	2.92	2.69	2.53	2.42	2.33	2.27	2.21	2.16	2.09	2.01	1.93	1.84	1.74	1.68	1.62
.975	30	5.57	4.18	3.59	3.25	3.03	2.87	2.75	2.65	2.57	2.51	2.41	2.31	2.20	2.07	1.94	1.87	1.79
.99		7.56	5.39	4.51	4.02	3.70	3.47	3.30	3.17	3.07	2.98	2.84	2.70	2.55	2.39	2.21	2.11	2.01
.995		9.18	6.35	5.24	4.62	4.23	3.95	3.74	3.58	3.45	3.34	3.18	3.01	2.82	2.63	2.42	2.30	2.18
.90		2.79	2.39	2.18	2.04	1.95	1.87	1.82	1.77	1.74	1.71	1.66	1.60	1.54	1.48	1.40	1.35	1.29
.95		4.00	3.15	2.76	2.53	2.37	2.25	2.17	2.10	2.04	1.99	1.92	1.84	1.75	1.65	1.53	1.47	1.39
.975	60	5.29	3.93	3.34	3.01	2.79	2.63	2.51	2.41	2.33	2.27	2.17	2.06	1.94	1.82	1.67	1.58	1.48
.99		7.08	4.98	4.13	3.65	3.34	3.12	2.95	2.82	2.72	2.63	2.50	2.35	2.20	2.03	1.84	1.73	1.60
.995		8.49	5.80	4.73	4.14	3.76	3.49	3.29	3.13	3.01	2.90	2.74	2.57	2.39	2.19	1.96	1.83	1.69
.90		2.75	2.35	2.13	1.99	1.90	1.82	1.77	1.72	1.68	1.65	1.60	1.54	1.48	1.41	1.32	1.26	1.19
.95		3.92	3.07	2.68	2.45	2.29	2.18	2.09	2.02	1.96	1.91	1.83	1.75	1.66	1.55	1.43	1.35	1.25
.975	120	5.15	3.80	3.23	2.89	2.67	2.52	2.39	2.30	2.22	2.16	2.05	1.94	1.82	1.69	1.53	1.43	1.31
.99		6.85	4.79	3.95	3.48	3.17	2.96	2.79	2.66	2.56	2.47	2.34	2.19	2.03	1.86	1.66	1.53	1.38
.995		8.18	5.54	4.50	3.92	3.55	3.28	3.09	2.93	2.81	2.71	2.54	2.37	2.19	1.98	1.75	1.61	1.43
.90		2.71	2.30	2.08	1.94	1.85	1.77	1.72	1.67	1.63	1.60	1.55	1.49	1.42	1.34	1.24	1.17	1.00
.95		3.84	3.00	2.60	2.37	2.21	2.10	2.01	1.94	1.88	1.83	1.75	1.67	1.57	1.46	1.32	1.22	1.00
.975	∞	5.02	3.69	3.12	2.79	2.57	2.41	2.29	2.19	2.11	2.05	1.94	1.83	1.71	1.57	1.39	1.27	1.00
.99		6.63	4.61	3.78	3.32	3.02	2.80	2.64	2.51	2.41	2.32	2.18	2.04	1.88	1.70	1.47	1.32	1.00
.995		7.88	5.30	4.28	3.72	3.35	3.09	2.90	2.74	2.62	2.52	2.36	2.19	2.00	1.79	1.53	1.36	1.00

Table IX

VALUES OF e^{-x}

x	e^{-x}	x	e^{-x}	x	e^{-x}	x	e^{-x}
0.00	1.00000	0.50	.60653	1.00	.36788	1.50	.22313
0.01	0.99005	0.51	.60050	1.01	.36422	1.51	.22091
0.02	.98020	0.52	.59452	1.02	.36059	1.52	.21871
0.03	.97045	0.53	.58860	1.03	.35701	1.53	.21654
0.04	.96079	0.54	.58275	1.04	.35345	1.54	.21438
0.05	.95123	0.55	.57695	1.05	.34994	1.55	.21225
0.06	.94176	0.56	.57121	1.06	.34646	1.56	.21014
0.07	.93239	0.57	.56553	1.07	.34301	1.57	.20805
0.08	.92312	0.58	.55990	1.08	.33960	1.58	.20598
0.09	.91393	0.59	.55433	1.09	.33622	1.59	.20393
0.10	.90484	0.60	.54881	1.10	.33287	1.60	.20190
0.11	.89583	0.61	.54335	1.11	.32956	1.61	.19989
0.12	.88692	0.62	.53794	1.12	.32628	1.62	.19790
0.13	.87810	0.63	.53259	1.13	.32303	1.63	.19593
0.14	.86936	0.64	.52729	1.14	.31982	1.64	.19398
0.15	.86071	0.65	.52205	1.15	.31664	1.65	.19205
0.16	.85214	0.66	.51685	1.16	.31349	1.66	.19014
0.17	.84366	0.67	.51171	1.17	.31037	1.67	.18825
0.18	.83527	0.68	.50662	1.18	.30728	1.68	.18637
0.19	.82696	0.69	.50158	1.19	.30422	1.69	.18452
0.20	.81873	0.70	.49659	1.20	.30119	1.70	.18268
0.21	.81058	0.71	.49164	1.21	.29820	1.71	.18087
0.22	.80252	0.72	.48675	1.22	.29523	1.72	.17907
0.23	.79453	0.73	.48191	1.23	.29229	1.73	.17728
0.24	.78663	0.74	.47711	1.24	.28938	1.74	.17552
0.25	.77880	0.75	.47237	1.25	.28650	1.75	.17377
0.26	.77105	0.76	.46767	1.26	.28365	1.76	.17204
0.27	.76338	0.77	.46301	1.27	.28083	1.77	.17033
0.28	.75578	0.78	.45841	1.28	.27804	1.78	.16864
0.29	.74826	0.79	.45384	1.29	.27527	1.79	.16696
0.30	.74082	0.80	.44933	1.30	.27253	1.80	.16530
0.31	.73345	0.81	.44486	1.31	.26982	1.81	.16365
0.32	.72615	0.82	.44043	1.32	.26714	1.82	.16203
0.33	.71892	0.83	.43605	1.33	.26448	1.83	.16041
0.34	.71177	0.84	.43171	1.34	.26185	1.84	.15882
0.35	.70469	0.85	.42741	1.35	.25924	1.85	.15724
0.36	.69768	0.86	.42316	1.36	.25666	1.86	.15567
0.37	.69073	0.87	.41895	1.37	.25411	1.87	.15412
0.38	.68386	0.88	.41478	1.38	.25158	1.88	.15259
0.39	.67706	0.89	.41066	1.39	.24908	1.89	.15107
0.40	.67032	0.90	.40657	1.40	.24660	1.90	.14957
0.41	.66365	0.91	.40252	1.41	.24414	1.91	.14808
0.42	.65705	0.92	.39852	1.42	.24171	1.92	.14661
0.43	.65051	0.93	.39455	1.43	.23931	1.93	.14515
0.44	.64404	0.94	.39063	1.44	.23693	1.94	.14370
0.45	.63763	0.95	.38674	1.45	.23457	1.95	.14227
0.46	.63128	0.96	.38289	1.46	.23224	1.96	.14086
0.47	.62500	0.97	.37908	1.47	.22993	1.97	.13946
0.48	.61878	0.98	.37531	1.48	.22764	1.98	.13807
0.49	.61263	0.99	.37158	1.49	.22537	1.99	.13670

For extensive tables of e^{-x} see G. F. Becker and C. E. Van Orstrand: *Hyperbolic Functions,* Smithsonian Mathematical Tables, Washington, D. C., 1909.

Table IX is used by permission from *Handbook of Probability and Statistics with Tables,* by Burington and May. Copyright, 1953. McGraw-Hill Book Co.

Values of e^{-x}

x	e^{-x}	x	e^{-x}	x	e^{-x}	x	e^{-x}
2.00	.13534	2.40	.09072	2.80	.06081	4.00	.01832
2.01	.13399	2.41	.08982	2.81	.06020	4.10	.01657
2.02	.13266	2.42	.08892	2.82	.05961	4.20	.01500
2.03	.13134	2.43	.08804	2.83	.05901	4.30	.01357
2.04	.13003	2.44	.08716	2.84	.05843	4.40	.01228
2.05	.12873	2.45	.08629	2.85	.05784	4.50	.01111
2.06	.12745	2.46	.08544	2.86	.05727	4.60	.01005
2.07	.12619	2.47	.08458	2.87	.05670	4.70	.00910
2.08	.12493	2.48	.08374	2.88	.05613	4.80	.00823
2.09	.12369	2.49	.08291	2.89	.05558	4.90	.00745
2.10	.12246	2.50	.08208	2.90	.05502	5.00	.00674
2.11	.12124	2.51	.08127	2.91	.05448	5.10	.00610
2.12	.12003	2.52	.08046	2.92	.05393	5.20	.00552
2.13	.11884	2.53	.07966	2.93	.05340	5.30	.00499
2.14	.11765	2.54	.07887	2.94	.05287	5.40	.00452
2.15	.11648	2.55	.07808	2.95	.05234	5.50	.00409
2.16	.11533	2.56	.07730	2.96	.05182	5.60	.00370
2.17	.11418	2.57	.07654	2.97	.05130	5.70	.00335
2.18	.11304	2.58	.07577	2.98	.05079	5.80	.00303
2.19	.11192	2.59	.07502	2.99	.05029	5.90	.00274
2.20	.11080	2.60	.07427	3.00	.04979	6.00	.00248
2.21	.10970	2.61	.07353	3.05	.04736	6.25	.00193
2.22	.10861	2.62	.07280	3.10	.04505	6.50	.00150
2.23	.10753	2.63	.07208	3.15	.04285	6.75	.00117
2.24	.10646	2.64	.07136	3.20	.04076	7.00	.00091
2.25	.10540	2.65	.07065	3.25	.03877	7.50	.00055
2.26	.10435	2.66	.06995	3.30	.03688	8.00	.00034
2.27	.10331	2.67	.06925	3.35	.03508	8.50	.00020
2.28	.10228	2.68	.06856	3.40	.03337	9.00	.00012
2.29	.10127	2.69	.06788	3.45	.03175	9.50	.00007
2.30	.10026	2.70	.06721	3.50	.03020	10.00	.00005
2.31	.09926	2.71	.06654	3.55	.02872		
2.32	.09827	2.72	.06587	3.60	.02732		
2.33	.09730	2.73	.06522	3.65	.02599		
2.34	.09633	2.74	.06457	3.70	.02472		
2.35	.09537	2.75	.06393	3.75	.02352		
2.36	.09442	2.76	.06329	3.80	.02237		
2.37	.09348	2.77	.06266	3.85	.02128		
2.38	.09255	2.78	.06204	3.90	.02024		
2.39	.09163	2.79	.06142	3.95	.01925		

Table X

NATURAL LOGARITHMS OF NUMBERS—0.00 TO 5.99 (Base $e = 2.718 \cdots$)

N	0	1	2	3	4	5	6	7	8	9
	Take tabular value −10									
0.0		5.395	6.088	6.493	6.781	7.004	7.187	7.341	7.474	7.592
0.1	7.697	7.793	7.880	7.960	8.034	8.103	8.167	8.228	8.285	8.339
0.2	8.391	8.439	8.486	8.530	8.573	8.614	8.653	8.691	8.727	8.762
0.3	8.796	8.829	8.861	8.891	8.921	8.950	8.978	9.006	9.032	9.058
0.4	9.084	9.108	9.132	9.156	9.179	9.201	9.223	9.245	9.266	9.287
0.5	9.307	9.327	9.346	9.365	9.384	9.402	9.420	9.438	9.455	9.472
0.6	9.489	9.506	9.522	9.538	9.554	9.569	9.584	9.600	9.614	9.629
0.7	9.643	9.658	9.671	9.685	9.699	9.712	9.726	9.739	9.752	9.764
0.8	9.777	9.789	9.802	9.814	9.826	9.837	9.849	9.861	9.872	9.883
0.9	9.895	9.906	9.917	9.927	9.938	9.949	9.959	9.970	9.980	9.990
1.0	0.0 0000	0995	1980	2956	3922	4879	5827	6766	7696	8618
1.1	9531	*0436	*1333	*2222	*3103	*3976	*4842	*5700	*6551	*7395
1.2	0.1 8232	9062	9885	*0701	*1511	*2314	*3111	*3902	*4686	*5464
1.3	0.2 6236	7003	7763	8518	9267	*0010	*0748	*1481	*2208	*2930
1.4	0.3 3647	4359	5066	5767	6464	7156	7844	8526	9204	9878
1.5	0.4 0547	1211	1871	2527	3178	3825	4469	5108	5742	6373
1.6	7000	7623	8243	8858	9470	*0078	*0682	*1282	*1879	*2473
1.7	0.5 3063	3649	4232	4812	5389	5962	6531	7098	7661	8222
1.8	8779	9333	9884	*0432	*0977	*1519	*2058	*2594	*3127	*3658
1.9	0.6 4185	4710	5233	5752	6269	6783	7294	7803	8310	8813
2.0	9315	9813	*0310	*0804	*1295	*1784	*2271	*2755	*3237	*3716
2.1	0.7 4194	4669	5142	5612	6081	6547	7011	7473	7932	8390
2.2	8846	9299	9751	*0200	*0648	*1093	*1536	*1978	*2418	*2855
2.3	0.8 3291	3725	4157	4587	5015	5442	5866	6289	6710	7129
2.4	7547	7963	8377	8789	9200	9609	*0016	*0422	*0826	*1228
2.5	0.9 1629	2028	2426	2822	3216	3609	4001	4391	4779	5166
2.6	5551	5935	6317	6698	7078	7456	7833	8208	8582	8954
2.7	9325	9695	*0063	*0430	*0796	*1160	*1523	*1885	*2245	*2604
2.8	1.0 2962	3318	3674	4028	4380	4732	5082	5431	5779	6126
2.9	6471	6815	7158	7500	7841	8181	8519	8856	9192	9527
3.0	9861	*0194	*0526	*0856	*1186	*1514	*1841	*2168	*2493	*2817
3.1	1.1 3140	3462	3783	4103	4422	4740	5057	5373	5688	6002
3.2	6315	6627	6938	7248	7557	7865	8173	8479	8784	9089
3.3	9392	9695	9996	*0297	*0597	*0896	*1194	*1491	*1788	*2083
3.4	1.2 2378	2671	2964	3256	3547	3837	4127	4415	4703	4990
3.5	5276	5562	5846	6130	6413	6695	6976	7257	7536	7815
3.6	8093	8371	8647	8923	9198	9473	9746	*0019	*0291	*0563
3.7	1.3 0833	1103	1372	1641	1909	2176	2442	2708	2972	3237
3.8	3500	3763	4025	4286	4547	4807	5067	5325	5584	5841
3.9	6098	6354	6609	6864	7118	7372	7624	7877	8128	8379
4.0	8629	8879	9128	9377	9624	9872	*0118	*0364	*0610	*0854
4.1	1.4 1099	1342	1585	1828	2070	2311	2552	2792	3031	3270
4.2	3508	3746	3984	4220	4456	4692	4927	5161	5395	5629
4.3	5862	6094	6326	6557	6787	7018	7247	7476	7705	7933
4.4	8160	8387	8614	8840	9065	9290	9515	9739	9962	*0185
4.5	1.5 0408	0630	0851	1072	1293	1513	1732	1951	2170	2388
4.6	2606	2823	3039	3256	3471	3687	3902	4116	4330	4543
4.7	4756	4969	5181	5393	5604	5814	6025	6235	6444	6653
4.8	6862	7070	7277	7485	7691	7898	8104	8309	8515	8719
4.9	8924	9127	9331	9534	9737	9939	*0141	*0342	*0543	*0744
5.0	1.6 0944	1144	1343	1542	1741	1939	2137	2334	2531	2728
5.1	2924	3120	3315	3511	3705	3900	4094	4287	4481	4673
5.2	4866	5058	5250	5441	5632	5823	6013	6203	6393	6582
5.3	6771	6959	7147	7335	7523	7710	7896	8083	8269	8455
5.4	8640	8825	9010	9194	9378	9562	9745	9928	*0111	*0293
5.5	1.7 0475	0656	0838	1019	1199	1380	1560	1740	1919	2098
5.6	2277	2455	2633	2811	2988	3166	3342	3519	3695	3871
5.7	4047	4222	4397	4572	4746	4920	5094	5267	5440	5613
5.8	5786	5958	6130	6302	6473	6644	6815	6985	7156	7326
5.9	7495	7665	7834	8002	8171	8339	8507	8675	8842	9009
N	0	1	2	3	4	5	6	7	8	9

$\log_e 0.10 = 7.69741\ 49070 - 10$

Table X is used by permission from *Handbook of Probability and Statistics with Tables*, by Burington and May. Copyright, 1953. McGraw-Hill Book Co.

Natural Logarithms of Numbers—6.00 to 10.09

N	0	1	2	3	4	5	6	7	8	9
6.0	1.7 9176	9342	9509	9675	9840	*0006	*0171	*0336	*0500	*0665
6.1	1.8 0829	0993	1156	1319	1482	1645	1808	1970	2132	2294
6.2	2455	2616	2777	2938	3098	3258	3418	3578	3737	3896
6.3	4055	4214	4372	4530	4688	4845	5003	5160	5317	5473
6.4	5630	5786	5942	6097	6253	6408	6563	6718	6872	7026
6.5	7180	7334	7487	7641	7794	7947	8099	8251	8403	8555
6.6	8707	8858	9010	9160	9311	9462	9612	9762	9912	*0061
6.7	1.9 0211	0360	0509	0658	0806	0954	1102	1250	1398	1545
6.8	1692	1839	1986	2132	2279	2425	2571	2716	2862	3007
6.9	3152	3297	3442	3586	3730	3874	4018	4162	4305	4448
7.0	4591	4734	4876	5019	5161	5303	5445	5586	5727	5869
7.1	6009	6150	6291	6431	6571	6711	6851	6991	7130	7269
7.2	7408	7547	7685	7824	7962	8100	8238	8376	8513	8650
7.3	8787	8924	9061	9198	9334	9470	9606	9742	9877	*0013
7.4	2.0 0148	0283	0418	0553	0687	0821	0956	1089	1223	1357
7.5	1490	1624	1757	1890	2022	2155	2287	2419	2551	2683
7.6	2815	2946	3078	3209	3340	3471	3601	3732	3862	3992
7.7	4122	4252	4381	4511	4640	4769	4898	5027	5156	5284
7.8	5412	5540	5668	5796	5924	6051	6179	6306	6433	6560
7.9	6686	6813	6939	7065	7191	7317	7443	7568	7694	7819
8.0	7944	8069	8194	8318	8443	8567	8691	8815	8939	9063
8.1	9186	9310	9433	9556	9679	9802	9924	*0047	*0169	*0291
8.2	2.1 0413	0535	0657	0779	0900	1021	1142	1263	1384	1505
8.3	1626	1746	1866	1986	2106	2226	2346	2465	2585	2704
8.4	2823	2942	3061	3180	3298	3417	3535	3653	3771	3889
8.5	4007	4124	4242	4359	4476	4593	4710	4827	4943	5060
8.6	5176	5292	5409	5524	5640	5756	5871	5987	6102	6217
8.7	6332	6447	6562	6677	6791	6905	7020	7134	7248	7361
8.8	7475	7589	7702	7816	7929	8042	8155	8267	8380	8493
8.9	8605	8717	8830	8942	9054	9165	9277	9389	9500	9611
9.0	9722	9834	9944	*0055	*0166	*0276	*0387	*0497	*0607	*0717
9.1	2.2 0827	0937	1047	1157	1266	1375	1485	1594	1703	1812
9.2	1920	2029	2138	2246	2354	2462	2570	2678	2786	2894
9.3	3001	3109	3216	3324	3431	3538	3645	3751	3858	3965
9.4	4071	4177	4284	4390	4496	4601	4707	4813	4918	5024
9.5	5129	5234	5339	5444	5549	5654	5759	5863	5968	6072
9.6	6176	6280	6384	6488	6592	6696	6799	6903	7006	7109
9.7	7213	7316	7419	7521	7624	7727	7829	7932	8034	8136
9.8	8238	8340	8442	8544	8646	8747	8849	8950	9051	9152
9.9	9253	9354	9455	9556	9657	9757	9858	9958	*0058	*0158
10.0	2.3 0259	0358	0458	0558	0658	0757	0857	0956	1055	1154
N	0	1	2	3	4	5	6	7	8	9

Natural Logarithms of Numbers—10 to 99

N	0	1	2	3	4	5	6	7	8	9
1	2.30259	39790	48491	56495	63906	70805	77259	83321	89037	94444
2	99573	*04452	*09104	*13549	*17805	*21888	*25810	*29584	*33220	*36730
3	3.40120	43399	46574	49651	52636	55535	58352	61092	63759	66356
4	68888	71357	73767	76120	78419	80666	82864	85015	87120	89182
5	91202	93183	95124	97029	98898	*00733	*02535	*04305	*06044	*07754
6	4.09434	11087	12713	14313	15888	17439	18965	20469	21951	23411
7	24850	26268	27667	29046	30407	31749	33073	34381	35671	36945
8	38203	39445	40672	41884	43082	44265	45435	46591	47734	48864
9	49981	51086	52179	53260	54329	55388	56435	57471	58497	59512

$\log_e 10 = 2.30258\ 50930$

Natural Logarithms of Numbers—100 to 609

N	0	1	2	3	4	5	6	7	8	9
10	4.6 0517	1512	2497	3473	4439	5396	6344	7283	8213	9135
11	4.7 0048	0953	1850	2739	3620	4493	5359	6217	7068	7912
12	8749	9579	*0402	*1218	*2028	*2831	*3628	*4419	*5203	*5981
13	4.8 6753	7520	8280	9035	9784	*0527	*1265	*1998	*2725	*3447
14	4.9 4164	4876	5583	6284	6981	7673	8361	9043	9721	*0395
15	5.0 1064	1728	2388	3044	3695	4343	4986	5625	6260	6890
16	7517	8140	8760	9375	9987	*0595	*1199	*1799	*2396	*2990
17	5.1 3580	4166	4749	5329	5906	6479	7048	7615	8178	8739
18	9296	9850	*0401	*0949	*1494	*2036	*2575	*3111	*3644	*4175
19	5.2 4702	5227	5750	6269	6786	7300	7811	8320	8827	9330
20	9832	*0330	*0827	*1321	*1812	*2301	*2788	*3272	*3754	*4233
21	5.3 4711	5186	5659	6129	6598	7064	7528	7990	8450	8907
22	9363	9816	*0268	*0717	*1165	*1610	*2053	*2495	*2935	*3372
23	5.4 3808	4242	4674	5104	5532	5959	6383	6806	7227	7646
24	8064	8480	8894	9306	9717	*0126	*0533	*0939	*1343	*1745
25	5.5 2146	2545	2943	3339	3733	4126	4518	4908	5296	5683
26	6068	6452	6834	7215	7595	7973	8350	8725	9099	9471
27	9842	*0212	*0580	*0947	*1313	*1677	*2040	*2402	*2762	*3121
28	5.6 3479	3835	4191	4545	4897	5249	5599	5948	6296	6643
29	6988	7332	7675	8017	8358	8698	9036	9373	9709	*0044
30	5.7 0378	0711	1043	1373	1703	2031	2359	2685	3010	3334
31	3657	3979	4300	4620	4939	5257	5574	5890	6205	6519
32	6832	7144	7455	7765	8074	8383	8690	8996	9301	9606
33	9909	*0212	*0513	*0814	*1114	*1413	*1711	*2008	*2305	*2600
34	5.8 2895	3188	3481	3773	4064	4354	4644	4932	5220	5507
35	5793	6079	6363	6647	6930	7212	7493	7774	8053	8332
36	8610	8888	9164	9440	9715	9990	*0263	*0536	*0808	*1080
37	5.9 1350	1620	1889	2158	2426	2693	2959	3225	3489	3754
38	4017	4280	4542	4803	5064	5324	5584	5842	6101	6358
39	6615	6871	7126	7381	7635	7889	8141	8394	8645	8896
40	9146	9396	9645	9894	*0141	*0389	*0635	*0881	*1127	*1372
41	6.0 1616	1859	2102	2345	2587	2828	3069	3309	3548	3787
42	4025	4263	4501	4737	4973	5209	5444	5678	5912	6146
43	6379	6611	6843	7074	7304	7535	7764	7993	8222	8450
44	8677	8904	9131	9357	9582	9807	*0032	*0256	*0479	*0702
45	6.1 0925	1147	1368	1589	1810	2030	2249	2468	2687	2905
46	3123	3340	3556	3773	3988	4204	4419	4633	4847	5060
47	5273	5486	5698	5910	6121	6331	6542	6752	6961	7170
48	7379	7587	7794	8002	8208	8415	8621	8826	9032	9236
49	9441	9644	9848	*0051	*0254	*0456	*0658	*0859	*1060	*1261
50	6.2 1461	1661	1860	2059	2258	2456	2654	2851	3048	3245
51	3441	3637	3832	4028	4222	4417	4611	4804	4998	5190
52	5383	5575	5767	5958	6149	6340	6530	6720	6910	7099
53	7288	7476	7664	7852	8040	8227	8413	8600	8786	8972
54	9157	9342	9527	9711	9895	*0079	*0262	*0445	*0628	*0810
55	6.3 0992	1173	1355	1536	1716	1897	2077	2257	2436	2615
56	2794	2972	3150	3328	3505	3683	3859	4036	4212	4388
57	4564	4739	4914	5089	5263	5437	5611	5784	5957	6130
58	6303	6475	6647	6819	6990	7161	7332	7502	7673	7843
59	8012	8182	8351	8519	8688	8856	9024	9192	9359	9526
60	9693	9859	*0026	*0192	*0357	*0523	*0688	*0853	*1017	*1182
N	0	1	2	3	4	5	6	7	8	9

$\log_e 100 = 4.60517\ 01860$

Natural Logarithms of Numbers—600 to 1109

N	0	1	2	3	4	5	6	7	8	9
60	6.3 9693	9859	*0026	*0192	*0357	*0523	*0688	*0853	*1017	*1182
61	6.4 1346	1510	1673	1836	1999	2162	2325	2487	2649	2811
62	2972	3133	3294	3455	3615	3775	3935	4095	4254	4413
63	4572	4731	4889	5047	5205	5362	5520	5677	5834	5990
64	6147	6303	6459	6614	6770	6925	7080	7235	7389	7543
65	7697	7851	8004	8158	8311	8464	8616	8768	8920	9072
66	9224	9375	9527	9677	9828	9979	*0129	*0279	*0429	*0578
67	6.5 0728	0877	1026	1175	1323	1471	1619	1767	1915	2062
68	2209	2356	2503	2649	2796	2942	3088	3233	3379	3524
69	3669	3814	3959	4103	4247	4391	4535	4679	4822	4965
70	5108	5251	5393	5536	5678	5820	5962	6103	6244	6386
71	6526	6667	6808	6948	7088	7228	7368	7508	7647	7786
72	7925	8064	8203	8341	8479	8617	8755	8893	9030	9167
73	9304	9441	9578	9715	9851	9987	*0123	*0259	*0394	*0530
74	6.6 0665	0800	0935	1070	1204	1338	1473	1607	1740	1874
75	2007	2141	2274	2407	2539	2672	2804	2936	3068	3200
76	3332	3463	3595	3726	3857	3988	4118	4249	4379	4509
77	4639	4769	4898	5028	5157	5286	5415	5544	5673	5801
78	5929	6058	6185	6313	6441	6568	6696	6823	6950	7077
79	7203	7330	7456	7582	7708	7834	7960	8085	8211	8336
80	8461	8586	8711	8835	8960	9084	9208	9332	9456	9580
81	9703	9827	9950	*0073	*0196	*0319	*0441	*0564	*0686	*0808
82	6.7 0930	1052	1174	1296	1417	1538	1659	1780	1901	2022
83	2143	2263	2383	2503	2623	2743	2863	2982	3102	3221
84	3340	3459	3578	3697	3815	3934	4052	4170	4288	4406
85	4524	4641	4759	4876	4993	5110	5227	5344	5460	5577
86	5693	5809	5926	6041	6157	6273	6388	6504	6619	6734
87	6849	6964	7079	7194	7308	7422	7537	7651	7765	7878
88	7992	8106	8219	8333	8446	8559	8672	8784	8897	9010
89	9122	9234	9347	9459	9571	9682	9794	9906	*0017	*0128
90	6.8 0239	0351	0461	0572	0683	0793	0904	1014	1124	1235
91	1344	1454	1564	1674	1783	1892	2002	2111	2220	2329
92	2437	2546	2655	2763	2871	2979	3087	3195	3303	3411
93	3518	3626	3733	3841	3948	4055	4162	4268	4375	4482
94	4588	4694	4801	4907	5013	5118	5224	5330	5435	5541
95	5646	5751	5857	5961	6066	6171	6276	6380	6485	6589
96	6693	6797	6901	7005	7109	7213	7316	7420	7523	7626
97	7730	7833	7936	8038	8141	8244	8346	8449	8551	8653
98	8755	8857	8959	9061	9163	9264	9366	9467	9568	9669
99	9770	9871	9972	*0073	*0174	*0274	*0375	*0475	*0575	*0675
100	6.9 0776	0875	0975	1075	1175	1274	1374	1473	1572	1672
101	1771	1870	1968	2067	2166	2264	2363	2461	2560	2658
102	2756	2854	2952	3049	3147	3245	3342	3440	3537	3634
103	3731	3828	3925	4022	4119	4216	4312	4409	4505	4601
104	4698	4794	4890	4986	5081	5177	5273	5368	5464	5559
105	5655	5750	5845	5940	6035	6130	6224	6319	6414	6508
106	6602	6697	6791	6885	6979	7073	7167	7261	7354	7448
107	7541	7635	7728	7821	7915	8008	8101	8193	8286	8379
108	8472	8564	8657	8749	8841	8934	9026	9118	9210	9302
109	9393	9485	9577	9668	9760	9851	9942	*0033	*0125	*0216
110	7.0 0307	0397	0488	0579	0670	0760	0851	0941	1031	1121
N	0	1	2	3	4	5	6	7	8	9

$\log_e 1000 = 6.90775\ 52790$

To find the logarithm of a number which is 10 (or 1/10) times a number whose logarithm is given, add to (or subtract from) the given logarithm the logarithm of 10.

Table XI

Common Logarithms of Numbers

N	0	1	2	3	4	5	6	7	8	9	Proportional parts 1	2	3	4	5
10	0000	0043	0086	0128	0170	0212	0253	0294	0334	0374	4	8	12	17	21
11	0414	0453	0492	0531	0569	0607	0645	0682	0719	0755	4	8	11	15	19
12	0792	0828	0864	0899	0934	0969	1004	1038	1072	1106	3	7	10	14	17
13	1139	1173	1206	1239	1271	1303	1335	1367	1399	1430	3	6	10	13	16
14	1461	1492	1523	1553	1584	1614	1644	1673	1703	1732	3	6	9	12	15
15	1761	1790	1818	1847	1875	1903	1931	1959	1987	2014	3	6	8	11	14
16	2041	2068	2095	2122	2148	2175	2201	2227	2253	2279	3	5	8	11	13
17	2304	2330	2355	2380	2405	2430	2455	2480	2504	2529	2	5	7	10	12
18	2553	2577	2601	2625	2648	2672	2695	2718	2742	2765	2	5	7	9	12
19	2788	2810	2833	2856	2878	2900	2923	2945	2967	2989	2	4	7	9	11
20	3010	3032	3054	3075	3096	3118	3139	3160	3181	3201	2	4	6	8	11
21	3222	3243	3263	3284	3304	3324	3345	3365	3385	3404	2	4	6	8	10
22	3424	3444	3464	3483	3502	3522	3541	3560	3579	3598	2	4	6	8	10
23	3617	3636	3655	3674	3692	3711	3729	3747	3766	3784	2	4	6	7	9
24	3802	3820	3838	3856	3874	3892	3909	3927	3945	3962	2	4	5	7	9
25	3979	3997	4014	4031	4048	4065	4082	4099	4116	4133	2	4	5	7	9
26	4150	4166	4183	4200	4216	4232	4249	4265	4281	4298	2	3	5	7	8
27	4314	4330	4346	4362	4378	4393	4409	4425	4440	4456	2	3	5	6	8
28	4472	4487	4502	4518	4533	4548	4564	4579	4594	4609	2	3	5	6	8
29	4624	4639	4654	4669	4683	4698	4713	4728	4742	4757	1	3	4	6	7
30	4771	4786	4800	4814	4829	4843	4857	4871	4886	4900	1	3	4	6	7
31	4914	4928	4942	4955	4969	4983	4997	5011	5024	5038	1	3	4	5	7
32	5051	5065	5079	5092	5105	5119	5132	5145	5159	5172	1	3	4	5	7
33	5185	5198	5211	5224	5237	5250	5263	5276	5289	5302	1	3	4	5	7
34	5315	5328	5340	5353	5366	5378	5391	5403	5416	5428	1	2	4	5	6
35	5441	5453	5465	5478	5490	5502	5514	5527	5539	5551	1	2	4	5	6
36	5563	5575	5587	5599	5611	5623	5635	5647	5658	5670	1	2	4	5	6
37	5682	5694	5705	5717	5729	5740	5752	5763	5775	5786	1	2	4	5	6
38	5798	5809	5821	5832	5843	5855	5866	5877	5888	5899	1	2	3	5	6
39	5911	5922	5933	5944	5955	5966	5977	5988	5999	6010	1	2	3	4	5
40	6021	6031	6042	6053	6064	6075	6085	6096	6107	6117	1	2	3	4	5
41	6128	6138	6149	6160	6170	6180	6191	6201	6212	6222	1	2	3	4	5
42	6232	6243	6253	6263	6274	6284	6294	6304	6314	6325	1	2	3	4	5
43	6335	6345	6355	6365	6375	6385	6395	6405	6415	6425	1	2	3	4	5
44	6435	6444	6454	6464	6474	6484	6493	6503	6513	6522	1	2	3	4	5
45	6532	6542	6551	6561	6571	6580	6590	6599	6609	6618	1	2	3	4	5
46	6628	6637	6646	6656	6665	6675	6684	6693	6702	6712	1	2	3	4	5
47	6721	6730	6739	6749	6758	6767	6776	6785	6794	6803	1	2	3	4	5
48	6812	6821	6830	6839	6848	6857	6866	6875	6884	6893	1	2	3	4	5
49	6902	6911	6920	6928	6937	6946	6955	6964	6972	6981	1	2	3	4	4
50	6990	6998	7007	7016	7024	7033	7042	7050	7059	7067	1	2	3	3	4
51	7076	7084	7093	7101	7110	7118	7126	7135	7143	7152	1	2	3	3	4
52	7160	7168	7177	7185	7193	7202	7210	7218	7226	7235	1	2	3	3	4
53	7243	7251	7259	7267	7275	7284	7292	7300	7308	7316	1	2	2	3	4
54	7324	7332	7340	7348	7356	7364	7372	7380	7388	7396	1	2	2	3	4
N	0	1	2	3	4	5	6	7	8	9	1	2	3	4	5

Table XI is used by permission from *Handbook of Probability and Statistics with Tables*, by Burington and May. Copyright, 1953. McGraw-Hill Book Co.

Common Logarithms of Numbers

N	0	1	2	3	4	5	6	7	8	9	Proportional parts 1	2	3	4	5
55	7404	7412	7419	7427	7435	7443	7451	7459	7466	7474	1	2	2	3	4
56	7482	7490	7497	7505	7513	7520	7528	7536	7543	7551	1	2	2	3	4
57	7559	7566	7574	7582	7589	7597	7604	7612	7619	7627	1	1	2	3	4
58	7634	7642	7649	7657	7664	7672	7679	7686	7694	7701	1	1	2	3	4
59	7709	7716	7723	7731	7738	7745	7752	7760	7767	7774	1	1	2	3	4
60	7782	7789	7796	7803	7810	7818	7825	7832	7839	7846	1	1	2	3	4
61	7853	7860	7868	7875	7882	7889	7896	7903	7910	7917	1	1	2	3	3
62	7924	7931	7938	7945	7952	7959	7966	7973	7980	7987	1	1	2	3	3
63	7993	8000	8007	8014	8021	8028	8035	8041	8048	8055	1	1	2	3	3
64	8062	8069	8075	8082	8089	8096	8102	8109	8116	8122	1	1	2	3	3
65	8129	8136	8142	8149	8156	8162	8169	8176	8182	8189	1	1	2	3	3
66	8195	8202	8209	8215	8222	8228	8235	8241	8248	8254	1	1	2	3	3
67	8261	8267	8274	8280	8287	8293	8299	8306	8312	8319	1	1	2	3	3
68	8325	8331	8338	8344	8351	8357	8363	8370	8376	8382	1	1	2	3	3
69	8388	8395	8401	8407	8414	8420	8426	8432	8439	8445	1	1	2	3	3
70	8451	8457	8463	8470	8476	8482	8488	8494	8500	8506	1	1	2	3	3
71	8513	8519	8525	8531	8537	8543	8549	8555	8561	8567	1	1	2	3	3
72	8573	8579	8585	8591	8597	8603	8609	8615	8621	8627	1	1	2	3	3
73	8633	8639	8645	8651	8657	8663	8669	8675	8681	8686	1	1	2	2	3
74	8692	8698	8704	8710	8716	8722	8727	8733	8739	8745	1	1	2	2	3
75	8751	8756	8762	8768	8774	8779	8785	8791	8797	8802	1	1	2	2	3
76	8808	8814	8820	8825	8831	8837	8842	8848	8854	8859	1	1	2	2	3
77	8865	8871	8876	8882	8887	8893	8899	8904	8910	8915	1	1	2	2	3
78	8921	8927	8932	8938	8943	8949	8954	8960	8965	8971	1	1	2	2	3
79	8976	8982	8987	8993	8998	9004	9009	9015	9020	9025	1	1	2	2	3
80	9031	9036	9042	9047	9053	9058	9063	9069	9074	9079	1	1	2	2	3
81	9085	9090	9096	9101	9106	9112	9117	9122	9128	9133	1	1	2	2	3
82	9138	9143	9149	9154	9159	9165	9170	9175	9180	9186	1	1	2	2	3
83	9191	9196	9201	9206	9212	9217	9222	9227	9232	9238	1	1	2	2	3
84	9243	9248	9253	9258	9263	9269	9274	9279	9284	9289	1	1	2	2	3
85	9294	9299	9304	9309	9315	9320	9325	9330	9335	9340	1	1	2	2	3
86	9345	9350	9355	9360	9365	9370	9375	9380	9385	9390	1	1	2	2	3
87	9395	9400	9405	9410	9415	9420	9425	9430	9435	9440	1	1	2	2	3
88	9445	9450	9455	9460	9465	9469	9474	9479	9484	9489	0	1	1	2	2
89	9494	9499	9504	9509	9513	9518	9523	9528	9533	9538	0	1	1	2	2
90	9542	9547	9552	9557	9562	9566	9571	9576	9581	9586	0	1	1	2	2
91	9590	9595	9600	9605	9609	9614	9619	9624	9628	9633	0	1	1	2	2
92	9638	9643	9647	9652	9657	9661	9666	9671	9675	9680	0	1	1	2	2
93	9685	9689	9694	9699	9703	9708	9713	9717	9722	9727	0	1	1	2	2
94	9731	9736	9741	9745	9750	9754	9759	9763	9768	9773	0	1	1	2	2
95	9777	9782	9786	9791	9795	9800	9805	9809	9814	9818	0	1	1	2	2
96	9823	9827	9832	9836	9841	9845	9850	9854	9859	9863	0	1	1	2	2
97	9868	9872	9877	9881	9886	9890	9894	9899	9903	9908	0	1	1	2	2
98	9912	9917	9921	9926	9930	9934	9939	9943	9948	9952	0	1	1	2	2
99	9956	9961	9965	9969	9974	9978	9983	9987	9991	9996	0	1	1	2	2
N	0	1	2	3	4	5	6	7	8	9	1	2	3	4	5

Table XII

Random Numbers

10	09	73	25	33	76	52	01	35	86	34	67	35	48	76	80	95	90	91	17	39	29	27	49	45
37	54	20	48	05	64	89	47	42	96	24	80	52	40	37	20	63	61	04	02	00	82	29	16	65
08	42	26	89	53	19	64	50	93	03	23	20	90	25	60	15	95	33	47	64	35	08	03	36	06
99	01	90	25	29	09	37	67	07	15	38	31	13	11	65	88	67	67	43	97	04	43	62	76	59
12	80	79	99	70	80	15	73	61	47	64	03	23	66	53	98	95	11	68	77	12	17	17	68	33
66	06	57	47	17	34	07	27	68	50	36	69	73	61	70	65	81	33	98	85	11	19	92	91	70
31	06	01	08	05	45	57	18	24	06	35	30	34	26	14	86	79	90	74	39	23	40	30	97	32
85	26	97	76	02	02	05	16	56	92	68	66	57	48	18	73	05	38	52	47	18	62	38	85	79
63	57	33	21	35	05	32	54	70	48	90	55	35	75	48	28	46	82	87	09	83	49	12	56	24
73	79	64	57	53	03	52	96	47	78	35	80	83	42	82	60	93	52	03	44	35	27	38	84	35
98	52	01	77	67	14	90	56	86	07	22	10	94	05	58	60	97	09	34	33	50	50	07	39	98
11	80	50	54	31	39	80	82	77	32	50	72	56	82	48	29	40	52	42	01	52	77	56	78	51
83	45	29	96	34	06	28	89	80	83	13	74	67	00	78	18	47	54	06	10	68	71	17	78	17
88	68	54	02	00	86	50	75	84	01	36	76	66	79	51	90	36	47	64	93	29	60	91	10	62
99	59	46	73	48	87	51	76	49	69	91	82	60	89	28	93	78	56	13	68	23	47	83	41	13
65	48	11	76	74	17	46	85	09	50	58	04	77	69	74	73	03	95	71	86	40	21	81	65	44
80	12	43	56	35	17	72	70	80	15	45	31	82	23	74	21	11	57	82	53	14	38	55	37	63
74	35	09	98	17	77	40	27	72	14	43	23	60	02	10	45	52	16	42	37	96	28	60	26	55
69	91	62	68	03	66	25	22	91	48	36	93	68	72	03	76	62	11	39	90	94	40	05	64	18
09	89	32	05	05	14	22	56	85	14	46	42	75	67	88	96	29	77	88	22	54	38	21	45	98
91	49	91	45	23	68	47	92	76	86	46	16	28	35	54	94	75	08	99	23	37	08	92	00	48
80	33	69	45	98	26	94	03	68	58	70	29	73	41	35	53	14	03	33	40	42	05	08	23	41
44	10	48	19	49	85	15	74	79	54	32	97	92	65	75	57	60	04	08	81	22	22	20	64	13
12	55	07	37	42	11	10	00	20	40	12	86	07	46	97	96	64	48	94	39	28	70	72	58	15
63	60	64	93	29	16	50	53	44	84	40	21	95	25	63	43	65	17	70	82	07	20	73	17	90
61	19	69	04	46	26	45	74	77	74	51	92	43	37	29	65	39	45	95	93	42	58	26	05	27
15	47	44	52	66	95	27	07	99	53	59	36	78	38	48	82	39	61	01	18	33	21	15	94	66
94	55	72	85	73	67	89	75	43	87	54	62	24	44	31	91	19	04	25	92	92	92	74	59	73
42	48	11	62	13	97	34	40	87	21	16	86	84	87	67	03	07	11	20	59	25	70	14	66	70
23	52	37	83	17	73	20	88	98	37	68	93	59	14	16	26	25	22	96	63	05	52	28	25	62
04	49	35	24	94	75	24	63	38	24	45	86	25	10	25	61	96	27	93	35	65	33	71	24	72
00	54	99	76	54	64	05	18	81	59	96	11	96	38	96	54	69	28	23	91	23	28	72	95	29
35	96	31	53	07	26	89	80	93	54	33	35	13	54	62	77	97	45	00	24	90	10	33	93	33
59	80	80	83	91	45	42	72	68	42	83	60	94	97	00	13	02	12	48	92	78	56	52	01	06
46	05	88	52	36	01	39	09	22	86	77	28	14	40	77	93	91	08	36	47	70	61	74	29	41
32	17	90	05	97	87	37	92	52	41	05	56	70	70	07	86	74	31	71	57	85	39	41	18	38
69	23	46	14	06	20	11	74	52	04	15	95	66	00	00	18	74	39	24	23	97	11	89	63	38
19	56	54	14	30	01	75	87	53	79	40	41	92	15	85	66	67	43	68	06	84	96	28	52	07
45	15	51	49	38	19	47	60	72	46	43	66	79	45	43	59	04	79	00	33	20	82	66	95	41
94	86	43	19	94	36	16	81	08	51	34	88	88	15	53	01	54	03	54	56	05	01	45	11	76
98	08	62	48	26	45	24	02	84	04	44	99	90	88	96	39	09	47	34	07	35	44	13	18	80
33	18	51	62	32	41	94	15	09	49	89	43	54	85	81	88	69	54	19	94	37	54	87	30	43
80	95	10	04	06	96	38	27	07	74	20	15	12	33	87	25	01	62	52	98	94	62	46	11	71
79	75	24	91	40	71	96	12	82	96	69	86	10	25	91	74	85	22	05	39	00	38	75	95	79
18	63	33	25	37	98	14	50	65	71	31	01	02	46	74	05	45	56	14	27	77	93	89	19	36
74	02	94	39	02	77	55	73	22	70	97	79	01	71	19	52	52	75	80	21	80	81	45	17	48
54	17	84	56	11	80	99	33	71	43	05	33	51	29	69	56	12	71	92	55	36	04	09	03	24
11	66	44	98	83	52	07	98	48	27	59	38	17	15	39	09	97	33	34	40	88	46	12	33	56
48	32	47	79	28	31	24	96	47	10	02	29	53	68	70	32	30	75	75	46	15	02	00	99	94
69	07	49	41	38	87	63	79	19	76	35	58	40	44	01	10	51	82	16	15	01	84	87	69	38

Reprinted by permission of The RAND Corporation, *A Million Random Digits with 100,000 Normal Deviates*, The Free Press, Glencoe, Illinois, 1955.

Random Numbers

09 18 82 00 97	32 82 53 95 27	04 22 08 63 04	83 38 98 73 74	64 27 85 80 44
90 04 58 54 97	51 98 15 06 54	94 93 88 19 97	91 87 07 61 50	68 47 66 46 59
73 18 95 02 07	47 67 72 62 69	62 29 06 44 64	27 12 46 70 18	41 36 18 27 60
75 76 87 64 90	20 97 18 17 49	90 42 91 22 72	95 37 50 58 71	93 82 34 31 78
54 01 64 40 56	66 28 13 10 03	00 68 22 73 98	20 71 45 32 95	07 70 61 78 13
08 35 86 99 10	78 54 24 27 85	13 66 15 88 73	04 61 89 75 53	31 22 30 84 20
28 30 60 32 64	81 33 31 05 91	40 51 00 78 93	32 60 46 04 75	94 11 90 18 40
53 84 08 62 33	81 59 41 36 28	51 21 59 02 90	28 46 66 87 95	77 76 22 07 91
91 75 75 37 41	61 61 36 22 69	50 26 39 02 12	55 78 17 65 14	83 48 34 70 55
89 41 59 26 94	00 39 75 83 91	12 60 71 76 46	48 94 97 23 06	94 54 13 74 08
77 51 30 38 20	86 83 42 99 01	68 41 48 27 74	51 90 81 39 80	72 89 35 55 07
19 50 23 71 74	69 97 92 02 88	55 21 02 97 73	74 28 77 52 51	65 34 46 74 15
21 81 85 93 13	93 27 88 17 57	05 68 67 31 56	07 08 28 50 46	31 85 33 84 52
51 47 46 64 99	68 10 72 36 21	94 04 99 13 45	42 83 60 91 91	08 00 74 54 49
99 55 96 83 31	62 53 52 41 70	69 77 71 28 30	74 81 97 81 42	43 86 07 28 34
33 71 34 80 07	93 58 47 28 69	51 92 66 47 21	58 30 32 98 22	93 17 49 39 72
85 27 48 68 93	11 30 32 92 70	28 83 43 41 37	73 51 59 04 00	71 14 84 36 43
84 13 38 96 40	44 03 55 21 66	73 85 27 00 91	61 22 26 05 61	62 32 71 84 23
56 73 21 62 34	17 39 59 61 31	10 12 39 16 22	85 49 65 75 60	81 60 41 88 80
65 13 85 68 06	87 64 88 52 61	34 31 36 58 61	45 87 52 10 69	85 64 44 72 77
38 00 10 21 76	81 71 91 17 11	71 60 29 29 37	74 21 96 40 49	65 58 44 96 98
37 40 29 63 97	01 30 47 75 86	56 27 11 00 86	47 32 46 26 05	40 03 03 74 38
97 12 54 03 48	87 08 33 14 17	21 81 53 92 50	75 23 76 20 47	15 50 12 95 78
21 82 64 11 34	47 14 33 40 72	64 63 88 59 02	49 13 90 64 41	03 85 65 45 52
73 13 54 27 42	95 71 90 90 35	85 79 47 42 96	08 78 98 81 56	64 69 11 92 02
07 63 87 79 29	03 06 11 80 72	96 20 74 41 56	23 82 19 95 38	04 71 36 69 94
60 52 88 34 41	07 95 41 98 14	59 17 52 06 95	05 53 35 21 39	61 21 20 64 55
83 59 63 56 55	06 95 89 29 83	05 12 80 97 19	77 43 35 37 83	92 30 15 04 98
10 85 06 27 46	99 59 91 05 07	13 49 90 63 19	53 07 57 18 39	06 41 01 93 62
39 82 09 89 52	43 62 26 31 47	64 42 18 08 14	43 80 00 93 51	31 02 47 31 67
59 58 00 64 78	75 56 97 88 00	88 83 55 44 86	23 76 80 61 56	04 11 10 84 08
38 50 80 73 41	23 79 34 87 63	90 82 29 70 22	17 71 90 42 07	95 95 44 99 53
30 69 27 06 68	94 68 81 61 27	56 19 68 00 91	82 06 76 34 00	05 46 26 92 00
65 44 39 56 59	18 28 82 74 37	49 63 22 40 41	08 33 76 56 76	96 29 99 08 36
27 26 75 02 64	13 19 27 22 94	07 47 74 46 06	17 98 54 89 11	97 34 13 03 58
91 30 70 69 91	19 07 22 42 10	36 69 95 37 28	28 82 53 57 93	28 97 66 62 52
68 43 49 46 88	84 47 31 36 22	62 12 69 84 08	12 84 38 25 90	09 81 59 31 46
48 90 81 58 77	54 74 52 45 91	35 70 00 47 54	83 82 45 26 92	54 13 05 51 60
06 91 34 51 97	42 67 27 86 01	11 88 30 95 28	63 01 19 89 01	14 97 44 03 44
10 45 51 60 19	14 21 03 37 12	91 34 23 78 21	88 32 58 08 51	43 66 77 08 83
12 88 39 73 43	65 02 76 11 84	04 28 50 13 92	17 97 41 50 77	90 71 22 67 69
21 77 83 09 76	38 80 73 69 61	31 64 94 20 96	63 28 10 20 23	08 81 64 74 49
19 52 35 95 15	65 12 25 96 59	86 28 36 82 58	69 57 21 37 98	16 43 59 15 29
67 24 55 26 70	35 58 31 65 63	79 24 68 66 86	76 46 33 42 22	26 65 59 08 02
60 58 44 73 77	07 50 03 79 92	45 13 42 65 29	26 76 08 36 37	41 32 64 43 44
53 85 34 13 77	36 06 69 48 50	58 83 87 38 59	49 36 47 33 31	96 24 04 36 42
24 63 73 87 36	74 38 48 93 42	52 62 30 79 92	12 36 91 86 01	03 74 28 38 73
83 08 01 24 51	38 99 22 28 15	07 75 95 17 77	97 37 72 75 85	51 97 23 78 67
16 44 42 43 34	36 15 19 90 73	27 49 37 09 39	85 13 03 25 52	54 84 65 47 59
60 79 01 81 57	57 17 86 57 62	11 16 17 85 76	45 81 95 29 79	65 13 00 48 60

Random Numbers

03	99	11	04	61	93	71	61	68	94	66	08	32	46	53	84	60	95	82	32	88	61	81	91	61
38	55	59	55	54	32	88	65	97	80	08	35	56	08	60	29	73	54	77	62	71	29	92	38	53
17	54	67	37	04	92	05	24	62	15	55	12	12	92	81	59	07	60	79	36	27	95	45	89	09
32	64	35	28	61	95	81	90	68	31	00	91	19	89	36	76	35	59	37	79	80	86	30	05	14
69	57	26	87	77	39	51	03	59	05	14	06	04	06	19	29	54	96	96	16	33	56	46	07	80
24	12	26	65	91	27	69	90	64	94	14	84	54	66	72	61	95	87	71	00	90	89	97	57	54
61	19	63	02	31	92	96	26	17	73	41	83	95	53	82	17	26	77	09	43	78	03	87	02	67
30	53	22	17	04	10	27	41	22	02	39	68	52	33	09	10	06	16	88	29	55	98	66	64	85
03	78	89	75	99	75	86	72	07	17	74	41	65	31	66	35	20	83	33	74	87	53	90	88	23
48	22	86	33	79	85	78	34	76	19	53	15	26	74	33	35	66	35	29	72	16	81	86	03	11
60	36	59	46	53	35	07	53	39	49	42	61	42	92	97	01	91	82	83	16	98	95	37	32	31
83	79	94	24	02	56	62	33	44	42	34	99	44	13	74	70	07	11	47	36	09	95	81	80	65
32	96	00	74	05	36	40	98	32	32	99	38	54	16	00	11	13	30	75	86	15	91	70	62	53
19	32	25	38	45	57	62	05	26	06	66	49	76	86	46	78	13	86	65	59	19	64	09	94	13
11	22	09	47	47	07	39	93	74	08	48	50	92	39	29	27	48	24	54	76	85	24	43	51	59
31	75	15	72	60	68	98	00	53	39	15	47	04	83	55	88	65	12	25	96	03	15	21	91	21
88	49	29	93	82	14	45	40	45	04	20	09	49	89	77	74	84	39	34	13	22	10	97	85	08
30	93	44	77	44	07	48	18	38	28	73	78	80	65	33	28	59	72	04	05	94	20	52	03	80
22	88	84	88	93	27	49	99	87	48	60	53	04	51	28	74	02	28	46	17	82	03	71	02	68
78	21	21	69	93	35	90	29	13	86	44	37	21	54	86	65	74	11	40	14	87	48	13	72	20
41	84	98	45	47	46	85	05	23	26	34	67	75	83	00	74	91	06	43	45	19	32	58	15	49
46	35	23	30	49	69	24	89	34	60	45	30	50	75	21	61	31	83	18	55	14	41	37	09	51
11	08	79	62	94	14	01	33	17	92	59	74	76	72	77	76	50	33	45	13	39	66	37	75	44
52	70	10	83	37	56	30	38	73	15	16	52	06	96	76	11	65	49	98	93	02	18	16	81	61
57	27	53	68	98	81	30	44	85	85	68	65	22	73	76	92	85	25	58	66	88	44	80	35	84
20	85	77	31	56	70	28	42	43	26	79	37	59	52	20	01	15	96	32	67	10	62	24	83	91
15	63	38	49	24	90	41	59	36	14	33	52	12	66	65	55	82	34	76	41	86	22	53	17	04
92	69	44	82	97	39	90	40	21	15	59	58	94	90	67	66	82	14	15	75	49	76	70	40	37
77	61	31	90	19	88	15	20	00	80	20	55	49	14	09	96	27	74	82	57	50	81	69	76	16
38	68	83	24	86	45	13	46	35	45	59	40	47	20	59	43	94	75	16	80	43	85	25	96	93
25	16	30	18	89	70	01	41	50	21	41	29	06	73	12	71	85	71	59	57	68	97	11	14	03
65	25	10	76	29	37	23	93	32	95	05	87	00	11	19	92	78	42	63	40	18	47	76	56	22
36	81	54	36	25	18	63	73	75	09	82	44	49	90	05	04	92	17	37	01	14	70	79	39	97
64	39	71	16	92	05	32	78	21	62	20	24	78	17	59	45	19	72	53	32	83	74	52	25	67
04	51	52	56	24	95	09	66	79	46	48	46	08	55	58	15	19	11	87	82	16	93	03	33	61
83	76	16	08	73	43	25	38	41	45	60	83	32	59	83	01	29	14	13	49	20	36	80	71	26
14	38	70	63	45	80	85	40	92	79	43	52	90	63	18	38	38	47	47	61	41	19	63	74	80
51	32	19	22	46	80	08	87	70	74	88	72	25	67	36	66	16	44	94	31	66	91	93	16	78
72	47	20	00	08	80	89	01	80	02	94	81	33	19	00	54	15	58	34	36	35	35	25	41	31
05	46	65	53	06	93	12	81	84	64	74	45	79	05	61	72	84	81	18	34	79	98	26	84	16
39	52	87	24	84	82	47	42	55	93	48	54	53	52	47	18	61	91	36	74	18	61	11	92	41
81	61	61	87	11	53	34	24	42	76	75	12	21	17	24	74	62	77	37	07	58	31	91	59	97
07	58	61	61	20	82	64	12	28	20	92	90	41	31	41	32	39	21	97	63	61	19	96	79	40
90	76	70	42	35	13	57	41	72	00	69	90	26	37	42	78	46	42	25	01	18	62	79	08	72
40	18	82	81	93	29	59	38	86	27	94	97	21	15	98	62	09	53	67	87	00	44	15	89	97
34	41	48	21	57	86	88	75	50	87	19	15	20	00	23	12	30	28	07	83	32	62	46	86	91
63	43	97	53	63	44	98	91	68	22	36	02	40	08	67	76	37	84	16	05	65	96	17	34	88
67	04	90	90	70	93	39	94	55	47	94	45	87	42	84	05	04	14	98	07	20	28	83	40	60
79	49	50	41	46	52	16	29	02	86	54	15	83	42	43	46	97	83	54	82	59	36	29	59	38
91	70	43	05	52	04	73	72	10	31	75	05	19	30	29	47	66	56	43	82	99	78	29	34	78

Random Numbers

94	01	54	68	74	32	44	44	82	77	59	82	09	61	63	64	65	42	58	43	41	14	54	28	20
74	10	88	82	22	88	57	07	40	15	25	70	49	10	35	01	75	51	47	50	48	96	83	86	03
62	88	08	78	73	95	16	05	92	21	22	30	49	03	14	72	87	71	73	34	39	28	30	41	49
11	74	81	21	02	80	58	04	18	67	17	71	05	96	21	06	55	40	78	50	73	95	07	95	52
17	94	40	56	00	60	47	80	33	43	25	85	25	89	05	57	21	63	96	18	49	85	69	93	26
66	06	74	27	92	95	04	35	26	80	46	78	05	64	87	09	97	15	94	81	37	00	62	21	86
54	24	49	10	30	45	54	77	08	18	59	84	99	61	69	61	45	92	16	47	87	41	71	71	98
30	94	55	75	89	31	73	25	72	60	47	67	00	76	54	46	37	62	53	66	94	74	64	95	80
69	17	03	74	03	86	99	59	03	07	94	30	47	18	03	26	82	50	55	11	12	45	99	13	14
08	34	58	89	75	35	84	18	57	71	08	10	55	99	87	87	11	22	14	76	14	71	37	11	81
27	76	74	35	84	85	30	18	89	77	29	49	06	97	14	73	03	54	12	07	74	69	90	93	10
13	02	51	43	38	54	06	61	52	43	47	72	46	67	33	47	43	14	39	05	31	04	85	66	99
80	21	73	62	92	98	52	52	43	35	24	43	22	48	96	43	27	75	88	74	11	46	61	60	82
10	87	56	20	04	90	39	16	11	05	57	41	10	63	68	53	85	63	07	43	08	67	08	47	41
54	12	75	73	26	26	62	91	90	87	24	47	28	87	79	30	54	02	78	86	61	73	27	54	54
60	31	14	28	24	37	30	14	26	78	45	99	04	32	42	17	37	45	20	03	70	70	77	02	14
49	73	97	14	84	92	00	39	80	86	76	66	87	32	09	59	20	21	19	73	02	90	23	32	50
78	62	65	15	94	16	45	39	46	14	39	01	49	70	66	83	01	20	98	32	25	57	17	76	28
66	69	21	39	86	99	83	70	05	82	81	23	24	49	87	09	50	49	64	12	90	19	37	95	68
44	07	12	80	91	07	36	29	77	03	76	44	74	25	37	98	52	49	78	31	65	70	40	95	14
41	46	88	51	49	49	55	41	79	94	14	92	43	96	50	95	29	40	05	56	70	48	10	69	05
94	55	93	75	59	49	67	85	31	19	70	31	20	56	82	66	98	63	40	99	74	47	42	07	40
41	61	57	03	60	64	11	45	86	60	90	85	06	46	18	80	62	05	17	90	11	43	63	80	72
50	27	39	31	13	41	79	48	68	61	24	78	18	96	83	55	41	18	56	67	77	53	59	98	92
41	39	68	05	04	90	67	00	82	89	40	90	20	50	69	95	08	30	67	83	28	10	25	78	16
25	80	72	42	60	71	52	97	89	20	72	68	20	73	85	90	72	65	71	66	98	88	40	85	83
06	17	09	79	65	88	30	29	80	41	21	44	34	18	08	68	98	48	36	20	89	74	79	88	82
60	80	85	44	44	74	41	28	11	05	01	17	62	88	38	36	42	11	64	89	18	05	95	10	61
80	94	04	48	93	10	40	83	62	22	80	58	27	19	44	92	63	84	03	33	67	05	41	60	67
19	51	69	01	20	46	75	97	16	43	13	17	75	52	92	21	03	68	28	08	77	50	19	74	27
49	38	65	44	80	23	60	42	35	54	21	78	54	11	01	91	17	81	01	74	29	42	09	04	38
06	31	28	89	40	15	99	56	93	21	47	45	86	48	09	98	18	98	18	51	29	65	18	42	15
60	94	20	03	07	11	89	79	26	74	40	40	56	80	32	96	71	75	42	44	10	70	14	13	93
92	32	99	89	32	78	28	44	63	47	71	20	99	20	61	39	44	89	31	36	25	72	20	85	64
77	93	66	35	74	31	38	45	19	24	85	56	12	96	71	58	13	71	78	20	22	75	13	65	18
38	10	17	77	56	11	65	71	38	97	95	88	95	70	67	47	64	81	38	85	70	66	99	34	06
39	64	16	94	57	91	33	92	25	02	92	61	38	97	19	11	94	75	62	03	19	32	42	05	04
84	05	44	04	55	99	39	66	36	80	67	66	76	06	31	69	18	19	68	45	38	52	51	16	00
47	46	80	35	77	57	64	96	32	66	24	70	07	15	94	14	00	42	31	53	69	24	90	57	47
43	32	13	13	70	28	97	72	38	96	76	47	96	85	62	62	34	20	75	89	08	89	90	59	85
64	28	16	18	26	18	55	56	49	37	13	17	33	33	65	78	85	11	64	99	87	06	41	30	75
66	84	77	04	95	32	35	00	29	85	86	71	63	87	46	26	31	37	74	63	55	38	77	26	81
72	46	13	32	30	21	52	95	34	24	92	58	10	22	62	78	43	86	62	76	18	39	67	35	38
21	03	29	10	50	13	05	81	62	18	12	47	05	65	00	15	29	27	61	39	59	52	65	21	13
95	36	26	70	11	06	65	11	61	36	01	01	60	08	57	55	01	85	63	74	35	82	47	17	08
49	71	29	73	80	10	40	45	54	52	34	03	06	07	26	75	21	11	02	71	36	63	36	84	24
58	27	56	17	64	97	58	65	47	16	50	25	94	63	45	87	19	54	60	92	26	78	76	09	39
89	51	41	17	88	68	22	42	34	17	73	95	97	61	45	30	34	24	02	77	11	04	97	20	49
15	47	25	06	69	48	13	93	67	32	46	87	43	70	88	73	46	50	98	19	58	86	93	52	20
12	12	08	61	24	51	24	74	43	02	60	88	35	21	09	21	43	73	67	86	49	22	67	78	37

Random Numbers

19 61 27 84 30	11 66 19 47 70	77 60 36 56 69	86 86 81 26 65	30 01 27 59 89
39 14 17 74 00	28 00 06 42 38	73 25 87 17 94	31 34 02 62 56	66 45 33 70 16
64 75 68 04 57	08 74 71 28 36	03 46 95 06 78	03 27 44 34 23	66 67 78 25 56
92 90 15 18 78	56 44 12 29 98	29 71 83 84 47	06 45 32 53 11	07 56 55 37 71
03 55 19 00 70	09 48 39 40 50	45 93 81 81 35	36 90 84 33 21	11 07 35 18 03
98 88 46 62 09	06 83 05 36 56	14 66 35 63 46	71 43 00 49 09	19 81 80 57 07
27 36 98 68 82	53 47 30 75 41	53 63 37 08 63	03 74 81 28 22	19 36 04 90 88
59 06 67 59 74	63 33 52 04 83	43 51 43 74 81	58 27 82 69 67	49 32 54 39 51
91 64 79 37 83	64 16 94 90 22	98 58 80 94 95	49 82 95 90 68	38 83 10 48 38
83 60 59 24 19	39 54 20 77 72	71 56 87 56 73	35 18 58 97 59	44 00 17 42 91
24 89 58 85 30	70 77 43 54 39	46 75 87 04 72	70 20 79 26 75	91 62 36 12 75
35 72 02 65 56	95 59 62 00 94	73 75 08 57 88	34 26 40 17 03	46 83 36 52 48
14 14 15 34 10	38 64 90 63 43	57 25 66 13 42	72 70 97 53 18	90 37 93 75 62
27 41 67 56 70	92 17 67 25 35	93 11 95 60 77	06 88 61 82 44	92 34 43 13 74
82 07 10 74 29	81 00 74 77 49	40 74 45 69 74	23 33 68 88 21	53 84 11 05 36
21 44 58 27 93	24 83 19 32 41	14 19 97 62 68	70 88 36 80 02	03 82 91 74 43
72 51 37 64 00	52 22 59 23 48	62 30 89 84 81	29 74 43 31 65	33 14 16 10 20
71 47 94 50 27	76 16 05 74 11	13 78 01 36 32	52 30 87 77 62	88 87 43 36 97
83 21 05 14 66	09 08 85 03 95	26 74 30 53 06	21 70 67 00 01	99 43 98 07 67
68 74 99 51 48	94 89 77 86 36	96 75 00 90 24	94 53 89 11 43	96 69 36 18 86
05 18 47 57 63	47 07 58 81 58	05 31 35 34 39	14 90 80 88 30	60 09 62 15 51
13 65 16 25 46	96 89 22 52 40	47 51 15 84 83	87 34 27 88 18	07 85 53 92 69
00 56 62 12 20	00 29 22 40 69	25 07 22 95 19	52 54 85 40 91	21 28 22 12 96
50 95 81 76 95	58 07 26 89 90	60 32 99 59 55	71 58 66 34 17	35 94 76 78 07
57 62 16 45 47	46 85 03 79 81	38 52 70 90 37	64 75 60 33 24	04 98 68 36 66
09 28 22 58 44	79 13 97 84 35	35 42 84 35 61	69 79 96 33 14	12 99 19 35 16
23 39 49 42 06	93 43 23 78 36	94 91 92 68 46	02 55 57 44 10	94 91 54 81 99
05 28 03 74 70	93 62 20 43 45	15 09 21 95 10	18 09 41 66 13	78 23 45 00 01
95 49 19 79 76	38 30 63 21 92	82 63 95 46 24	72 43 49 26 06	23 19 17 46 93
78 52 10 01 04	18 24 87 55 83	90 32 65 07 85	54 03 46 62 51	35 77 41 46 92
96 34 54 45 79	85 93 24 40 53	75 70 42 08 40	86 58 38 39 44	52 45 67 37 66
77 96 33 11 51	32 36 49 16 91	47 35 74 03 38	23 43 52 40 65	08 45 89 53 66
07 52 01 12 94	23 23 80 17 48	41 69 06 73 28	54 81 43 77 77	10 05 74 23 32
38 42 30 23 09	70 70 38 57 36	46 14 81 42 58	29 23 61 21 52	05 08 86 58 25
02 46 36 55 33	21 19 96 05 55	33 92 80 18 17	07 39 68 92 15	30 72 22 21 02
15 88 09 22 61	17 29 28 81 90	61 78 14 88 98	92 52 52 12 83	88 58 16 00 98
71 92 60 08 19	59 14 40 02 24	30 57 09 01 94	18 32 90 69 99	26 85 71 92 38
64 42 52 81 08	16 55 41 60 16	00 04 28 32 29	10 33 33 61 68	65 61 79 48 34
79 78 22 39 24	49 44 03 04 32	81 07 73 15 43	95 21 66 48 65	13 65 85 10 81
35 33 77 45 38	44 55 36 46 72	90 96 04 18 49	93 86 54 46 08	93 17 63 48 51
05 24 92 93 29	19 71 59 40 82	14 73 88 66 67	43 70 86 63 54	93 69 22 55 27
56 46 39 93 80	38 79 38 57 74	19 05 61 39 39	46 06 22 76 47	66 14 66 32 10
96 29 63 31 21	54 19 63 41 08	75 81 48 59 86	71 17 11 51 02	28 99 26 31 65
98 38 03 62 69	60 01 40 72 01	62 44 84 63 85	42 17 58 83 50	46 18 24 91 26
52 56 76 43 50	16 31 55 39 69	80 39 58 11 14	54 35 86 45 78	47 26 91 57 47
78 49 89 08 30	25 95 59 92 36	43 28 69 10 64	99 96 99 51 44	64 42 47 73 77
49 55 32 42 41	08 15 08 95 35	08 70 39 10 41	77 32 38 10 79	45 12 79 36 86
32 15 10 70 75	83 15 51 02 52	73 10 08 86 18	23 89 18 74 18	45 41 72 02 68
11 31 45 03 63	26 86 02 77 99	49 41 68 35 34	19 18 70 80 59	76 67 70 21 10
12 36 47 12 10	87 05 25 02 41	90 78 59 78 89	81 39 95 81 30	64 43 90 56 14

Table XIII

95%-POINTS $\epsilon_{N,.95}$ AND 99%-POINTS $\epsilon_{N,.99}$ FOR KOLMOGOROV'S STATISTIC

$$Pr\{\delta_N < \epsilon_{N,.95}\} = .95, \; Pr\{\delta_N < \epsilon_{N,.99}\} = .99$$

(1) N	(2) $\epsilon_{N,\ .95}$	(3) $\epsilon_{N,\ .99}$
2	.8419	.9293
3	.7076	.8290
4	.6239	.7341
5	.5633	.6685
10	.4087	.4864
15	.3375	.4042
20	.2939	.3524
25	.2639	.3165
30	.2417	.2898
40	.2101	.2521
50	.1884	.2260
60	.1723	.2067
70	.1597	.1917
80	.1496	.1795
90	.1412	
100	.1340	

Index

ANSWERS

Pages 7–9

1. (a) 0.2; (b) 0.8; (c) 0.15; (d) 0.65.
2. (a) 3/5; (b) 12/25; (c) 4/5; (d) 2/25.
3. (a) 7/10; (b) 1/10; (c) 2/10.
4. (a) 36 elementary events, probability 1/36 each; (b) 5; (c) 1/36; (d) 2/9; (e) 1/9; (f) 5/12.
5. (a) 4 elementary events, probability 1/4 each; (b) 1/4; (c) 1/2.
7. 6 elementary events, probability 1/6 each; (0,0,2), (0,2,0), (0,1,1); 1/2.
8. (a) 23/38; (b) 0.
9. (a) 8 elementary events, probability 1/8 each; (b) 1/4.
10. 2/5.
11. $18/(47)(46) \doteq 0.008$; $188/(47)(46) \doteq 0.09$.
12. (a) 8/15; (b) 2/3.

Page 12

2. True: (b), (c), (d), (f), (g), (i), (j), (k), (l), (m).
3. $O \subset AB \subset AB \cup AC \subset A \subset A \cup B \subset S$.
4. $\overline{AB} \subset \bar{B} \subset \bar{A} \subset \bar{A} \cup \bar{B}$.
5. (a) $\bar{A}\bar{B}\bar{C}$ or $\overline{A \cup B \cup C}$; (b) ABC; (c) $\bar{A}\bar{B}C$; (d) AB; (e) $AB\bar{C}$ or $AB - C$; (f) $A\bar{B}\bar{C} \cup \bar{A}B\bar{C} \cup \bar{A}\bar{B}C$; (g) $A \cup B \cup C$; (h) $\bar{A}\bar{B}\bar{C} \cup A\bar{B}\bar{C} \cup \bar{A}B\bar{C} \cup \bar{A}\bar{B}C$; (i) $AB\bar{C} \cup A\bar{B}C \cup \bar{A}BC$.

Page 15

$P(A) + P(B) + P(C) - P(AB) - P(AC) - P(BC) + P(ABC)$.

Pages 17–18

1. 7/12, 3/4, 1/2, 1.
2. 2/3, 3/4, 2/3.
3. (a) 1/6; (b) 1/6; (c) $P(AB) = P(A \mid B)P(B) = (1/6)(1/6) = 1/36$.
4. (b) $P(A) = P(AB_1) + P(AB_2)$; (c) $P(A) = P(A \mid B_1)P(B_1) + P(A \mid B_2)P(B_2)$.
5. 0.65.
6. (a) 15/26; (b) 5/13; (c) 1/26; (d) 59/130.
7. 0.26.
8. 11/108.
9. 0.846.
10. 0.948.
11. 4/75.

Pages 19–20

1. (a) $(1/6)^4$; (b) $(1/2)^4$; (c) $(1/6)^3$.
2. (a) $(1/2)^N$; (b) $(1/2)^N$; (c) $1 - (1/2)^N$.
3. 29.
6. (a) 1/6; (b) 2/3; (c) 2/9; (d) 7/18.
7. 0.518; 0.491.
8. Yes; yes.
9. (a) Of 36 elementary events, 12 favorable to first, 12 to second, 12 to third.
(b) No, $1/6 = P(AB) \neq P(A)P(B) = (1/3)(1/3) = 1/9$; no.

Pages 26–28

2. 0.01; independence.

3. (a) 0.216; (b) 0.064; (c) 0.144; (d) 0.432; (e) 0.648.

4. (a) $\bar{A}$, $P(\bar{A}) = 1 - P(A)$; (b) $P(B|A) = P(AB)/P(A)$; (c) AB, $P(AB)$; (d) $P(A|B) = P(AB)/P(B)$.

5. 3/1600.

6. (a) $(1/2)^N$; (b) $(1/2)^N$; (c) $1 - (1/2)^N$.

7. (a) 0.343, 0.027; (b) 0.91.

8. (a) 1/24; (b) 1/4; (c) 3/4; (d) 1/12.

9. (a) $\bar{A}\bar{B}\bar{C}$, 0.072; (b) $AB \cup BC \cup CA$, 0.604.

11. (a) 0.1; (*b*) 7.

12. (a) 1/8; (b) 7/8.

13. (a) $(1/8) + (3/4)c + c^2$; (b) $(7/8) - (3/4)k - k^2$.

14. (a) $(51/52)^{52}$; (b) $(1 - 1/n)^n \to e^{-1}$ as $n \to \infty$.

Pages 30–31

1. 2/9.

2. 7/12.

3. 8/11.

4. 12/21.

5. 4/13.

6. 1/3.

7. 3/4.

8. 6/7.

Pages 35–36

1. (a) 5 spot; 1 spot, 2 spot, 3 spot; all; none. (b) 1/6, 1/2, 1, 0.

2. (b) 0, 1, 1.

3. (a) Real numbers between 0 and 1. (b) The real number 1/2; 0. (c) Real numbers between 1/2 and 1, real numbers between 1/3 and 1, 1/2; 2/3.

4. (b) All individuals less than 150 lb.; all individuals of weight greater than 100 lb. but less than 150 lb.

Page 38

1. (a) The real numbers; (b) 1/2; (c) 1/6; (d) 1; (e) 0.

Page 51

2. $h(z) = 1/(b - a)$ for $a < z < b$, $h(z) = 0$ for $z < a$ and for $z > b$; $H(z) = 0$ for $z < a$, $H(z) = (z - a)/(b - a)$ for $a < z < b$, $H(z) = 1$ for $z > b$.

5. $F(w) = w^2$ for $0 < w < 1$, $F(w) = 0$ for $w < 0$, $F(w) = 1$ for $w > 1$; $f(w) = 2w$ for $0 < w < 1$, $f(w) = 0$ for $w < 0$ and for $w > 1$.

6. $f(w) = e^{-\lambda}\lambda^{½(w-4)}/[\frac{1}{2}(w - 4)]!$ for $w = 4, 6, 8, \cdots$; $f(w) = 0$ for all other w.

8. $F(x) = (\text{Arctan } x + \pi/2)/\pi$; $f(x) = 1/[\pi(1 + x^2)]$.

Pages 54–56

1. 3.5, 35/12, $\sqrt{35/12}$.

2. $(a + b)/2$, $(b - a)^2/12$, $(b - a)/\sqrt{12}$.

3. 2/3, 2/9, $\sqrt{2}/3$.

4. 2/3, 2/9, $\sqrt{2}/3$.

5. 2/3, 1/18, $\sqrt{2}/6$.

6. 1/6, 0, 0.

7. Do not exist.

8. (b) $F(x) = x^2(3 - 2x)$ for $0 < x < 1$, $F(x) = 0$ for $x < 0$, $F(x) = 1$ for $x > 1$; (c) 1/2; (d) 1/2.
9. (b) $G(y) = 0$ for $y < 0$, $G(y) = 3y - 2y^{3/2}$ for $0 < y < 1$, $G(y) = 1$ for $y > 1$; $g(y) = 3 - 3y^{1/2}$ for $0 < y < 1$, $g(y) = 0$ for $y < 0$ and for $y > 1$.
10. $E(\mathbf{y}) = 3/4$, $V(\mathbf{y}) = 11/16$.
11. (a) 18/25, 13/50, 1/50; (c) \$0.30.
12. $f(x) = 2x$ for $0 < x < 1$, $f(x) = 0$ for $x < 0$, $x > 1$; $E(\mathbf{x}) = 2/3$, $V(\mathbf{x}) = 1/18$, $\sigma_x = \sqrt{2}/6$.
13. a, 0.
14. p, $\sqrt{pq}$.
16. $E(\mathbf{x}) = 11/8$, $V(\mathbf{x}) = 47/64$.
17. (a) $g(y) = \theta e^{-\theta y}$ for $y > 0$; (b) $1/\theta$, $1/\theta^2$.
18. $E(\mathbf{x}) = ck/(c - 1)$ (exists if $c > 1$), $V(\mathbf{x}) = ck^2/(c - 2)(c - 1)^2$ (exists if $c > 2$).
19. 1/2.
20. 2/3.
22. $2/\sqrt{\pi b}$.
23. $E(\mathbf{x}) = r/(1 - r)$; $V(\mathbf{x}) = [r/(1 - r)]^2 + r/(1 - r)$.

Pages 64–65

1. $f(1) = 1/2, f(2) = 3/8, f(3) = 1/8$; $g(1) = 1/2, g(2) = 1/4, g(3) = 1/4$.
2. $f(-1) = 1/3, f(0) = 0, f(1) = 2/3$; $g(-1) = 1/4, g(0) = 1/4, g(1) = 1/2$.
3. (a) 1/2; (b) $G(y) = 0$ for $y \leq -1$, $G(y) = 1/4$ for $-1 < y \leq 0$, $G(y) = \frac{1}{2}$ for $0 \leq y < 1$, $G(y) = 1$ for $y \geq 1$.

4. (b)

$x \backslash y$	0	1	2
0	4/9	4/18	1/36
1	4/18	1/18	0
2	1/36	0	0

(c), (d) $f(0) = g(0) = 25/36$,
$f(1) = g(1) = 5/18$,
$f(2) = g(2) = 1/36$.

5. (a)

$x \backslash y$	0	1	2	3	4	5	6
0	1/4	1/4	0	0	0	0	0
1	0	1/12	1/12	1/12	1/12	1/12	1/12

(b) $f(0) = f(1) = 1/2$; $g(0) = 1/4, g(1) = 1/3$, $g(2) = g(3) = g(4) = g(5) = g(6) = 1/12$; (c) 2/3.

6. (a)

$x \backslash y$	0	1	2
0	1/16	1/4	1/4
1	1/8	1/4	0
2	1/16	0	0

(b) $f(0) = 9/16, f(1) = 3/8$, $f(2) = 1/16$; $g(0) = 1/4$, $g(1) = 1/2, g(2) = 1/4$.

(c) $E(\mathbf{y}) = 1$, $V(\mathbf{y}) = 1/2$, $\sigma_y = 1/\sqrt{2}$.

Pages 70–71

1. (a) $g(y) = 0$ for $|y| > 1$, $g(y) = 2\sqrt{1 - y^2}/\pi$ for $|y| < 1$; (b) $G(y) = 0$ for $y \leq -1$, $G(y) = [y\sqrt{1 - y^2} + \text{Arc sin } y + \pi/2]/\pi$ for $-1 \leq y \leq 1$, $G(y) = 1$ for $y \geq 1$; (c) 0; (d) 1/4.

2. $\sqrt{7/2}$, $\sqrt{17/2}$.

3. (a) $f(r) = 0$ for $r < 0$, $f(r) = e^{-r}$ for $r > 0$; (b) $E(\mathbf{r}) = 1$; (c) $V(\mathbf{r}) = 1$.

4. (a) $k = 1/2\pi$; (b) $f(x) = \dfrac{1}{\sqrt{2\pi}} e^{-x^2/2}$; (c) 0; (d) 1.

5. (a) 1/4; (b) 1/2; (c) 2/3; (d) $\pi/16$.

6. (a) 0, $z^2/2$, $1 - \frac{1}{2}(2 - z)^2$, 1; (b) $h(z) = 0$ for $z < 0$, $z > 2$, $h(z) = z$ for $0 < z < 1$, $h(z) = 2 - z$ for $1 < z < 2$.

Pages 76–77

1. $g(1|1) = 1/4$, $g(1|2) = 1$, $g(1|3) = 0$.

2. (a) $f(-1) = 1/4$, $f(1) = 3/4$; (*b*) $g(-1|1) = 2/3$, $g(0|1) = 1/3$, $g(1|1) = 0$.

3. Dependent, independent, dependent, dependent.

4.

$x \backslash y$	1	2
1	1/12	1/6
2	1/12	1/6
3	1/6	1/3

5. (a) $G(5|x) = 1$ for $x = 3, 4, 5, 6$; $G(5|7) = G(5|8) = 2/3$, $G(5|9) = G(5|10) = 1/2$; (b) 19/24.

6. (a) $f(x) = 1/4$ for $x = 1, 2, 3, 4$, $f(x) = 0$ for other x; $g(y|1) = 1/4$ for $y = 1, 2, 3, 4$, $g(y|2) = 1/3$ for $y = 2, 3, 4$, $g(y|3) = 1/2$ for $y = 3, 4$, $g(4|4) = 1$.

(b)

$x \backslash y$	1	2	3	4
1	1/16	1/16	1/16	1/16
2	0	1/12	1/12	1/12
3	0	0	1/8	1/8
4	0	0	0	1/4

(c) $g(1) = 1/16$, $g(2) = 7/48$, $g(3) = 13/48$, $g(4) = 25/48$.

7. (a) 7/8; (b) No.

Pages 80–81

1. (a) $(1 - 1/e)^2$; (b) 1/2; (c) $g(y|x) = e^{-y}$ for $y > 0$, $x > 0$, $g(y|x) = 0$ for $y < 0$, $x > 0$.

2. (a) 1; (b) $f(x) = 0$ for $x < 0$, $x > 1$, $f(x) = x + 1/2$ for $0 < x < 1$; $g(y) \equiv f(y)$; (c) 1/2; (d) $g(y|x) = 0$ for $y < 0$, $0 < x < 1$, $g(y|x) = 0$ for $y > 1$, $0 < x < 1$, $g(y|x) = (x + y)/(x + 1/2)$ for $0 < y < 1$, $0 < x < 1$.

3. (a) $f(x,y) = 14x^4y$ for $0 < y < x$, $0 < x < 1$, $f(x,y) = 0$ for other x,y; (b) $g(y) = 14y(1 - y^5)/5$ for $0 < y < 1$, $g(y) = 0$ for $y < 0$, $y > 1$; (c) 1/4.

4. (a) $f(r,s) = 2e^{-(s+r)}$ for $0 < r < s$; $f(r,s) = 0$ for other r,s; (b) $g(s) = 2e^{-s}(1 - e^{-s})$ for $s > 0$, $g(s) = 0$ for $s < 0$; (c) $(1 - e^{-3})^2$.

5. (a) $k = 4$; (b) $g(y) = 2y$ for $0 < y < 1$; $g(y) = 0$ for $y < 0$, $y > 1$; $G(y) = 0$ for $y < 0$, $G(y) = y^2$ for $0 < y < 1$, $G(y) = 1$ for $y > 1$; (c) $f(x|y) = 2x$ for $0 < x < 1$, $0 < y < 1$, $f(x|y) = 0$ for $x < 0$ or $x > 1$, $0 < y < 1$.

6. (a) $f(x,y) = 1/4\sqrt{1 - x^2}$ for $|x| < 1$, $|y| < \sqrt{1 - x^2}$, $f(x,y) = 0$ for other x,y; (b) $\pi/4\sqrt{2}$.

Page 83

1. Independent, dependent.
2. Dependent, independent, independent.
3. Dependent, dependent, dependent.
4. (a) $f(x) = 0$ for $x < 0$, $x > 1$, $f(x) = \frac{\pi}{4}(\cos \pi x/2 + \sin \pi x/2)$ for $0 < x < 1$;
(b) $g(y|x) = \frac{\pi}{2}\left[\sin \frac{\pi}{2}(x + y)\right] \Big/ \left[\cos \frac{\pi x}{2} + \sin \frac{\pi x}{2}\right]$ for $0 < y < 1$, $0 < x < 1$, $g(y|x) = 0$ for $y < 0$ or $y > 1$ if $0 < x < 1$; (c) no; (d) $1/2 - \sqrt{2}/6$.
5. $1/4$.
6. $\ln 2 - 1/2$.
7. y^2.
8. $Pr\{\max(\mathbf{x}_1, \mathbf{x}_2, \cdots, \mathbf{x}_n) < y\} = (y/\theta)^n$ for $0 < y < \theta$.
9. $\int_{-\infty}^{\infty} \int_{x_1}^{\infty} f(x_1)f(x_2)\,dx_2\,dx_1 = \int_{-\infty}^{\infty} [1 - F(x_1)]f(x_1)\,dx_1 = 1 - \{\frac{1}{2}[F(x_1)]^2\}_{-\infty}^{\infty} = 1/2.$

Pages 91–92

1. p, pq.
2. (a) 4/3, 2/9; (b) 8, 4/3.
3. 2 with probability p, 0 with probability q; 1 with probability p, -1 with probability q; 1 with probability p, 0 with probability q; $2p$, $4pq$; $2p - 1$, $4pq$; p, pq.
4. (a) 1; (b) -2; (c) 20; (d) b, c.
5. (a) np; (b) p.
6. (a) npq; (b) pq/n.
7. $\sum_{i=1}^{n} E(\mathbf{x}_i)$, $\frac{1}{n}\sum_{i=1}^{n} E(\mathbf{x}_i)$.
8. $\sum_{i=1}^{n} V(\mathbf{x}_i)$, $\frac{1}{n^2}\sum_{i=1}^{n} V(\mathbf{x}_i)$.
9. 7, 35/6; $7n/2$, $35n/12$.
18. $\min_{\lambda} E[(\mathbf{x} - \lambda)^2] = V(\mathbf{x})$.

Page 95

1. $g(1|1) = g(2|1) = 1/4$, $g(3|1) = 1/2$, $E(\mathbf{y}|1) = 9/4$; $g(1|2) = 1$, $E(\mathbf{y}|2) = 1$; $g(2|3) = 1$, $E(\mathbf{y}|3) = 2$; $E(\mathbf{y}) = 7/4$.
2. $E(\mathbf{y}|1) = 5/2$; $E(\mathbf{y}|2) = 3$; $E(\mathbf{y}|3) = 7/2$; $E(\mathbf{y}|4) = 4$; $E(\mathbf{y}) = 13/4$.
4. $E(\mathbf{y}|x) = (3x + 2)/3(2x + 1)$ for $0 < x < 1$; $E(\mathbf{y}) = 7/12$.
5. $E(\mathbf{y}|x) = (x + 1)/2$ for $0 < x < 1$; $E(\mathbf{y}) = 3/4$.

Pages 112–115

1. (b) 0.2401, 0.4116, 0.2646, 0.0756, 0.0081; (c) 0.3483.
2. 19/27.
3. $1 - [q^{25} + 25pq^{24}] \doteq 7.4(10^{-5})$, $p = 0.0005$, $q = 1 - p$.
4. (a) $\binom{5}{x}(1/6)^x(5/6)^{5-x}$;

(b) $\sum_{x=y}^{5} \binom{5}{x} (1/6)^x(5/6)^{5-x}$;

(c) $\sum_{x=0}^{y} \binom{5}{x} (1/6)^x(5/6)^{5-x}$;

(d) 5/6, 25/36.

5. (a) $\sum_{x=60}^{100} \binom{100}{x} (2/3)^x(1/3)^{100-x}$; (b) $\sum_{x=60}^{75} \binom{100}{x} (2/3)^x(1/3)^{100-x}$.

6. (a) 80; (b) 16; (c) 0.04.

7. $(1/2)^{20} \sum_{x=15}^{20} \binom{20}{x} = 0.021$.

8. $\sum_{x=5}^{10} \binom{10}{x} (1/7)^x(6/7)^{10-x} = 0.008$.

9. $\sum_{x=4}^{6} \binom{6}{x} (10^{-6})^x(1 - 10^{-6})^{6-x} = (1.5)10^{-23}$.

10. (a) $(b - a)/\theta$; (b) a^3/θ^3.

11. (a) Each is $f(x) = 1/\theta$ for $0 < x < \theta, f(x) = 0$ for $x < 0, x > \theta$; (b) $f(x_1,x_2,x_3) = f(x_1)f(x_2)f(x_3) = 1/\theta^3$ if $\theta > \max(x_1,x_2,x_3)$, $f(x_1,x_2,x_3) = 0$ if $\theta < \max(x_1,x_2,x_3)$.

12. (b) $g(y)$; $g(y_1)g(y_2)$; (c) 31/36.

13. (a) $e^{-z^2/2}/\sqrt{2\pi}$; $\exp(-\frac{1}{2}\sum_{i=1}^{n} z^2{}_i)/(\sqrt{2\pi})^n$; (b) $\frac{1}{\sqrt{2\pi}}\int_{-1}^{2} e^{-z^2/2}\,dz$; (c) $\frac{1}{2\pi}\int_{-\infty}^{\infty}\int_{-z_2}^{\alpha-z_2} e^{-\frac{1}{2}(z_1{}^2+z_2{}^2)}\,dz_1\,dz_2$.

14. (a) 19/26; (b) $\binom{10}{7}$ $(19/26)^7$ $(7/26)^3$; (c) 8; (d) 190/26; (e) $\sqrt{1330}/26$.

15. (a) 0.0385; (b) A, 0.374; B, 0.382; C, 0.244.

16. (a) $\binom{n}{k} p^kq^{n-k}$.

17. When $(n + 1)p$ is an integer.

18. $Pr\{\mathbf{y} = y\} = pq^y$ $(q = 1 - p)$; $E(\mathbf{y}) = q/p$; $V(\mathbf{y}) = q/p^2$.

Pages 123–125

1. $f(x) = e^{-2}2^x/x!$, $x = 0, 1, 2, \cdots$; $F(x) = e^{-2}\sum_{t<x} 2^t/t!$, for $x > 0$, $F(x) = 0$ for $x < 0$.

2. (b) $\sum_{x=0}^{10} e^{-20}20^x/x! = 0.0108$ (by table).

6. (a) 5/4; (b) $1 - e^{-5/4}$.

7. (a) 10; (b) $e^{-10}\sum_{x=5}^{\infty} 10^x/x!$.

8. (a) $e^{-0.03}$; (b) $e^{-0.3}$.

9. (a) $1 - e^{-5} = 0.993$; (b) $1 - e^{-5}(1 + 5) = 0.960$.

10. $6!(1/6)^3(1/18)^3/(3!)^2$.

11. (a) 3/8, 1/8, 1/2; (b) 27/256.

12. $\lambda = 0.051$, $n = 51$.

13. $\sum_{x=4}^{50} \binom{50}{x} (0.03)^x(0.97)^{50-x} \doteq \sum_{x=4}^{\infty} e^{-1.5}(1.5)^x/x! = 0.066$ (from summed Poisson tables).

14. $\lambda = 2.1$ from summed Poisson table, $p = 0.0105$.

15. Approximately $e^{-6(10^{-6})}[6(10^{-6})]^4/4! = 54(10^{-24})$.

16. $\lambda - 1$, λ.

20. $F(t) = 1 - e^{-\lambda t}$ for $t > 0$, $F(t) = 0$ for $t < 0$; $f(t) = 0$ for $t < 0$, $f(t) = \lambda e^{-\lambda t}$ for $t > 0$; $E(\mathbf{t}) = 1/\lambda$; $V(\mathbf{t}) = 1/\lambda^2$.

Pages 133–135

1. (a) 200/3, 200/9; (b) 2/9; (c) $\mathbf{x} = 1$ with probability 2/3, $\mathbf{x} = 0$ with probability 1/3.

2. (b) 1/10; (c) 1/10; (d) $\epsilon = \sqrt{2}$ (using Chebyshev's inequality).

3. (a) 21/25; (b) 320.

4. (a) $\binom{10}{9}(1/4)^9(3/4)$; (b) $\sum_{k=5}^{10}\binom{10}{k}(1/4)^k(3/4)^{10-k}$; (c) 6.

5. (a) $\sum_{|x-50p|\le\epsilon}\binom{50}{x}p^x(1-p)^{50-x}$; (b) 0.22.

6. (a) \$2; (b) 4 (squared dollars!); (c) 0.1.

Pages 156–161

1. $\bar{x}$.

2. s.

3. $\bar{x}$.

5. min $(x_1, x_2, \cdots, x_n)$, max $(x_1, x_2, \cdots, x_n)$.

6. (a) 0.26, 0.74, $p = 1/2$; (b) $p = 1/3$.

7. $1/\bar{x}$.

8. Positive.

9. Any number which is within distance 1 of the largest sample value and also within distance 1 of the smallest sample value.

10. $\frac{1}{2}(A - B + \pi/2)$, $\frac{1}{2}(\pi/2 + B - A)$.

11. $(m\pi/2 + \sum_{i=1}^{n} A_i - \sum_{j=1}^{m} B_j)/(n + m)$, $(n\pi/2 + \sum_{j=1}^{m} B_j - \sum_{i=1}^{n} A_i)/(n + m)$.

12. $2(N_1 + N_2)/3N$, $(N_1 + N_2)/3N$.

13. $Pr\{\mathbf{t}_n < t\} = 1 - (1 - t/n\theta)^n \to 1 - e^{-t/\theta}$ as $n \to \infty$.

14. (b) $F(t) = \frac{1}{2}e^t$ $(t < 0)$, $F(t) = 1 - \frac{1}{2}e^{-t}$ $(t > 0)$, $f(t) = \frac{1}{2}e^{-|t|}$.

16. (a) $\sum_{i=1}^{n} x_i/mn$; (b) 0.499.

17. (a) $e^{-\bar{x}}$; (b) $e^{-1.12} \doteq 0.326$.

18. (a) $10^{\mu+\sigma^2/2 \log_{10}e}$; (b) $10^{\bar{z}+s^2/2 \log_{10}e}$; where $s^2 = \sum_{i=1}^{n}(z_i - \bar{z})^2/n$; (c) 28.3.

19. (a) max $(x_1, x_2, \cdots, x_n)$ − min $(x_1, x_2, \cdots, x_n)$; preceding multiplied by $(n + 1)/(n - 1)$; (b) 2704, 2884.3.

20. (a) $\dfrac{1}{\sqrt{2\pi}}\displaystyle\int_{-\infty}^{(t-\bar{x})/s} e^{-z^2/2}\,dz$; (b) 0.008.

24. $f(x_1, x_2, \cdots, x_n|y) = (1/y)[1/(y - 1)] \cdots [1/(y - n + 1)] = (y - n)!/y!$ is independent of k.

Pages 161–163

1. (a) 0.683; (b) $c = 3.29$; (c) $d = -1.56$.

2. (a) 0.136; (b) $(-1.36, \infty)$.

3. (a) $c = 1.28$; (b) 0.067.

4. (a) $\left(\dfrac{1}{\sqrt{2\pi}}\displaystyle\int_{-\infty}^{1.5} e^{-z^2/2}\,dz\right)\left(\dfrac{1}{\sqrt{2\pi}}\displaystyle\int_{-\infty}^{1} e^{-z^2/2}\,dz\right)$

or $\left(\dfrac{1}{2\sqrt{2\pi}}\displaystyle\int_{-\infty}^{3} e^{-x^2/8}\,dx\right)\left(\dfrac{1}{3\sqrt{2\pi}}\displaystyle\int_{-\infty}^{3} e^{-y^2/18}\,dy\right)$;

(b) $1 - \left(\dfrac{1}{\sqrt{2\pi}}\displaystyle\int_{1.5}^{\infty} e^{-z^2/2}\,dz\right)\left(\dfrac{1}{\sqrt{2\pi}}\displaystyle\int_{1}^{\infty} e^{-z^2/2}\,dz\right)$

or $1 - \left(\dfrac{1}{2\sqrt{2\pi}}\displaystyle\int_{3}^{\infty} e^{-x^2/8}\,dx\right)\left(\dfrac{1}{3\sqrt{2\pi}}\displaystyle\int_{3}^{\infty} e^{-y^2/18}\,dy\right)$;

(c) 0.7851, 0.9894.

5. (a) $\left(\frac{1}{\sqrt{2\pi}}\int_{-\infty}^{3} e^{-z^2/2}\,dz\right)^n$, $(0.9987)^n$;

(b) $1 - \left(\frac{1}{\sqrt{2\pi}}\int_{-3}^{\infty} e^{-z^2/2}\,dz\right)^n$, $1 - (0.9987)^n$;

(c) $\left(\frac{1}{\sqrt{2\pi}}\int_{-3}^{3} e^{-z^2/2}\,dz\right)^n$, $(0.9974)^n$; (d) $n = 156$.

6. An ordered set of 10 real numbers, a 10-tuple; $e^{-(x-\mu)^2/2\sigma^2}/\sqrt{2\pi}\,\sigma$; $1/\sqrt{2\pi}\,\sigma)^{10}e^{-\sum_{i=1}^{10}(x_i-\mu)^2/2\sigma^2}$

7. (b) Normal (μ,σ); $e^{-(x-\mu)^2/2\sigma^2}/\sqrt{2\pi}\,\sigma$; they are independent; $(1/\sqrt{2\pi}\,\sigma)^n e^{-\sum_{i=1}^{n}(x_i-\mu)^2/2\sigma^2}$

8. $\frac{1}{\sqrt{2\pi}}\int_{-\infty}^{\log y} e^{-t^2/2}\,dt$, $y > 0$; $(1/\sqrt{2\pi})(1/y)^{\frac{1}{2}\log y + 1}$, $y > 0$.

9. (a) 0.1336; (b) 4/9.

10. $\mu \pm \sigma$.

11. Binomial, with $n = 10{,}000$, $p = 0.1587$; 1587; 1335.

12. (a) 1.4; (b) $\sum_{x=8}^{10}\binom{10}{x}(0.2024)^x(0.7976)^{10-x} = 0.0001$ (from tables); (c) 17.

13. $h(z) = (0.8/\sqrt{2\pi})e^{-2(z-3.5)^2} + (2/\sqrt{2\pi})e^{-(z-3)^2/0.18}$; $E(\mathbf{z}) = 3.2$, $\sigma_z = 0.46$.

14. $h(z) = e^{-(z-\mu)^2/2\sigma^2}\Big/\int_{x_0}^{\infty} e^{-(t-\mu)^2/2\sigma^2}\,dt$ for $z > x_0$, $h(z) = 0$ for $z < x_0$; $E(\mathbf{z}) = \mu + [\sigma^2 e^{-(x_0-\mu)^2/2\sigma^2}]\Big/\left[\int_{x_0}^{\infty} e^{-(t-\mu)^2/2\sigma^2}\,dt\right]$.

Pages 171–173

1. 0.52.
2. 271.
3. 0.465.
4. (a) 0.0228, 0.1587, 0.8413; (b) 1065.
5. (a) 0.988; (b) 62.
6. 663.
7. (a) 125; (b) 41.
8. (a) 0.92; (b) 0.02; (c) 0.08; (d) 676.
9. (a) $100p$; $100p(1-p)$; (b) $\sum_{|s-100p|>10}\binom{100}{s}p^s(1-p)^{100-s}$; (c) 2/9, $1/4 = \max p(1-p)$; (d) 0.034; (e) 0.046 (since $\sigma_s \le 5$); (f) 384.

11. (a) $\mu = np = 80$, $\sigma = \sqrt{npq} = 4$; use normal approximation at 74.5 probability $= 0.085$; (b) $p = 0.8$, $\beta = np^2 = 64$, $\lambda = np - \beta = 16$, probability $\doteq 0.077$; or, using $\sum_{s=0}^{74}\binom{100}{s}(0.8)^s(0.2)^{100-s} = \sum_{r=26}^{100}\binom{100}{r}(0.2)^r(0.8)^{100-r}$, with $p = 0.2$, $\beta = np^2 = 4$, $\lambda = np - \beta = 16$, probability is approximately 0.089.

12. (a) 1/8; (b) Poisson: $\beta = 2$, $\lambda = np - \beta = 10.5$, probability $\doteq 0.82$; normal, $\mu = np = 12.5$, $\sigma = \sqrt{npq} = 3.31$, probability is approximately 0.82.

Pages 184–187

1. (172, 178).
2. (a) (48.4, 51.6); (b) fail to reject, reject.
3. (a) (−1,15); (b) fail to reject.
4. (3.92, 4.08).
5. Reject.
6. Yes.

7. 217.
8. No, yes.
9. Fail to reject.
10. (70.6,73.4).
11. 11,000 ± 60; 11,000 ± 25.
12. $(\bar{x} - 1/4)/\sqrt{(1/4)(3/4)/125} = -1.29$, fail to reject.
13. 2.27, yes; no.
14. 3.27, significant.
15. 2.79, significant at 1% level.
16. 2.43, significant at 1.6% level.
17. (0.61,0.78).
18. (a) (0.20,0.38); (b) fail to reject.
19. $2(1.96)\sqrt{pq/n} < 0.05$ if $n > 1537$.
21. (a) Reject $p = 1/2$; (b) (0.237,0.491).
22. (a) (−0.16,0.25); (b) don't reject; (c) yes.

Pages 205–207

2. Choose A with probability 3/5, B with probability 2/5.
3. Discard.
4. Sell, \$−20.
5. Genus 1 if $-2.9 < s < 6.1$, Genus 2 if $s < -2.9$ or if $s > 6.1$.

Pages 218–220

1. (a) $\frac{1}{2\pi\sigma^2}\int_0^{2\pi}\int_0^a re^{-r^2/2\sigma^2}\,dr\,d\theta = 1 - e^{-a^2/2\sigma^2}$; (b) $C = \sigma\sqrt{2\log 2}$.

2. (a) 5/2, 5/4; (b) 13/4, 41/48; (c) 5/8; (d) $\sqrt{15/41}$, (e) $x - 2y + 4 = 0$; (f) $41x - 30y - 5 = 0$.

3. $R(1) = 2.5$, $R(2) = 3$, $R(3) = 3.5$, $R(4) = 4$; e.g., $y = \frac{1}{2}x + 2$.

4. (a) 7/12, 11/144; 7/12, 11/144; (b) −1/144, −1/11; (c) $x + 11y - 7 = 0$; (d) $11x + y - 7 = 0$.

5. (a) $y + \frac{1}{2}$ for $0 < y < 1$; (b) $y = (3x + 2)/3(2x + 1)(0 < x < 1)$.

6. (a) $y = 0$; (b) 0, 1/3, 0, 2/9; (c) 0, $y = 0$; (d) no.

7. 0.93.

8. (a) 0.75; (b) $x - y = 25$; (c) 85; regression curve coincides with regression line.

9. 136.

10. $d = 0.882w + 18.90$.

14. (a) $\mathbf{l} = \mathbf{r}\mathbf{s}_y/s_x$, $\mathbf{b} = \bar{\mathbf{y}} - \mathbf{r}\mathbf{s}_y\bar{x}/s_x$, where $s_x = \sum_{i=1}^n x_i^2/n - \bar{x}^2$, $\mathbf{s}_y = \sum_{i=1}^n \mathbf{y}_i^2/n - \bar{\mathbf{y}}^2$, $\mathbf{r} = \left[\sum_{i=1}^n x_i\mathbf{y}_i - \overline{x\mathbf{y}}\right]/s_x\mathbf{s}_y$.

17. (b) $a\mu_x + b\mu_y$, $a^2\sigma_x^2 + 2\rho ab\sigma_x\sigma_y + b^2\sigma_y^2$.

Page 223

1. Yes.

2. No.

3. (a) Fail to reject; (b) $0.02 < \rho < 0.59$.

4. Significant at $\frac{1}{2}$% level.

5. (a) $r = 0.97$; (b) The theorem on p. 207 is obviously not valid for $\rho = 1$; if $\rho = 1$ then $\mathbf{r} = 1$ with probability 1.

Pages 238–240

1. (a) Fail to reject, fail to reject; (b) $1.45 < \sigma < 5.31$; $1.31 < \sigma < 6.83$.
2. Reject, reject.

3. (a) Reject, fail to reject; (b) (7.8, 12.1), (7.2, 12.8).
4. (a) $5269.52 < \mu < 5269.62$; (b) $0.077 < \sigma < 0.15$.
5. (23.4,26.6).
6. 0.997, 0.72.
7. (a) 10^{μ}; (b) $(10^{\bar{z}-(st_{1-\alpha/2})/\sqrt{n-1}}, 10^{\bar{z}-(st_{\alpha/2}/\sqrt{n-1})})$, where $s^2 = \sum_{i=1}^{n}(z_i - \bar{z})^2/n$ and t_β is the $\beta\%$ point of the t-distribution with $n - 1$ degrees of freedom; (c) (15.6, 30.9).
8. (96, 216).
9. $\mathbf{x} - \mathbf{y}$ normal (5,4.1), $Pr\{\mathbf{x} - \mathbf{y} < 0\} = 0.11$.
10. (a) X^2 with n degrees of freedom; (b) $0.22 < \sigma^2 < 1.02$.
11. (a) $pe^t + q$; (b) $(pe^t + q)^n$.

Pages 245–248

1. (b) $10\sqrt{10}$, 150; (c) $0.225 < \lambda < 0.375$, $43.4 < \beta < 66.6$; (d) fail to reject.
2. (a) $52.5 < \beta < 56.1$; (b) $0.15 < \lambda < 0.23$.
3. (a) $\hat{\boldsymbol{\lambda}} = 2(\mathbf{y}_2 - \bar{\mathbf{y}})$; (b) normal $(\lambda, \sigma\sqrt{2})$.
4. (a) $y = 0.0513x + 1.777$; (b) $t = 1.83$, 2 degrees of freedom, not significant at the 10% level against the alternative $\lambda \neq 0$; not quite significant at the 10% level against alternatives $\lambda > 0$ (cf. pp. 240 ff.)
5. (a) $y = (0.86)(10^{-5})x - 1.321(10^{-2})$; (b) $0.78(10^{-5}) < \lambda < 0.94(10^{-5})$; (c) $0.14(10^{-4}) < \sigma^2 < 0.89(10^{-4})$.
6. $\gamma = -\hat{\lambda} = 0.90$.
8. The statistic

$$\sqrt{n+m-4}\left[(\hat{\boldsymbol{\lambda}}_1 - \hat{\boldsymbol{\lambda}}_2) - (\lambda_1 - \lambda_2)\Big/\sqrt{(n\hat{\boldsymbol{\sigma}}_1^2 + m\hat{\boldsymbol{\sigma}}_2^2)\left(\frac{1}{ns_x^2} + \frac{1}{ms_z^2}\right)}\right]$$

has Student's t-distribution with $n + m - 4$ degrees of freedom.
12. $\mathbf{t} = (\bar{\mathbf{y}}_1 - \bar{\mathbf{y}}_2)\sqrt{n-2}/\sqrt{\hat{\boldsymbol{\sigma}}_1^2 + \hat{\boldsymbol{\sigma}}_2^2}$; $t = 1.04$; not significant at the 5% level.

Pages 269–274

1. Yes.
2. (a) Fail to reject; (b) $197.9 < \mu < 232.1$.
3. (a) Fail to reject; (b) $-3.1 < \mu < 9.1$.
4. Reject.
5. Reject.
6. Fail to reject.
7. Reject.
8. Yes.
9. Fail to reject ($t = 0.9$).
10. $t = 1.15$, not significant.
11. (a) $F = 0.72$, do not reject; (b) $t = 1.73$, not significant.
12. $\mathrm{X}^2 = 80$, with 19 degrees of freedom; critical value 38.6, therefore reject.
13. (a) $|\bar{x}| > 0.258$; (b) 0.06, 0.66; (c) 0.94, 0.34; (e) No, since $\bar{x}$ will be nearly normal even if the population differs fairly markedly from normality (Central Limit Theorem).
14. (a) Reject only if all heads or all tails are thrown; (b) 0.33, 0.09.
15. (a) More than 58; (b) 1.00, 0.93, 0.27.
16. (a) 1.25; (b) Poisson mean = 1.25, $N = 4$.
17. (a) Yes, yes; (b) $0.20 < \rho < 0.77$.
18. (a) 31; (b) 0.98.
19. 455.
21. Reject $\sigma_1^2 = \sigma_2^2$; (1.2,8.4).

22. (a) Reject the null hypothesis; (b) $(1.1,\infty)$, 0.99.

23. Reject if $|\bar{x} - \mu_0| > t$, where t is chosen so that $Pr\{|\bar{x} - \mu_0| > t\} = \alpha$ when $\mu = \mu_0$.

24. The likelihood ratio test coincides with the t test.

25. Reject when $\chi^2 = -2 \log \lambda = 2n[\bar{x} \log \bar{x} - \bar{x} - \log \mu_0 + \mu_0]$ is too large; $\chi^2 = 200[\bar{x} \log \bar{x} - \bar{x} + 1] > 3.84$, reject if $\bar{x} < 0.81$ or if $\bar{x} > 1.20$.

Pages 280–285

1. $D^2 = 2$, critical value 2.71, hence cannot reject.

2. $D^2 = 35$, critical value 9.2, hence reject.

3. $D^2 = 2.78$, yes, no.

4. $D^2 = 21.3$, critical value 6.6, hence not consistent.

5. $D^2 = 4.17$, 1 degree of freedom, not significant.

6. $D^2 = 5.8$, 1 degree of freedom, significant.

7. $D^2 = 3.77$, 1 degree of freedom, not significant (but almost).

8. $D^2 = 26$, 4 degrees of freedom, significant at 1% level.

9. $D^2 = 2.0$, 1 degree of freedom, significant at about 18% level.

10. (a) $D^2 = 0.005$, 1 degree of freedom, not significant; (b) $D^2 = 9.6$, 3 degrees of freedom, significant at 5% level.

11. $D^2 = 4$; 9 degrees of freedom, do not reject; 0.9.

12. $D^2 = 5.06$, 3 degrees of freedom, not significant at 5% level.

13. $D^2 = 3683.88$, 12 degrees of freedom; reject the hypothesis of independence.

14. $\delta_{20} = 1.003$; don't reject $N(0,1)$.

15. $D^2 = 2.4$, 4 degrees of freedom; don't reject hypothesis of independence.

16. $D^2 = 2.484$, 3 degrees of freedom, don't reject.

17. $D^2 = 37$, 11 degrees of freedom; reject the hypothesis of homogeneity.

Pages 305–313

3. $F = 11.25$; 2, 27 degrees of freedom; significant.

4. $F = 2.03$; 3, 8 degrees of freedom, not significant; critical 4.07.

5. $F = 16.5$; 4, 5 degrees of freedom; significant at 1% level.

6. (a) $F = 4.74$, not significant at the 10% level; (b) $F = 9.32$, significant at the 10% level.

7. (a) $F = \infty$; (b) $\sigma^2 = 0$; would occur with probability 0.

8. (a) $F = 16.3$; 2, 6 degrees of freedom; significant at the 1% level; (b) homoscedasticity is suspect.

9. $F = 0.09$; 3,9 degrees of freedom, not significant.

13. $F = 36.5/14 = 2.61$; 4, 12 degrees of freedom; not significant at 5% level.

14. $3.5 < \sigma^2 < 10$.

16. $F = 6.81$; 2, 40 degrees of freedom; reject the hypothesis.

17. (a) $F = 10.33$; 1, 9 degrees of freedom; don't reject the null hypothesis; (b) $t = \sqrt{F} = 3.22$, for $N - 0$; 9 degrees of freedom; yes.

18. Treatments: $F = 120$; 3, 6 degrees of freedom; reject.
Rows: $F = 1.74$; 3, 6 degrees of freedom; don't reject.
Columns: $F = 3.85$; 3, 6 degrees of freedom; reject.

19. $F = 4.20$; 4, 11 degrees of freedom; reject null hypothesis.

20. (a) $F = 2.69$; 3, 15 degrees of freedom; accept the hypothesis; (b) $F = 5.33$; 5, 15 degrees of freedom; reject the hypothesis.

21. $F = 0.93$; 4, 12 degrees of freedom; don't reject.

22. $F = 0.48$; 2, 9 degrees of freedom; don't reject.

23. $F = 5.2$; 3, 6 degrees of freedom; reject.

Pages 323–325

1. $66.8 < \mu < 73.2$.

2. 37.1.

3. $(\bar{x} - \mu)\sqrt{nN}/\sigma\sqrt{N-n} = 2.71$; probability $= 0.0034$.

4. (a) None; (b) 1.06.

5. No, no.

6. $3\sigma^2$.

7. (a) 150 men, 50 women; (b) 164 men, 36 women; reduction to variance, 0.00094; relative reduction, 0.024; ratio of standard deviations = 1.01; (c) reduction in variance, 0.00375; relative reduction, 0.094; ratio of standard deviations 1.05.

8. 28%; $\sigma/\sqrt{n}$ is 1.28 times too large.

9. $\mu = 21/5$, $\sigma = \sqrt{14}/5$, $\rho = -1/4$; $x + 4y - 21 = 0$.

10. (a) $E(\bar{x}) = \sum_{j=1}^{m} p_j\mu_j$, $V(\bar{x}) = \sum_{j=1}^{m} \frac{p_j^2\sigma_j^2}{n_j}\frac{N_j - n_j}{N_j - 1}$;
(b) $p_j = N_j/N (j = 1,2,\cdots, m)$, where $N = \sum_{j=1}^{m} N_j$.

11. (b) \$6.21 ($\lambda = 35/11$).

Pages 342–345

1. (a) $\bar{x} = 6.53, 7.47$; (b) $s^2 = 0.54$.

2. $s^2 = 0.0053, 0.239$.

3. 1, by Corollary B. Let $\mathbf{z}_i$ denote the amount to be won, positive or negative, by Player I at the i-th play; let $-b$ $(b < 0)$ be the amount of money with which he enters the game; let a be the amount with which Player II enters the game. Player I loses all his money if, for some k, $\sum_{i=1}^{k} \mathbf{z}_i \leq b$, while Player II loses his money if, for some k, $\sum_{i=1}^{k} \mathbf{z}_i \geq a$.

4. (b) No.

5. $y = n/4 \pm 9.2$.

6. (a) Normal, mean $\frac{\mu_1 - \mu_0}{\sigma^2}\left[\mu - \frac{\mu_0 + \mu_1}{2}\right]$, standard deviation $\frac{\mu_1 - \mu_0}{\sigma}$.

7. About 36; about 36.

8. $y = [\log A + n(\lambda_1 - \lambda_0)]/\log(\lambda_1/\lambda_0)$, $y = [\log B + n(\lambda_1 - \lambda_0)]/\log(\lambda_1/\lambda_0)$.

9. About 11.

10. $n = 130$, $d = 7$.

11. Accept when number defective $< 0.59n - 2.30$, reject when $> 0.59n + 2.30$; here n = number tested.

12. (a) Reject when sum of squares $> 2.47n + 5.07$, accept when sum of squares $< 2.47n - 6.50$; (b) yes; reject.

13. (a) Reject when total number of defectives $> 0.0473n + 3.36$, accept when $< 0.0473n - 5.12$. (b) 271.

Pages 353–354

1. 66%.

2. $y_3 < \xi_{0.25} < y_8$; i.e., $11 < \xi_{0.25} < 17$.

3. $y_{18} \leq \xi_{0.75} \leq y_{27}$.

4. 37.

5. About 660.

10. $H(u) = Pr\{\mathbf{z}_n - \mathbf{z}_1 < u\} = u^n + nu^{n-1}(1 - u)$,
$h(u) = H'(u) = n(n-1)u^{n-2}(1 - u)$, $0 < u < 1$.

11. $G(t) = Pr\{\mathbf{y}_n - \mathbf{y}_1 < t\} = [2nt^{n-1} - (n-1)t^n]/2^n$,
$g(t) = n(n-1)t^{n-2}(2 - t)/2^n$, $0 < t < 2$.

Pages 368–371

1. Yes, with one-sided test; almost significant at 5% level with two-sided test.
2. Yes, critical value 19.7 in one-tail test; $E(\mathbf{m}_1) = 14.8$, $\sigma_{m_1} = 2.1$.
3. $30L$ and $30H$ gives 26 runs; $\mu = 31$, $\sigma = 3.84$; not significant at 5% level.
4. (a) 30 runs, $\mu = 38.5$, $\sigma = 4.16$; barely significant at 2% level (one tail test); (b) $21x$, $19y$ above median (z_{40}); $\tau = 1.83$; barely significant at the 3% level.
5. D replaced by L, two H selected at random to be replaced by L (first and last H); 9 runs, $\mu = 11$, $\sigma = 2.18$, fail to reject at 10% significance level with one-tail test.
6. 23 runs (depends on table of random digits), $\mu = 26$, $\sigma = 3.5$, not significant at 10% level.
7. Let $\mathbf{A} = \max_x |F_1^\circ(\mathbf{x}) - F_2^\circ(\mathbf{x})|$. Possible values of $\mathbf{A}$ are 0.1, 0.2, ⋯, 1.0. The observed value is $A = 0.7$, hence reject at 5% level (critical value 0.56). Interpolation yields $Pr\{\mathbf{A} \geq 0.7\} = Pr\{\mathbf{A} \geq 0.65\} = 1 - Pr\{\mathbf{A} < 0.65\} \doteq 0.99$.
8. $r = 4$, reject the null hypothesis; 3%; suspect actual trend toward smaller catches.
$\binom{5}{1}\binom{5}{0}\Big]\Big/\binom{2}{6} = 0.07$; reject.
9. $r = 16$, reject the null hypothesis.
10. $r = 4$, reject the hypothesis.
11. $\binom{5}{4}\binom{5}{2}\Big/\binom{10}{4} = \binom{5}{1}\binom{5}{3}\Big/\binom{10}{4} = 0.24$.
12. $\binom{9}{4} = 126$.
13. (a) $Pr\{\mathbf{r} = 2\} = 2/3$, $Pr\{\mathbf{r} = 3\} = 1/3$; (b) $E(\mathbf{r}) = 7/3$, $V(\mathbf{r}) = 2/9$.

CDEFGHI 706987

Printed in the United States of America